INSTRUCTOR'S
SOLUTIONS MANUAL

MILTON LOYER
Penn State University

to accompany

ESSENTIALS OF STATISTICS
SECOND EDITION

Mario F. Triola
Dutchess Community College

PEARSON
Addison
Wesley

Boston   San Francisco   New York
London   Toronto   Sydney   Tokyo   Singapore   Madrid
Mexico City   Munich   Paris   Cape Town   Hong Kong   Montreal

Reproduced by Pearson Addison-Wesley from electronic files supplied by the author.

Copyright © 2005 Pearson Education, Inc.
Publishing as Pearson Addison-Wesley, 75 Arlington Street, Boston, MA 02116

ISBN   0-321-22910-X

1 2 3 4 5 6 VHG 06 05 04

PEARSON
Addison
Wesley

TABLE OF CONTENTS

INTRODUCTION

This *Instructor's Solutions Manual* contains solutions to all the exercises in the text. For convenience, we include all the information given in the **Student's Solutions Manual** as it appears in that volume – except that the student solutions are sometimes given in an expanded format made more user-friendly by the inclusion of additional white space. Bold-face type identifies the exercise numbers and NOTE designations for material appearing only in the instructor's manual. Accordingly, even numbers not in bold-face type identify solutions appearing for one reason or another in the student's manual.

STUDENT'S SOLUTIONS MANUAL PREFACE

This manual contains the solutions to the odd-numbered exercises for each section of the textbook Essentials of Statistics, Second Edition, by Mario Triola, and the solutions for all of the end-of-chapter review and cumulative review exercises of that text. To aid in the comprehension of calculations, worked problems typically include intermediate steps of algebraic and/or computer/calculator notation. When appropriate, additional hints and comments are included and prefaced by NOTE.

Many statistical problems are best solved using particular formats. Recognizing and following these patterns promote understanding and develop the capacity to apply the concepts to other problems. This manual identifies and employs such formats whenever practicable.

For best results, read the text carefully before attempting the exercises, and attempt the exercises before consulting the solutions. This manual has been prepared to provide a check and extra insights for exercises that have already been completed and to provide guidance for solving exercises that have already been attempted but have not been successfully completed.

I would like to thank Mario Triola for writing an excellent elementary statistics book and for inviting me to prepare this solutions manual.

Chapter 1

Introduction to Statistics

1-2 Types of Data

1.   Parameters, since 87 and 13 refer to the entire population.

2.   Statistic, since 4.2 refers to the selected sample.

3.   Statistic, since 0.65 refers to the selected sample.

4.   Parameter, since 706 refers to the entire population.

5.   Discrete, since annual salary cannot assume any value over a continuous span – as an annual salary of $98,765.4321, for example, is not a physical possibility. The annual presidential salary is typically stated in multiples of $1000 - and it cannot be paid in US currency in units smaller than a cent.

6.   Continuous, since weight can be any value over a continuous span.

7.   Discrete, since the calculated percent cannot be any value over a continuous span. Because the number having guns in their homes must be an integer, the possible values for the percent are limited to multiples of 100/1059.

8.   Discrete, since the number of defective masks must be an integer.

9.   Ratio, since differences are meaningful and zero height has a natural meaning.

10. Ordinal, since the ratings give relative position in a hierarchy.

11. Interval, since differences are meaningful but ratios are not. Refer to exercise #21.

12. Nominal, since the number are for identification only. The numbers on the jerseys are merely numerical names for the players.

13. Ordinal, since the ratings give relative position in a hierarchy.

14. Nominal, since the numbers are used for identification only. Even though SS numbers are assigned chronologically within regions and can be placed in numerical order, there is no meaningful way to compare 208-34-3337 and 517-94-1439. If all the numbers had been assigned chronologically beginning with 000-00-0001, like the order of finishers in a race, then SS numbers would illustrate the ordinal level of measurement.

15. Ratio, since differences are meaningful and zero "yes" responses has a natural meaning.

16. Nominal, since the numbers are used for identification only. Even though they are assigned alphabetically within regions, zip codes are merely numerical names for post offices. If the numbers had resulted from placing all the post offices in one large list alphabetically (or by city size, or by mail volume, etc.), so that 17356 [Red Lion, PA] was the 17,356th post office in the list, like the order of finishers in a race, then zip codes would illustrate the ordinal level of measurement.

17. a. The sample is the ten adults who were asked for an opinion.
     b. There is more than one possible answer. The population the reporter had in mind may have been all the adults living in that particular city.
     No. People living in that city but who do not pass by that corner (shut-ins, those with no business in that part of town, etc.) will not be represented in the sample. Furthermore, it was not specified that the reported selected the ten adults in an unbiased manner - e.g., he may have (consciously or subconsciously) selected ten friendly-looking people.

18. **NOTE:** This is a non-trivial problem. By definition, the sample must be a subset of the population – i.e., the sample and the population must have the same units. In this particular problem, the researchers appear to be interested in the TV sets that are in use at a particular time – and, of course, the number of TV sets in use at a selected household may be 0, 1, or more than 1.
    a. The sample is the TV's that are in use at that time the randomly selected households.
    b. The population is all the TV's in use at that time in the entire country.
    Yes. If the households are selected at random, then each TV in use at the time has the same chance of being included - which means that there are no biases that would prevent the sample from being representative .

19. a. The sample is the 1059 randomly selected adults.
    b. The population is all the adults in the entire country. NOTE: While it is not specified that the adults were selected from within USA, this is the logical assumption.
    Yes. If the adults in the sample were randomly selected, there are no biases that would prevent the sample from being representative. NOTE: This is a sample of adults, not of homes. The appropriate inference is that about 39% of the adults live in a home with a gun, not that there is a gun in about 39% of the homes. Since adults were selected at random, homes with more adults are more likely to be represented in the survey – and that bias would prevent the survey from being representative of all homes.

20. a. The sample is the 65 adults who responded to the survey.
    b. The population for this portion of the project is all the adults that the graduate student knows.
    No. The sample includes only those who cared enough about the graduate student and/or the issue in question to offer a response. Those who did not care enough to respond will not be represented in the sample.

21. Temperature ratios are not meaningful because a temperature of 0° does not represent the absence of temperature in the same sense that $0 represents the absence of money. The zero temperature in the example (whether Fahrenheit or Centigrade) was determined by a criterion other than "the absence of temperature."

22. That value has no meaning.
    NOTE: When there are only two categories coded 0 and 1, the average gives the proportion of cases in the category coded 1. When there are more than two categories, such calculations with nominal data have no meaning.

23. This is an example of ordinal data. It is not interval data because differences are not meaningful – i.e., the difference between the ratings +4 and +5 does not necessarily represent the same differential in the quality of the food as the difference between the ratings 0 and +1.

1-3 Critical Thinking

NOTE: The alternatives given in exercises #1-4 are not the only possible answers.

1. Males weigh more than females – and truck drivers tend to be male, while about half the adults who do not drive trucks are female.

2. Homeowners tend to be more affluent than renters – and thus they can afford better medical care.

3. There are more minority drivers than white drivers in Orange County – if the rates of speeding were the same for both types of drivers, you would expect the more numerous type of driver to be issued more tickets.

4. Colds generally do not last more than two weeks – you would expect all the subjects to be improved in two weeks no matter what medicine they took or didn't take.

5. The study was financed by those with a vested interest in promoting chocolate, who would be more likely to report only the favorable findings. While chocolate contains an antioxidant associated with decreased risk of heart disease and stroke, it may also contain other ingredients associated with an increased risk of those or other health problems.

6. The census counting process is not 100% accurate, especially among those (such as illegal aliens) who may not wish to be counted. Giving such a precise figure suggests a degree of accuracy not actually warranted.

7. No. The sample was self-selected and therefore not necessarily representative of the general population (or even of the constituencies of the various women's groups contacted).

8. Because the 186,000 respondents were self-selected and not randomly chosen, they are not necessarily representative of the general population and provide no usable information about the general population. In addition, the respondents were self-selected from a particular portion of the general population – viz., persons watching "Nightline" and able to spend the time and money to respond.

9. Telephone directories do not contain unlisted numbers, and consumer types electing not be listed would not be represented in the survey. In addition, sometimes numbers appear in directories more than once (e.g., under the husband's name and under the wife's name), and consumer types electing multiple listings would be over-represented in the survey. Also excluded from the survey would be those without telephones (for economic, religious, or other reasons), transient persons (both frequent movers and those who just happened to have moved) not in the current directory, and persons whose living arrangements (group housing, extended families, etc.) do not include a phone in their own name.

10. A person could make the same claim about anything found in cities but not in rural areas. Consider, for example, the claim that fire hydrants cause crime – because crime rates are higher in cities with fire hydrants than in rural areas that have no fire hydrants.

11. Motorcyclists that died in crashes in which helmets may have saved their lives could not be present to testify.

12. They survey may not produce honest responses. A financial consultant, or any person dealing with the public, will probably give better service to those he likes – and so a respondent who knows that his name will be linked with the answers he supplies might hesitate to give responses that would upset his financial consultant.

13. No. While 0.94 is the average of the 29 different brands in the survey, it is not a good estimate of the average of all the cigarettes smoked for at least two significant reasons. First, the 29 brands in the survey are not representative of all brands on the market – they include only 100mm filtered brands that are not menthol or light. Secondly, some brands are much more popular than others. Even if every brand on the market were in the survey, the average would not be a good estimate of all the cigarettes smoked – the values of the popular brands will carry more weight when the amounts of each brand that are actually smoked are taken into consideration.

14. There are several possible answers. (1) Since tallness is perceived to be a favorable attribute, people tend to overstate their heights; at the very least, people would tend to round to the next highest inch and not to the nearest inch. (2) Many people do not really accurately know their height. (3) Because Americans tend to express height in feet and inches, errors might occur either in converting heights to all inches or in misstatements like 52" for 5'2". (4) Because many cultures express height in centimeters, some people might not know or be able to readily calculate their heights in inches.

15. Most people born after 1945 are still living. This means the sample would include only those who did not reach their normal life expectancy and would not be representative.

16. The decreased rate that occurred after the recommendation to use the supine position was not necessarily *caused* by the use of that position. It could be that general medical

advances were lowering the rates of all infant mortality, including death by SIDS.

NOTE for exercises #17-20: Multiplying or dividing by 1 will not change a value. Since 100% is the same as 1, multiplying or dividing by 100%will not change a value – but remember that the percent sign is a necessary unit (just like inches or pounds) that cannot be ignored.

17. a. $17/25 = .68 = .68 \times 100\% = 68\%$
     b. $35.2\% = 35.2\%/100\% = .352$
     c. $57\% = 57\%/100\% = .57; .57 \times 1500 = 855$
     d. $.486 = .486 \times 100\% = 48.6\%$

18. a. $26\% = 26\%/100\% = .26; .26 \times 950 = 247$
     b. $5\% = 5\%/100\% = .05$
     c. $.01 = .01 \times 100\% = 1\%$
     d. $527/1200 = .439 = .439 \times 100\% = 43.9\%$

19. a. There is not enough accuracy in the reported percent to determine an exact answer. While $.52 \times 1038 = 539.76$ suggests an answer of 540, x/1038 rounds to 52% for $535 \leq x \leq 544$. The actual number could be anywhere from 535 to 544 inclusive.
     b. $52/1038 = .05 = 5\%$

20. a. $19/270 = .07 = 7\%$
     b. $270 \times .030 = 8$

21. There is not enough accuracy in the reported percents to determine an exact answer. It is tempting to conclude that
     $.08 \cdot (1875) = 150$ admit to committing a campus crime
     $.62 \cdot (150) = 93$ say they did so under the influence of alcohol or drugs.
     But x/1875 rounds to 8% for $141 \leq x \leq 159$, and so the number admitting to a crime could be anywhere from 141 to 159 inclusive. Similarly, the number that say they committed the crime under the influence of alcohol or drugs could be anywhere from 87 to 99 inclusive – since 87/141 and 99/159 both round to 62%.

22. Since 100% is the totality of whatever is being measured, a decrease of 100% would mean that nothing is left. A decrease of more than 100% would be possible only in situations (e.g., those involving money) where negative amounts have meaning. An increase of more than 100%, however, presents no problems – as an increase of 200%, for example, means an addition of twice the original amount to produce three times the starting quantity.
     a. Refer to the explanation above. Since negative plaque has no meaning, the amount of plaque cannot be reduced by more than 100%.
     b. Refer to the explanation above. Since negative investment generally has no meaning, the amount of foreign investment cannot fall more than 100%. The only possible literal interpretation is that the net flow of foreign money is now negative, and four times what it used to be when it was positive.

23. Assuming that each of the 20 individual subjects is ultimately counted as a success or not (i.e., that there are no "dropouts" or "partial successes"), the success rates in fraction form must be one of 0/20, 1/20, 2/20,..., 19/20, 20/20. In percentages, these rates are multiples of 5 (0%, 5%, 10%,..., 95%, 100%), and values such as 53% and 58% are not mathematical possibilities.

24. a. Since 100% is the totality of whatever is being measured, removing 100% of some quantity means that none of it is left.
     b. Reducing plaque by over 300% would mean removing three times as much plaque as is there, and then removing even more!

25. The answers will vary according to student interests. Here is one example.
     a. Should our school consider a dress code?
     b. Should our school consider a dress code outlawing lewd or unsanitary practices?
     c. Should our school consider a dress code limiting personal freedom and diverting attention from more important educational issues?

26.   The following figures meet the stated criteria.
   a. The graph on the left is an objective presentation of the data, for the height (and area) of
      the female bar is 74% of the height (and area) of the male bar.
   b. The graph on the right exaggerates the differences by "cutting off" the bottom of the
      figure and starting at 70. Even though the vertical labeling gives the correct values, the
      graph is misleading since the height (and area) of the female bar is only 4/30 = 13% of
      the height (and area) of the male bar – and so the visual impression is that the female
      salary is only 13% of the male salary.

 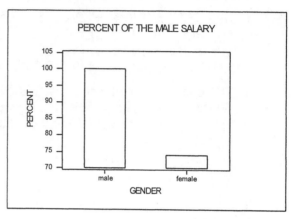

1-4 Design of Experiments

1.   Experiment, since the effect of an applied treatment is measured.

2.   Observational study, since specific characteristics are measured on unmodified subjects

3.   Observational study, since specific characteristics are measured on unmodified subjects.

4.   Experiment, since the effect of an applied treatment is measured.

5.   Retrospective, since the data are collected by going back in time.

6.   Prospective, since the data are to be collected in the future from a group sharing a common
     factor.

7.   Cross-sectional, since the data are collected at one point in time.

8.   Retrospective, since the data are collected by going back in time.

9.   Convenience, since the sample was simply those who happen to pass by.

10. Systematic, since every 100th element in the population was chosen.

11. Random, since each adult has an equal chance of being selected.
     NOTE: This is a complex situation. The above answer ignores the fact that there is not a 1
     to 1 correspondence between adults and phone numbers. An adult with more than one
     number will have a higher chance of being selected. An adult who shares a phone number
     with other adults will have a lower chance of being selected. And, of course, adults with
     no phone numbers have no chance of being selected at all.

12. Stratified, since the population of interest (assumed to be all car owners) was divided into
     5 subpopulations from which the actual sampling was done.

13. Cluster, since the population of interest (assumed to be all students at The College of
     Newport) was divided into classes which were randomly selected in order to interview all
     the students in each selected class.
     NOTE: Ideally the division into classes should place each student into one and only one

class (e.g., if every student must take exactly one PE class each semester, select the PE classes at random). In practice such divisions are often made in ways that place some students in none of the classes (e.g., by selecting from all 2 pm M-W-F classes) or in more than one of the classes (e.g., by selecting from all the classes offered in the college). With careful handling, imperfect divisions should not significantly affect the results.

14. Random, since each Corvette owner has an equal chance of being selected.
NOTE: this is also an example of simple random sampling, since every possible group of 50 Corvette owners has the same chance of being chosen.

15. Systematic, since every fifth element in the population (assumed to be all drivers passing the checkpoint during its operation) was sampled.

16. Cluster, since the population (assumed to be all voters) will be divided into polling stations which will be randomly selected in order to interview all the voters at each station.

17. Stratified, since the population of interest (assumed to be all workers) was divided into 3 subpopulations from which the actual sampling was done.

18. Convenience, since the sample is those who happen to be in his family.

19. Cluster, since the population of interest (assumed to be all cardiac patients) were divided into hospitals which were randomly selected in order to survey all such patients at each hospital.

20. Stratified, since the population of interest will be divided into subpopulations from which the actual sampling will be done.

21. Yes, this is a random sample because each of the 1000 tablets (assumed to be the population) has an equal chance of being selected. Yes, this is a simple random sample because every possible group of 50 tablets has the same chance of being chosen.

22. Yes, this is a random sample of the class because each of the 30 students has an equal chance (viz., 1/5) of being selected. No, it is not a simple random sample because every possible group of 6 students does not have the same chance of being chosen – groups of 6 with students from different rows have no chance of being chosen.

23. No, this is not a random sample because each element in the population does not have an equal chance of being selected. If the population of interest is all the residents of the city, then those who do not pass that street corner have no chance of being selected. Even if the population of interest is all those who pass that street corner, the reporter's personal preferences would likely prevent each person from having an equal chance of being selected – e.g., the reporter might not want to stop a woman with three noisy children, or a man walking very fast and obviously in a hurry to get somewhere. Since the sample is not random, it cannot be a simple random sample.

24. Yes, this is a random sample because each unit on the conveyor belt has an equal chance (viz., 1/100) of being selected. No, this is not a simple random sample because all possible samples do not have the same chance of being chosen – samples containing two consecutive units, for example, cannot occur.
NOTE: The above answer assumes the units are placed on the conveyor belt in random order, or that the engineer begins his sampling at a random moment. If the units are placed on the conveyor belt in some order and the engineer wants to begin sampling as soon as the first units are placed on the belt, then he should randomly choose a number from 1 to 100 to identify the first unit to be selected.

25. Yes, this is a random sample because each person in Orange County has an equal chance of being selected. No, this is not a simple random sample because every possible sample of 200 Orange County residents does not have the same chance of being chosen – a sample with 75 men and 45 women, for example, is not possible. The survey will include a simple random sample of Orange County men and a simple random sample of Orange County women, but not a simple random sample of Orange County adults.

26. Yes, this is a random sample because each adult resident of Newport has an equal chance (viz, 10/n – where n is the total number of blocks in Newport) of being selected. No, this is not a simple random sample because every possible sample does not have the same chance of being chosen – a sample with at least one adult from every block, for example, cannot occur.

27. Assume that "students who use this book" refers to a particular semester (or other point in time). Before attempting any sampling procedure below, two preliminary steps are necessary: (1) obtain from the publisher a list of each school that uses the book and (2) obtain from each school the number of students enrolled in courses requiring the text. Note that using only the number of books sold to the school by the publisher will miss those students purchasing used copies turned in from previous semesters. "Students" in parts (a)-(e) below is understood to mean students using this book.
   a. Random - conceptually (i.e., without actually doing so) make a list of all N students by assigning to each school one place on the list for each of its students; pick 100 random numbers from 1 to N -- each number identifies a particular school and a conceptual student; for each identified school select a student at random (or more than one student, if that school was identified more than once). In this manner every student has the same chance of being selected -- in fact, every group of 100 has the same chance of being selected, and the sample is a simple random sample.
   b. Systematic - place the n schools in a list, pick a random number between 1 and (n/10) to determine a starting selection, select every (n/10)th school; at each of the 10 systematically selected schools, randomly (or systematically) select and survey 10 students.
   c. Convenience - randomly (or conveniently) select and survey 100 students from your school.
   d. Stratified - divide the schools into categories (e.g., 2 year, 4 year private, 4 year public, proprietary) and select 1 school from each category; at each school randomly (or by a stratified procedure) select and survey the number of students equal to the percent of the total students that are in that category.
   e. Cluster - select a school at random and survey all the students (or cluster sample again by grouping the students in classes and selecting a class at random in which to survey all the students); repeat (i.e., select another school at random) as necessary until the desired sample of 100 is obtained.

28. Confounding occurs when the researcher is not able to determine which factor (often one planned and one unplanned) produced an observed effect. If a restaurant tries adding an evening buffet for one week and it happens to be the same week that a nearby theater shows a real blockbuster that attracts unusual crowds to the neighborhood, the restaurant cannot know whether its increased business is due to the new buffet or to the extra traffic created by the theater.

29. No. Even though every state has the same chance of being selected, not every voter has the same chance of being selected. Once a state is selected, any particular registered voter in a small state is competing against fewer peers and has a higher chance of being selected than any particular registered voter in a large state.

30. The study may be described as
   a. prospective because the data are to be collected in the future, after the patients are assigned to different treatment groups.
   b. randomized because the patients were assigned to one of the three treatment groups at random.
   c. double-blind because neither the patient nor the evaluating physician knew which treatment had been administered.
   d. placebo-controlled because there was a treatment with no drug that allowed the researchers to distinguish between real effects of the drugs in question and (1) the psychological effects of "being treated" and/or (2) the results of not receiving any drugs.

31. a. The two samples are self-selected, and the participants were not randomly assigned to
their respective groups. It appears that the researchers asked a group of drivers without
cell phones to participate, and then approached a group of drivers who already had cell
phones. It could be that drivers who self-select to have cell phones are anxious types
that would have more accidents anyway.

   b. Those with cell phones were specifically asked to use the phones while driving. This is
not likely to produce the same results as "normal" usage – not to mention the fact that
knowing they are part of a study will likely put them on their best behavior and not
represent their typical conduct in such a situation.

Review Exercises

1. No, the responses cannot be considered representative of the population of the United
States for at least the following reasons.
   a. Only AOL subscribers were contacted. Those who are not AOL subscribers, not to
mention those with no Internet connections at all, will not be represented. This will
introduce a significant bias – since non-Internet users might to be the less affluent, less
educated and less business-oriented.

   b. The sample was self-selected. The responses represent only those who had enough time
and/or interest in the question. Typically, those with strong feelings one way or the
other are more likely to respond and will be over-represented in the results.

2. Let N be the total number of full-time students and n be the desired sample size.
   a. Random. Obtain a list of all N full-time students, number the students from 1 to N,
select n random numbers from 1 to N, and poll each student whose number on the list is
one of the random numbers selected.

   b. Systematic. Obtain a list of all N full-time students, number the students from 1 to N,
let m be the largest integer less than the fraction N/n, select a random number between
1 and m, begin with the student whose number is the random number selected, and poll
that student and every mth student thereafter.

   c. Convenience. Select a location (e.g., the intersection of major campus walkways) by
which most of the students usually pass, and poll the first n full-time students that pass.

   d. Stratified. Obtain a list of all N full-time students and the gender of each, divide the list
by gender, and randomly select and poll n/2 students from each gender.

   e. Cluster. Obtain a list of all the classes meeting at a popular time (e.g., 10 am Monday),
estimate how many of the classes would be necessary to include n students, select that
many of the classes at random, and poll all of the students in each selected class.

3. a. Ratio, since differences are valid and there is a meaningful 0.
   b. Ordinal, since there is a hierarchy but differences are not valid.
   c. Nominal, since the categories have no meaningful inherent order.
   d. Interval, since differences are valid but the 0 is arbitrary.

4. a. Discrete, since the number of shares held must be an integer.
NOTE: Even if partial shares are allowed (e.g., 5½ shares), the number of shares must
be some fractional value and not any value on a continuum -- e.g., a person could not
own π shares.

   b. Ratio, since differences between values are consistent and there is a natural zero.

   c. Stratified, since the set of interest (all stockholders) was divided into subpopulations (by
states) from which the actual sampling was done.

   d. Statistic, since the value is determined from a sample and not the entire population.

   e. There is no unique correct answer, but the following are reasonable possibilities.
(1) The proportion of stockholders holding above that certain number of shares (which
would vary from company to company) that would make them "influential." (2) The
proportion of stockholders holding below that certain number of shares (which would
vary from company to company) that would make them "insignificant." (3) The
numbers of shares (and hence the degree of influence) held by the largest stockholders.

f. There are several possible valid answers. (1) The results would be from a self-selected group (i.e., those who chose to respond) and not necessarily a representative group. (2) If the questionnaire did not include information on the numbers of shares owned, the views of small stockholders (who are probably less knowledgeable about business and stocks) could not be distinguished from those of large stockholders (whose views should carry more weight).

5. a. Systematic, since the selections are made at regular intervals.
    b. Convenience, since those selected were the ones who happened to attend.
    c. Cluster, since the stockholders were organized into groups (by stockbroker) and all the stockholders in the selected groups were chosen.
    d. Random, since each stockholder has the same chance of being selected.
    e. Stratified, since the stockholders were divided into subpopulations from which the actual sampling was done.

6. a. Blinding occurs when those involved in an experiment (either as subjects or evaluators) do not know whether they are dealing with a treatment or a placebo. It might be used in this experiment by (a) not telling the subjects whether they are receiving Sleepeze or the placebo and/or (b) not telling any post-experiment interviewers or evaluators which subjects received Sleepeze and which ones received the placebo. Double-blinding occurs when neither the subjects nor the evaluators know whether they are dealing with a treatment or a placebo.
    b. The data reported will probably involve subjective assessments (e.g., "On a scale of 1 to 10, how well did it work?") that may be subconsciously influenced by whether the subject was known to have received Sleepeze or the placebo.
    c. In a completely randomized block design, subjects are assigned to the groups (in this case to receive Sleepeze or the placebo) at random.
    d. In a rigorously controlled block design, subjects are assigned to the groups (in this case to receive Sleepeze or the placebo) in such a way that the groups are similar with respect to extraneous variables that might affect the outcome. In this experiment it may be important to make certain each group has approximately the same age distribution, degree of insomnia, number of males, number users of alcohol and/or tobacco, etc.
    e. Replication involves repeating the experiment on a sample of subjects large enough to ensure that atypical responses of a few subjects will not give a distorted view of the true situation.

Cumulative Review Exercises

NOTE: Throughout the text intermediate mathematical steps will be shown as an aid to those who may be having difficulty with the calculations. In practice, most of the work can be done continuously on calculators and the intermediate values are unnecessary. Even when the calculations cannot be done continuously, DO NOT WRITE AN INTERMEDIATE VALUE ON YOUR PAPER AND THEN RE-ENTER IT IN THE CALCULATOR. That practice can introduce round-off errors and copying errors. Store any intermediate values in the calculator so that you can recall them with infinite accuracy and without copying errors.

1. $$\frac{169.1+144.2+179.3+178.5+152.6+166.8+135.0+201.5+175.2+139.0}{10} = \frac{1638.5}{10}$$
    $$= 163.85$$

2. $$\frac{98.20 - 98.60}{.62} = \frac{-.40}{.62} = -.645$$

3. $\dfrac{98.20 - 98.60}{0.62/\sqrt{106}} = \dfrac{-.40}{.0602} = -6.642$

4. $\left[\dfrac{(1.96)(15)}{2}\right]^2 = \left[\dfrac{29.4}{2}\right]^2 = [14.7]^2 = 216.09$

5. $\sqrt{\dfrac{(5\text{-}7)^2 + (12\text{-}7)^2 + (4\text{-}7)^2}{3\text{-}1}} = \sqrt{\dfrac{(\text{-}2)^2 + (5)^2 + (\text{-}3)^2}{2}} = \sqrt{\dfrac{4 + 25 + 9}{2}} = \sqrt{\dfrac{38}{2}}$

$= \sqrt{19} = 4.359$

6. $\dfrac{(183 - 137.09)^2}{137.09} + \dfrac{(30 - 41.68)^2}{41.68} = \dfrac{(45.91)^2}{137.09} + \dfrac{(\text{-}11.68)^2}{41.68} = \dfrac{2107.7281}{137.09} + \dfrac{136.4224}{41.68}$

$= 15.375 + 3.273 = 18.647$

7. $\sqrt{\dfrac{10(513.27) - 71.5^2}{10(9)}} = \sqrt{\dfrac{5132.7 - 5112.25}{90}} = \sqrt{\dfrac{20.45}{90}} = \sqrt{.2272} = .477$

8. $\dfrac{8(151{,}879) - (516.5)(2176)}{\sqrt{8(34{,}525.75) - 516.5^2}\,\sqrt{8(728{,}520) - 2176^2}} = \dfrac{1215032 - 1123904}{\sqrt{9433.75}\,\sqrt{1093184}} = \dfrac{91128}{1015522} = .897$

9. $0.95^{500} = 7.27\text{E-}12 = 7.27 \cdot 10^{-12}$
$= .00000000000727;$ moving the decimal point left 12 places

NOTE: Calculators and computers vary in their representation of such numbers. This manual assumes they will be given in scientific notation as a two-decimal number between 1.00 and 9.99 inclusive followed by an indication (usually E for *exponent* of the multiplying power of ten) of how to adjust the decimal point to obtain a number in the usual notation (rounded to three significant digits).

10. $8^{14} = 4.40\text{E}+12 = 4.40 \cdot 10^{12}$
$= 4{,}400{,}000{,}000{,}000;$ moving the decimal point right 12 places

11. $9^{12} = 2.82\text{E}+11 = 2.82 \cdot 10^{11}$
$= 282{,}000{,}000{,}000;$ moving the decimal point right 11 places

12. $.25^{17} = 5.82\text{E-}11 = 5.82 \cdot 10^{-11}$
$= .0000000000582;$ moving the decimal point left 11 places

Chapter 2

Describing, Exploring, and Comparing Data

2-2 Frequency Distributions

1. Subtracting the first two consecutive lower class limits indicates that the class width is 100 - 90 = 10. Since there is a gap of 1.0 between the upper class limit of one class and the lower class limit of the next, class boundaries are determined by increasing or decreasing the appropriate class limits by (1.0)/2 = 0.5. The class boundaries and class midpoints are given in the table below.

pressure	class boundaries	class midpoint	frequency
90 - 99	89.5 - 99.5	94.5	1
100 - 109	99.5 - 109.5	104.5	4
110 - 119	109.5 - 119.5	114.5	17
120 - 129	119.5 - 129.5	124.5	12
130 - 139	129.5 - 139.5	134.5	5
140 - 149	139.5 - 149.5	144.5	0
150 - 159	149.5 - 159.5	154.5	1
			40

NOTE: Although they often contain extra decimal points and may involve consideration of how the data were obtained, class boundaries are the key to tabular and pictorial data summaries. Once the class boundaries are obtained, everything else falls into place. Here the first class width is readily seen to be 99.5 - 89.5 = 10.0 and the first midpoint is (89.5 + 99.5)/2 = 94.5. In this manual, class boundaries will typically be calculated first and then used to determine other values. In addition, the sum of the frequencies is an informative number used in many subsequent calculations and will be shown as an integral part of each table.

2. Since the gap between classes as presented is 1.0, the appropriate class limits are increased or decreased by (1.0)/2 = 0.5 to obtain the class boundaries and the following table.

pressure	class boundaries	class midpoint	frequency
80 - 99	79.5 - 99.5	89.5	9
100 - 119	99.5 - 119.5	109.5	24
120 - 139	119.5 - 139.5	129.5	5
140 - 159	139.5 - 159.5	149.5	1
160 - 179	159.5 - 179.5	169.5	0
180 - 199	179.5 - 199.5	189.5	1
			40

The class width is 99.5 - 79.5 = 20; the first midpoint is (79.5 + 99.5)/2 = 89.5.

3. Since the gap between classes as presented is 1.0 the appropriate class limits are increased or decreased by (1.0)/2 = .05 to obtain the class boundaries and the following table.

cholesterol	class boundaries	class midpoint	frequency
0 - 199	-0.5 - 199.5	99.5	13
200 - 399	199.5 - 399.5	299.5	11
400 - 599	399.5 - 599.5	499.5	5
600 - 799	599.5 - 799.5	699.5	8
800 - 999	799.5 - 999.5	899.5	2
1000 - 1199	999.5 - 1199.5	1099.5	0
1200 - 1399	1199.5 - 1399.5	1299.5	1
			40

The class width is 199.5 - (-0.5) = 200; the first midpoint is (-0.5 + 199.5)/2 = 99.5.

4. Since the gap between classes as presented is 0.1, the appropriate class limits are increased or decreased by $(0.1)/2 = 0.05$ to obtain the class boundaries and the following table.

mass index	class boundaries	class midpoint	frequency
15.0 - 20.9	14.95 - 20.95	17.95	10
21.0 - 26.9	20.95 - 26.95	23.95	15
27.0 - 32.9	26.95 - 32.95	29.95	11
33.0 - 38.9	32.95 - 38.95	35.95	2
39.0 - 44.9	38.95 - 44.95	41.95	2
			40

The class width is $20.95 - 14.95 = 6$; the first midpoint is $(14.95 + 20.95)/2 = 17.95$.

5. The relative frequency for each class is found by dividing its frequency by 40, the sum of the frequencies. NOTE: As before, the sum is included as an integral part of the table. For relative frequencies, this should always be 1.000 (i.e., 100%) and serves as a check for the calculations.

pressure	relative frequency
90 - 99	.025
100 - 109	.100
110 - 119	.425
120 - 129	.300
130 - 139	.125
140 - 149	.000
150 - 159	.025
	1.000

6. The relative frequency for each class is found by dividing its frequency by 40, the sum of the frequencies. **NOTE:** As before, the sum is as an integral part of the table. For relative frequencies, this should always be 1.000 (i.e., 100%) and serves as a check for the calculations.

pressure	relative frequency
80 - 99	.225
100 - 119	.600
120 - 139	.125
140 - 159	.025
160 - 179	.000
180 - 199	.025
	1.000

7. The relative frequency for each class is found by dividing its frequency by 40, the sum of the frequencies. NOTE: In #5, the relative frequencies were expressed as decimals; here they are expressed as percents. The choice is arbitrary.

cholesterol	relative frequency
0 - 199	.325
200 - 399	.275
400 - 599	.125
600 - 799	.200
800 - 999	.050
1000 -1199	.000
1200 -1399	.025
	1.000

8. The relative frequency for each class is found by dividing its frequency by 40, the sum of the frequencies. **NOTE:** In #6, the relative frequencies were expressed as decimals; here they are expressed as percents. The choice is arbitrary.

mass index	relative frequency
15.0 - 20.9	.250
21.0 - 26.9	.375
27.0 - 32.9	.275
33.0 - 38.9	.050
39.0 - 44.9	.050
	1.000

9. The cumulative frequencies are determined by repeated addition of successive frequencies to obtain the combined number in each class and all previous classes. NOTE: Consistent with the emphasis that has been placed on class boundaries, we choose to use upper class boundaries in the "less than" column. Conceptually, pressures occur on a continuum and the integer values reported are assumed to be the nearest whole number representation of the precise measure. An exact pressure of 99.7, for example, would be reported as 100 and fall in the second class. The values in the first class, therefore, are better described as being "less than 99.5" (using the upper class boundary) than as being "less than 100."

This distinction becomes crucial in the construction of pictorial representations in the next section. In addition, the fact that the final cumulative frequency must equal the total number (i.e, the sum of the frequency column) serves as a check for calculations. The sum of cumulative frequencies, however, has absolutely no meaning and is not included.

(#9) pressure	cumulative frequency		(#10) pressure	cumulative frequency
less than 99.5	1		less than 99.5	9
less than 109.5	5		less than 119.5	33
less than 119.9	22		less than 139.5	38
less than 129.5	34		less than 159.5	39
less than 139.5	39		less than 179.5	39
less than 149.5	39		less than 199.5	40
less than 159.5	40			

10. The cumulative frequencies are determined by repeated addition of successive frequencies to obtain the combined number in each class and all previous classes. **NOTE:** See NOTE for #9.

11. The cumulative frequencies are determined by repeated addition of successive frequencies to obtain the combined number in each class and all previous classes. NOTE: Consistent with the emphasis that has been placed on class boundaries, we choose to use upper class boundaries in the "less than" column.

(#11) cholesterol	cumulative frequency		(#12) mass index	cumulative frequency
less than 199.5	13		less than 20.95	10
less than 399.5	24		less than 26.95	25
less than 599.5	29		less than 32.95	36
less than 799.5	37		less than 38.95	38
less than 999.5	39		less than 44.95	40
less than 1199.5	39			
less than 1399.5	40			

12. The cumulative frequencies are determined by repeated addition of successive frequencies to obtain the combined number in each class and all previous classes. **NOTE:** See NOTE for #11.

13. The relative frequencies are determined by dividing the given frequencies by 200, the sum of the given frequencies. The fact that the sum of the relative frequencies is 1.000 provides a check to the arithmetic. For a fair die, we expect each relative frequency to be close to $1/6 = .167$. As these relative frequencies all fall between .135 and .210, they do not appear to differ significantly from the values expected for a fair die.

(#13) outcome	relative frequency		(#14) digit	relative frequency
1	.135		0	11.250%
2	.155		1	7.500%
3	.210		2	8.750%
4	.200		3	5.625%
5	.140		4	10.625%
6	.160		5	12.500%
	1.000		6	13.125%
			7	16.250%
			8	4.375%
			9	10.000%
				100.000%

14. The relative frequencies are determined by dividing the given frequencies by 160, the sum of the given frequencies. The fact that the sum of the relative frequencies is 1.000 provides a check to the arithmetic. For random selection with all digits equally likely, we expect each relative frequency to be close to $1/10 = 10\%$. As these relative frequencies range from 4% (less than ½ of expectation) to 16% (more than 1½ of the expectation,

they appear to differ significantly from the values for random selection with all digits equally likely.

15. For a lower class limit of 0 for the first class and a class width of 50, the frequency distribution is given at the right.
NOTE: The class limits for the first class are 0-49 and not 0-50.

weight (lbs)	frequency
0 - 49	6
50 - 99	10
100 - 149	10
150 - 199	7
200 - 249	8
250 - 299	2
300 - 349	4
350 - 399	3
400 - 449	3
450 - 499	0
500 - 549	1
	54

16. For a lower class limit of 96.5 for the first class and a class width of 0.4, the frequency distribution is given at the right.
NOTE: The classes may be identified using either class limits or class boundaries. While class boundaries typically introduce another decimal place in the presentation, they eliminate the impression that some data might have occurred in gaps between the classes.

temperature	frequency
96.45 - 96.85	1
96.85 - 97.25	8
97.25 - 97.65	14
97.65 - 98.05	22
98.05 - 98.45	19
98.45 - 98.85	32
98.85 - 99.25	6
99.25 - 99.65	4
	106

Two notable features of the frequency table are: [**NOTE:** Answers will vary]
(1) The class containing 98.6 has the greatest frequency, but the data do not center around that class.
(2) The data appear to have two peaks (near 97.85 and 98.65) with a slight valley between them – that could signify the placing together of two unimodal subpopulations (e.g., male/female, athletic/non-athletic, etc.).

17. The separate frequency distributions are given below.

male head circumference	frequency
34.0 - 35.9	2
36.0 - 37.9	0
38.0 - 39.9	5
40.0 - 41.9	29
42.0 - 43.9	14
	50

female head circumference	frequency
34.0 - 35.9	1
36.0 - 37.9	3
38.0 - 39.9	14
40.0 - 41.9	27
42.0 - 43.9	5
	50

It appears that the head circumferences tend to be larger for baby boys than for baby girls.

18. The separate frequency distributions are given below.

tobacco use (seconds)	frequency
0 - 99	39
100 - 199	6
200 - 299	4
300 - 399	0
400 - 499	0
500 - 599	1
	50

alcohol use (seconds)	frequency
0 - 99	46
100 - 199	3
200 - 299	0
300 - 399	0
400 - 499	1
	50

There does not appear to be a significant difference between the lengths of tobacco use and the lengths of alcohol use in animated movies for children.

19.   The separate relative frequency distributions are given below, to the right of the figure
       giving the actual frequencies. The relative frequencies were obtained by dividing the
       actual frequencies for each gender by the total frequencies for that gender.

M	age	F		male ages	relative frequency		female ages	relative frequency
11	19-28	8		19-28	.099		19-28	.205
43	29-38	18		29-38	.387		29-38	.462
31	39-48	4		39-48	.279		39-48	.103
22	49-58	7		49-58	.198		49-58	.179
4	59-68	2		59-68	.036		59-68	.051
111		39			1.000			1.000

Both genders have more runners in the 29-38 age group than in any other ten year spread.
But the second most populous category is the one above that for the males, and the one
below that for the females. It appears that the male runners tend to be slightly older than
the female runners.

20.   Assuming that "start the first class at" refers to the first lower class limit produces the
       following frequency tables for Regular and Diet Coke. In each case the relative
       frequencies were obtained by dividing the observed frequencies by 36.

REGULAR COKE weight (lbs)	relative frequency		DIET COKE weight (lbs)	relative frequency
.7900 - .7949	.028		.7750 - .7799	.111
.7950 - .7999	.000		.7800 - .7849	.361
.8000 - .8049	.028		.7850 - .7899	.417
.8050 - .8099	.083		.7900 - .7949	.111
.8100 - .8149	.111			1.000
.8150 - .8199	.472			
.8200 - .8249	.167			
.8250 - .8299	.111			
	1.000			

There are two significant differences between the data sets: the weights for Regular Coke
are considerably larger than those for Diet Coke, the weights for Regular Coke cover a
much wider range than those for Diet Coke. The first difference might be explained by the
weight of the sugar present in Regular Coke but not in Diet Coke. The second difference
suggests that the sugar might not be evenly distributed throughout the large amounts of
Regular Coke from which the cans are filled - assuming the cans are filled by volume, the
lighter cans could be coming from a portion of the mixture containing less sugar.

NOTE: The Diet Coke frequency table has only 4 categories, which is usually not
sufficient to give a picture of the nature of the distribution. This is allowable in this
context, since the class width and class limits employed work well with the other cola data
and permit meaningful comparisons across the data sets.

21.   Assuming that "start the first class at 200 lb"
       refers to the first lower class limit produces
       the frequency table given at the right.

weight (lbs)	frequency
200 - 219	6
220 - 239	5
240 - 259	12
260 - 279	36
280 - 299	87
300 - 319	28
320 - 339	0
340 - 359	0
360 - 379	0
380 - 399	0
400 - 419	0
420 - 439	0
440 - 459	0
460 - 479	0
480 - 499	0
500 - 519	1
	175

In general, an outlier can add several rows
to a frequency table. Even though most of
the added rows have frequency zero, the
table tends to suggest that these are possible
valid values – thus distorting the reader's
mental image of the distribution.

22. Let n = the number of data values
       x = the number of classes.
Solve the given formula x = 1 + (log n)/(log 2)
          for n to get $n = 2^{x-1}$.
Use the value x = 5.5, 6.5, 7.5,... to get the cut-ff values for n as follows.

x	$n = 2^{x-1}$	
5.5	22.63	(for n < 22.63, x rounds to 5; for n > 22.63, n rounds to 6)
6.5	45.25	(for n < 45.25, x rounds to 6; for n > 45.25, x rounds to 7)
7.5	90.51	(etc.)
8.5	181.02	
9.5	362.04	
10.5	724.04	
11.5	1448.15	
12.5	2896.31	

Assuming n ≥ 16, use the cut-off values to complete the table as follows.

n	ideal # of classes
16– 22	5
23– 45	6
46– 90	7
91– 181	8
182– 362	9
363– 724	10
725–1448	11
1449–2896	12

2-3 Visualizing Data

1. The answer depends upon what is meant by "the center." Since the ages seem to range from about 10 to about 70, 40 could be called the center value - in the sense that it is half way between the lowest and highest points on the horizontal axis that represent observed data. Since the ages are concentrated at the lower end of the scale, an age near 24 could be called the center value - in the sense that about ½ of the 131 ages appear to be below 24 and about ½ of the ages appear to be above 24. Or an age near 26 could be called the center value - in the sense that a fulcrum placed under 26 on the horizontal would appears to nearly "balance" the histogram.

2. The lowest and highest possible ages appear to be about 10 and 70 respectively.

3. The percentage younger than 30 is about (1+38+38+16)/131 = 93/131 = .710 = 71.0%.

4. The class width is 5 - the class at the left with frequency 1 appears to extend from about 10 to 15, and the adjacent class with frequency 38 appear to extend from about 15 to 20.

5. Since, the shading representing Group A covers about 40% of the "pie," the approximate percentage of people with Group A blood is 40%. If the chart is based on a sample of 500 people, approximately (.40)(500) = 200 people had Group A blood.

6. Since, the shading representing Group B covers about 10% of the "pie," the approximate percentage of people with Group B blood is 10%. If the chart is based on a sample of 500 people, approximately (.10)(500) = 50 people had Group B blood.

7.   Obtain the relative frequencies by dividing each frequency by the total frequency for each sample. The two relative frequency histograms are given, using the same scale, below at the right. Each sample distribution spreads out in both directions from a "typical" (or most frequently occurring value), but the faculty data appears to be shifted to the left by about one interval. Since each interval represents 3 years, the faculty cars are about 3 years newer than the student cars. In addition, the majority of the student car ages fall below the class with the highest frequency, while faculty car ages tend to occur above their most populous class.

NOTE: The class boundaries in the histograms are -0.5, 2.5, 5.5, etc. Assuming the car ages were obtained by subtracting the model year from the calendar year, that boundary scheme is consistent with the new models being introduced ½ year "early" and sold at a steady rate during the calendar year. In truth, this data is difficult to present in a graph that accounts for the underlying continuity of the ages. The figures given below are probably the best for the level of this text.

STUDENTS

age	frequency	relative frequency
0- 2	23	.106
3- 5	33	.152
6- 8	63	.290
9-11	68	.313
12-14	19	.088
15-17	10	.046
18-20	1	.005
21-23	0	.000
	217	1.000

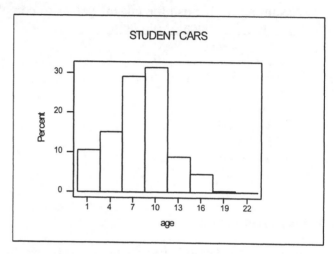

FACULTY

age	frequency	relative frequency
0- 2	30	.197
3- 5	47	.309
6- 8	36	.237
9-11	30	.197
12-14	8	.053
15-17	0	.000
18-20	0	.000
21-23	1	.007
	152	1.000

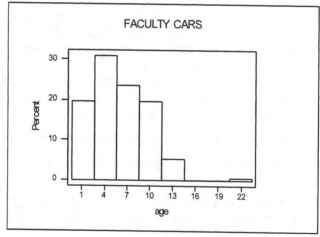

8. See the figure below. The bars extend from class boundary to class boundary. Each axis is labeled numerically <u>and</u> with the name of the quantity represented. Although the posted limit is 30 mph, it appears that the police ticket only those traveling at least 42 mph.

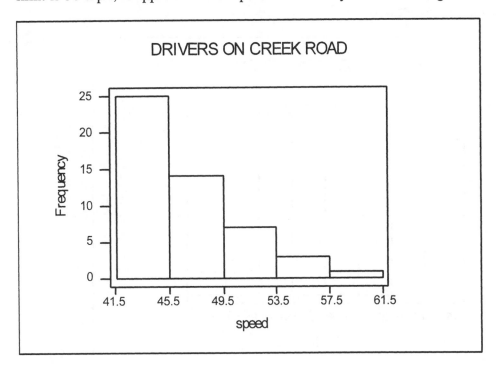

9. See the figure below. The class boundaries are -0.5, 49.5, 99.5, 149.5, ... 549.5. The bars extend from class boundary to class boundary. For visual simplicity, the horizontal axis has been labeled 0, 50, 150, etc. The "center" of the weights (i.e., the "balance point" of the histogram) appears to be about 190.

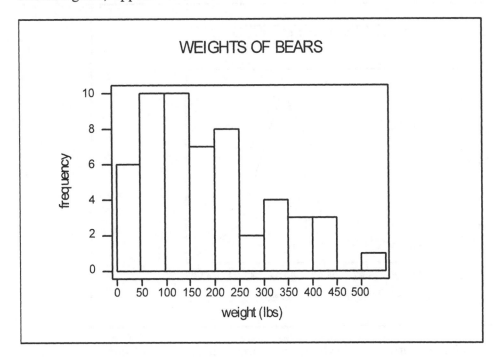

10.   See the figure below. The distribution appears to be approximately bell-shaped and suggests that the average body temperature may be less than the commonly believed 98.6°F. The distribution of normal temperatures is important because it may be used to identify abnormal temperatures.

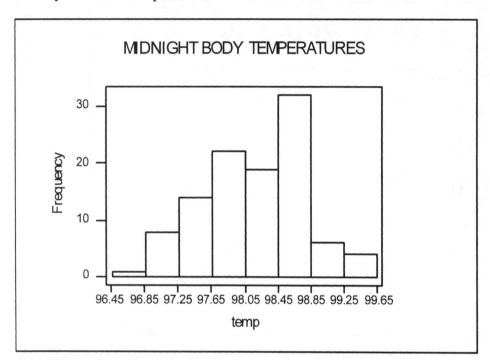

11.   See the figure below. The frequencies are plotted above the class midpoints, and "extra" midpoints are added so that both polygons begin and end with a frequency of zero. The females are represented by the solid line, and the males by the dashes.

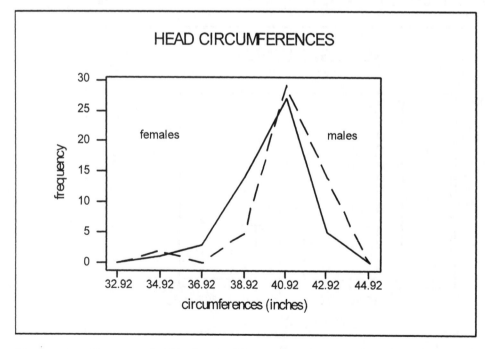

Both polygons have approximately the same shape, but the male circumferences appear to be slightly larger.

12. See the figure below. The frequencies are plotted above the class midpoints, and "extra midpoints are added so that both polygons begin and end with a frequency of zero. Tobacco is represented by the solid line, and alcohol by the dashes.

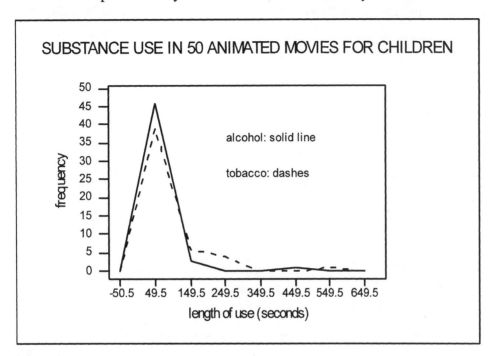

The two polygons are virtually on top of each other. There appears to be no significant difference in the lengths of time that alcohol and tobacco use are shown in the films.

13. See the figures below. Since ages are reported as of the last birthday, the class boundaries are 19,29,39,49,59,69 – i.e., the first class in each figure includes all ages from 19.000 to 28.999.

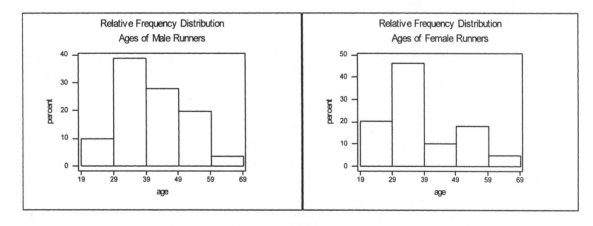

The two histograms are almost identical, except for the "dip" at age 39-49 for the females. It could be that physical or family conditions that typically occur about that age for females are not conducive to running marathons. Because of that dip, it appears that the male runners are slightly older than their female counterparts.

14. See the figure below. The frequencies are plotted above the class midpoints, and "extra" midpoints are added so that both polygons begin and end with a frequency of zero. The horizontal axis is labeled for convenience of presentation, but the frequencies are plotted beginning at .77245 and every .005 thereafter – .77245, .77745,…,.82745,.83245.

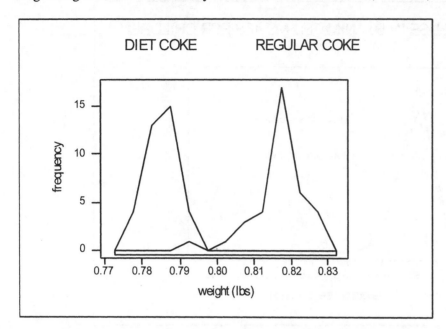

The two distributions have similar shapes, but the diet Coke weights are less than those of regular Coke - probably because of the weight of the sugar in regular Coke.

15. The original numbers are listed by the row in which they appear in the stem-and-leaf plot.

stem	leaves	original numbers
20	0005	200, 200, 200, 205
21	69999	216, 219, 219, 219, 219
22	2233333	222, 222, 223, 223, 223, 223, 223
23		
24	1177	241, 241, 247, 247

16. The original numbers are listed by the row in which they appear in the stem-and-leaf plot.

stem	leaves	original numbers
50	12 12 12 55	5012, 5012, 5012, 5055
51		
52	00 00 00 00	5200, 5200, 5200, 5200
53	27 27 35	5327, 5327, 5335
54	72	5472

17. The dotplot is constructed using the original scores as follows. Each space represents 1 unit.

18. The dotplot is constructed using the original scores as follows.

19.   The expanded stem-and-leaf plot below on the left is one possibility. NOTE: The text claims that stem-and-leaf plots enable us to "see the distribution of data and yet keep all the information in the original list." Following the suggestion to round the nearest inch not only loses information but also uses subjectivity to round values exactly half way between. Since always rounding such values "up" creates a slight bias, many texts suggest rounding toward the even digit – so that 33.5 becomes 34, but 36.5 becomes 36. The technique below of using superscripts to indicate the occasional decimals is both mathematically clear and visually uncluttered.

```
stem│leaves
   3│6  7
   4│0  0  1  3  3⁵
   4│6  6  7  8  8  9
   5│0  2  2⁵ 3  3  4
   5│7³ 7⁵ 8  9  9  9
   6│0  0⁵ 1  1  1⁵ 2  3  3  3  3⁵ 4  4  4
   6│5  5  6⁵ 7  7⁵ 8⁵
   7│0  0⁵ 2  2  2  2  3  3⁵
   7│5  6⁵
```

20.   The stem-and-left plot below is one possibility. **NOTE:** The text claims that stem-and-leaf plots enable us to "see the distribution of data and yet keep all the information in the original list." Following the suggestion to round the nearest tenth not only loses information but also uses subjectivity to round values exactly half way between. Since always rounding such values "up" creates a slight bias, many texts suggest rounding toward the even digit – so that 2.35 becomes 2.4, but 3.05 becomes 3.0. The figure below is accurate and uncluttered.

```
stem│leaves
  0.│15  27  38
  0.│58  63  65  72  74  80  85  89  92  92  93
  1.│14  15  28  36  40  41  41  44  44  45  45  48  49
  1.│53  53  58  61  68  74  81
  2.│00  04  10  13  13  17  19  19  30  31  35  44
  2.│66  68  83  83  87  88  93  96  97
  3.│05  36  42
  3.│53
  4.│37
  4.│69
  5.│28
```

21.   See the figure below, with bars arranged in order of magnitude. Networking appears to be the most effective job-seeking approach.

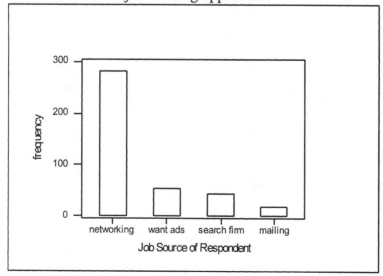

22.   The pie chart is given below at the left. The Pareto chart appears to be more effective in showing the relative importance of job sources.

Job Source of Responder

Causes of Train Derailments

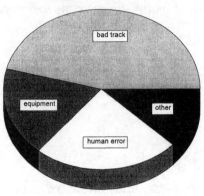

23.   See the figure above at the right. The sum of the frequencies is 50; the relative frequencies are 23/50 = 46%, 9/50 = 18%, 12/50 = 24%, and 6/50 = 12%. The corresponding central angles are (.46)360° = 165.6°, (.18)360° = 64.8°, (.24)360° = 86.4°, and (.12)360° = 43.2°. To be complete, the figure needs to be titled with the name of the quantity being measured.

24.   See the following figure, with bars arranged in order of magnitude. The Pareto chart appears to be more effective in showing the relative importance of the causes of train derailments.

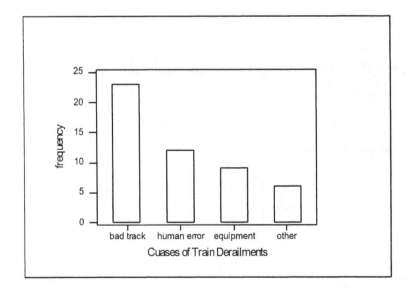

25. The scatter diagram is given below. The figure should have a title, and each axis should be labeled both numerically and with the name of the variable. An "x" marks a single occurrence, while numbers indicate multiple occurrences at a point. Cigarettes high in tar also tend to be high in CO. The points cluster about a straight line from (0,0) to (18,18), indicating that the mg of CO tends to be about equal to the mg of tar.

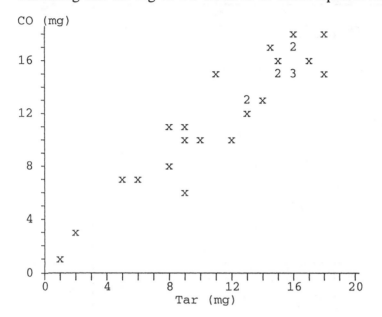

26. The scatter diagram is given below. The figure should have a title, and each axis should be labeled both numerically and with the name of the variable. An "x" marks a single occurrence, while numbers indicate the multiple occurrences at a point. The pattern indicates that bears with large necks also tend to have high weights.

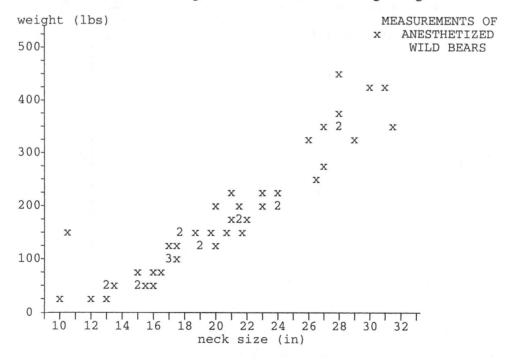

27.   The time series graph is given below. An investor could use this graph to project where the market might be next year and invest accordingly. The flat portion at the right might be suggesting that the market has reached a point at which it will level off for a while – and that the rapid growth of the last several years may be at end..

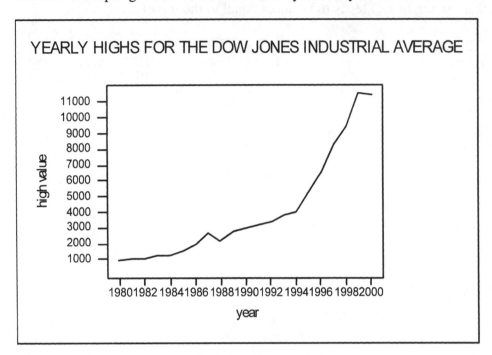

28.   The time series graph is given below. There appears to be a downward trend – which may be due to increased seat belt use and/or safety improvements in both automobiles and the highways.

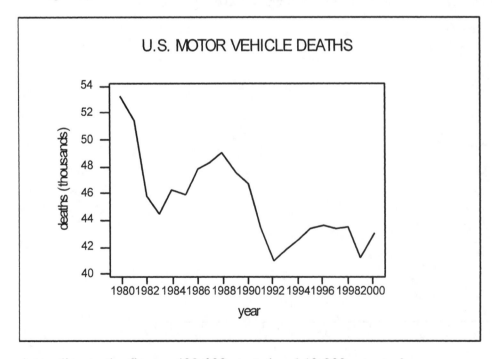

29.   According to the figure, 422,000 started and 10,000 returned.
       10,000/422,000 = 2.37%

30.   According to the figure, there were 50,000 men prior to crossing the Berezina River on the

return trip and 28,000 after crossing the river. The number who died was 22,000 or
22,000/50,000 = 44%.
NOTE: The figure is a summary that gives only periodic counts, and it is not necessarily
true that 22,000 died <u>while</u> crossing the river.

31.   The figure indicates the number of men had just dropped to 37,000 on November 9 when
the temperature was 16°F (-9°C), and had just dropped to 24,000 on November 14 when
the temperature was -6°F (-21°C). The number who died during that time, therefore, was
37,000 - 24,000 = 13,000.

32.   The figure indicates that 100,000 men reached Moscow and that 20,000 of those survived
to rejoin about 30,000 of their comrades at Botr. The number who died on that portion of
the return trip, therefore, was 100,000 - 20,000 = 80,000.

33.   NOTE: Exercise #20 of section 2-2 dealt with frequency table representations of this data
and specified a class width of 20. Using a class width with an odd number of units of
measure allows the class midpoint to have the same number of decimal places as the
original data and often produces more appealing visual representations. Here we use a
class width of 25 – with class midpoints of 200, 225, etc. – and so the figures will differ
from ones made using the previous classes. The histogram bars extend from class
boundary to class boundary (i.e., from 187.5 to 212.5 for the first class), but for
convenience the labels have been placed at the class midpoints.

a. The histogram with the outlier is as shown below.

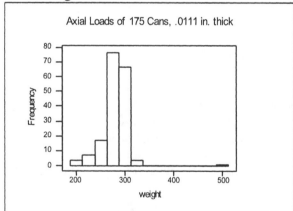

b. The histogram without the outlier is as shown below.

c. The basic shape of the histogram does not change, except that a distant piece has been
"broken off." NOTE: The redrawn histogram in part (b) should not be an exact copy of
the one in part (a) with the distant bar erased. Since removing the distant bar reduces

the effective width of the figure significantly, the rule that the height should be approximately 3/4 of the width requires either making the remaining bars wider (and keeping the figure's height) or making them shorter (and keeping the figure's reduced width). To do otherwise produces a figure too tall for its width – and one that tends to visually overstate the differences between classes.

2-4 Measures of Center

NOTE: As it is common in mathematics and statistics to use symbols instead of words to represent quantities that are used often and/or that may appear in equations, this manual employs symbols for the measures of central tendency as follows:

mean = $\bar{x}$ mode = M
median = $\tilde{x}$ midrange = m.r.

Also, this manual generally follows the author's guideline of presenting means, medians and midranges accurate to one more decimal place than found in the original data. The mode, the only measure which must be one of the original pieces of data, is presented with the same accuracy as the original data. This manual will, however, recognize the following two exceptions to these guidelines.
(1) When there are an odd number of data, the median will be one of the original values and will not be reported to one more decimal place. And so the median of 1,2,3,4,5 would be reported as 3.
(2) When the mean falls exactly halfway between two values that meet the guidelines, an extra decimal place ending in 5 will be used. And so the mean of 1,2,3,3 would be reported as 9/4 = 2.25.

1. Arranged in order, the 6 scores are: 0 0 0 176 223 548
    a. $\bar{x}$ = $(\Sigma x)/n$ = (947)/6 = 157.8   c. M = 0
    b. $\tilde{x}$ = (0 + 176)/2 = 88.0   d. m.r. = (0 + 548)/2 = 274.0
    Whether or not there is a problem with scenes of tobacco use in animated children's films depends on the scene. If a likeable character uses tobacco without any criticism or ill effects, this would suggest to children that such usage is appropriate and acceptable. In most children's films, however, tobacco usage is typically associated with evil and undesirable characters and situations – suggesting that tobacco usage is not appropriate or acceptable for decent persons.

NOTE: The median is the middle score when the scores are arranged in order, and the midrange is halfway between the first and last score when the scores are arranged in order. It is therefore usually helpful to begin by placing the scores in order. This will not affect the mean, and it may also aid in identifying the mode. In addition, no measure of central tendency can have a value lower than the smallest score or higher than the largest score – remembering this helps to protect against gross errors, which most commonly occur when calculating the mean.

2. Arranged in order, the 12 scores are:
    70.9 74.0 78.6 79.2 79.5 80.2 82.5 83.7 84.3 84.6 85.3 86.2
    a. $\bar{x}$ = $(\Sigma x)/n$ = (969.0)/12 = 80.75   c. M = [none]
    b. $\tilde{x}$ = (80.2 + 82.5)/2 = 81.35   d. m.r. = (70.9 + 86.2)/2 = 78.55
    Yes; if the pages were randomly selected, their sample mean is likely to be a reasonable estimate of the mean level of the whole book.

3. Arranged in order, the 16 scores are:
    .03 .07 .09 .13 .13 .17 .24 .30 .39 .43 .43 .44 .45 .47 .47 .48
    a. $\bar{x}$ = $(\Sigma x)/n$ = (4.72)/16 = .295   c. M = .13,.43,.47 [tri-modal]
    b. $\tilde{x}$ = (.30 + .39)/2 = .345   d. m.r. = (.03 + .48)/2 = .255
    No; this sample means weights each brand of cereal equally and does not take into account

which of the cereals have higher (or lower) rates of consumption.

4. Arranged in order, the 15 scores are:
    17.7 19.9 19.6 20.6 21.4 22.0 23.8 24.0 25.2 27.5 28.9 29.1 29.9 33.5 37.7
    a. $\bar{x} = (\Sigma x)/n = (380.5)/15 = 25.37$ c. M = 19.6
    b. $\tilde{x} = 24.0$ d. m.r. = (17.7 + 37.7)/2 = 27.70
    Yes; the mean of this sample is reasonably close to 25.74, the overall mean of all 40
    values.

5. Arranged in order, the 15 scores are:
    .12 .13 .14 .16 .16 .16 .17 .17 .17 .18 .21 .24 .24 .27 .29
    a. $\bar{x} = (\Sigma x)/n = (2.81)/15 = .187$ c. M = .16,.17 [bi-modal]
    b. $\tilde{x} = .17$ d. m.r. = (.12 + .29)/2 = .205
    Yes; these values appear to be significantly above the allowed maximum.

6. Arranged in order, the 18 scores are:
    14 16 17 18 20 21 23 24 25 27 28 30 31 34 37 38 40 42
    a. $\bar{x} = (\Sigma x)/n = (485)/18 = 26.9$ c. M = [none]
    b. $\tilde{x} = (25 + 27)/2 = 26.0$ d. m.r. = (14 + 42)/2 = 28.0
    Yes; these results support the common belief that those killed in motorcycle accidents
    come from among the younger drivers.

7. Arranged in order, the 20 scores are:
    15 17 17 17 17 17 17 18 18 18 18 18 19 19 19 19 20 21 21 21
    a. $\bar{x} = (\Sigma x)/n = (366)/20 = 18.3$ c. M = 17
    b. $\tilde{x} = (18 + 18)/2 = 18.0$ d. m.r. = (15 + 21)/2 = 18.0
    The sample results appear to be very consistent – i.e., there appears to be little variation
    from person to person. This suggests that there is little variation in the population, and
    that the sample mean should be a good estimate of the population mean – in the sense that
    other samples would likely produce similar results that vary little from this sample

8. Arranged in order, the 12 scores are:
    654.2 661.3 662.2 662.7 667.0 667.4 669.8 670.7 672.2 672.2 672.6 679.2
    a. $\bar{x} = (\Sigma x)/n = (8011.5)/12 = 667.625$ c. M = 672.2
    b. $\tilde{x} = (667.4 + 669.8)/2 = 668.60$ d. m.r. = (654.2 + 679.2)/2 = 666.70
    A serious consequence of having weights that vary too much would be the uncertainty
    about how much medication was actually being taken.

9. Arranged in order, the scores are as follows.
    JV: 6.5 6.6 6.7 6.8 7.1 7.3 7.4 7.7 7.7 7.7
    Pr: 4.2 5.4 5.8 6.2 6.7 7.7 7.7 8.5 9.3 10.0

Jefferson Valley	Providence
n = 10	n = 10
$\bar{x} = (\Sigma x)/n = (71.5)/10 = 7.15$	$\bar{x} = (\Sigma x)/n = (71.5)/10 = 7.15$
$\tilde{x} = (7.1 + 7.3)/2 = 7.20$	$\tilde{x} = (6.7 + 7.7)/2 = 7.20$
M = 7.7	M = 7.7
m.r. = (6.5 + 7.7)/2 = 7.10	m.r. = (4.2 + 10.0)/2 = 7.10

    Comparing only measures of central tendency, one might suspect the two sets are identical.
    The Jefferson Valley times, however, are considerably less variable.
    NOTE: This is the reason most banks have gone to the single waiting line. While it
    doesn't make service faster, it makes service times more equitable by eliminating the "luck
    of the draw" – i.e., ending up by pure chance in a fast or slow line and having unusually
    short or long waits.

10. Arranged in order, the scores are as follows.
     Regular: .8150 .8163 .8181 .8192 .8211 .8247
         Diet: .7758 .7773 .7844 .7861 .7868 .7896

Regular

$n = 6$
$\bar{x} = (\Sigma x)/n = (4.9144)/6 = .81907$
$\tilde{x} = (.8181 + .8192)/2 = .81865$
$M = $ [none]
m.r. $= (.8150 + .8247)/2 = .81985$

Diet

$n = 6$
$\bar{x} = (\Sigma x)/n = (4.7000)/6 = .78333$
$\tilde{x} = (.7844 + .7861)/2 = .78525$
$M = $ [none]
m.r. $= (.7758 + .7896)/2 = .78270$

Diet Coke appears to weigh less than regular Coke, perhaps because it contains less sugar.

11. Arranged in order, the scores are as follows.
     McDonald's: 92 118 128 136 153 176 192 193 240 254 267 287
     Jack in the Box: 74 109 109 190 229 255 270 300 328 377 428 481

McDonald's

$n = 12$
$\bar{x} = (\Sigma x)/n = (2236)/12 = 186.3$
$\tilde{x} = (176 + 192)/2 = 184.0$
$M = $ [none]
m.r. $= (92 + 287)/2 = 189.5$

Jack in the Box

$n = 12$
$\bar{x} = (\Sigma x)/n = (3150)/12 = 262.5$
$\tilde{x} = (255 + 270)/2 = 262.5$
$M = 109$
m.r. $= (74 + 481)/2 = 277.5$

McDonald's appears to be faster. Yes; the difference appears to be significant.

12. Arranged in order, the scores are as follows.
     BC: 119 125 126 126 128 128 129 131 131 131 132 138
     AD: 126 126 129 130 131 133 134 136 137 138 139 141

4000 BC skulls

$n = 12$
$\bar{x} = (\Sigma x)/n = (1544)/12 = 128.7$
$\tilde{x} = (128 + 129)/2 = 128.5$
$M = 131$
m.r. $= (119 + 138)/2 = 128.5$

150 AD skulls

$n = 12$
$\bar{x} = (\Sigma x)/n = (1600)/12 = 133.3$
$\tilde{x} = (133 + 134)/2 = 133.5$
$M = 126$
m.r. $= (126 + 141)/2 = 133.5$

Yes; the head sizes appear to have changed, indicating possible interbreeding.
NOTE: This example illustrates the difficulty with using the mode to measure what is typical. When the observed values are approximately evenly spread out across all the scores and do not "bunch up" around a most popular score, the mode could be any score (no matter how unrepresentative) that just happened to occur twice.

13. The following values were obtained for the head circumference data, where x_i indicates the ith score from the ordered list.

males

$n = 50$
$\bar{x} = (\Sigma x)/n = 2054.9/50 = 41.10$
$\tilde{x} = (x_{25} + x_{26})/2$
     $= (41.1 + 41.1)/2 = 41.10$

females

$n = 50$
$\bar{x} = (\Sigma x)/n = 2002.4/50 = 40.05$
$\tilde{x} = (x_{25} + x_{26})/2)/2$
     $= (40.2 + 40.2 = 40.20$

No; on the basis of the means and medians alone, there does not appear to be a significant difference between the genders.

14. The following Flesch-Kincaid Grade Level Rating values were obtained for the three authors, where x_i indicates the ith score from the ordered list.

Clancy	Rowling	Tolstoy
n = 12	n = 12	n = 12
$\bar{x} = (\Sigma x)/n$	$\bar{x} = (\Sigma x)/n$	$\bar{x} = (\Sigma x)/n$
= 78.0/12 = 6.50	= 60.9/12 = 5.075	= 101.2/12 = 8.43
$\tilde{x} = (x_6 + x_7)/2$	$\tilde{x} = (x_6 + x_7)/2$	$\tilde{x} = (x_6 + x_7)/2$
= (5.4+6.1)/2 = 5.75	= (4.9+5.2)/12 = 5.05	= (8.2+8.3)/2 = 8.30

Yes; the ratings appear to be different.

15. The following values were obtained for Boston rainfall, where x_i indicates the ith score from the ordered list.

Thursday	Sunday
n = 52	n = 52
$\bar{x} = (\Sigma x)/n = 3.57/52 = .069$	$\bar{x} = (\Sigma x)/n = 3.52/52 = .068$
$\tilde{x} = (x_{26}+x_{27})/2 = (.00 + .00)/2 = .000$	$\tilde{x} = (x_{26}+x_{27})/2 = (.00 + .00)/2 = .000$

If "it rains more on weekends" refers to the amount of rain, the data do not support the claim. The amount of rainfall appears to be virtually the same for Thursday and Sunday. If "it rains more on weekends" refers to the frequency of rain (regardless of the amount), then the proportions of days on which there was rain would have to be compared.

16. The following lengths (in seconds) of scenes showing tobacco and alcohol use were obtained for the animated children's movies, where x_i indicates the ith score from the ordered list.

tobacco	alcohol
n = 50	n = 50
$\bar{x} = (\Sigma x)/n = 2872/50 = 57.4$	$\bar{x} = (\Sigma x)/n = 1623/50 = 32.5$
$\tilde{x} = (x_{25}+x_{26})/2 = (5+6)/2 = 5.5$	$\tilde{x} = (x_{25}+x_{26})/2 = (0+3)/2 = 1.5$

Yes; there does appear to be a difference in the times. Whether or not "more time" is synonymous with a "larger problem" depends on the nature of the scenes. If the scenes where the product is used present the product in a negative manner, then "more time" spent in a manner critical of the product corresponds to a "more wholesome" attitude being conveyed.

17. The x values below are the class midpoints from the given frequency table.

x	f	x·f
44.5	8	356.0
54.5	44	2398.0
64.5	23	1483.5
74.5	6	447.0
84.5	107	9041.5
94.5	11	1039.5
104.5	1	104.5
	200	14870.0

$$\bar{x} = (\Sigma x \cdot f)/n$$
$$= (14870.0)/200$$
$$= 74.35$$

NOTE: The mean time was calculated to be 74.35 minutes. According to the rule given in the text, this value should be rounded to one decimal place. The text describes how many decimal places to present in an answer, but not the actual rounding process. When the figure to be rounded is <u>exactly</u> half-way between two values (i.e., the digit in the position to be discarded is a 5, and there are no further digits because the calculations have "come out even"), there is no universally accepted rounding rule. Some authors say to always round up such a value; others correctly note that always rounding up introduces a consistent bias, and that the value should actually be rounded up half the time and rounded down half the time. And so some authors suggest rounding toward the even value (e.g., .65 becomes .6 and .75 becomes .8), while others simply suggest flipping a coin. In this manual, answers <u>exactly</u> half-way between will be reported without rounding (i.e., stated to one more decimal than usual).

18.   The individual x values may be used directly ion the calculations as follows.

x	f	x·f
1	27	27
2	31	62
3	42	126
4	40	160
5	28	140
6	32	192
	200	707

$$\overline{x} = (\Sigma x \cdot f)/n$$
$$= (707)/200$$
$$= 3.5$$

This sample mean of 3.5 is identical (to one decimal accuracy) to the true mean of the equally-weighted values 1,2,3,4,5,6. While loading the die might be expected to affect the relative frequency of occurrence of some of the values, it this case it appears not to have affected the overall mean value that occurs.

19.   The x values below are the class midpoints from the given frequency table.

x	f	x·f
43.5	25	1087.5
47.5	14	665.0
51.5	7	360.5
55.5	3	166.5
59.5	1	59.5
	50	2339.0

$$\overline{x} = (\Sigma x \cdot f)/n$$
$$= (2339.0)/50$$
$$= 46.8$$

The mean speed of 46.8 mi/hr of those ticketed by the police is more than 1.5 times the posted speed limit of 30 mi/hr. NOTE: This indicates nothing about the mean speed of *all* drivers, a figure which may or may not be higher than the posted limit.

20.   The x values below are the class midpoints from the given frequency table.

x	f	x·f
96.65	1	96.65
97.05	8	776.40
97.45	14	1634.30
97.85	22	2152.70
98.25	19	1866.75
98.65	32	3156.80
99.05	6	594.30
99.45	4	397.80
	106	10405.70

$$\overline{x} = (\Sigma x \cdot f)/n$$
$$= (10405.70)/106$$
$$= 98.17$$

This sample mean of 98.17°F appears to be significantly less than the commonly assumed population mean of 98.6°F.

21.   a. Arranged in order, the original 54 scores are:

26   29   34   40   46   48   60   62   64   65   76   79   80   86   90
94 105 114 116 120 125 132 140 140 144 148 150 150 154 166
166 180 182 202 202 204 204 212 220 220 236 262 270 316 332
344 348 356 360 365 416 436 446 514

$\overline{x} = (\Sigma x)/n = (9876)/54 = 182.9$

b. Trimming the highest and lowest 10% (or 5.4 = 5 scores), the remaining 44 scores are:

48   60   62   64   65   76   79   80   86   90   94 105 114 116 120
125 132 140 140 144 148 150 150 154 166 166 180 182 202 202
204 204 212 220 220 236 262 270 316 332 344 348 356 360

$\overline{x} = (\Sigma x)/n = (7524)/44 = 171.0$

c. Trimming the highest and lowest 20% (or $10.8 = 11$ scores), the remaining 32 scores are:

```
 79   80   86   90   94 105 114 116 120 125 132 140 140 144 148
150 150 154 166 166 180 182 202 202 204 204 212 220 220 236
262 270
```

$\bar{x} = (\Sigma x)/n = (5093)/32 = 159.2$

In this case, the mean gets smaller as more scores are trimmed. In general, means can increase, decrease, or stay the same as more scores are trimmed. The mean decreased here because the higher scores were farther from the original mean than were the lower scores.

22. No, the result is not the national average teacher's salary. Since there are many more teachers in California, for example, than Nevada, those state averages should not be counted equally – a weighted average (where the weights are the numbers of teachers in each state) should be used.

23. Let $\bar{x}_h$ stand for the harmonic mean: $\bar{x}_h = n/[\Sigma(1/x)] = 2/[1/40 + 1/60] = 2/[.0417]$
$= 48.0$

24. The geometric mean of the five values is the fifth root of their product.
$\sqrt[5]{(1.10)(1.08)(1.09)(1.12)(1.07)} = 1.092$

25. R.M.S. $= \sqrt{\Sigma x^2/n} = \sqrt{[(110)^2 + (0)^2 + (-60)^2 + (12)^2]/4} = \sqrt{15844/4} = \sqrt{3961} = 62.9$

2-5 Measures of Variation

NOTE: Although not given in the text, the symbol R will be used for the range throughout this manual. Remember that the range is the difference between the highest and the lowest scores, and not necessarily the difference between the last and the first values as they are listed. Since calculating the range involves only the subtraction of 2 original pieces of data, that measure of variation will be reported with the same accuracy as the original data.

1.

x	$x - \bar{x}$	$(x-\bar{x})^2$	x^2
0	-157.83	24910.3089	0
0	-157.83	24910.3089	0
0	-157.83	24910.3089	0
176	18.17	330.1489	30976
223	65.17	4247.1289	49729
548	390.17	152232.6289	300304
947	0.02	231540.8834	381009

$\bar{x} = (\Sigma x)/n = 947/6 = 157.83$

$R = 548 0 = 548$

by formula 2-4,
$s^2 = \Sigma(x-\bar{x})^2/(n-1)$
$= 231540.8834/5$
$= 46308.17$
$= 46308.2$

by formula 2-5,
$s^2 = [n(\Sigma x^2) - (\Sigma x)^2]/[n(n-1)]$
$= [6(381009) - (947)^2]/[6(5)]$
$= [1388888889245]/[30]$
$= 46308.17$
$= 46308.2$

$s = \sqrt{46308.17} = 215.2$

The times appear to vary widely.

NOTE: When finding the square root of the variance to obtain the standard deviation, use <u>all</u> the decimal places of the variance, and not the rounded value reported as the answer. The best way to do this is either to keep the value on the calculator display or to place it in the memory. Do <u>not</u> copy down all the decimal places and then re-enter them to find the square root, as that could introduce round-off and/or copying errors.

When using formula 2-4, constructing a table having the first three columns shown above helps to organize the calculations and makes errors less likely. In addition, verify that $\Sigma(x-\bar{x}) = 0$ [except for a possible small discrepancy at the last decimal, due to using a rounded value for the mean] before proceeding – if such is not the case, there is an error and further calculation is fruitless. For completeness, and as a check, both formulas 2-4 and 2-5 were used above. In general, only formula 2-5 will be used throughout the remainder of this manual for the following reasons:

(1) When the mean does not "come out even," formula 2-4 involves round-off error and/or many messy decimal calculations.

(2) The quantities Σx and Σx^2 needed for formula 2-5 can be found directly and conveniently on the calculator from the original data without having to construct a table like the one above.

2. preliminary values: $n = 12$, $\Sigma x = 969.0$, $\Sigma x^2 = 78487.82$
$R = 86.2 - 70.9 = 15.3$
$s^2 = [n(\Sigma x^2) - (\Sigma x)^2]/[n(n-1)] = [12(78487.82) - (969.0)^2]/[12(11)]$
     $= (2892.84)/132 = 21.92$
$s = 4.68$

Yes; since the 12 pages were selected at random, s =4.68 should be a reasonable estimate for the entire book.

3. preliminary values: $n = 16$, $\Sigma x = 4.72$, $\Sigma x^2 = 1.8144$
$R = .48 - .03 = .45$
$s^2 = [n(\Sigma x^2) - (\Sigma x)^2]/[n(n-1)] = [16(1.8144) - (4.72)^2]/[16(15)]$
     $= (6.7520)/240 = .028$
$s = .168$

No; this value is not likely to be a good estimate for the standard deviation among the amounts in each gram consumed by the population. This value gives equal weight to each cereal in the sample, no matter how popular (or unpopular) it is with consumers. The sample is not representative of the consumption patters.

NOTE: The quantity $[n(\Sigma x^2) - (\Sigma x)^2]$ cannot be less than zero. A negative value indicates that there is an error and that further calculation is fruitless. In addition, remember to find the value for s by taking the square root of the precise value of s^2 showing on the calculator display <u>before</u> it is rounded to one more decimal place than the original data.

4. preliminary values: $n = 15$, $\Sigma x = 380.5$, $\Sigma x^2 = 10101.23$
$R = 37.7 - 17.7 = 20.0$
$s^2 = [n(\Sigma x^2) - (\Sigma x)^2]/[n(n-1)] = [15(1010.23) - (380.5)^2]/[15(14)]$
     $= (6738.20)/210 = 32.09$
$s = 5.66$

Yes; this sample value is reasonably close to the true value for all women in the data set.

5. preliminary values: $n = 15$, $\Sigma x = 2.81$, $\Sigma x^2 = .5631$
$R = .29 - .12 = .17$
$s^2 = [n(\Sigma x^2) - (\Sigma x)^2]/[n(n-1)] = [15(.5631) - (2.81)^2]/[15(14)]$
     $= (.5504)/210 = .00262$
$s = .051$

No; the intent is to lower the mean amount. If all drivers had high concentrations (e.g., between .35 and .30), there would be a low s – but a high level of drunk driving.
NOTE: Following the usual round-off rule of giving answers with one more decimal than the original data produces a variance of .003, which has only one significant digit.
This is an unusual situation occurring because values less than 1.0 become smaller when they are squared. Since the original data had 2 significant digits, we provide 3 significant digits for the variance.

6. preliminary values: n = 18, Σx = 485, Σx^2 = 14343
R = 42 - 14 = 28
$s^2 = [n(\Sigma x^2) - (\Sigma x)^2]/[n(n-1)] = [18(14343) - (485)^2]/[18(17)] = (22949)/306 = 75.0$
s = 8.7
Since motorcycle drivers tend to come from a particular age group (viz., the younger drivers), their ages would vary less than those in the general population of all licensed drivers.

7. preliminary values: n = 20, Σx = 366, Σx^2 = 6746
R = 21 - 15 = 6
$s^2 = [n(\Sigma x^2) - (\Sigma x)^2]/[n(n-1)] = 20(6746) - (366)^2]/[20(19)] = (964)/380 = 2.5$
s = 1.6
The fact that both R and s are small (relative to the recorded data values) means that reaction times tended to be consistent and showed little variation.

8. preliminary values: n = 12, Σx = 8011.5, Σx^2 = 5349166.83
R = 679.2 - 654.2 = 25.0
$s^2 = [n(\Sigma x^2) - (\Sigma x)^2]/[n(n-1)] = [12(5349166.83) - (8011.5)^2]/[12(11)]$
   $= (5869.71)/132 = 44.47$
s = 6.67
While there is always room for improvement, it appears that the variability from pill to pill is at an acceptable level. The standard deviation is about 1% of the typical weight, and the values of s and R are consistent with the Range Rule of Thumb – that s $\approx$ R/4.

9. Jefferson Valley   Providence
n = 10, Σx = 71.5, Σx^2 = 513.27   n = 10, Σx = 71.5, Σx^2 = 541.09
R = 7.7 - 6.5 = 1.2   R = 10.0 - 4.2 = 5.8
$s^2 = [n(\Sigma x^2) - (\Sigma x)^2]/[n(n-1)]$ $s^2 = [n(\Sigma x^2) - (\Sigma x)^2]/[n(n-1)]$
   $= [10(513.27) - (71.5)^2]/[10(9)]$ $= [10(541.09) - (71.5)^2]/[10(9)]$
   $= 20.45/90 = 0.23$ $= 298.65/90 = 3.32$
s = 0.48   s = 1.82
Exercise #9 of section 2-4 indicated that the mean waiting time was 7.15 minutes at each bank. The Jefferson Valley waiting times, however, are considerably less variable. The range measures the difference between the extremes. The longest and shortest waits at Jefferson Valley differ by a little over 1 minute (R=1.2), while the longest and shortest waits at Providence differ by almost 6 minutes (R=5.8). The standard deviation measures the typical difference from the mean. A Jefferson Valley customer usually receives service within about ½ minute (s=0.48) of 7.15 minutes, while a Providence customer usually receives service within about 2 minutes (s=1.82) of the mean.

10. Regular   Diet
n = 6, Σx = 4.9144, Σx^2 = 4.02528224 n = 6, Σx = 4.7000, Σx^2 = 3.68181990
R = .8247 - .8150 = .0097   R = .7896 - .7758 = .0138
$s^2 = [n(\Sigma x^2) - (\Sigma x)^2]/[n(n-1)]$ $s^2 = [n(\Sigma x^2) - (\Sigma x)^2]/[n(n-1)]$
   $= [6(4.02528224) - (4.9144)^2]/[6(5)]$ $= [6(3.68181990) - (4.7000)^2]/[6(5)]$
   $= .00036608/30 = .000012202$ $= .00091940/30 = .000030633$
s = .00349   s = .00554
There appears to be slightly more variation among the Diet Coke weights than among those for Regular Coke.

11. McDonald's
$n = 12$, $\Sigma x = 2236$, $\Sigma x^2 = 461540$
$R = 287 - 92 = 195$
$s^2 = [n(\Sigma x^2) - (\Sigma x)^2]/[n(n-1)]$
$\quad = [12(461540) - (2236)^2]/[12(11)]$
$\quad = 538784/132 = 4081.7$
$\ s = 63.9$

Jack in the Box
$n = 12$, $\Sigma x = 3150$, $\Sigma x^2 = 1009962$
$R = 481 - 74 = 407$
$s^2 = [n(\Sigma x^2) - (\Sigma x)^2]/[n(n-1)]$
$\quad = [12(1009962) - (3150)^2]/[12(11)]$
$\quad = .2197044/132 = 16644.3$
$\ s = 129.0$

There appears to be about twice the variability among the times at Jack in the Box as there is at McDonald's. In other words, McDonald's seems to be doing better at producing a uniform system for dealing with all orders.

12. 4000 BC
$n = 12$, $\Sigma x = 1544$, $\Sigma x^2 = 198898$
$R = 138 - 119 = 19$
$s^2 = [n(\Sigma x^2) - (\Sigma x)^2]/[n(n-1)]$
$\quad = [12(198898) - (1544)^2]/[12(11)]$
$\quad = 2840/132 = 21.5$
$s\ = 4.6$

150 AD
$n = 12$, $\Sigma x = 1600$, $\Sigma x^2 = 213610$
$R = 141 - 126 = 15$
$s^2 = [n(\Sigma x^2) - (\Sigma x)^2]/[n(n-1)]$
$\quad = [12(213610) - (1600)^2]/[12(11)]$
$\quad = 3320/132 = 25.2$
$s\ = 5.0$

There is approximately the same amount of variability in skull breadths within each period.

13. males
$n = 50$, $\Sigma x = 2054.9$, $\Sigma x^2 = 84562.23$
$s^2 = [n(\Sigma x^2) - (\Sigma x)^2]/[n(n-1)]$
$\quad = [50(84562.23) - (2054.9)^2]/[50(49)]$
$\quad = 5497.49/2450 = 2.24$
$s\ = 1.50$

females
$n = 50$, $\Sigma x = 2002.4$, $\Sigma x^2 = 80323.82$
$s^2 = [n(\Sigma x^2) - (\Sigma x)^2]/[n(n-1)]$
$\quad = [50(80323.82) - (2002.4)^2]/[50(49)]$
$\quad = 6585.24/2450 = 2.69$
$s\ = 1.64$

While there was slightly more variability among the female values in this particular sample, there does not appear to be a significant difference between the genders.

14. Clancy
$n = 12$, $\Sigma x = 78.0$
$\Sigma x^2 = 572.94$
$s^2 = [n(\Sigma x^2) - (\Sigma x)^2]/[n(n-1)]$
$\quad = [12(572.94) - (78.0)^2]/[12(11)]$
$\quad = 791.28/132 = 5.99$
$s = 2.45$

Rowling
$n = 12$, $\Sigma x = 60.9$
$\Sigma x^2 = 572.94$
$s^2 = [n(\Sigma x^2) - (\Sigma x)^2]/[n(n-1)]$
$\quad = [12(324.07) - (60.9)^2]/[12(11)]$
$\quad = 180.03/132 = 1.36$
$s = 1.17$

Tolstoy
$n = 12$, $\Sigma x = 101.2$
$\Sigma x^2 = 572.94$
$s^2 = [n(\Sigma x^2) - (\Sigma x)^2]/[n(n-1)]$
$\quad = [12(897.82) - (101.2)^2]/[12(11)]$
$\quad = 532.40/132 = 4.03$
$s = 2.01$

The reading difficulty level seems to vary from page to page most in the Clancy book and least in the Rowling book. As 2.45 is more than twice 1.17, it appears that the difference may be significant.

15. Thursday
$n = 52$, $\Sigma x = 3.57$, $\Sigma x^2 = 1.6699$
$s^2 = [n(\Sigma x^2) - (\Sigma x)^2]/[n(n-1)]$
$\quad = [52(1.6699) - (3.57)^2]/[52(51)]$
$\quad = 74.0899/2652 = .02793$
$s\ = .167$

Sunday
$n = 52$, $\Sigma x = 3.52$, $\Sigma x^2 = 2.2790$
$s^2 = [n(\Sigma x^2) - (\Sigma x)^2]/[n(n-1)]$
$\quad = [52(2.2790) - (3.52)^2]/[52(51)]$
$\quad = 106.1176/2652 = .04001$
$s\ = .200$

The values are close, although there may be slightly more variation among the amounts for Sundays than among the amounts for Thursdays.

16. tobacco
$n = 50$, $\Sigma x = 2872$, $\Sigma x^2 = 694918$
$s^2 = [n(\Sigma x^2) - (\Sigma x)^2]/[n(n-1)]$
$\quad = [50(694918) - (2872)^2]/[50(49)]$
$\quad = 26497516/2450 = 10815.3$
$s\ = 104.0$

alcohol
$n = 50$, $\Sigma x = 1623$, $\Sigma x^2 = 268331$
$s^2 = [n(\Sigma x^2) - (\Sigma x)^2]/[n(n-1)]$
$\quad = [50(268331) - (1623)^2]/[50(49)]$
$\quad = 10782421/2450 = 4401.0$
$s\ = 66.3$

While there was slightly more variability among the lengths of tobacco usage in this particular sample, there does not appear to be a significant difference between the products.

17.

x	f	f·x	f·x^2
44.5	8	356.0	15842.00
54.5	44	2398.0	130691.00
64.5	23	1483.5	95685.75
74.5	6	447.0	33301.50
84.5	107	9041.5	764006.75
94.5	11	1039.5	98232.75
104.5	1	104.5	10920.25
	200	14870.0	1148680.00

$s^2 = [n(\Sigma f \cdot x^2) - (\Sigma f \cdot x)^2]/[n(n-1)]$
$= [200(1148680.00) - (1487.0)^2]/[200(199)] = (8619100.00)/29800 = 216.56$
$s = 14.7$

18.

x	f	f·x	f·x^2
1	27	27	27
2	31	62	124
3	42	126	378
4	40	160	640
5	28	140	700
6	32	192	1152
	200	707	3021

$s^2 = [n(\Sigma f \cdot x^2) - (\Sigma f \cdot x)^2]/[n(n-1)]$
$= [200(3021) - (707)^2]/[200(199)] = (104351)/39800 = 2.6$
$s = 1.6$

NOTE: This compares favorably with $\sigma = 1.708$, the true standard deviation among the values produced by a balanced die.

19.

x	f	f·x	f·x^2
43.5	25	1087.5	47305.25
47.5	14	665.0	31587.50
51.5	7	360.5	18565.75
55.5	3	166.5	9240.75
59.5	1	59.5	3540.25
	50	2339.0	110239.50

$s^2 = [n(\Sigma f \cdot x^2) - (\Sigma f \cdot x)^2]/[n(n-1)]$
$= [50(110239.50) - (2339.0)^2]/[50(49)] = (41054.00)/2450 = 16.76$
$s = 4.1$

20.   The x values below are the class midpoints from the given frequency table.

x	f	f·x	f·x^2
96.65	1	96.65	9341.2225
97.05	8	776.40	75349.6200
97.45	14	1634.30	132951.0350
97.85	22	2152.70	210641.6950
98.25	19	1866.75	183408.1875
98.65	32	3156.80	311418.3200
99.05	6	594.30	58865.5150
99.45	4	397.80	39561.2100
	106	10405.70	1021536.7050

$s^2 = [n(\Sigma f \cdot x^2) - (\Sigma f \cdot x)^2]/[n(n-1)]$
$= [106(1021536.7050) - (10504.70)^2]/[106(105)] = (4297.71)/11130 = .3861$
$s = .62$

21.   Answers will vary. Assuming that the ages range from 25 to 75, the Range Rule of Thumb suggests $s \approx$ range/4 $= (75-25)/4 = 50/4 = 12.5$.

22.   Answers will vary. Assuming that the grades range from 50 to 100, the Range Rule of Thumb suggests s ≈ range/4 = (100-50)/4 = 50/4 = 12.5.

23.   Given $\overline{x}$=38.86 and s=3.78, the Range Rule of Thumb suggests
    minimum "usual" value = $\overline{x}$ – 2s = 38.86 – 2(3.78) = 38.86 – 7.56 = 31.30
    maximum "usual" value = $\overline{x}$ + 2s = 38.86 + 2(3.78) = 38.86 + 7.56 = 46.42
    Yes, in this context a length of 47.0 cm would be considered unusual.

24.   Given $\overline{x}$=63.6 and s=2.5, the Range Rule of Thumb suggests
    minimum "usual" value = $\overline{x}$ – 2s = 63.6 – 2(2.5) = 63.6 – 5.0 = 58.6
    maximum "usual" value = $\overline{x}$ + 2s = 63.6 + 2(2.5) = 63.6 + 5.0 = 68.6
    Yes, in this context a woman 72" tall would be considered unusually tall.

25.   a. The limits 61.1 and 66.1 are 1 standard deviation from the mean. The Empirical Rule for Data with a Bell-shaped Distribution states that about 68% of the heights should fall within those limits.
    b. The limits 56.1 and 76.1 are 3 standard deviations from the mean. The Empirical Rule for Data with a Bell-shaped Distribution states that about 99.7% of the heights should fall within those limits.

26.   a. The limits .80931 and .82433 are 1 standard deviation from the mean. The Empirical Rule for Data with a Bell-shaped Distribution states that about 68% of the weights should fall within those limits.
    b. The limits .80180 and .83184 are 2 standard deviations from the mean. The Empirical Rule for Data with a Bell-shaped Distribution states that about 95% of the weights should fall within those limits.

27.   The limits 58.6 and 68.6 are 2 standard deviations from the mean. Chebyshev's Theorem states that there must be at least $1 - 1/k^2$ of the scores within k standard deviations of the mean. Here k = 2, and so the proportion of the heights within those limits is at least $1 - 1/2^2 = 1 - 1/4 = 3/4 = 75\%$.

28.   The limits .79429 and .83935 are 3 standard deviations from the mean. Chebyshev's Theorem states that there must be at least $1 - 1/k^2$ of the scores within k standard deviations of the mean. Here k = 3, and so the proportion of the heights within those limits is at least $1 - 1/3^2 = 1 - 1/9 = 8/9 = 89\%$.

29.   The following values were obtained using computer software. Using the accuracy for $\overline{x}$ and s given by the computer, we calculate the coefficient of variation to the nearest .01%.

calories	grams of sugar
n = 16	n = 16
$\overline{x}$ = 3.7625	$\overline{x}$ = .2950
s = .2217	s = .1677
CV = s/$\overline{x}$	CV = s/$\overline{x}$
= .2217/3.7625	= .1677/.2950
= .0589 = 5.89%	= .5685 = 56.85%

Relative to their mean amounts, there is considerably more variability in the grams of sugar than in the calories. There are two possible explanations: (1) The amount of calories may be easier to control than the weight of sugar. (2) The weights of sugar are so small that any slight deviation seems large by comparison.

30. The following values were obtained using computer software. Using the accuracy for $\bar{x}$ and s given by the computer, we calculate the coefficient of variation to the nearest .01%.

<u>Regular Coke</u>
n = 36
$\bar{x}$ = .81682
s = .00751
CV = $s/\bar{x}$
     = .00751/.81682
     = .0092 = 0.92%

<u>Regular Pepsi</u>
n = 36
$\bar{x}$ = .82410
s = .00570
CV = $s/\bar{x}$
     = .00570/.82410
     = .0069 = 0.69%

As each of the coefficients falls between ½% and 1%, they do not appear to differ significantly.

31. A standard deviation of s = 0 is possible only when s^2 = 0, and $s^2 = \Sigma(x-\bar{x})^2/(n-1) = 0$ only when $\Sigma(x-\bar{x})^2 = 0$. Since each $(x-\bar{x})^2$ is non-negative, $\Sigma(x-\bar{x})^2 = 0$ only when every $(x-\bar{x})^2 = 0$ – i.e., only when every x is equal to $\bar{x}$. In simple terms, zero variation occurs only when all the scores are identical.

32. a. dollars; the units for the standard deviation are always the same as the original units
b. dollars squared; the units for the variance are always the square of the original units

33. The Everlast brand is the better choice. In general, a smaller standard deviation of lifetimes indicates more consistency from battery to battery – signaling a more dependable production process and a more dependable final product. Assuming a bell-shaped distribution of lifetimes, for example, that empirical rule states that about 68% of the lifetimes will fall within one standard deviation of the mean. Here, those limits would be
for Everlast: 50 ± 2 or 48 months to 52 months
for Endurance: 50 ± 6 or 44 months to 56 months
While a person might be lucky and purchase a long-lasting Endurance battery, an Everlast battery is much more likely to last for the advertised 48 months.

34. A large effect; the new standard deviation will be much higher.
NOTE: Very roughly, standard deviation measures "typical spread." If 20 scores have s=1, then the "total spread" is about 20. If the new score is about 20 away from the others (either higher or lower), the new total spread will be about 40 and the new typical spread will be about 2.

35. section 1
n = 11, Σx = 201, Σx^2 = 4001
R = 20 - 1 = 19
$s^2 = [n(\Sigma x^2) - (\Sigma x)^2]/[n(n-1)]$
    $= [11(4001) - (201)^2]/[11(10)]$
    = 3610/110 = 32.92
s = 5.7

section 2
n = 11, Σx = 119, Σx^2 = 1741
R = 19 - 2 = 17
$s^2 = [n(\Sigma x^2) - (\Sigma x)^2]/[n(n-1)]$
    $= [11(1741) - (119)^2]/[11(10)]$
    = 1990/110 = 45.36
s = 6.7

The range values give the impression that section 1 had more variability than section 2. The range can be misleading because it is based only on the extreme scores. In this case, the lowest score in section 1 was so distinctly different from the others that to include it in any measure trying to give a summary about the section as a whole would skew the results. For the mean, where the value is only one of 11 used in the calculation, the effect is minimal; for the range, where the value is one of only 2 used in the calculation, the effect is dramatic. The standard deviation values give the impression that section 2 had slightly more variability.
NOTE: In this case, section 2 seems considerably more variable (or diverse), and even the standard deviation by itself fails to accurately distinguish between the sections.

36. The following values were obtained for the smokers in Table 2-1 using computer software. All subsequent calculations use the accuracy of these values.

n = 40 $\bar{x}$ = 172.5 $\tilde{x}$ = 170.0   s = 119.5

Pearson's index is skewness is

I = 3($\bar{x}$ - $\tilde{x}$)/s = 3(172.5 - 170.0)/119.5 = 3(2.5)/119.5 = .063

Since -1.00 < I < 1.00 for these data, there is not significant skewness.

37. For greater accuracy and understanding, we use 3 decimal places and formula 2-4.

a. the original population

x	x-μ	(x-μ)²
3	-3	9
6	0	0
9	3	9
18	0	18

μ = (Σx)/N = 18/3 = 6

σ^2 = Σ(x-μ)²/N = 18/3 = 6

[σ = 2.449]

b. the nine samples: using $s^2 = \Sigma(x-\bar{x})^2/(n-1)$ [for each sample, n = 2]

sample	$\bar{x}$	s²	s
3,3	3.0	0	0
3,6	4.5	4.5	2.121
3,9	6.0	18.0	4.245
6,3	4.5	4.5	2.121
6,6	6.0	0	0
6,9	7.5	4.5	2.121
9,3	6.0	18.0	4.245
9,6	7.5	4.5	2.121
9,9	9.0	0	0
	54.0	54.0	16.974

mean of the 9 s² values

(Σs²)/9 = 54.0/9 = 6

c. the nine samples: using $\sigma^2 = \Sigma(x-\mu)^2/N$ [for each sample, N = 2]

sample	μ	σ²
3,3	3.0	0
3,6	4.5	2.25
3,9	6.0	9.00
6,3	4.5	2.25
6,6	6.0	0
6,9	7.5	2.25
9,3	6.0	9.00
9,6	7.5	2.25
9,9	9.0	0
	54.0	27.00

mean of the 9 σ² values

(Σσ²)/9 = 27.00/9 = 3

d. The approach in (b) of dividing by n-1 when calculating the sample variance gives a better estimate of the population variance. On the average, the approach in (b) gave the correct population variance of 6. The approach in (c) of dividing by n underestimated the correct population variance. When computing sample variances, divide by n-1 and not by n.

e. No. An unbiased estimator is one that gives the correct answer on the average. Since the average value of s² in part (b) was 6, which was the correct value calculated for σ² in part (a), s² is an unbiased estimator of σ². Since the average value of s in part (b) is (Σs)/9 = 16.974/9 = 1.886, which is not the correct value of 2.449 calculated for σ in part (a), s is not an unbiased estimator of σ.

NOTE: Since the average value of $\bar{x}$ in part (b) is ($\Sigma \bar{x}$)/9 = 54.0/9 = 6.0, which is the correct value calculated for μ in part (a), $\bar{x}$ is an unbiased estimator of μ.

38. a. the original population

x	x-μ	|x-μ|
3	-3	3
6	0	0
9	3	3
18	0	6

μ = (Σx)/N = 18/3 = 6

MAD = Σ|x-μ|/N = 6/3 = 2

b. the nine samples: using MAD $= \Sigma|x-\bar{x}|/n$ [for each sample, n = 2]

sample	$\bar{x}$	MAD
3,3	3.0	0
3,6	4.5	1.5
3,9	6.0	3.0
6,3	4.5	1.5
6,6	6.0	0
6,9	7.5	1.5
9,3	6.0	3.0
9,6	7.5	1.5
9,9	9.0	0
	54.0	12.0

mean of the 9 MAD values

$[\Sigma(MAD)]/9 = 12.0/9 = 1.33$

c. Since the average value of the sample MAD's in part (b), does not equal the true population MAD in part (a), the sample MAD is not an unbiased estimator of the population MAD. In the given example, dividing by (n-1) instead of n would be dividing by 1 instead of 2. That would double each of the sample MAD's and make the average MAD 24/9 = 2.67, which is still not equal to the value in part (a). Therefore division by n-1 instead of n does not produce an unbiased estimator for the mean absolute deviation as it did for the variance.

2-6 Measures of Relative Standing

1. a. $x - \mu = 160 - 100 = 60$
    b. $60/\sigma = 60/16 = 3.75$
    c. $z = (x - \mu)/\sigma = (160 - 100)/16 = 60/16 = 3.75$
    d. Since Einstein's IQ converts to a z score of $3.75 > 2$, it is considered unusually high.

2. a. $x - \mu = 48 - 72.9 = -24.9$
    b. $-24.9/\sigma = -24.9/12.3 = -2.02$
    c. $z = (x - \mu)/\sigma = (48 - 72.9)/12.3 = -24.9/12.3 = -2.02$
    d. Since the author's pulse rate converts to a z score of $-2.02 < -2$, it would be considered unusually low. Athletes and people who exercise regularly tend to have low pulse rates; it could be that the author falls into that category.
    NOTE: It is also acceptable to use $|x - \mu| = 24.9$ in part (a). This means that the answer in (b) is +2.02. The z score is the *signed* number of standard deviations from the mean.

3. In general, $z = (x - \mu)/\sigma$.
    a. $z_{60} = (60 - 69.0)/2.8 = -3.21$
    b. $z_{85} = (85 - 69.0)/2.8 = 5.71$
    c. $z_{69.72} = (69.72 - 69.0)/2.8 = 0.26$

4. In general, $z = (x - \mu)/\sigma$.
    a. $z_{100} = (100 - 98.20)/.62 = 2.90$
    b. $z_{96.96} = (96.96 - 98.20)/.62 = -2.00$
    c. $z_{98.20} = (98.20 - 98.20)/.62 = 0.00$

5. $z = (x - \mu)/\sigma$
    $z_{70} = (70 - 63.6)/2.5 = 2.56$
    Yes, that height is considered unusual since $2.56 > 2.00$.

6. $z = (x - \mu)/\sigma$
    $z_{308} = (308 - 268)/15 = 2.67$
    Yes, the length is considered unusual since $2.67 > 2.00$. The length is unusual, but not necessarily impossible.

7. $z = (x - \mu)/\sigma$
     $z_{101} = (101 - 98.20)/0.62 = 4.52$
     Yes, that temperature is unusually high, since $4.52 > 2.00$. It suggests that either the person is healthy but has a very unusual temperature for a healthy person, or that person is sick (i.e., has an elevated temperature attributable to some cause).

8. $z = (x - \mu)/\sigma$
     $z_{259.0} = (259.1 - 178.1)/40.7 = 1.99$
     No, this level is not considered unusually high since $1.99 < 2.00$.
     NOTE: While this level is not unusually high compared to the general population, it still might be high enough to be of concern – i.e., it could be that the levels in the general population are unhealthily high.

9.   In general $z = (x - \overline{x})/s$
     psychology: $z_{85} = (85 - 90)/10 = -5/10 = -0.50$
     economics: $z_{45} = (45 - 55)/5 = -10/5 = -2.00$
     The psychology score has the better relative position since $-0.50 > -2.00$.

10. In general, $z = (x - \mu)/\sigma$.
     a. $z_{144} = (144 - 128)/34 = .47$
     b. $z_{90} = (90 - 86)/18 = .22$
     c. $z_{18} = (18 - 15)/5 = .60$
     The score in part (c) has the highest z score and therefore is the highest relative score.

11. preliminary values: $n = 36$, $\Sigma x = 29.4056$, $\Sigma x^2 = 24.02111984$
     $\overline{x} = (\Sigma x)/n = 29.4056/36 = .81682$
     $s^2 = [n(\Sigma x^2) - (\Sigma x)^2]/[n(n-1)]$
     $\quad = [36(24.02111984) - (29.4056)^2]/[36(35)] = .07100288/1260 = .000056351$
     $s = .007507$
     $z = (x - \overline{x})/s$
     $z_{.7901} = (.7901 - .81682)/.007507 = -3.56$
     Yes; since $-3.56 < -2.00$, .7901 is an unusual weight for regular Coke.

12. For the green M&M's, computer software gives the following relevant values.
     $\quad n=7 \qquad \overline{x}=.9266 \qquad s=.0387 \qquad max=1.002$
     $z = (x - \overline{x})/s$
     $z_{1.002} = (1.002 - .9266)/.0387 = 1.95$
     No; since 1.95 2.00, 1.002 is not an unusual weight for a green M&M.

13. Let b = # of scores below x; n = total number of scores.
     In general, the percentile of score x is $(b/n) \cdot 100$.
     The percentile for a cotinine level of 149 is $(17/40) \cdot 100 = 42.5$.

14. Let b = # of scores below x; n = total number of scores.
     In general, the percentile of score x is $(b/n) \cdot 100$.
     The percentile for a cotinine level of 210 is $(24/40) \cdot 100 = 60$.

15. Let b = # of scores below x; n = total number of scores.
     In general, the percentile of score x is $(b/n) \cdot 100$.
     The percentile for a cotinine level of 35 is $(6/40) \cdot 100 = 15$.

16. Let b = # of scores below x; n = total number of scores.
     In general, the percentile of score x is $(b/n) \cdot 100$.
     The percentile for a cotinine level of 250 is $(29/40) \cdot 100 = 72.5$.

17. To find P_{20}, L = (20/100)·40 = 8 – a whole number.
The mean of the 8th and 9th scores, P_{20} = (44+48)/2 = 46.

18. To find $Q_3 = P_{75}$, L = (75/100)·40 = 30 – a whole number.
The mean of the 30th and 31st scores, P_{75} = (250+253)/2 = 251.5.

19. To find P_{75}, L = (75/100)·40 = 30 – a whole number.
The mean of the 30th and 31st scores, P_{75} = (250+253)/2 = 251.5.

20. To find $Q_2 = P_{50}$, L = (50/100)·40 = 20 – a whole number.
The mean of the 20th and 21st scores, P_{50} = (167+173)/2 = 170.

#	level
1	2
2	8
3	44
4	62
5	62
6	89
7	94
8	98
9	98
10	112
11	123
12	125
13	126
14	130
15	146
16	149
17	149
18	173
19	175
20	181
21	207
22	223
23	237
24	254
25	264
26	267
27	271
28	280
29	293
30	301
31	309
32	318
33	325
34	384
35	447
36	462
37	531
38	596
39	600
40	920

21. To find P_{33}, L = (33/100)·40 = 13.2, rounded up to 14.
Since the 14th score is 121, P_{33} = 121.

22. To find P_{21}, L = (21/100)·40 = 8.4, rounded up to 9.
Since the 9th score is 48, P_{21} = 48.

23. To find P_{01}, L = (1/100)·40 = 0.4, rounded up to 1.
Since the 1st score is 0, P_{01} = 0.

24. To find P_{85}, L = (85/100)·40 = 34 – a whole number.
The mean of the 34th and 35th scores, P_{85} = (277+284)/2 = 280.5.

NOTE: For exercises 25-36, refer to the ordered list at the right.

25. Let b = # of scores below x; n = total number of scores
In general, the percentile of score x is (b/n)·100.
The percentile of score 123 is (10/40)·100 = 25.

26. Let b = # of scores below x; n = total number of scores
In general, the percentile of score x is (b/n)·100.
The percentile of score 309 is (30/40)·100 = 75.

27. Let b = # of scores below x; n = total number of scores
In general, the percentile of score x is (b/n)·100.
The percentile of score 271 is (26/40)·100 = 65.

28. Let b = # of scores below x; n = total number of scores
In general, the percentile of score x is (b/n)·100.
The percentile of score 126 is (12/40)·100 = 30.

29. To find P_{85}, L = (85/100)·40 = 34 – a whole number.
The mean of the 34th and 35th scores, P_{85} = (384+447)/2 = 415.5.

30. To find P_{35}, L = (35/100)·40 = 14 – a whole number.
The mean of the 14th and 15th scores, P_{35} = (130+146)/2 = 138.

31. To find $Q_1 = P_{25}$, L = (25/100)·40 = 10 – a whole number.
The mean of the 10th and 11th scores, P_{25} = (112+123)/2 = 117.5.

32. To find $Q_3 = P_{75}$, L = (75/100)·40 = 30 – a whole number.
The mean of the 30th and 31st scores, P_{75} = (301+309)/2 = 305.

33. To find P_{18}, L = (18/100)·40 = 7.2 rounded up to 8.
Since the 8th score is 98, P_{18} = 98.

34.   To find P_{36}, $L = (36/100) \cdot 40 = 14.4$ rounded up to 15.
Since the 15th score is 146, $P_{36} = 146$.

35.   To find P_{58}, $L = (58/100) \cdot 40 = 23.2$ rounded up to 24.
Since the 23rd score is 237, $P_{58} = 254$.

36.   To find P_{96}, $L = (96/100) \cdot 40 = 38.4$ rounded up to 39.
Since the 39th score is 600, $P_{96} = 600$.

37.   In general, z scores are not affected by the particular unit of measurement that is used. The relative position of a score (whether it is above or below the mean, its rank in an ordered list of the scores, etc.) is not affected by the unit of measurement, and relative position is what a z score communicates. Mathematically, the same units (feet, centimeters, dollars, etc.) appear in both the numerator and denominator of $(x-\mu)/\sigma$ and cancel out to leave the z score unit-free. In fact the z score is also called the *standard score* for that very reason – it is a standardized value that is independent of the unit of measure employed.

NOTE: In more technical language, changing from one unit of measure to another (feet to centimeters, °F to °C, dollars to pesos, etc.) is a linear transformation – i.e., if x is the score in one unit, then (for some appropriate values of a and b) $y = ax + b$ is the score in the other unit. In such cases it can be shown that
$\mu_y = a\mu_x + b$ and
$\sigma_y = a\sigma_x$.
The new z score is the same the old one, since
$z_y = (y - \mu_y)/\sigma_y = [(ax + b) - (a\mu_x + b)]/a\sigma_x = [ax - a\mu_x]/a\sigma_x = (x - \mu_x)/\sigma_x = z_x$

38.   Solve $z = (x - \mu)/\sigma$ to get
$x = \mu + z\sigma$
a. $x_{2.16} = 63.6 + (2.16)(2.5) = 63.6 + 5.4 = 69.0$ inches
b. $x_{-1.84} = 63.6 + (-1.84)(2.5) = 63.6 - 4.6 = 59.0$ inches

39.   a. The interquartile range is $Q_3 - Q_1$.
   For $Q_3 = P_{75}$, $L = (75/100) \cdot 40 = 30$ – a whole number.
    The mean of the 30th and 31st scores, $Q_3 = (250+253)/2 = 251.5$.
   For $Q_1 = P_{25}$, $L = (25/100) \cdot 40 = 10$ – a whole number.
    The mean of the 10th and 11th scores, $Q_1 = (86+87)/2 = 86.5$.
   The interquartile range is $251.5 - 86.5 = 165$.
b. The midquartile is $(Q_1 + Q_3)/2 = (251.5+86.5)/2 = 169$.
c. The 10-90 percentile range is $P_{90} - P_{10}$.
   For P_{90}, $L = (90/100) \cdot 40 = 36$ – a whole number.
    The mean of the 36th and 37th scores, $P_{90} = (289+290)/2 = 289.5$.
   For P_{10}, $L = (10/100) \cdot 40 = 4$ – a whole number.
    The mean of the 4th and 5th scores, $P_{10} = (3+17)/2 = 10$.
   The 10-90 percentile range is $289.5 - 10 = 279.5$
d. Yes, $Q_2 = P_{50}$ by definition. Yes, they are always equal.
e. For $Q_2 = P_{50}$, $L = (50/100) \cdot 40 = 20$ – a whole number.
    The mean of the 20th and 21st scores, $Q_2 = (167+173)/2 = 170$.
   No; in this case $170 = Q_2 \neq (Q_1 + Q_3)/2 = 169$, which demonstrates that the median does not necessarily equal the midquartile.

40.   a. $D_1 = P_{10}$, $D_5 = P_{50}$, $D_8 = P_{80}$

b. In each case D_d, $L = (10d/100) \cdot 40 = 4d$ – a whole number.
  $D_d = (x_{4d} + x_{4d+1})/2$ for $d = 1,2,3,4,5,6,7,8,9$
  $D_1 = (x_4 + x_5)/2 = (3+17)/2 = 10.0$
  $D_2 = (x_8 + x_9)/2 = (44+48)/2 = 46.0$
  $D_3 = (x_{12} + x_{13})/2 = (103+112)/2 = 107.5$
  $D_4 = (x_{16} + x_{17})/2 = (130+131)/2 = 130.5$
  $D_5 = (x_{20} + x_{21})/2 = (167+173)/2 = 170.0$
  $D_6 = (x_{24} + x_{25})/2 = (208+210)/2 = 209.0$
  $D_7 = (x_{28} + x_{29})/2 = (234+245)/2 = 239.5$
  $D_8 = (x_{32} + x_{33})/2 = (265+266)/2 = 265.5$
  $D_9 = (x_{36} + x_{37})/2 = (289+290)/2 = 289.5$

c. In each case Quintile_q, $L = (20q/100) \cdot 40 = 8q$ – a whole number.
  $\text{Quintile}_q = (x_{8d} + x_{8d+1})/2$ for $q = 1,2,3,4$
  $\text{Quintile}_1 = (x_8 + x_9)/2 = (44+48)/2 = 46.0$
  $\text{Quintile}_2 = (x_{16} + x_{17})/2 = (130+131)/2 = 130.5$
  $\text{Quintile}_3 = (x_{24} + x_{25})/2 = (208+210)/2 = 209.0$
  $\text{Quintile}_4 = (x_{32} + x_{33})/2 = (265+266)/2 = 265.5$

2-7 Exploratory Data Analysis (EDA)

The exercises in this section may be done much more easily when ordered lists of the values are available. On the next page appear ordered lists for the data of exercises #1-8. The left-most column gives the ordered ID numbers 1-50. Data sets with more than 50 values (except for the 54 bear lengths in exercise #6) have more than one column – the second column being ordered values 51-100, etc.

NOTE: A boxplot can be misleading if an extreme value artificially extends the whisker beyond the reasonable data. This manual follows the convention of extending the whisker only to the highest and lowest values within $1.5(Q_3 - Q_1)$ of Q_2 – any point more than 1.5 times the width of the box away from the median will be considered an outlier and represented separately. This type of boxplot is discussed in exercise #13. The boxplots given in this manual can be converted to the ones presented in the text by extending the whisker to the most extreme outlier.

1. Consider the 40 digits.
      For $Q_1 = P_{25}$, $L = (25/100) \cdot 40 = 10$ – a whole number, use 10.5.
      For $\tilde{x} = Q_2 = P_{50}$, $L = (50/100) \cdot 40 = 20$ – a whole number, use 20.5.
      For $Q_3 = P_{75}$, $L = (75/100) \cdot 40 = 30$ – a whole number, use 30.5.

  $\min = x_1 = 0$
  $Q_1 = (x_{10} + x_{11})2 = (2+2)/2 = 2$
  $Q_2 = (x_{20} + x_{21})2 = (5+5)/2 = 5$
  $Q_3 = (x_{30} + x_{31})2 = (7+7)/2 = 7$
  $\max = x_{40} = 9$

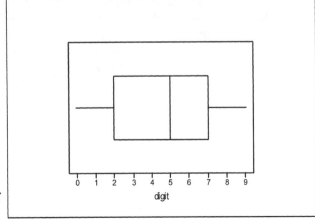

Since the quartiles (indicated by the vertical bars) divide the figure into four approximately equal segments, the boxplot suggests the values follow a uniform distribution. This is what one would expect if the digits were selected with a random procedure.

2.   Consider the 15 movie budgets, as given in millions of dollars.
For $Q_1 = P_{25}$, $L = (25/100) \cdot 15 = 3.75$ rounded up to 4.
For $\tilde{x} = Q_2 = P_{50}$, $L = (50/100) \cdot 15 = 7.5$ rounded up to 8.
For $Q_3 = P_{75}$, $L = (75/100) \cdot 15 = 11.25$ rounded up to 12.

min $= x_1 = .25$
$Q_1 = x_4 = 8$
$Q_2 = x_8 = 18.5$
$Q_3 = x_{12} = 70$
max $= x_{15} = 100$

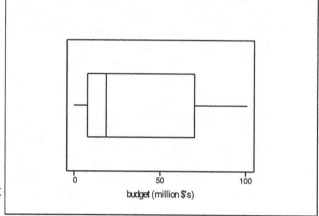

Since some the films date from the
1970's, and the budgets presumably
are the actual amounts spent in the year
of production, the sample values are not
likely to be representative of the actual
dollar amounts (i.e., in current dollars) of movies made this year.

3.   Consider the 16 calorie amounts.
For $Q_1 = P_{25}$, $L = (25/100) \cdot 16 = 4$ – a whole number, use 4.5.
For $\tilde{x} = Q_2 = P_{50}$, $L = (50/100) \cdot 16 = 8$ – a whole number, use 8.5.
For $Q_3 = P_{75}$, $L = (75/100) \cdot 16 = 12$ – a whole number, use 12.5.

min $= x_1 = 3.3$
$Q_1 = (x_4 + x_5)2 = (3.6 + 3.6)/2 = 3.6$
$Q_2 = (x_8 + x_9)2 = (3.7 + 3.8)/2 = 3.75$
$Q_3 = (x_{12} + x_{13})2 = (3.9 + 4.0)/2 = 3.95$
max $= x_{16} = 4.1$

These values are not necessarily representative of the cereals consumed by the general
population. Although cereals like "Corn Flakes" and "Bran Flakes" are not identified by
manufacturer, it is likely that the values given are for cereals produced by the major companies
(General Mills, Kellogg's, etc) and not the less expensive generic imitations used by many
consumers. In addition, each cereals is given equal weight in the data set – regardless of how
popular (or unpopular) it is with consumers.

The following ordered lists are used for exercises #1-8.

	#1 dig	#2 bud	#3 cal	#4 nic	#5 wgt	#6 lgn	#7 alc	#8 temp	#8 temp	#8 temp
01	0	0.250	3.3	0.1	.870	36.0	0	96.5	98.3	99.1
02	0	0.325	3.5	0.2	.872	37.0	0	96.9	98.3	99.2
03	0	6.400	3.6	0.5	.874	40.0	0	97.0	98.4	99.4
04	0	8.000	3.6	0.6	.882	40.0	0	97.0	98.4	99.4
05	0	10.000	3.6	0.7	.888	41.0	0	97.0	98.4	99.5
06	0	15.000	3.6	0.7	.891	43.0	0	97.1	98.4	99.6
07	1	17.000	3.7	0.8	.897	43.5	0	97.1	98.4	
08	1	18.500	3.7	0.8	.898	46.0	0	97.1	98.4	
09	1	25.000	3.8	0.8	.908	46.0	0	97.2	98.4	
10	2	50.000	3.9	0.8	.908	47.0	0	97.3	98.4	
11	2	55.000	3.9	0.9	.908	48.0	0	97.3	98.4	
12	2	70.000	3.9	1.0	.911	48.0	0	97.3	98.4	
13	2	70.000	4.0	1.0	.912	49.0	0	97.4	98.4	
14	3	72.000	4.0	1.0	.913	50.0	0	97.4	98.4	
15	3	100.000	4.0	1.0	.920	52.0	0	97.4	98.5	
16	4		4.1	1.0	.924	52.5	0	97.5	98.5	
17	4			1.0	.924	53.0	0	97.5	98.5	
18	4			1.0	.933	53.0	0	97.6	98.5	
19	5			1.1	.936	54.0	0	97.6	98.6	
20	5			1.1	.952	57.3	0	97.6	98.6	
21	5			1.1	.983	57.5	0	97.6	98.6	
22	5			1.2		58.0	0	97.6	98.6	
23	5			1.2		59.0	0	97.6	98.6	
24	5			1.2		59.0	0	97.7	98.6	
25	5			1.2		59.0	0	97.8	98.6	
26	6			1.2		60.0	3	97.8	98.6	
27	6			1.3		60.5	4	97.8	98.6	
28	6			1.4		61.0	5	97.8	98.6	
29	7			1.4		61.0	7	97.8	98.6	
30	7					61.5	8	97.9	98.6	
31	7					62.5	13	97.9	98.6	
32	7					63.0	20	97.9	98.6	
33	7					63.0	28	98.0	98.6	
34	8					63.0	33	98.0	98.7	
35	8					63.5	34	98.0	98.7	
36	9					64.0	38	98.0	98.7	
37	9					64.0	39	98.0	98.7	
38	9					64.0	39	98.0	98.7	
39	9					65.0	46	98.0	98.7	
40	9					65.0	51	98.0	98.8	
41						66.5	72	98.0	98.8	
42						67.0	73	98.0	98.8	
43						67.5	74	98.0	98.8	
44						68.5	76	98.0	98.8	
45						70.0	80	98.0	98.8	
46						70.5	88	98.2	98.8	
47						72.0	113	98.2	98.9	
48						72.0	123	98.2	98.9	
49						72.0	142	98.2	99.0	
50						72.0	414	98.2	99.0	
						73.0				
						73.5				
						75.0				
						76.5				

4. Consider the 29 nicotine amounts.

For $Q_1 = P_{25}$, $L = (25/100) \cdot 29 = 7.25$ rounded up to 8.
For $\tilde{x} = Q_2 = P_{50}$, $L = (50/100) \cdot 29 = 14.5$ rounded up to 15.
For $Q_3 = P_{75}$, $L = (75/100) \cdot 29 = 21.75$ rounded up to 22.

min $= x_1 = 0.1$
$Q_1 = x_8 = 0.8$
$Q_2 = x_{15} = 1.0$
$Q_3 = x_{22} = 1.2$
max $= x_{29} = 1.4$

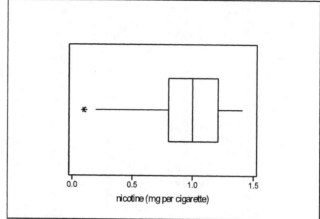

No; the sample values are not likely to be representative of cigarettes smoked by "an individual consumer" – no matter how that phrase is interpreted. The values would not be representative of cigarettes smoked by any one individual, since most consumers are faithful to a single brand and would not experience such a wide range of nicotine content. The values are not representative of those smoked by consumers in general because they include only cigarettes that are "100 mm long, filtered, and not menthol or light." In addition, each cigarette brand is given equal weight in the data set – regardless of how popular (or unpopular) it is with consumers.

5. Consider the 21 weights.

For $Q_1 = P_{25}$, $L = (25/100) \cdot 21 = 5.25$ rounded up to 6.
For $\tilde{x} = Q_2 = P_{50}$, $L = (50/100) \cdot 21 = 10.5$ rounded up to 11.
For $Q_3 = P_{75}$, $L = (75/100) \cdot 21 = 15.75$ rounded up to 16.

min $= x_1 = .870$
$Q_1 = x_6 = .891$
$Q_2 = x_{11} = .908$
$Q_3 = x_{16} = .924$
max $= x_{21} = .983$

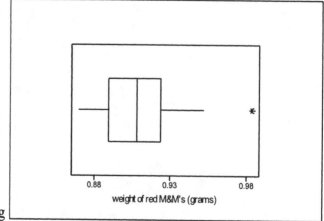

Yes; assuming there is no significant difference in the weights of the coloring agents, the weights of the red M&M's are likely to be representative of the weights of all the colors.

6. Consider the 54 lengths.

For $Q_1 = P_{25}$, $L = (25/100) \cdot 54 = 13.5$ rounded up to 14.
For $\tilde{x} = Q_2 = P_{50}$, $L = (50/100) \cdot 54 = 27$ – a whole number, use 27.5
For $Q_3 = P_{75}$, $L = (75/100) \cdot 54 = 40.5$ rounded up to 41.

$min = x_1 = 36.0$
$Q_1 = x_{14} = 50.0$
$Q_2 = (x_{27} + x_{28})2 = (60.5 + 61.0)/2$
$\qquad\qquad = 60.75$
$Q_3 = x_{41} = 66.5$
$max = x_{54} = 76.5$

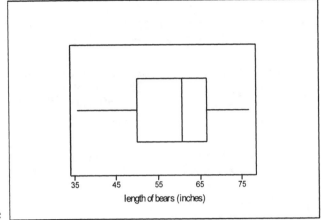

While the median is slightly toward the higher end (indicating a slight negative skew), the distribution is approximately symmetric.

7. Consider the 50 times.
     For $Q_1 = P_{25}$, $L = (25/100) \cdot 50 = 12.5$ rounded up to 13.
     For $\tilde{x} = Q_2 = P_{50}$, $L = (50/100) \cdot 50 = 25$ -- an integer, use 25.5.
     For $Q_3 = P_{75}$, $L = (75/100) \cdot 50 = 37.5$ rounded up to 38.

$min = x_1 = 0$
$Q_1 = x_{13} = 0$
$Q_2 = x_{25.5} = (0+3)/2 = 1.5$
$Q_3 = x_{38} = 39$
$max = x_{50} = 414$

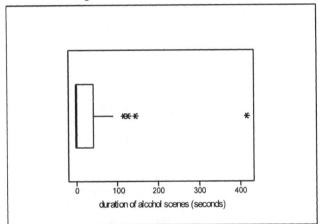

Based on the boxplot, the distribution appears to be extremely positively skewed.

8. Consider the 106 temperatures.
     For $Q_1 = P_{25}$, $L = (25/100) \cdot 106 = 26.5$ rounded up to 27.
     For $\tilde{x} = Q_2 = P_{50}$, $L = (50/100) \cdot 106 = 53$ -- an integer, use 53.5.
     For $Q_3 = P_{75}$, $L = (75/100) \cdot 106 = 79.5$ rounded up to 80.

$min = x_1 = 96.5$
$Q_1 = x_{27} = 97.8$
$Q_2 = x_{53.5} = (98.4 + 98.4)/2 = 98.4$
$Q_3 = x_{80} = 98.6$
$max = x_{106} = 99.6$

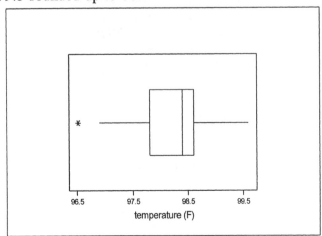

The values are <u>not</u> centered around the 98.6, which is actually P_{75}.

On the next page appear ordered lists for the data of exercises #9-12. They follow the same format as the ordered lists given previously for exercises #1-8.

9. Consider the 39 actor and 39 actress values.
    For $Q_1 = P_{25}$, L = (25/100)·39 = 9.75 rounded up to 10.
    For x̄ = $Q_2 = P_{50}$, L = (50/100)·39 = 19.5 rounded up to 20.
    For $Q_3 = P_{75}$, L = (75/100)·39 = 29.25 rounded up tp 30.
    For the actors,
        min = x_1 = 31
        $Q_1 = x_{10}$ = 37
        $Q_2 = x_{20}$ = 43
        $Q_3 = x_{30}$ = 51
        max = x_{39} = 76
    For the actresses,
        min = x_1 = 21
        $Q_1 = x_{10}$ = 30
        $Q_2 = x_{20}$ = 34
        $Q_3 = x_{30}$ = 41
        max = x_{39} = 80

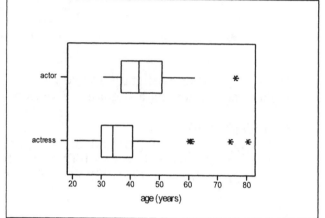

The ages for the actresses cover a wider range and cluster around a lower value than do the ages of the actors.

10. Consider the 36 regular and 36 diet values.
    For $Q_1 = P_{25}$, L = (25/100)·36 = 9 – an integer, use 9.5.
    For x̃ = $Q_2 = P_{50}$, L = (50/100)·38 = 18 – an integer, use 18.5.
    For $Q_3 = P_{75}$, L = (75/100)·36 = 27 – an integer, use 27.5.
    For the regular Coke,
        min = x_1 = .7901
        $Q_1 = x_{9.5}$ = (.8143+.8150)/2 = .81465
        $Q_2 = x_{18.5}$ = (.8170+.8172)/2 = .8171
        $Q_3 = x_{27.5}$ = (.8207+.8211)/2 = .8209
        max = x_{36} = .8295
    For the diet Coke,
        min = x_1 = .7758
        $Q_1 = x_{9.5}$ = (.7822+.7822)/2
            = .7822
        $Q_2 = x_{18.5}$ = (.7852+.7852)/2
            = .7852
        $Q_3 = x_{27.5}$ = (.7879+.7879)/2
            = .7879
        max = x_{36} = .7923

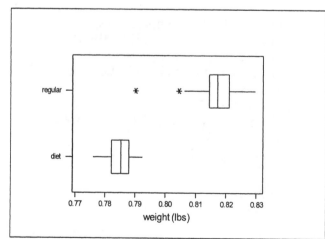

The weights for the diet sodas are lower and less variable.

The following ordered lists are used for exercises #9-12.

	#9 mal	#9 fem	#10 requ	#10 diet	#11 smo	#11 ets	#11 no	#12 clan	#12 rowl	#12 tols
01	31	21	.7901	.7758	0	0	0	43.9	70.9	51.9
02	32	24	.8044	.7760	1	0	0	58.2	74.0	52.8
03	32	25	.8062	.7771	1	0	0	64.4	78.6	58.4
04	32	26	.8073	.7773	3	0	0	69.4	79.2	64.2
05	33	26	.8079	.7802	17	0	0	72.7	79.5	65.4
06	35	26	.8110	.7806	32	0	0	72.9	80.2	68.5
07	36	26	.8126	.7811	35	0	0	73.1	82.5	69.4
08	36	27	.8128	.7813	44	0	0	73.4	83.7	71.4
09	37	28	.8143	.7822	48	0	0	76.3	84.3	71.6
10	37	30	.8150	.7822	86	1	0	76.4	84.6	72.2
11	38	30	.8150	.7822	87	1	0	79.8	85.3	73.6
12	39	31	.8152	.7826	103	1	0	89.2	86.2	74.4
13	39	31	.8152	.7830	112	1	0			
14	40	33	.8161	.7833	121	1	0			
15	40	33	.8161	.7837	123	1	0			
16	40	33	.8163	.7839	130	1	0			
17	41	34	.8165	.7844	131	1	0			
18	42	34	.8170	.7852	149	1	0			
19	42	34	.8172	.7852	164	1	0			
20	43	34	.8176	.7859	167	1	0			
21	43	35	.8181	.7861	173	2	0			
22	44	35	.8189	.7868	173	2	0			
23	45	35	.8192	.7870	198	3	0			
24	45	37	.8192	.7872	208	3	0			
25	46	37	.8194	.7874	210	3	0			
26	46	38	.8194	.7874	222	4	0			
27	47	39	.8207	.7879	227	13	0			
28	48	41	.8211	.7879	234	13	0			
29	48	41	.8299	.7881	245	17	0			
30	51	41	.8244	.7885	250	19	0			
31	53	42	.8244	.7892	253	45	0			
32	55	44	.8247	.7896	265	51	0			
33	56	49	.8251	.7907	266	69	0			
34	56	50	.8264	.7910	277	74	0			
35	60	60	.8284	.7923	284	178	1			
36	60	61	.8295	.7923	289	197	1			
37	61	61			290	241	9			
38	62	74			313	384	90			
39	76	80			477	543	244			
40					491	551	309			

11.   Consider the 40 values for each group.
    For $Q_1 = P_{25}$, L = (25/100)·40 = 10 – an integer, use 10.5.
    For $\tilde{x} = Q_2 = P_{50}$, L = (50/100)·40 = 20 – an integer, use 20.5.
    For $Q_3 = P_{75}$, L = (75/100)·40 = 30 – an integer, use 30.5.
For the smokers,
    min = x_1 = 0
    $Q_1 = x_{10.5}$ = (86+87)/2 = 86.5
    $Q_2 = x_{20.5}$ = (167+173)/2 = 170
    $Q_3 = x_{30.5}$ = (250+253)/2 = 251.5
    max = x_{40} = 491
For the ETS group,
    min = x_1 = 0
    $Q_1 = x_{10.5}$ = (1+1)/2 = 1
    $Q_2 = x_{20.5}$ = (1+2)/2 = 1.5
    $Q_3 = x_{30.5}$ = (19+45)/2 = 32
    max = x_{40} = 551
For the no ETS group,
    min = x_1 = 0
    $Q_1 = x_{10.5}$ = (0+0)/2 = 0
    $Q_2 = x_{20.5}$ = (0+0)/2 = 0
    $Q_3 = x_{30.5}$ = (0+0)/2 = 0
    max = x_{40} = 309

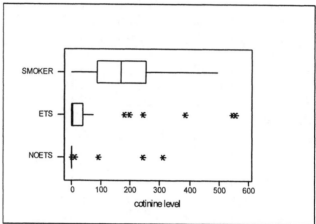

Even though all three groups cover approximately the same range, the boxplot makes it clear that the typical values are highest for the smokers and essentially zero (except for outliers) for the no ETS group.

12.   Consider the 12 values for each group.
    For $Q_1 = P_{25}$, L = (25/100)·12 = 3 – an integer, use 3.5.
    For $\tilde{x} = Q_2 = P_{50}$, L = (50/100)·12 = 6 – an integer, use 6.5.
    For $Q_3 = P_{75}$, L = (75/100)·12 = 9 – an integer, use 9.5.
For the Clancy book.
    min = x_1 = 43.9
    $Q_1 = x_{3.5}$ = (64.4+69.4)/2 = 66.9
    $Q_2 = x_{6.5}$ = (72.9+73.1)/2 = 73.0
    $Q_3 = x_{9.5}$ = (76.3+76.4)/2 = 76.35
    max = x_{12} = 89.2
For the Rowling book,
    min = x_1 = 70.9
    $Q_1 = x_{3.5}$ = (78.6+79.2)/2 = 78.9
    $Q_2 = x_{6.5}$ = (80.2+82.5)/2 = 81.35
    $Q_3 = x_{9.5}$ = (84.3+84.6)/2 = 84.45
    max = x_{12} = 86.2
For the Tolstoy book,
    min = x_1 = 51.9
    $Q_1 = x_{3.5}$ = (58.4+64.2)/2 = 61.3
    $Q_2 = x_{6.5}$ = (68.5+69.4)/2 = 68.95
    $Q_3 = x_{9.5}$ = (71.6+72.2)/2 = 71.9
    max = x_{12} = 74.4

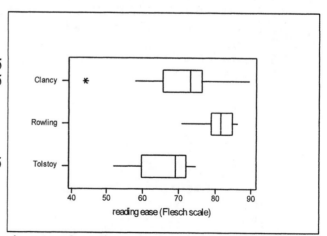

Yes; there does appear to be a difference in ease of reading. Yes; considering that high scores indicate easier reading and the intended audience of each author, the results are consistent with what most people would expect – Rowling writes for children, Clancy writes for as broad a range of adults as possible (trying to sell as many books as possible), Tolstoy writes for the more educated adults (caring more about producing a work of literature than selling it).

13. The following given values are also calculated in detail in exercise #11.
$Q_1 = 86.5$ $Q_2 = 170$ $Q_3 = 251.5$

a. IQR $= Q_3 - Q_1 = 251.5 - 86.5 = 165$

b. Since $1.5(IQR) = 1.5(165) = 247.5$, the modified boxplot line extends to
the smallest value above $Q_1 - 247.5 = 86.5 - 247.5 = -161$, which is 0
the largest value below $Q_3 + 247.5 = 251.5 + 247.5 = 499$, which is 491

c. Since $3.0(IQR) = 3.0(165) = 495$, mild outliers are x values for which
$Q_1 - 495 \le x < Q_1 - 247.5$ or $Q_3 + 247.5 < x \le Q_3 + 495$
$-408.5 \le x < -161$ $499 < x \le 746.5$
There are no such values.

d. Extreme outliers in this exercise are x values for which $x < -408.5$ or $x > 746.5$. There are no such values.

Review Exercises

1. The scores arranged in order are:
42 43 46 46 47 48 49 49 50 51 51 51 51 51 52 52 54 54 54 54 54
55 55 55 55 56 56 56 57 57 57 57 58 60 61 61 61 62 64 64 65 68 69
preliminary values: $n = 43$, $\Sigma x = 2358$, $\Sigma x^2 = 130{,}930$

a. $\bar{x} = (\Sigma x)/n = (2358)/43 = 54.8$

b. $\tilde{x} = 55$

c. M = 51,54 [bi-modal]

d. m.r. $= (42 + 69)/2 = 55.5$

e. R $= 69 - 42 = 27$

f. s = 6.2 (from part g)

g. $s^2 = [n(\Sigma x^2) - (\Sigma x)^2]/[n(n-1)]$
$= [43(130{,}930) - (2358)^2]/[43(42)]$
$= (69{,}826)/1806 = 38.7$

h. For $Q_1 = P_{25}$, L $= (25/100) \cdot 43 = 10.75$ rounded up to 11. And so $Q_1 = x_{11} = 51$.

i. For $Q_3 = P_{75}$, L $= (75/100) \cdot 43 = 32.25$ rounded up to 33. And so $Q_3 = x_{33} = 58$.

j. For P_{10}, L $= (10/100) \cdot 43 = 4.3$ rounded up to 5. And so $P_{10} = x_5 = 47$.

2. a. $z = (x - \bar{x})/s$
$z_{43} = (43 - 54.837)/6.218 = -1.90$

b. No; Kennedy's inaugural age is not unusual since $-2.00 < -1.90 < -2.00$.

c. According to the Range Rule of Thumb, the usual values are within 2s of $\bar{x}$
usual minimum: $\bar{x} - 2s = 54.8 - 2(6.2) = 42.4$
usual maximum: $\bar{x} + 2s = 54.8 + 2(6.2) = 67.2$
The ages 42, 68 and 69 are unusual.

d. Yes; an age of 35 would be unusual – even if $\bar{x}$ and s were recalculated with the value 35 included. It is likely that a presidential candidate of age 35 would find that age would be a campaign issue – especially during the primaries and other preliminary stages of the campaign, but probably not so much so if the candidate wins the nomination of a major party. Presumably a candidate who wins the nomination of a major party will have enough positive qualities to overcome an unusual age - after all, Ronald Reagan (the 69 on the list) was elected despite his "unusual" age.

3.

age	frequency
40 – 44	2
45 – 49	6
50 – 54	13
55 – 59	12
60 – 64	7
65 – 69	3
	43

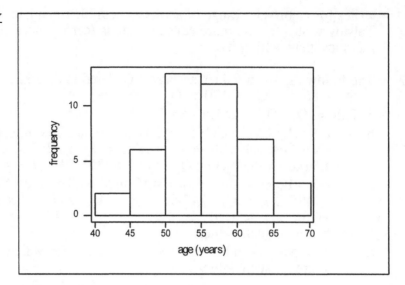

4. See the figure above at the right.
    NOTE: Unlike other data, age is not reported to the nearest unit. The bars in a histogram
    extend from class boundary to class boundary. Because of the way that ages are reported,
    the boundaries here are 40, 45, 50, etc -- i.e., someone 44.9 years old still reports an age
    of 44 and crosses into the next class only upon turning 45, not upon turning 44.5.

5. From results in exercise #1,
    $$\text{min} = x_1 = 42$$
    $$Q_1 = x_{11} = 51$$
    $$Q_2 = x_{22} = 55$$
    $$Q_3 = x_{33} = 58$$
    $$\text{max} = x_{43} = 69$$

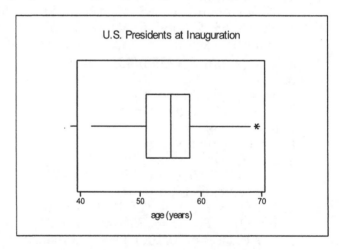

6. a. Since scores 48.6 to 61.0 are within 1·s of $\bar{x}$, the Empirical Rule for Data with a Bell-
       Shaped Distribution states that about 68% of such persons fall within those limits.
    b. Since scores 42.4 to 67.2 are within 2·s of $\bar{x}$, the Empirical Rule for Data with a Bell-
       Shaped Distribution states that about 95% of such persons fall within those limits.

7. In general, $z = (x - \bar{x})/s$.
    management, $z_{72} = (72 - 80)/12 = -0.67$
    production, $z_{19} = (19 - 20)/5 = -0.20$
    The score on the test for production employees has the better relative position since
    $-0.20 > -0.67$.

8. In general, the Range Rule of Thumb states that the range typically covers about 4 standard
    deviations -- with the lowest and highest scores being about 2 standard deviations below
    and above the mean respectively. While answers will vary, the following answers assume
    the cars driven by students have ages that range from $x_1 = 0$ years to $x_n = 12$ years.
    a. The estimated mean age is $(x_1 + x_n)/2 = (0 + 12)/2 = 6$ years.
    b. The estimated standard deviation of the ages is $R/4 = (x_n - x_1)/4 = (12 - 0)/4 = 3$
       years.

Cumulative Review Exercises

1. The scores arranged in order are:
    -241 -151 -125 -85 -65 20 20 27 30 41 80 105 140 186 325
    preliminary values: n = 15, Σx = 307, Σx^2 = 289313
    a. $\bar{x}$ = (Σx)/n = (307)/15 = 20.5
        $\tilde{x}$ = 27
        M = 20
        m.r. = (-241 + 325)/2 = 42
    b. R = 325 - (-241) = 566
        s^2 = [n(Σx^2) - (Σx)^2]/[n(n-1)]
            = [15(289313) - (307)^2]/[15(14)]
            = (4245446)/210 = 20216.4
        s = 142.2
    c. continuous. Even though the values were reported rounded to whole seconds, time can be any value on a continuum.
    d. ratio. Differences are consistent and there is a meaningful zero; 8 seconds is twice as much time as 4 seconds.

2. a. mode. The median requires at least ordinal level data, and the mean and the midrange require at least interval level data.
    b. convenience. The group was not selected by any process other than the fact that they happened to be the first names on the list.
    c. cluster. The population was divided into units (election precincts), some of which were selected at random to be examined in their entirety.
    d. The standard deviation, since it is the only measure of variation in the list. The standard deviation should be lowered to improve the consistency of the product.

3. No; using the mean of the state values counts each state equally, while states with more people will have a greater affect on the per capita consumption for the population in all 50 states combined. Use the state populations as weights to find the weighted mean.

Chapter 3

Probability

3-2 Fundamentals

1. A probability value is a number between 0 and 1 inclusive.
   a. 50-50 = 50% = .50
   b. 20% = .20
   c no chance = 0% = 0

2. A probability value is a number between 0 and 1 inclusive.
   a. 90% = .90
   b. definitely = 100% = 1
   c. 1/10 = .10

3. Since $0 \leq P(A) \leq 1$ is always true, the following values less than 0 or greater than 1 cannot be probabilities.
   values less than 0: -1
   values greater than 1: 2 5/3 $\sqrt{2}$

4. a. 1.00   b. 0   c. 1/10   d. 1/2   e. 1/5

5. Assuming boys (B) and girls (G) are equally likely, the 8 equally likely
   possibilities for a family of 3 children are given at the right. Rule #2
   can be used to find the desired probabilities as follows.
   a. P(1G) = 3/8
   b. P(2G's) = 3/8
   c. P(3G's) = 1/8

   BBB
   GBB
   BGB
   BBG
   GGB
   GBG
   BGG
   GGG

6. Let C = developing cancer of the brain or nervous system; use Rule #1
   P(C) = 135/420,000 = .000321
   No; this is not very different form the general population value of .000340. This suggests
       that cell phones are not the cause of such cancers.

7. Let H = getting a home run.
   P(H) = 73/476 = .1534
   Yes; this is very different from his lifetime probability of 567/7932 = .0715. It is about
   twice as high.

8. Let L = being struck by lightning; use Rule #1.
   P(L) = 389/281,421,906 = .00000138

9. Consider only the 85 women who were pregnant.
   a. Let W = the test wrongly concludes a woman is not pregnant.
      P(W) = 5/85 = .059
   b. No; since .059 > .05, it is not unusual for the test to be wrong for pregnant women..

10. Consider only the 14 women who were not pregnant.
    a. Let W = the test wrongly concludes a woman is pregnant.
       P(W) = 3/14 = .214
    b. No; since .214 > .05, it is not unusual for the test to be wrong for women who are not
       pregnant.

11. Let N = selecting someone who feels that secondhand smoke is not at all harmful.
   a. P(N) = 52/1038 = .0501
   b. By Rule #1, .0501 is an appropriate approximation for the proportion of people who believe that secondhand smoke is not at all harmful. No; since .0501 > .05, it is not unusual for someone to believe that secondhand smoke is not at all harmful.

12. Consider only the 19+844 = 863 patients who took the drug.
   Let F = a patient experiences flu symptoms.
   a. By Rule #1, an appropriate approximation is P(F) = 19/863 = .0220
   b. Yes; since .0220 < .05, it is considered unusual for a patient taking the drug to experience flu symptoms.

13. Consider only the 2624 + 168,262 = 170,886 American Airlines passenger who were bumped.
   Let I = a passenger is bumped involuntarily.
   a. By Rule #1, an appropriate approximation is P(I) = 2624/170,866 = .0154
   b. Yes; since .0164 < .05, such involuntary bumpings are considered unusual.

14. Let L = an American Airlines flight arrives late.
   a. By Rule #1, an appropriate estimate is P(L) = 42/150 = .280.
   b. No; since .280 > .05, it is not considered unusual for such a flight to arrive late.

15. a. Let C = selecting the correct birthdate.
      P(C) = 1/365
   b. Yes; since 1/365 = .003 < .05.
   c. Since P(C) = .003 is so small, C is unlikely to occur by chance. It appears that Mike had inside information and was not operating on chance.
   d. Depends. Most likely Mike was on the spot and gave an obviously incorrect response in an attempt to handle the situation humorously. If Kelly appreciates his spontaneity and sense of humor, the probability may be quite high.

16. **NOTE**: This problem can be approached two ways. Finding P(1 of your 2 numbers matches the winning number), the usual approach, requires using the Addition Rule of section 3-3. Finding P(the winning number matches one of your 2 numbers), which is an equivalent event, requires only the methods of this section.
   a. The winning number can be selected in 25,827,165 equally likely ways.
      Let W = you winning the grand prize
      W can occur 2 ways, if either of your numbers is selected; use Rule #2.
      P(W) = 2/25,827,165 = .0000000774
   b. Yes; since .0000000774 < .05, winning the grand prize is an unusual event.

17. a. Let B = a person's birthday is October 18.
      B is one of 365 (assumed) equally likely outcomes; use Rule #2.
      P(B) = 1/365 = .00274
   b. Let O = a person's birthday is in October.
      O includes 31 of 365 (assumed) equally likely outcomes; use Rule #2.
      P(N) = 31/365 = .0849
   c. Let D = a person's birthday was on a day that ends in the letter y.
      D includes all 7 of the (assumed) equally likely outcomes; use Rule #2.
      P(D) = 7/7 = 1
      NOTE: Since event D is a certainty, P(D) = 1 without reference to Rule #2 – i.e., even if all 7 outcomes are not equally likely

18. a. There were 831 + 18 = 849 consumers surveyed.
      Let C = a consumer recognizes the Campbell's Soup brand name; use Rule #1.
      P(C) = 831/849 = .979

b. Let B = a consumer recognizes the McDonald's brand name; use Rule #3.
   P(B) = .99 [This answer is subjective, and there is no single correct response.]
c. Let V = a consumer recognizes the Veeco Instruments brand name; use Rule #3.
   P(V) = .01 [This answer is subjective, and there is no single correct response.]

19. There were 132 + 880 = 1012 respondents.
    Let D = getting a respondent who gave the doorstop answer.
    D includes 132 of 1012 equally likely outcomes; use Rule #2.
    P(D) = 132/1012 = .130

20. Let A = selecting a driver in that age bracket has an accident.
    A occurred 136 times in a sample of 400; use Rule #1.
    P(A) ≈ 136/400 = .340

    Yes; since this indicates more than 1 such driver in every 3 is likely to have an accident, this should be a concern.

    NOTE: This is properly an estimate that such a person <u>had</u> an accident last year, and not that such a person <u>will have</u> an accident next year. To extend the estimate as desired requires the additional assumption that relevant factors (speed limits, weather, alcohol laws, the economy, etc.) remain the same.

21. The following table summarizes the relevant information from Data Set 27, where a win is defined as a positive result.

column	1	2	3	4	5	6	7	8	9	10	total
# of values	50	50	50	50	50	50	50	50	50	50	500
# of wins	6	6	10	8	7	6	8	9	6	11	77
# of 208's	0	1	1	3	1	1	3	2	0	1	13

    a. Let W = winning; use Rule #1.
       P(W) = 77/500 = .154
    b. Let R = running the deck; use Rule #1.
       P(R) = 13/500 = .026

22. There were 117 + 617 = 734 patients in the clinical test.
    Let H = experiencing a headache; use Rule #1.
    P(H) = 117/734 = .159
    Perhaps; the .159 should be compared to the probability of experiencing a headache when not using Viagra – which cannot be assumed to be 0.00, especially if the clinical trial involved activity beyond merely taking the drug.

23. a. Assuming boys (B) and girls (G) are equally likely, the 4 equally likely   BB
       possibilities for a family of 2 children are given at the right. Rule #2   BG
       can be used to find the desired probabilities as follows.   GB
    b. P(2G's) = 1/4   GG
    c. P(1 of each)= 2/4 = 1/2

24. a. Assuming boys (Br) and girls (Bl) are equally likely, the 4 equally likely   BrBr
       possibilities are given at the right. Rule #2 can be used to find the desired   BrBl
       probabilities as follows.   BlBr
    b. P(BlBl) = 1/4   BlBl
    c. P(brown eyes) = P(BrBr or BrBl or BlBr) = 3/4

25. a. net profit = (winnings received) – (amount bet) = $23 – $2 = $21
    b. payoff odds = (net profit):(amount bet) = 21:2
    c. actual odds = P(lose)/P(win) = (14/15)/(1/15) = 14/1 or 14:1
    d. Payoff odds of 14:1 mean a profit of $14 for every $1 bet.
       A winning bet of $2 means a profit of $28, which implies winnings received of $30.

26. Let O = an odd number occurs.
   a. P(O) = 18/38 = .474
   b. odds against winning = P($\overline{O}$)/P(O) = (20/38)/(18/38) = 10/9 = 10:9
   c. Payoff odds of 1:1 mean a profit of $1 for every $1 bet.
     A winning bet of $18 means a profit of $18.
   d. Payoff odds of 10:9 mean a profit of $10 for every $9 bet.
     A winning bet of $18 means a profit of $20.

27. Chance fluctuations in testing situations typically prevent subjects from scoring exactly the same each time the test is given. When treated subjects show an improvement, there are two possibilities: (1) the treatment was effective and the improvement was due to the treatment or (2) the treatment was not effective and the improvement was due to chance. The accepted standard is that an event whose probability of occurrence is less than .05 is an unusual event. In this scenario, the probability that the treatment group shows an improvement even if the drug has no effect is calculated to be .04. If the treatment group does show improvement, then, either the treatment truly is effective or else an unusual event has occurred. Operating according to the accepted standard, one should conclude that the treatment was effective.

28. Probably, but not on the basis of those calculations. For a population that is 1/2 female, the probability that 20 randomly selected people are all women is $(1/2)^{20} = 1/(1,048,576)$. To determine bias by the court the relevant probability is not the probability that "20 randomly selected people are all women" but that "20 randomly selected people available for jury duty are all women" – i.e., those available for jury duty may not be evenly divided between the genders.

29. If the odds against A are a:b, then P(A) = b/(a+b).
Let M = Millennium wins the next race.
If the odds against M are 3:5, then a=3 and b=5 in the statement above.
P(M) = 5/(3+5) = 5/8 = .625

3-3 Addition Rule

1. a. No, it's possible for a cardiac surgeon to be a female.
   b. No, it's possible for a female college student to drive a motorcycle.
   c. Yes, a person treated with Lipitor would not be in the group that was given no treatment.

2. a. Yes, a person watching NBC would not be watching CBS at precisely the same time.
   b. Yes, a person opposing all government taxation would not approve of government taxation.
   c. No, there are currently United States senators who are females.

3. a. P($\overline{A}$) = 1 – P(A) = 1 – .05 = .95
   b. Let B = a randomly selected woman over the age of 25 has a bachelor's degree.
   c. P($\overline{B}$) = 1 – P(B) = 1 – .218 = .782

4. a. P($\overline{A}$) = 1 – P(A) = 1 – .0175 = .9825
   b. Let B = selecting an American who believes that life exists elsewhere in the galaxy.
   c. P($\overline{B}$) = 1 - P(B) = 1 – .61 = .39

5. Make a chart like the one on the right.
   Let G = getting a green pod.
   Let W = getting a white flower.

   There are two approaches.

		POD		
		Green	Yellow	
FLOWER	Purple	5	4	9
	White	3	2	5
		8	6	14

* Use broad categories and allow for double-counting (i.e., the "formal addition rule").
P(G or W) = P(G) + P(W) - P(G and W)
$$= 8/14 + 5/14 - 3/14$$
$$= 10/14 = 5/7 \text{ or } .714$$

* Use individual mutually exclusive categories that involve no double-counting (i.e., the "intuitive addition rule"). For simplicity in this problem, we use GP for "G and P" and GW for "G and W" and so on, as indicated in the table.
P(G or W) = P(GP or GW or YW)
$$= P(GP) + P(GW) + P(YW)$$
$$= 5/14 + 3/14 + 2/14$$
$$= 10/14 = 5/7 \text{ or } .714$$

NOTE: In general, using broad categories and allowing for double-counting is a "more powerful" technique that "lets the formula do the work" and requires less analysis by the solver. Except when such detailed analysis is instructive, this manual uses the first approach.

NOTE: Throughout the manual we follow the pattern in exercise #5 of using the first letter [or other natural designation] of each category to represent that category. And so in exercises #9-13 P(S) = P(selecting a person who survived) and P(M) = P(selecting a man) and so on. If there is ever cause for ambiguity, the notation will be clearly defined. Since mathematics and statistics use considerable notation and formulas, it is important to clearly define what various letters stand for.

6. Refer to exercise #5.
P(Y or P) = P(Y) + P(P) - P(F and R)
$$= 6/14 + 9/14 - 4/14$$
$$= 11/14 \text{ or } .786$$

7. Let O = a person's birthday falls on October 18; then P(O) = 1/365.
$$P(\bar{O}) = 1 - P(O) = 1 - 1/365 = 364/365 \text{ or } .997$$

8. Let O = a person's birthday falls in October; then P(O) = 31/365.
$$P(\bar{O}) = 1 - P(O) = 1 - 31/365 = 334/365 \text{ or } .915$$

9. Make a chart like the one on the right.
P(W or C) = P(W) + P(C) - P(W and C)
$$= 422/2223 + 109/2223 - 0/2223$$
$$= 531/2223 = .239$$
Note: Let C stand for child – i.e., boys and girls together. And so P(C) = 109/2223, P(C and S) = 56/2223, etc.

	FATE		
GROUP	Survived	Died	
Men	332	1360	1692
Women	318	104	422
Boys	29	35	64
Girls	27	18	45
	706	1517	2223

10. Refer to exercise #9.
P(M or S) = P(M) + P(S) - P(M and S)
$$= 1692/2223 + 706/2223 - 332/2223$$
$$= 2066/2223 = .929$$

11. Refer to exercise #9
P(C or S) = P(C) + P(S) - P(C and S)
$$= 109/2223 + 706/2223 - 56/2223$$
$$= 759/2223 = .341$$

12. Refer to exercise #9.
P(W or D) = P(W) + P(D) - P(W and D)
$$= 422/2223 + 1517/2223 - 104/2223$$
$$= 1835/2223 = .825$$

13. Make a chart like the one on the right.
$P(\bar{A}) = 1 - P(A)$
$\qquad = 1 - 40/100 = 60/100 = .60$

	Rh FACTOR		
GROUP	+	−	
A	35	5	40
B	8	2	10
AB	4	1	5
O	39	6	45
	86	14	100

14. Refer to exercise #13.
$P(Rh\text{-}) = 14/100 = .14$

15. Refer to exercise #13.
$P(A \text{ or } Rh\text{-}) = P(A) + P(Rh\text{-}) - P(A \text{ and } Rh\text{-})$
$\qquad = 40/100 + 14/100 - 5/100 = 49/100 = .49$

16. Refer to exercise #13.
$P(A \text{ or } B) = P(A) + P(B)$
$\qquad = 40/100 + 10/100 = 50/100 = .50$

17. Refer to exercise #13.
$P(\overline{Rh+}) = 1 - P(Rh+)$
$\qquad = 1 - 86/100$
$\qquad = 14/100 = .14$

18. Refer to exercise #13.
$P(B \text{ or } Rh+) = P(B) + P(Rh+) - P(B \text{ and } Rh+)$
$\qquad = 10/100 + 86/100 - 8/100$
$\qquad = 88/100 = .88$

19. Refer to exercise #13.
$P(AB \text{ or } Rh+) = P(AB) + P(Rh+) - P(AB \text{ and } Rh+)$
$\qquad = 5/100 + 86/100 - 4/100$
$\qquad = 87/100 = .87$

20. Refer to exercise #13.
$P(A \text{ or } O \text{ or } Rh+) = P(A) + P(O) + P(Rh+) - P(A \text{ and } Rh+) - P(O \text{ and } Rh+)$
$\qquad = 40/100 + 45/100 + 86/100 - 35/100 - 39/100$
$\qquad = 97/100 = .97$

21. Make a chart like the one on the right.
$P(M \text{ or } 6) = P(M) + P(6) - P(M \text{ and } 6)$
$\qquad = 6/20 + 6/20 - 2/20$
$\qquad = 10/20 = .50$

		TRANSMISSION		
		A	M	
CYLINDERS	4	6	3	9
	6	4	2	6
	8	4	1	5
		14	6	20

22. Of the 107 subjects in Data Set 4, only four (#'s 19,46,66,83) are female non-smokers. Each of the other 103 subjects is either a male or a smoker. By Rule #2 of section 3.2, $P(M \text{ or } S) = 103/107 = .963$

23. Make a chart like the one on the right.
Let A = a person is age 18-21
$\qquad$ N = a person does not respond
$P(A \text{ or } N) = P(A) + P(N) - P(A \text{ and } N)$
$\qquad = 84/359 + 31/359 - 11/359$
$\qquad = 104/359 = .290$

		RESPOND?		
		Yes	No	
AGE	18-21	73	11	84
	22-29	255	20	275
		328	31	359

24. Refer to exercise #23.
$P(A \text{ or } Y) = P(A) + P(Y) - P(A \text{ and } Y)$
$\qquad = 84/359 + 328/359 - 73/359$
$\qquad = 339/359 = .944$

25. The general formula is: P(A or B) = P(A) + P(B) - P(A and B).
    Solving for P(A and B) yields: P(A and B) = P(A) + P(B) - P(A or B)
    a. For P(A) = 3/11 and P(B) = 4/11 and P(A or B) = 7/11, the Addition Rule produces
       P(A and B) = P(A) + P(B) - P(A or B)
                  = 3/11 + 4/11 - 7/11
                  = 0
    This means that A and B are mutually exclusive.
    b. For P(A) = 5/18 and P(B) = 11/18 and P(A or B) = 13/18, the Addition Rule
       produces
       P(A and B) = P(A) + P(B) - P(A or B)
                  = 5/18 + 11/18 - 13/18
                  = 3/18
    This means that A and B are not mutually exclusive.

26. No, as illustrated by the following example.
    Let A = has prostate cancer
    Let B = is a female
    Let C = has testicular cancer

27. If the *exclusive or* is used instead of the *inclusive or*, then the double-counted probability
    must be completely removed (i.e., must be subtracted twice) and the formula becomes
    P(A or B) = P(A) + P(B) - 2·P(A and B)

28. P(A or B or C)
        = P[(A or B) or C]
        = P(A or B) + P(C) - P[(A or B) and C]
        = [P(A) + P(B) - P(A and B)] + P(C) - P[(A and C) or (B and C)]
        = [P(A) + P(B) - P(A and B)] + P(C) - [P(A and C) + P(B and C) - P(A and B and C)]
        = P(A) + P(B) - P(A and B) + P(C) - P(A and C) - P(B and C) + P(A and B and C)
        = P(A) + P(B) + P(C) - P(A and B) - P(A and C) - P(A and B) + P(A and B and C)

3-4 Multiplication Rule: Basics

1. a. Independent, since getting a 5 when rolling a die does not affect the likelihood of getting
      heads when flipping a coin.
   b. Independent, since random selection means that the viewing preferences of the first
      person chosen in no way affect the viewing preferences of the second person.
   c. Dependent, since getting a positive response to a request for a date generally depends on
      the personal opinions of the one being asked – and dress is one of the factors that people
      consider when forming opinions of each other.
      NOTE: This manual views such subjective situations "in general" and without reading
      too much into the problem. The problem doesn't say, for example, how the invitation
      was extended – if it were extended over the phone, then dress would be irrelevant. And
      the problem doesn't say the nature of the relationship prior to the invitation – if the
      people already know each other fairly well, then the dress one happens to be wearing at
      the time of the invitation would probably have little if any affect on the response.

2. a. Independent, since the calculator (assumed to be battery operated) and the refrigerator
      (assumed to be electric) have difference power sources totally unrelated to each other.
      NOTE: One could argue that a refrigerator's failure may be due to improper maintenance
      – the same type of behavior that would put off replacing weak calculator batteries. If so,
      then a person's refrigerator not working suggests he may be one who doesn't properly
      maintain things – which suggests that his calculator might not be working either. This
      manual ignores such highly speculative hypothetical scenarios.

   b. Dependent, since the kitchen light and the refrigerator have the same power source – the electric service supplied to the house. Finding that one of them is not working makes it more likely that the other is not working – just as finding that one of them is working indicates there is electricity to the house and makes it likely that other electric appliances are working.
     NOTE: If the light and the refrigerator are not working, they could have failed independently of each other – but that is irrelevant. The notion of statistical dependence rests upon whether the occurrence of one event <u>could</u> reasonably be related to the occurrence of another.
   c. Dependent, since impaired driving ability makes a car crash more likely.

3. Let T = getting tails when tossing a coin.
   Let 3 = getting a three then rolling a die.
   $P(T \text{ and } 3) = P(T) \cdot P(3|T) = (1/2) \cdot (1/6) = 1/12$

4. Let K = randomly selecting K from the 26 letters in the alphabet.
   Let 9 = randomly selecting 9 from the 10 base ten digits.
   $P(K \text{ and } 9) = P(K) \cdot P(9|K) = (1/26) \cdot (1/10) = 1/260$
   This password would not be an effective deterrent against someone who knew that the password consisted of one letter followed by one digit – since there are only 260 possible combinations, which could all be tried in a reasonably short period of time. If the person trying to gain access knew only that the password could be any phrase of 8 or fewer characters, with at least $26 + 10 = 36$ possibilities for each character, then K9 is one of millions of possibilities and would be as effective as any other password.

5. There are 1 blue + 3 green + 2 red + 1 yellow = 7 items.
   Let A = the first item selected is colored green.
   Let B = the second item selected is colored green.
   In general, $P(A \text{ and } B) = P(A) \cdot P(B|A)$
   a. $P(A \text{ and } B) = P(A) \cdot P(B|A) = (3/7) \cdot (3/7) = 9/49 = .184$
   b. $P(A \text{ and } B) = P(A) \cdot P(B|A) = (3/7) \cdot (2/6) = 6/42 = .143$

6. Refer to exercise #5.
   Let R = selecting an item colored red.
   Let G = selecting an item colored green.
   Let B = selecting an item colored blue.
   a. $P(R_1 \text{ and } G_2 \text{ and } B_3) = P(R_1) \cdot P(G_2|R_1) \cdot P(B_3|R_1 \text{ and } G_2)$
                $= (2/7) \cdot (3/7) \cdot (1/7) = 6/343 = .0175$
   b. $P(R_1 \text{ and } G_2 \text{ and } B_3) = P(R_1) \cdot P(G_2|R_1) \cdot P(B_3|R_1 \text{ and } G_2)$
                $= (2/7) \cdot (3/6) \cdot (1/5) = 6/210 = .0286$

7. Let D = selecting a defective gas mask
   $P(D) = 10322/19218 = .5371$, for the first selection1from the population
   a. $P(D_1 \text{ and } D_2) = P(D_1) \cdot P(D_2|D_1) = (10322/19218) \cdot (10322/19218) = .288477$
   b. $P(D_1 \text{ and } D_2) = P(D_1) \cdot P(D_2|D_1) = (10322/19218) \cdot (10321/19217) = .288464$
   c. The results differ only slightly and are identical to the usual accuracy with which probabilities are reported.
   d. Selecting without replacement. Replacement could lead to re-testing the same unit, which would not yield any new information.

8. Let O = selecting a a hunter who was wearing orange.
   $P(O) = 6/123 = .0488$, for the first selection1from the sample
   a. $P(O_1 \text{ and } O_2) = P(O_1) \cdot P(O_2|O_1) = (6/123) \cdot (6/123) = .00238$
   b. $P(O_1 \text{ and } O_2) = P(O_1) \cdot P(O_2|O_1) = (6/123) \cdot (5/122) = .00200$
   c. Selecting without replacement. Replacement could lead to re-interviewing the same hunter, which would lead to no new information.

9. Let C = a student guesses the correct response.
   P(C) = ½ for each question.
   a. $P(C_1$ and C_2 and C_3 and C_4 and C_5 and C_6 and C_7 and $\overline{C}_8$ and $\overline{C}_9$ and $\overline{C}_{10})$
      $= P(C_1) \cdot P(C_2) \cdot P(C_3) \cdot P(C_4) \cdot P(C_5) \cdot P(C_6) \cdot P(C_7) \cdot P(\overline{C}_8) \cdot P(\overline{C}_9) \cdot P(\overline{C}_{10})$
      $= (½) \cdot (½) \cdot (½) \cdot (½) \cdot (½) \cdot (½) \cdot (½) \cdot (½) \cdot (½) \cdot (½) = 1/1032$
   b. No; getting the first 7 correct and the last 3 incorrect is only one possible way of passing the test.

10. Let W = selecting a woman.
    P(W) = 13/100, for the first selection only
    $P(W_1$ and W_2 and $W_3) = P(W_1) \cdot P(W_2 \mid W_1) \cdot P(W_3 \mid W_1$ and $W_2)$
    $= (13/100) \cdot (12/99) \cdot (11/98) = .00177$
    No; depending on the purpose for contacting the senators, the lobbyist would likely choose the ones that would best help him achieve that purpose.

11. a. Let N = a person is born on November 27.
       P(N) = 1/365, for each selection
       $P(N_1$ and $N_2) = P(N_1) \cdot P(N_2)$
       $= (1/365) \cdot (1/365) = 1/133225 = .00000751$
    b. Let S = a person's birthday is favorable to being the same.
       P(S) = 365/365 for the first person, but then the second person must match
       P(the birthdays are the same) $= P(S_1$ and $S_2) = P(S_1) \cdot P(S_2 \mid S_1)$
       $= (365/365) \cdot (1/365) = 1/365 = .00274$

12. a. Let J = being born on July 4.
       $P(J_1$ and J_2 and $J_3) = P(J_1) \cdot P(J_2) \cdot P(J_3)$
       $= (1/365) \cdot (1/365) \cdot (1/365) = .0000000206$
       Probably not. This probability is about 1 in 50 million, which means that the event can be expected to occur about once in every 50 million such situations.
    b. Let F = a birthday is favorable to producing the desired 3-way match.
       $P(F_1$ and F_2 and $F_3) = P(F_1) \cdot P(F_2 \mid F_1) \cdot P(F_3 \mid F_1$ and $F_2)$
       $= (365/365) \cdot (1/365) \cdot (1/365) = .00000751$

13. Since the sample size is no more than 5% of the size of the population, treat the selections as being independent even though the selections are made without replacement.
    Let G = a selected CD is good.
    P(G) = .97, for each selection
    P(batch accepted) = P(all good)
    $= P(G_1$ and G_2 and...and $G_{12})$
    $= P(G_1) \cdot P(G_2) \cdot ... \cdot P(G_{12}) = (.97)^{12} = .694$

14. Let A = a poll is accurate as claimed.
    P(A) = .95, for each poll
    $P(A_1$ and A_2 and A_3 and A_4 and $A_5) = P(A_1) \cdot P(A_2) \cdot P(A_3) \cdot P(A_4) \cdot P(A_5)$
    $= (.95) \cdot (.95) \cdot (.95) \cdot (.95) \cdot (.95) = (.95)^5 = .774$
    No; the more polls one considers, the less likely it us that they all will be within the claimed margin of error.

15. Let G = a girl is born.
    P(G) = .50, for each couple
    $P(G_1$ and G_2 and...and $G_{10}) = P(G_1) \cdot P(G_2) \cdot ... \cdot P(G_{10}) = (.50)^{10} = .000977$
    Yes, the gender selection method appears to be effective. The choice is between two possibilities: (1) the gender selection method has no effect and a very unusual event occurred or (2) the gender selection method is effective.

16. Let O = the valve opens properly.

P(O) = .9968, for each valve

P(water gets through) = P(O_1 and O_2) = P(O_1)·P(O_2) = (.9968)·(.9968) = .9936

Yes; since the systems is used only in emergencies, and not on a routine basis – but because the probability of a failure is .0064, the system can be expected to fail about 64 times in every 10,000 uses. That means if it is used 28 times a day [28x365 = 10,220 times a year], we expect about 64 failures annually – and after one such failure in a nuclear reactor, there might not be a next time for anything.

17. Let T = the tire named is consistent with all naming the same tire.

P(T) = 4/4 for the first person, but then the others must match him

P(all name the same tire) = P(T_1 and T_2 and T_3 and T_4)

$\qquad$ = P(T_1)·P($T_2 | T_1$)·P($T_3 | T_1$ and T_2)·P($T_4 | T_1$ and T_2 and T_3)

$\qquad$ = (4/4)(1/4)(1/4)(1/4) = 1/64 = .0156

18. Let F = a selection is favorable to producing the desired 9-way match

P(F) = 5/5 for the first selection, and 1/5 thereafter

P(F_1 and F_2 and…and F_9) = P(F_1)·P(F_2)·…·P(F_9)

$\qquad$ = (5/5)·(1/5)·…·(1/5) = 1·(1/5)^8 = .00000256

There is no reasonable doubt if the voices are similar, but not otherwise. If the criminal had a high voice, for example, and only one of the five suspects had a high voice, all nine victims would probably select the suspect with the high voice even if he were not the guilty person.

19. Since the sample size is no more than 5% of the size of the population, treat the selections as being independent even though the selections are made without replacement.

Let N = a CD is not defective

P(N) = 1 – .02 = .98, for each selection

P(N_1 and N_2 and…and N_{15}) = P(N_1)·P(N_2)·…·P(N_{15}) = (.98)^{15} = .739

No, there is not strong evidence to conclude that the new process is better. Even if the new process made no difference, the observed result is not considered unusual and could be expected to occur about 74% of the time.

20. Let A = the alarm clock works properly.

P(A) = .975, for each alarm clock

a. P($\bar{A}$) = 1 – .975 = .025

b. P($\bar{A}_1$ and $\bar{A}_2$) = P($\bar{A}_1$) P($\bar{A}_2 | \bar{A}_1$) = (.025)·(.025) = .000625

c. P(A_1 or A_2) = P(A_1) + P(A_2) – P(A_1 and A_2)

$\qquad$ = .975 + .975 – (.975)·(.975) = .999

21. Refer to the table at the right.

P(Pos_1 and Pos_2) = P(Pos_1)·P(Pos_2)

$\qquad$ = (83/99)·(.82/98)

$\qquad$ = .702

		TEST RESULT		
		Pos	Neg	
PREGNANT?	Yes	80	5	85
	No	3	11	14
		83	16	99

22. Refer to the table for exercise #21.

P(Neg or No) = P(Neg) + P(No) – P(Neg and No)

$\qquad$ = 16/99 + 14/99 – 11/99 = 19/99 = .192

23. Refer to the table for exercise #21.

P(Yes_1 and Yes_2) = P(Yes_1)·P(Yes_2) = (85/99)·(84/98) = .736

24. Refer to the table for exercise #21.

P(Neg_1 and Neg_2 and Neg_3) = P(Neg_1)·P($Neg_2 | Neg_1$)·P($Neg_3 | Neg_1$ and Neg_2)

$\qquad$ = (16/99)·(15/98)·(14/97) = .00357

25. let D = a birthday is different from any yet selected
$P(D_1)$ = 366/366   NOTE: With nothing to match, it <u>must</u> be different.
$P(D_2|D_1)$ = 365/366
$P(D_3|D_1 \text{ and } D_2)$ = 364/366
...
$P(D_5|D_1 \text{ and } D_2 \text{ and}...\text{and } D_4)$ = 362/366
...
$P(D_{25}|D_1 \text{ and } D_2 \text{ and}...\text{and } D_{24})$ = 342/366
   a. P(all different) = $P(D_1 \text{ and } D_2 \text{ and } D_3)$
                     = $P(D_1) \cdot P(D_2) \cdot P(D_3)$
                     = $(366/366) \cdot (365/366) \cdot (364/366)$ = .992
   b. P(all different) = $P(D_1 \text{ and } D_2 \text{ and}...\text{and } D_5)$
                     = $P(D_1) \cdot P(D_2) \cdot ... \cdot P(D_5)$
                     = $(366/366) \cdot (365/366) \cdot ... \cdot (362/366)$ = .973
   c. P(all different) = $P(D_1 \text{ and } D_2 \text{ and}...\text{and } D_{25})$
                     = $P(D_1) \cdot P(D_2) \cdot ... \cdot P(D_{25})$
                     = $(366/366) \cdot (365/366) \cdot ... \cdot (342/366)$ = .432
   NOTE: A program to perform this calculation can be constructed using a programming language, or using most spreadsheet or statistical software packages. In BASIC, for example, use

```
10 LET P=1
15 PRINT "How many birthdays?"
20 INPUT D
30   FOR K=1 TO D-1
40   LET P=P*(366-K)/366
50   NEXT K
55 PRINT "The probability they all are different is"
60 PRINT P
70 END
```

26. let F = a birth is favorable to producing the desired 8-way match
$P(F)$ = 2/2 for the first birth, and 1/2 thereafter
$P(F_1 \text{ and } F_2 \text{ and}...\text{and } F_8)$ = $P(F_1) \cdot P(F_2) \cdot ... \cdot P(F_8)$
$= (2/2) \cdot (1/2) \cdot ... \cdot (1/2)$ = $1 \cdot (1/2)^7$ = .00781

27. This is problem can be done by two different methods. In either case,
   let A = getting an ace
      S = getting a spade
   * consider the sample space
   The first card could be any of 52 cards; for each first card, there are 51 possible second cards. This makes a total of $52 \cdot 51$ = 2652 equally likely outcomes in the sample space. How many of them are A_1S_2?
   The aces of hearts, diamonds and clubs can be paired with any of the 13 clubs for a total of $3 \cdot 13$ = 39 favorable possibilities. The ace of spades can only be paired with any of the remaining 12 members of that suit for a total of 12 favorable possibilities. Since there are 39 + 12 = 51 favorable possibilities among the equally likely outcomes,
   $P(A_1S_2)$ = 51/2652
           = .0192
   * use the formulas
   Let As and Ao represent the ace of spades and the ace of any other suit respectively. Break A_1S_2 into mutually exclusive parts so the probability can be found by adding and without having to consider double-counting.
   $P(A_1S_2)$ = $P[(As_1 \text{ and } S_2) \text{ or } (Ao_1 \text{ and } S_2)]$
           = $P(As_1 \text{ and } S_2) + P(Ao_1 \text{ and } S_2)$
           = $P(As_1) \cdot P(S_2|As_1) + P(Ao_1) \cdot P(S_2|Ao_1)$
           = $(1/52)(12/51) + (3/52)(13/51)$
           = 12/2652 + 39/2652
           = 51/2652 = .0192

28. The following English/logic facts are used in this exercise.
   * not (A or B) = not A and not B
      Is your sister either artistic or bright?
      No? Then she is not artistic and she is not bright.
   * not (A and B) = not A or not B
      Is your brother artistic and bright?
      No? Then either he is not artistic or he is not bright.
   a. $P(\overline{A \text{ or } B}) = P(\overline{A} \text{ and } \overline{B})$ [from the first fact above]
      or____
      $P(\overline{A \text{ or } B}) = 1 - P(A \text{ or } B)$ [rule of complimentary events]
   b. $P(\overline{A} \text{ or } \overline{B}) = 1 - P(A \text{ and } B)$ [from the second fact above]
   c. They are different: part (a) gives the complement of "A or B"
                while part (b) gives the complement of "A and B."

3-5 Multiplication Rule: Complements and Conditional Probability

1. If it is not true that "at least one of them has Group A blood," then "none of them has Group A blood."

2. If it is not true that "all of them are free of defects," then "at least one of them is defective."

3. If it is not true that "none of them is correct," then "at least one of them is correct."

4. If it is not true that "at least one of them accepts," then "none of them accepts."

5. Let L = selecting someone with long hair.
   Let W = selecting a woman.
   $P(W|L) = .90$ seems like a reasonable estimate. No; while someone with long hair is likely to be a woman, one cannot say such will "almost surely" be the case.

6. Let C = selecting someone who owns a motorcycle.
   Let M = selecting a male.
   $P(M|C) = .95$ seems like a reasonable estimate. Yes; it would be "reasonable to believe" that Pat is a male.

7. Let B = a child is a boy
   $P(B) = .5$, for each birth
   $$P(\text{at least one girl}) = 1 - P(\text{all boys})$$
   $$= 1 - P(B_1 \text{ and } B_2 \text{ and } B_3 \text{ and } B_4 \text{ and } B_5)$$
   $$= 1 - P(B_1) \cdot P(B_2) \cdot P(B_3) \cdot P(B_4) \cdot P(B_5)$$
   $$= 1 - (.5) \cdot (.5) \cdot (.5) \cdot (.5) \cdot (.5) = 1 - .03125 = .96875$$
   Yes; that probability is high enough to be "very confident" of getting at least one girl – since .03125 is less than .05, the accepted probability of an unusual event.

8. Refer to the notation of exercise #7.
   $$P(\text{at least one girl}) = 1 - P(\text{all boys})$$
   $$= 1 - P(B_1 \text{ and } B_2 \text{ and}...\text{and } B_{12})$$
   $$= 1 - P(B_1) \cdot P(B_2) \cdot ... \cdot P(B_{12})$$
   $$= 1 - (.5) \cdot (.5) \cdot ... \cdot (.5) = 1 - (.5)^{12} = 1 - .000244 = .999756$$
   Either an extremely rare event has occurred or (more likely) there is some genetic factor present for this couple that makes $P(B) > .5$.

9. Let N = not getting cited for a traffic violation.
   $P(N) = .9$ for each such infraction
   P(at least violation citation) = 1 - P(no violation citations)
   $$= 1 - P(N_1 \text{ and } N_2 \text{ and } N_3 \text{ and } N_4 \text{ and } N_5)$$
   $$= 1 - P(N_1) \cdot P(N_2) \cdot P(N_3) \cdot P(N_4) \cdot P(N_5)$$
   $$= 1 - (.9) \cdot (.9) \cdot (.9) \cdot (.9) \cdot (.9)$$
   $$= 1 - .590 = .410$$

10. Let E = erroneously answering a question.
    $P(E) = 4/5 = .8$, for each question
    P(at least one correct) = 1 - P(all erroneous)
    $$= 1 - P(E_1 \text{ and } E_2 \text{ and } E_3 \text{ and } E_4)$$
    $$= 1 - P(E_1) \cdot P(E_2) \cdot P(E_3) \cdot P(E_4)$$
    $$= 1 - (.8) \cdot (.8) \cdot (.8) \cdot (.8) = 1 - .410 = .590$$
    Since $.590 > .5$, you are more likely to pass than to fail – whether or not you can
    "reasonably expect" to pass depends on your perception of what is reasonable.

11. Let G = getting a girl.
    $P(G) = .5$, for each birth
    $P(G_3 \mid G_1 \text{ and } G_2) = P(G_3) = .5$
    No; this is not the same as $P(G_1 \text{ and } G_2 \text{ and } G_3) = P(G_1) \cdot P(G_2) \cdot P(G_3)$
    $$= (.5) \cdot (.5) \cdot (.5) = .125$$

12. Make a chart like the one on the right.
    Let Gr = getting a green pod.
    Let Pu = getting a purple flower.
    $P(Pu \mid Gr) = 5/8 = .625$

		POD		
		Green	Yellow	
FLOWER	Purple	5	4	9
	White	3	2	5
		8	6	14

13. Refer to the table at the right.
    $P(Neg \mid No) = 11/14 = .786$
    Since $P(Neg \mid Yes) = 5/85 = .059 > .05$,
    it would not be considered unusual for

		TEST RESULT		
		Pos	Neg	
PREGNANT?	Yes	80	5	85
	No	3	11	14
		83	16	99

    the test to read negative even if she were
    pregnant. If a woman wanted to be more sure that she were not pregnant, she could take
    another test. Assuming independence of tests (i.e., that errors occur at random and there is
    no biological reason why the test should err in her particular case), P(2 false negatives) =
    $(.059)^2 = .003$.

14. Refer to the table for exercise #13.
    $P(No \mid Neg) = 11/16 = .6875$
    No; $P(No \mid Neg)$ is not equal to $P(Neg \mid No)$ calculated in exercise #13.

15. Let F = the alarm clock fails.
    $P(F) = .01$, for each clock
    P(at least one works) = 1 - P(all fail) = $1 - P(F_1 \text{ and } F_2 \text{ and } F_3)$
    $$= 1 - P(F_1) \cdot P(F_2) \cdot P(F_3)$$
    $$= 1 - (.01)(.01)(.01) = 1 - .000001 = .999999$$
    Yes; the student appears to gain, because now the probability of a timely alarm is virtually a
    certainty. There may be something else going on, however, if the student "misses many
    classes because of malfunctioning alarm clocks" when his clock works correctly 99% of the
    time.
    NOTE: Rounded to 3 significant digits as usual, the answer is 1.00. In cases when
    rounding to 3 significant digits produces a probability of 1.00, this manual gives the
    answer with sufficient significant digits to distinguish the answer from a certainty.

16. Let G = a selected CD is good [i.e., the CD is good, not necessarily the music].

P(G) = .97, for each CD

$$
\begin{aligned}
\text{P(reject the batch)} &= \text{P(at least one defective)} \\
&= 1 - \text{P(all good)} \\
&= 1 - \text{P(G}_1 \text{ and G}_2 \text{ and...and G}_{10}\text{)} \\
&= 1 - \text{P(G}_1)\cdot\text{P(G}_2)\cdot...\cdot\text{P(G}_{10}) \\
&= 1 - (.97)(.97)...(.97) = 1 - (.97)^{10} = 1 - .737 = .263
\end{aligned}
$$

NOTE: Since the sample is less than 5% of the population (i.e., 10/5000 = .002 < .05), treat the selections as independent and ignore that the sampling is without replacement.

17. Let N = a person is HIV negative

P(N) = .9, for each person in the at-risk population

$$
\begin{aligned}
\text{P(HIV positive result)} &= \text{P(at least person is HIV positive)} \\
&= 1 - \text{P(all persons HIV negative)} \\
&= 1 - \text{P(N}_1 \text{ and N}_2 \text{ and N}_3\text{)} \\
&= 1 - \text{P(N}_1)\cdot\text{P(N}_2)\cdot\text{P(N}_3) \\
&= 1 - (.9)(.9)(.9) = 1 - .729 = .271
\end{aligned}
$$

NOTE: This plan is very efficient. Suppose, for example, there were 3,000 people to be tested. Only in .271 = 27.1% of the groups would a retest need to be done for each of the 3 individuals. Those (.271)·(1,000) = 271 groups would generate 271·3 = 813 retests. The total number of tests required is then 1813 (1000 original tests + 813 retests), only 60% of the 3,000 tests that would have been required to test everyone individually.

18. Let S = a swimming pool passes the test.

P(S) = .98, for each pool

$$
\begin{aligned}
\text{P(the combined sample fails)} &= \text{P(at least one pool fails)} \\
&= 1 - \text{P(all pools pass)} \\
&= 1 - \text{P(S}_1 \text{ and S}_2 \text{ and...and S}_6\text{)} \\
&= 1 - \text{P(S}_1)\cdot\text{P(S}_2)\cdot...\cdot\text{P(S}_6) \\
&= 1 - (.98)(.98)...(.98) = 1 - (.98)^6 = 1 - .886 = .114
\end{aligned}
$$

NOTE: This plan is very efficient. Suppose, for example, there were 60 pools to be tested. Only in .114 = 11.4% of the groups would a retest need to be done for each of the 6 pools. That (.114)·(10) = 1 case would generate 1·6 = 6 retests. The total number of tests required is then 16 (10 original tests + 6 retests), only 27% of the 60 tests that would have been required to test each pool individually.

19. Refer to the table at the right.

This problem may be done two ways.

		FATE Survived	FATE Died	
	Men	332	1360	1692
GROUP	Women	318	104	422
	Boys	29	35	64
	Girls	27	18	45
		706	1517	2223

* reading directly from the table

P(M|D) = 1360/1517 = .897

* using the formula

$$
\begin{aligned}
\text{P(M}|\text{D)} &= \text{P(M and D)/P(D)} \\
&= (1360/2223)/(1517/2223) \\
&= .6118/.6824 = .897
\end{aligned}
$$

NOTE: In general, the manual will use the most obvious approach -- which most often is the first one of applying the basic definition by reading directly from the table.

20. Refer to the table and comments for exercise #19.

P(M|D) = 1360/1517 = .897

21. Refer to the table and comments for exercise #19.

P([B or G]|S) = [29 + 27]/706 = 56/706 = .0793

22. Refer to the table and comments for exercise #19.

P([M or W]|D) = [1360 + 104]/1517 = 1464/1517 = .965

23. Let F = getting a seat in the front row. $(11/12)^{31} = .0674$
$P(F) = 2/24 = 1/12 = .083$ $(11/12)^{32} = .0618$
P(at least one F in n rides) = 1 - P(no F in n rides) = 1 - $(11/12)^n$. $(11/12)^{33} = .0566$
P(at least one F in n rides) > .95 requires that $(11/12)^n < .05$. $(11/12)^{34} = .0519$
According to the table at the right, this first occurs for n = 35. $(11/12)^{35} = .0476$

24. Make a chart like the one on the right.
Let D = getting a defective one
Let A = getting one made in Atlanta
$P(A \mid D) = 3/5 = .600$

		RESULT		
		Good	Def.	
PLANT	Atlanta	397	3	400
	Balto.	798	2	800
		1195	5	1200

25. a. The table is given below: 300 = 0.3% of 100,000; 285 = 95% of 300; etc.

		TEST RESULT		
		Pos	Neg	
HIV?	Yes	285	15	300
	No	4985	94,715	99,700
		5270	94,730	100,000

b. $P(\text{Yes} \mid \text{Pos}) = 285/5270 = .0541$

26. For 25 randomly selected people,
a. P(no 2 share the same birthday) = .432 [see exercise #25c in section 3-4]
b. P(at least 2 share the same birthday) = 1 - P(no 2 share the same birthday)
= 1 - .432 = .568

27. When 2 coins are tossed, there are 4 equally likely possibilities: HH HT TH TT.
There are two possible approaches.
* counting the sample space directly
   If there is at least one H, that leaves only 3 equally likely possibilities: HH HT TH
   Since HH is one of those 3, P(HH | at least one H) = 1/3
* applying an appropriate formula
   Use $P(B \mid A) = P(A \text{ and } B)/P(A)$, where   B = HH
                                                         A = at least one H
   P(HH | at least one H) = P(at least one H and HH)/P(at least one H)
   = (1/4)/(3/4)
   = 1/3

3-6 Counting

1. $6! = 6 \cdot 5 \cdot 4 \cdot 3 \cdot 2 \cdot 1 = 720$

2. $15! = 15 \cdot 14 \cdot 13 \cdot 12 \cdot 11 \cdot 10 \cdot 9 \cdot 8 \cdot 7 \cdot 6 \cdot 5 \cdot 4 \cdot 3 \cdot 2 \cdot 1 = 1,307,674,368,000$
NOTE: It's staggering how such a small number like 15 can have such a large value for its factorial. In practice this means that if you have 15 books on a shelf you could arrange them in over 1.3 trillion different orders!

3. $_{25}P_2 = 25!/23! = (25 \cdot 24 \cdot 23!)/23! = 25 \cdot 24 = 600$
NOTE: This technique of "cancelling out" or "reducing" the problem by removing the factors 23! = $23 \cdot 22 \cdot \ldots \cdot 1$ from both the numerator and the denominator is preferred over actually evaluating 25!, actually evaluating 23!, and then dividing those two very large numbers. In general, a smaller factorial in the denominator can be completely divided into a larger factorial in the numerator to leave only the "excess" factors not appearing the in the denominator. This is the technique employed in this manual -- e.g., see #5 below, where the 23! is cancelled from both the numerator and the denominator. In addition, $_nP_r$ and $_nC_r$ will always be integers; calculating a non-integer value for either expression

indicates an error has been made. More generally, the answer to any <u>counting</u> problem (but not a <u>probability</u> problem) must always be a whole number; a fractional number indicates that an error has been made.

4. $_{100}P_3 = 100!/97! = (100 \cdot 99 \cdot 98 \cdot 97!)/97! = 100 \cdot 99 \cdot 98 = 970,200$

5 $_{25}C_2 = 25!/(2!23!) = (25 \cdot 24)/2! = 300$

6. $_{100}C_3 = 100!/(3!97!) = (100 \cdot 99 \cdot 98)/3! = 161,700$

7. $_{52}C_5 = 52!/(5!47!) = (52 \cdot 51 \cdot 50 \cdot 49 \cdot 48)/5! = 2,598,960$

8. $_{52}P_5 = 52!/47! = (52 \cdot 51 \cdot 50 \cdot 49 \cdot 48 \cdot 47!)/47! = 52 \cdot 51 \cdot 50 \cdot 49 \cdot 48 = 311,875,200$

9. Let W = winning the described lottery with a single selection.
   The total number of possible combinations is
   $_{49}C_6 = 49!/(43!6!) = (49 \cdot 48 \cdot 47 \cdot 46 \cdot 45 \cdot 44)/6! = 13,983,816$.
   Since only one combination wins, P(W) = 1/13,983,816.

10. Let W = winning the described lottery with a single selection.
   The total number of possible combinations is
   $_{69}C_6 = 69!/(63!6!) = (69 \cdot 68 \cdot 67 \cdot 66 \cdot 65 \cdot 64)/6! = 119,877,472$
   Since only one combination wins, P(W) = 1/119,877,472.

11. Let W = winning the described lottery with a single selection.
   The total number of possible combinations is
   $_{59}C_6 = 59!/(53!6!) = (59 \cdot 58 \cdot 57 \cdot 56 \cdot 55 \cdot 54)/6! = 45,057,474$
   Since only one combination wins, P(W) = 1/45,047,474.

12. Let W = winning the described lottery with a single selection.
   The total number of possible combinations is
   $_{39}C_5 = 39!/(34!5!) = (39 \cdot 38 \cdot 37 \cdot 36 \cdot 35)/5! = 575,757$.
   Since only one combination wins, P(W) = 1/575,757.

13. Let C = choosing the 4 oldest at random.
   The total number of possible groups of 4 is
   $_{32}C_4 = 32!/4!28! = 32 \cdot 31 \cdot 30 \cdot 29/4! = 35,960$.
   Since only one group of 4 is the 4 oldest, P(C) = 1/35,960 = .0000278.
   Yes; P(C) is low enough to suggest the event did not happen randomly.

14. There are $2 \cdot 2 \cdot 2 \cdot 2 \cdot 2 \cdot 2 \cdot 2 \cdot 2 = 2^8 = 256$ possible sequences. Yes; the keyboard being used to prepare this manual has 47 character keys – considering both lower and upper cases, it appears that $2 \cdot 47 = 94$ sequences would be needed.

15. Let W = winning the described lottery with a single selection.
   The total number of possible permutations is
   $_{42}C_6 = 42!/36! = 42 \cdot 41 \cdot 40 \cdot 39 \cdot 38 \cdot 37 = 3,776,965,920$.
   Since only one permutation wins, P(W) = 1/3,776,965,920.

16. Let S = rolling a 6.
   P(S) = 1/6, for each trial.
   $P(S_1 S_2 S_3 S_4 S_5) = P(S_1) \cdot P(S_2) \cdot P(S_3) \cdot P(S_4) \cdot P(S_5) = (1/6)^5 = 1/7776 = .000128$
   Yes; that probability is low enough to suggest the event did not occur by chance alone.

17. Let Y = the 6 youngest are chosen.
   The total number of possible groups of 6 is $_{15}C_6 = 15!/(6!9!) = 5005$.

Since only of the possibilities consists of the 6 youngest, $P(Y) = 1/5005 = .000200$.
Yes; that probability is low enough to suggest the event did not occur by chance alone.

18. $_{10}P_3 = 10!/7! = 10 \cdot 9 \cdot 8 = 720$

19. For 3 cities there are $3! = 6$ possible sequences; and so there are 4 more possible routes.
For 8 cities there are $8! = 40,320$ possible sequences.

20. The total number of possibilities is $10^9 = 1,000,000,000$.
P(randomly generating any particular number) $= 1/1,000,000,000$

21. $_5C_2 = 5!/(2!3!) = (5 \cdot 4)/2! = 10$

22. a. Since a different arrangement of selected names is a different slate, use
$_{12}P_4 = 12!/8! = 12 \cdot 11 \cdot 10 \cdot 9 = 11,880$
b. Since a different arrangement of selected names is the same committee, use
$_{12}C_4 = 12!/(8!4!) = (12 \cdot 11 \cdot 10 \cdot 9)/4! = 495$

23. For 6 letters there are $6! = 720$ possible sequences.
The only English word possible from those letters is "satire."
Since there is only one correct sequence, P(correct sequence by chance) $= 1/720$.

24. The first note is given by *. There are 3 possibilities (R,U,D) for each of the next 15
notes. There are $3 \cdot 3 \cdot 3 \cdot 3 \cdot 3 \cdot 3 \cdot 3 \cdot 3 \cdot 3 \cdot 3 \cdot 3 \cdot 3 \cdot 3 \cdot 3 \cdot 3 = 3^{15} = 14,348,907$ possible sequences.
NOTE: This assumes each song has at least 16 notes, and it does not guarantee that two
different melodies will not have the same representation – if one goes up steps every time
the other goes up one step, for example, they both will show a U in that position.

25. Let O = opening the lock on the first try.
The total number of possible "combinations" is $50 \cdot 50 \cdot 50 = 125,000$.
Since only of the possibilities is correct, $P(O) = 1/125,000$.

26. This problem may be approached in two different ways.
* general probability formulas of earlier sections
Let F = selecting a card favorable for getting a flush.
$P(F_1) = 52/52$, since the first card could be anything
$P(F_2) = 12/51$, since the second card must be from the same suit as the first
etc.
P(getting a flush) $= P(F_1$ and F_2 and F_3 and F_4 and $F_5)$
$= P(F_1) \cdot P(F_2) \cdot P(F_3) \cdot P(F_4) \cdot P(F_5)$
$= (52/52) \cdot (12/51) \cdot (11/50) \cdot (10/49) \cdot (9/48) = .00198$
* counting techniques of this section
The total number of possible 5 card selections is
$_{52}C_5 = 52!/(47!5!) = 2,598,960$
The total number of possible 5 card selections from one particular suit is
$_{13}C_5 = 13!/(8!5!) = 1287$
The total number of possible 5 card selections from any of the 4 suits is
$4 \cdot 1287 = 5148$
P(getting a flush) $= 5148/2598960 = .00198$

27. a. There are 2 possibilities (B,G) for each baby. The number of possible sequences is
$2 \cdot 2 \cdot 2 \cdot 2 \cdot 2 \cdot 2 \cdot 2 \cdot 2 = 2^8 = 256$
b. The number of ways to arrange 8 items consisting of 4 B's and 4 G's is $8!/(4!4!) = 70$.
c. Let E = getting equal numbers of boys and girls in 8 births.
Based on parts (a) and (b), P(E) 70/256 = .273

28. a. There are 2 possibilities (B,G) for each baby. The number of possible sequences is
$2 \cdot 2 \cdot 2 \cdot 2 \cdot 2 \cdot 2 \cdot 2 \cdot 2 \cdot 2 \cdot 2 \cdot 2 \cdot 2 \cdot 2 \cdot 2 \cdot 2 \cdot 2 \cdot 2 \cdot 2 \cdot 2 \cdot 2 = 2^{20} = 1,048,576$

  b. The number of ways to arrange 20 items consisting of 10 B's and 10 G's is
$20!/(10!10!) = 20 \cdot 19 \cdot 18 \cdot 17 \cdot 16 \cdot 15 \cdot 14 \cdot 13 \cdot 12 \cdot 11/10! = 184,756$

  c. Let E = getting equal numbers of boys and girls in 20 births.
Based on parts (a) and (b), P(E) = 184756/1048576 = .176.

  d. The preceding results indicate that getting 10 boys and 10 girls when 20 babies are randomly selected is not an unusual event – for one such random selection. But the probability of getting that result twice in a row would be (.176)·(.176) = .0310, which would be considered unusual since .0310 < .05. Getting 10 boys and 10 girls "consistently" should arouse suspicion.

29. The 1st digit may be any of 8 (any digit except 0 or 1).
The 2nd digit may be any of 2 (0 or 1).
The 3rd digit may be any of 9 (any digit except whatever the 2nd digit is).
There are $8 \cdot 2 \cdot 9 = 144$ possibilities.

30. The total number of ways of selecting 5 eggs from among 12 is
$_{12}C_5 = 12!/(7!5!) = (12 \cdot 11 \cdot 10 \cdot 9 \cdot 8)/5! = 792$.

  a. Let A = selecting all 3 of the cracked eggs. The total number of ways of selecting 3 eggs from among the 3 cracked ones and 2 eggs from among the 9 good ones is
$_3C_3 \cdot _9C_2 = [3!/(0!3!)] \cdot [9!/(7!2!)] = [1] \cdot [36] = 36$
$P(A) = 36/792 = .0455$

  b. Let N = selecting none of the cracked eggs. The total number of ways of selecting 0 eggs from among the 3 cracked ones and 5 eggs from among the 9 good ones is
$_3C_0 \cdot _9C_5 = [3!/(3!0!)] \cdot [9!/(4!5!)] = [1] \cdot [126] = 126$
$P(N) = 126/792 = .1591$

  c. Let T = selecting 2 of the cracked eggs. The total number of ways of selecting 2 eggs from among the 3 cracked ones and 3 eggs from among the 9 good ones is
$_3C_2 \cdot _9C_3 = [3!/(1!2!)] \cdot [9!/(6!3!)] = [3] \cdot [84] = 252$
$P(T) = 252/792 = .3182$

NOTE 1: Since the answer in part (a) required 4 decimal places to provide 3 significant digit accuracy, the answers in parts (b) and (c) are also given to 4 decimal places for consistency and ease of comparison. In general, this pattern will apply throughout the manual.

NOTE 2: There is only one possibility not covered in parts (a)-(c) above -- viz., one of the cracked eggs is selected. As a check, it is recommended that this probability be calculated. If these 4 mutually exclusive and exhaustive probabilities do not sum to 1.000, then an error has been made.

  Let O = selecting 1 of the cracked eggs.
  The total number of ways of selecting 1 egg from among the 3 cracked ones and 4 eggs from among the 9 good ones is $_3C_1 \cdot _9C_4 = [3!/(2!1!)] \cdot [9!/(5!4!)] = [3] \cdot [126] = 378$
  $P(O) = 378/792 = .4773$
  P(N or O or T or A) = P(N) + P(O) + P(T) + P(A)
  $= .1591 + .4773 + .3182 + .0455$
  $= 1.000$ [the 4 values actually sum to 1.0001 due to round-off]
And so everything seems in order. Performing an extra calculation that can provide a check to both the methodology and the mathematics is a good habit that is well worth the effort.

31. Winning the game as described requires two events A and B as follows.
    A = selecting the correct 5 numbers between 1 and 47
        There are $_{47}C_5 = 47!/(42!5!) = 1,533,939$ possible selections.
        Since there is only 1 winning selection, $P(A) = 1/1,533,939$
    B = selecting the correct number between 1 and 27 in a separate drawing
        There are $_{27}C_1 = 27!/(26!1!) = 27$ possible selections.
        Since there is only 1 winning selection, $P(B) = 1/27$.
    P(winning the game) = P(A and B)
        $= P(A) \cdot P(B|A)$
        $= (1/1,533,939) \cdot (1/27) = 1/41,416,353$

32. a. Since there are 64 teams at the start and only 1 team left at the end, 63 teams must be
        eliminated. Since each game eliminates 1 team, it takes 63 games to eliminate 63 teams.
    b. Let W = picking all 63 winners by random guessing.
        Since there are 2 outcomes for each of the 63 games, there are $2^{63} = 9.223 \cdot 10^{18}$ possible
        sets of results. Since only one such result gives all the correct winners,
        $P(W) = 1/2^{63} = 1/9.223 \cdot 10^{18} = 1.084 \cdot 10^{-19}$.
    c. Let E = picking all 63 winners by expert guessing, where each guess has a 70% chance.
        $P(E) = (.7)^{63} = 1.743 \cdot 10^{-10}$. This is about 10^9 (one billion) times more likely than
        winning by random guessing, but it still represents a chance of only 1 in $1/(.7)^{63} =$
        $1/(1.743 \cdot 10^{-10}) = 5,738,831,575$ of correctly picking all 63 winners.
        NOTE: The logic employed above is as follows: If E is to have 1 chance in x of
        occurring, then $P(E) = 1/x$ and solving for x yields $x = 1/P(E)$.

33. There are 26 possible first characters, and 36 possible characters for the other positions.
    Find the number of possible names using 1,2,3,...,8 characters and then add to get the
    total.

characters	possible names		
1	26	=	26
2	26·36	=	936
3	26·36·36	=	33,696
4	26·36·36·36	=	1,213,056
5	26·36·36·36·36	=	43,670,016
6	26·36·36·36·36·36	=	1,572,120,576
7	26·36·36·36·36·36·36	=	56,596,340,736
8	26·36·36·36·36·36·36·36	=	2,037,468,266,496
	total	=	2,095,681,645,538

34. a. The number of handshakes is the number of ways 2 people can be chosen from 5,
        $_5C_2 = 5!/(3!2!) = (5 \cdot 4)/2! = 10$.
    b. The number of handshakes is the number of ways 2 people can be chosen from n,
        $_nC_2 = n!/[(n-2)!2!] = n \cdot (n-1)/2! = n \cdot (n-1)/2$.
    c. Visualize the people entering one at a time, each person sitting to the right of the
        previous person who entered. Where the first person sits is irrelevant – i.e., it merely
        establishes a reference point but does not affect the number of arrangements. Once the 1st
        person sits, there are 4 possibilities for the person at his right. Once the 2nd person sits,
        there are 3 possibilities for the person at his right. Once the 3rd person sits, there are 2
        possibilities for the person at his right. Once the 4th person sits, there is only 1 remaining
        person to sit as his right. And so the number of possible arrangements is $4 \cdot 3 \cdot 2 \cdot 1 = 24$.
    d. Use the same reasoning as in part (c). Once the 1st person sits, there are n-1 possibilities
        for the person at his right. Once the 2nd person sits, there are n-2 possibilities for the
        person at his right. And so on... Once the next to the last person sits, there is only 1
        possibility for the person at his right. And so the number of possible arrangements is
        $(n-1) \cdot (n-2) \cdot ... \cdot 1 = (n-1)!$.

Review Exercises

1. Refer to the table at the right.

		POLYGRAPH		
		Truth	Lie	
SUBJECT	Truth	65	15	80
	Lie	3	17	20
		68	32	100

   Let PT = the polygraph indicates truth
   PL = the polygraph indicates lie
   AT = the subject is actually telling the truth
   AL = the subject is actually telling a lie
   $P(AL) = 20/100 = .200$

2. Refer to the table and notation of exercise #1.
   $P(PL) = 32/100 = .320$

3. Refer to the table and notation of exercise #1.
   $P(AL \text{ or } PL) = P(AL) + P(PL) - P(AL \text{ and } PL)$
   $= 20/100 + 32/100 - 17/100 = 35/100 = .350$

4. Refer to the table and notation of exercise #1.
   $P(AT \text{ or } PT) = P(AT) + P(PT) - P(AT \text{ and } PT)$
   $= 80/100 + 68/100 - 65/100 = 83/100 = .830$

5. Refer to the table and notation of exercise #1.
   $P(AT_1 \text{ and } AT_2) = P(AT_1) \cdot P(AT_2 \mid AT_1)$
   $= (80/100) \cdot (79/99) = .638$

6. Refer to the table and notation of exercise #1.
   $P(PL_1 \text{ and } PL_2) = P(PL_1) \cdot P(PL_2 \mid PL_1)$
   $= (32/100) \cdot (31/99) = .100$

7. Refer to the table and notation of exercise #1.
   $P(AT \mid PL) = 15/32 = .469$

8. Refer to the table and notation of exercise #1.
   $P(PL \mid AT) = 15/80 = .1875$

9. Let B = a computer breaks down during the first two years
   a. $P(B) = 992/4000 = .248$
   b. $P(B_1 \text{ and } B_2) = P(B_1) \cdot P(B_2) = (.248) \cdot (.248) = .0615$
   c. $P(\text{at least 1 breaks down}) = 1 - P(\text{all good})$
   $= 1 - P(\overline{B}_1 \text{ and } \overline{B}_2 \text{ and } \overline{B}_3)$
   $= 1 - P(\overline{B}_1) \cdot P(\overline{B}_2) \cdot P(\overline{B}_3) = 1 - (.752)^3 = .575$

10. Since the sample size is no more than 5% of the size of the population, treat the selections as being independent even though the selections are made without replacement.
    Let G = a CD is good.
    $P(G) = .98$, for each selection
    $P(\text{reject batch}) = P(\text{at least one is defective})$
    $= 1 - P(\text{all are good})$
    $= 1 - P(G_1 \text{ and } G_2 \text{ and } G_3 \text{ and } G_4)$
    $= 1 - P(G_1) \cdot P(G_2) \cdot P(G_3) \cdot P(G_4) = 1 - (.98)^4 = .0776$
    NOTE: $P(\text{reject batch}) = 1 - (2450/2500) \cdot (2449/2499) \cdot (2448/2498) \cdot (2447/2497) = .0777$
    if the problem is done considering the effect of the non-replacement.

11. Let G = getting a girl
    $P(G) = \frac{1}{2}$, for each child
    $P(\text{all girls}) = P(G_1 \text{ and } G_2 \text{ and } G_3 \text{ and} \ldots \text{and } G_{12})$
    $= P(G_1) \cdot P(G_2) \cdot P(G_3) \cdot \ldots \cdot P(G_{12}) = (\frac{1}{2})^{12} = 1/4096$

Yes; since the probability of the getting all girls by chance alone is so small, it appears the company's claim is valid.

12. a. Let W = the committee of 3 is the 3 wealthiest members.
   The number of possible committees of 3 is $_{10}C_3 = 10!/(7!3!) = 120$.
   Since only one of those committees is the 3 wealthiest members,
   P(W) = 1/120 = .00833
   b. Since order is important, the number of possible slates of officers is
   $_{10}P_3 = 10!/7! = 720$

13. Let E = a winning even number occurs.
   a. P(E) = 18/38 [=9/19]
   b. odds against E = $P(\overline{E})/P(E)$
   = (20/38)/(18/38) = 20/18 = 10/9, usually expressed as 10:9
   c. payoff odds = (net profit):(amount bet)
   If the payoff odds are 1:1, the net profit is $5 for a winning $5 bet.

14. Since the sample size is no more than 5% of the size of the population, treat the selections as being independent even though the selections are made without replacement.
   Let R = getting a Republican.
   P(R) = .30, for each selection
   $P(R_1 \text{ and } R_2 \text{ and}...\text{and } R_{12}) = P(R_1) \cdot P(R_2) \cdot ... \cdot P(R_{12}) = (.30)^{12} = .000000531$
   No, the pollster's claim is not correct.

15. Let L = a selected 27 year old male lives for one more year.
   P(L) = .9982, for each such person
   $P(L_1 \text{ and } L_2 \text{ and}...\text{and } L_{12}) = P(L_1) \cdot P(L_2) \cdot ... \cdot P(L_{12}) = (.9982)^{12} = .979$

16. a. Let W = winning the described lottery with a single selection.
   The total number of possible combinations is
   $_{52}C_6 = 52!/(46!6!) = (52 \cdot 51 \cdot 50 \cdot 49 \cdot 48 \cdot 47)/6! = 20,358,520$.
   Since only one combination wins, P(W) = 1/20,358,520.
   b. Let W = winning the described lottery with a single selection.
   The total number of possible combinations is
   $_{30}C_5 = 30!/(25!5!) = (30 \cdot 29 \cdot 28 \cdot 27 \cdot 26)/5! = 142,506$.
   Since only one combination wins, P(W) = 1/142,506.
   c. Two events need to occur to win the Big Game.
   *Let A = selecting the winning 5 from among the 50.
   The total number of possible combinations is
   $_{50}C_5 = 50!/(45!5!) = (50 \cdot 49 \cdot 48 \cdot 47 \cdot 46)/5! = 2,118,760$.
   Since only one combination wins, P(A) = 1/2,118,760.
   *Let B = selecting the winning 1 from among the 36, and P(B) = 1/36.
   P(winning the Big Game) = P(A and B)
   = $P(A) \cdot P(B|A)$
   = $(1/2,118,760) \cdot (1/36)$
   = 1/76,275,360

Cumulative Review Exercises

1. scores arranged in order: 0 0 0 2 3 3 3 3 4 4 4 5 5 5 5 6 6 6 6 7 7
   summary statistics: n = 21, $\Sigma x = 84$, $\Sigma x^2 = 430$
   a. $\overline{x} = (\Sigma x)/n = 84/21 = 4.0$
   b. $\tilde{x} = 4$, the 11th score in the ordered list
   c. $s^2 = [n \cdot (\Sigma x^2) - (\Sigma x)^2]/[n(n-1)] = [21(430) - (84)^2]/[(21)(20)] = 4.7$

$s = 2.2$

d. $s^2 = 4.7$ [from part (c)]

e. Yes; all of the scores are either 0 or positive.

f. Let G = randomly selecting a positive value

   $P(G) = 18/21 = 6/7$.

g. Let G = randomly selecting a positive value

   $P(G_1 \text{ and } G_2) = P(G_1) \cdot P(G_2 | G_1)$
   $= (18/21) \cdot (17/20) = .729$

h. Let E = the treatment is effective.

   $P(E) = ½$, under the given assumptions, for each person

   $P(E_1 \text{ and } E_2 \text{ and...and } E_{18}) = P(E_1) \cdot P(E_2) \cdot ... \cdot P(E_{18}) = (½)^{18} = 1/262,144$

   Yes; this probability is low enough to reject the idea that the treatment is ineffective.

   Yes; the treatment appears to be effective.

2. Let x = the height selected.

   The values identified on the boxplot are: x_1 [minimum] = 56.1

   $\qquad\qquad\qquad\qquad\qquad\qquad\qquad\qquad\quad P_{25} = 62.2$

   $\qquad\qquad\qquad\qquad\qquad\qquad\qquad\qquad\quad P_{50} = 63.6$

   $\qquad\qquad\qquad\qquad\qquad\qquad\qquad\qquad\quad P_{75} = 65.0$

   $\qquad\qquad\qquad\qquad\qquad\qquad\qquad\qquad\quad x_n$ [maximum] = 71.1

   NOTE: Assume that the number of heights is so large that (1) repeated sampling does not affect the probabilities for subsequent selections and (2) it can be said that P_a has a% of the heights below it and (100-a)% of the heights above it.

   a. The exact values of $\overline{x}$ and s cannot be determined from the information given. The Range Rule of Thumb [the highest and lowest values are approximately 2 standard deviations above and below the mean], however, indicates that $s \approx (x_n - x_1)/4$ and $\overline{x} \approx (x_1 + x_n)/2$. In this case we estimate $\overline{x} \approx (56.1 + 71.1)/2 = 63.6$

   NOTE: The boxplot, which gives $\tilde{x} = P_{50} = 63.6$, is symmetric. This suggests that the original distribution is approximately so. In a symmetric distribution the mean and median are equal. This also suggests $\overline{x} \approx 63.6$.

   b. $P(56.1 < x < 62.2) = P(x_1 < x < P_{25})$
   $\qquad\qquad\qquad\qquad\qquad\quad = .25 - 0 = .25$

   c. $P(x < 62.2 \text{ or } x > 63.6) = P(x < 62.2) + P(x > 63.6)$
   $\qquad\qquad\qquad\qquad\qquad\qquad\quad = P(x < P_{25}) + P(x > P_{50})$
   $\qquad\qquad\qquad\qquad\qquad\qquad\quad = .25 + .50 = .75$

   NOTE: No height is less than 62.2 <u>and</u> greater than 63.6 – i.e., the addition rule for mutually exclusive events can be used.

   d. Let B = selecting a height between 62.2 and 63.6.

   $P(B) = P(P_{25} < x < P_{50})$
   $\qquad\; = .50 - .25 = .25$

   $P(B_1 \text{ and } B_2) = P(B_1) \cdot P(B_2 | B_1)$
   $\qquad\qquad\qquad\quad = (.25) \cdot (.25) = .0625$

   e. Let S = a selected woman is shorter than the mean.

   $\qquad$T = a selected woman is taller than the mean.

   $\qquad$E = the event that a group of 5 women consists of 3 T's and 2 S's.

   There are $2 \cdot 2 \cdot 2 \cdot 2 \cdot 2 = 32$ equally likely [see the NOTE below] sequences of T's and S's. The number of arrangements of 3 T's and 2 S's is $5!/(3!2!) = 10$.

   $\qquad P(E) = 10/32 = .3125$

   NOTE: The exact value of the mean cannot be determined from the information given. From part (a) we estimate $\overline{x} \approx 63.6$, which is also the median. If this is true then *in this particular problem* $P(x < \overline{x}) = P(S) = .50$ and $P(x > \overline{x}) = P(T) = .50$. This means that all arrangements of T's and S's are equally likely and

   $\qquad P(E) = (\# \text{ of ways E can occur})/(\text{total number of possible outcomes})$

Chapter 4

Probability Distributions

4-2 Random Variables

1. a. Continuous, since height can be any value on a continuum.
   b. Discrete, since the number of points must be an integer.
   c. Continuous, since time can be any value on a continuum.
   d. Discrete, since the number of players must be an integer.
   e. Discrete, since salary is typically stated in whole dollars – and it cannot be stated in units smaller than whole number of cents.

2. a. Discrete, since monetary cost must be stated in units of .01 dollars.
   b. Discrete, since the number of movies must be an integer.
   c. Continuous, since time can be any value on a continuum.
   d. Discrete, since the number of actors must be an integer.
   e. Continuous, since weight can be any value on a continuum.

NOTE: When working with probability distributions and formulas in the exercises that follow, always keep these important facts in mind.
   * If one of the conditions for a probability distribution does not hold, the formulas do not apply and produce numbers that have no meaning.
   * $\Sigma x \cdot P(x)$ gives the mean of the x values and must be a number between the highest and lowest x values.
   * $\Sigma x^2 \cdot P(x)$ gives the mean of the x^2 values and must be a number between the highest and lowest x^2 values.
   * $\Sigma P(x)$ must always equal 1.000.
   * Σx and Σx^2 have no meaning and should not be calculated.
   * The quantity $[\Sigma x^2 \cdot P(x) - \mu^2]$ cannot possibly be negative; if it is, then there is a mistake.
   * Always be careful to use the <u>unrounded</u> mean in the calculation of the variance and to take the square root of the <u>unrounded</u> variance to find the standard deviation.

3. This is a probability distribution since $\Sigma P(x)=1$ is true and $0 \le P(x) \le 1$ is true for each x.

x	P(x)	x·P(x)	x²	x²P(x)	
0	.125	0	0	0	$\mu = \Sigma x \cdot P(x)$
1	.375	.375	1	.375	$= 1.500$, rounded to 1.5
2	.375	.750	4	1.500	$\sigma^2 = \Sigma x^2 \cdot P(x) - \mu^2$
3	.125	.375	9	1.125	$= 3.000 - (1.500)^2$
	1.000	1.500		3.000	$= .750$
					$\sigma = .866$, rounded to 0.9

4. This is not a probability distribution since $\Sigma P(x)=.977 \ne 1$.

5. This is not a probability distribution since $\Sigma P(x)=.94 \ne 1$.

6. This is a probability distribution since $\Sigma P(x)=1$ is true and $0 \le P(x) \le 1$ is true for each x.

x	P(x)	x·P(x)	x²	x²P(x)	
0	.0000	0	0	0	$\mu = \Sigma x \cdot P(x)$
1	.0001	.0001	1	.0001	$= 3.9598$, rounded to 4.0
2	.0006	.0012	4	.0024	$\sigma^2 = \Sigma x^2 \cdot P(x) - \mu^2$
3	.0387	.1161	9	.3483	$= 15.7204 - (3.9598)^2$
4	.9606	3.8424	16	15.3696	$= .0404$
	1.0000	3.9598		15.7204	$\sigma = .2010$, rounded to 0.2

7. This is a probability distribution since $\Sigma P(x)=1$ is true and $0 \le P(x) \le 1$ is true for each x.

x	P(x)	x·P(x)	x²	x²P(x)	
0	.512	0	0	0	$\mu = \Sigma x \cdot P(x)$
1	.301	.301	1	.301	$= .730$, rounded to 0.7
2	.132	.264	4	.528	$\sigma^2 = \Sigma x^2 \cdot P(x) - \mu^2$
3	.055	.165	9	.495	$= 1.324 - (.73)^2$
	1.000	.730		1.324	$= .791$
					$\sigma = .889$, rounded to 0.9

8. This is not a probability distribution since $\Sigma P(x) = .986 \neq 1$.

9. This is a probability distribution since $\Sigma P(x)=1$ is true and $0 \le P(x) \le 1$ is true for each x.

x	P(x)	x·P(x)	x²	x²P(x)	
4	.1809	.7236	16	2.8944	$\mu = \Sigma x \cdot P(x)$
5	.2234	1.1170	25	5.5850	$= 5.7871$, rounded to 5.8
6	.2234	1.3404	36	8.0424	$\sigma^2 = \Sigma x^2 \cdot P(x) - \mu^2$
7	.3723	2.6061	49	18.2427	$= 34.7645 - (5.7871)^2$
	1.0000	5.7871		34.7645	$= 1.2740$
					$\sigma = 1.129$, rounded to 1.1

No; since $.1809 > .05$, a four g ame sweep is not considered an unusual event.

10. This is not a probability distribution since $\Sigma P(x) = .9686 \neq 1$.

11.

x	P(x)	x·P(x)	
5	244/495	2.4646	$E = \Sigma x \cdot P(x)$
-5	251/495	-2.5353	$= \$-0.0707$ [i.e., a loss of 7.07¢]
	495/495	-0.0707	

Since the expected loss is 7.07¢ for a $5 bet, the expected (or long run) loss is 7.07/5 = 1.41¢ for each $1 a person bets.

12. a.

x	P(x)	x·P(x)	
175	1/38	175/38	$E = \Sigma x \cdot P(x)$
-5	37/38	-185/38	$= -10/38$
	38/38	-10/38	$= \$-0.263$ [i.e., a loss of 26.3¢]

The expected loss is 26.3¢ for a $5 bet.

b.

x	P(x)	x·P(x)	
5	18/38	90/38	$E = \Sigma x \cdot P(x)$
-5	20/38	-100/38	$= -10/38$
	38/38	-10/38	$= \$-0.263$ [i.e., a loss of 26.3¢]

The expected loss is 26.3¢ for a $5 bet.

c. Since the bets in parts (a) and (b) each have (exactly the same) negative expectation, the best option is not to bet at all.

NOTE: Problems whose probabilities do not "come out even" as decimals can be very sensitive to rounding errors. Since the P(x) values are used in several subsequent calculations, express them as exact fractions instead of rounded decimals. If it is not convenient to continue with fractions throughout the entire problem, then use sufficient decimal places (typically one more than "usual") in the x·P(x) and x²·P(x) columns to guard against cumulative rounding errors.

13. a. Mike "wins" $100,000 - $250 = $99,750 if he dies.
   Mike "loses" $250 if he lives.

b.

x	P(x)	x·P(x)	
99750	.0015	149.625	$E = \Sigma x \cdot P(x)$
-250	.9985	-249.625	$= -100.000$ [i.e., a loss of $100]
	1.0000	-100.000	

c. Since the company is making a $100 profit at this price, it would break even if it sold the policy for $100 less – i.e. for $150. NOTE: This oversimplified analysis ignores the cost of doing business. If the costs (printing, salaries, etc.) associated with offering the policy is $25, for example, then the company's profit is only $75 and selling the policy for $75 less (i.e., for $175) would represent the break even point for the company.

d. Buying life insurance is similar to purchasing other services. You let someone make a profit off you by shoveling the snow in your driveway because the cost is worth the effort and frustration you save. You let someone make a profit off you by selling you life insurance because the cost is worth the peace you have from providing for the financial security of your heirs.

14.

x	P(x)	x·P(x)
1,000,000	.000000011	.011111111
100,000	.000000009	.000909091
25,000	.000000009	.000227273
5,000	.000000027	.000136362
2,500	.000000036	.000090909
0	.999999908	0
	1.000000000	.012474746

a. E = Σx·P(x)
   = .012 [i.e., 1.2 cents]

b. mean loss
   = price of stamp - 1.2¢
   = 37¢ - 1.2¢
   = 35.8¢ [as of spring 2003]

No; from a purely financial point of view, it is not worth entering this contest.

15. a. 10·10·10·10 = 10,000
    b. 1/10,000 = .0001
    c.

x	P(x)	x·P(x)
2787.50	.0001	.27875
-.50	.9999	-.49995
	1.0000	-.22120

E = Σx·P(x)
   = -.2212   [i.e., a loss of 22.12¢]

d. The Pick 4 game is the better of the two. Even though they both are losing propositions, the expected value is higher for the Pick 4 game – i.e., -22.12 > -22.5.

16. a. 10·10·10 = 1,000
     b. 1/1,000 = .001
     c.

x	P(x)	x·P(x)
249.50	.001	.2495
-.50	.999	-.4995
	1.000	-.2500

E = Σx·P(x)
   = -.25   [i.e., a loss of 25¢]

d. The New Jersey Pick 3 is the better of the two. Even though they both are losing propositions, the expected value is higher for the New Jersey version – i.e., -22.5 > -25.

17. a. P(x=9) = .122
    b. P(x≥9) = P(x=9 or x=10 or x=11 or x=12 or x=13 or x=14)
       = P(x=9) + P(x=10) + P(x=11) + P(x=12) + P(x=13) + P(x=14)
       = .122 + .061 + .022 + .006 + .001 + .000 = .212
    c. Part (b). In determining whether a particular event in some hierarchy of events is unusual, one should consider both that event and the events that are more extreme. Even though the probability of a particular event may be very low, that event might not be unusual in a practical sense. P(35 girls in 60 births) = .045 < .05, for example, but getting 35 girls in 60 births is one of the more common outcomes – it's just that there are so many possible outcomes that the probability of any one particular outcome is small.
    d. No; this is not evidence that the technique is effective. Getting 9 or more girls by chance alone is not unusual, since P(x≥9) = .212 > .05.

18. a. P(x=12) = .006
     b. P(x≥12) = P(x=12 or x=13 or x=14)
        = P(x=12) + P(x=13) + P(x=14)
        = .006 + .001 + .000 = .007
     c. Part (b). In determining whether a particular event in some hierarchy of events is unusual, one should consider both that event and the events that are more extreme. Even though the probability of a particular event may be very low, that event might not be unusual in a practical sense. P(35 girls in 60 births) = .045 < .05, for example, but getting 35 girls in 60 births is one of the more common outcomes – it's just that there are

so many possible outcomes that the probability of any one particular outcome is small.
   d. Yes; this is evidence that the technique is effective. Getting 12 or more girls by chance alone would be unusual, since $P(x \geq 12) = .007 < .05$.

19. a. $P(x \geq 11) = P(x=11 \text{ or } x=12 \text{ or } x=13 \text{ or } x=14)$
    $= P(x=11) + P(x=12) + P(x=13) + P(x=14)$
    $= .022 + .006 + .001 + .000 = .029$
    b. Yes; this is evidence that the technique is effective. Getting 11 or more girls by chance alone would be unusual, since $P(x \geq 11) = .029 < .05$.

20. a. $P(x \geq 10) = P(x=10 \text{ or } x=11 \text{ or } x=12 \text{ or } x=13 \text{ or } x=14)$
    $= P(x=10) + P(x=11) + P(x=12) + P(x=13) + P(x=14)$
    $= .061 + .022 + .006 + .001 + .000 = .090$
    b. No; this is not evidence that the technique is effective. Getting 10 or more girls by chance alone is not unusual, since $P(x \geq 10) = .090 > .05$.

21. $P(x \geq 8) = P(x=8 \text{ or } x=9 \text{ or } x=10 \text{ or } x=11 \text{ or } x=12 \text{ or } x=13 \text{ or } x=14)$
    $= P(x=8) + P(x=9) + P(x=10) + P(x=11) + P(x=12) + P(x=13) + P(x=14)$
    $= .183 + .122 + .061 + .022 + .006 + .001 + .000 = .395$
    No; Bob's claim is not valid. Getting 8 or more answers correct by chance alone is not unusual, since $P(x \geq 8) = .395 > .05$.

22. $P(x \leq 2) = P(x=0 \text{ or } x=1 \text{ or } x=2)$
    $= P(x=0) + P(x=1) + P(x=2)$
    $= .000 + .001 + .006 = .007$
    Yes; the number of Bob's correct answers is unusual. Getting 2 or fewer answers correct by chance alone would be unusual, since $P(x \leq 2) = .007 < .05$.
    No; Bob's claim that he can pass true/false tests by guessing is not valid. Since his number of correct answers was unusually low rather than unusually high, he would not pass.

23. For every $1000, Bond A gives a profit of $(.06)(\$1000) = \$60$ with probability .99.

x	P(x)	x·P(x)	
60	.99	59.40	$E = \Sigma x \cdot P(x)$
-1000	.01	-10.00	$= 49.40$ [i.e., a profit of \$49.40]
	1.00	49.40	

For every $1000, Bond B gives a profit of $(.08)(\$1000) = \$80$ with probability .95.

x	P(x)	x·P(x)	
80	.95	76.00	$E = \Sigma x \cdot P(x)$
-1000	.05	-50.00	$= 26.00$ [i.e., a profit of \$26.00]
	1.00	26.00	

Bond A is the better bond since it was the higher expected value – i.e., $49.40 > 26.00$. Since both bonds have positive expectations, either one would be a reasonable selection. Although bond A has a higher expectation, a person willing to assume more risk in hope of a higher payoff might opt for Bond B.

24. The distribution and calculations are given below.

x	P(x)	x·P(x)	x²	x²P(x)	
1	.2	.2	1	.2	$\mu = \Sigma x \cdot P(x)$
2	.2	.4	2	.8	$= 3.0$
3	.2	.6	9	1.8	$\sigma^2 = \Sigma x^2 \cdot P(x) - \mu^2$
4	.2	.8	16	3.2	$= 11.0 - (3.0)^2$
5	.2	1.0	25	5.0	$= 2.0$
	1.0	3.0		11.0	$\sigma = 1.414$

   a. For $n=5$, $\mu = (n+1)/2 = 6/2 = 3.0$. This agrees with the calculations above.
   b. For $n=5$, $\sigma^2 = (n^2-1)/12 = 24/12 = 2$.
         $\sigma = \sqrt{2} = 1.414$. This agrees with the calculations above.

c. For n=20,
   $\mu = (n+1)/2 = 21/2 = 10.5$.
   $\sigma^2 = (n^2-1)/12 = 399/12 = 33.25$
   $\sigma = \sqrt{33.25} = 5.766$, rounded to 5.8

4-3 Binomial Probability Distributions

NOTE: The four requirements for a binomial experiment are
#1 There are a fixed number of trials.
#2 The trials are independent.
#3 Each trial has two possible named outcomes.
#4 The probabilities remain constant for each trial.

1. No; requirement #3 is not met. There are more than 2 possible outcomes.

2. Yes; all four requirements are met.

3. No; requirement #3 is not met. There are more than 2 possible outcomes.

4. Yes; all four requirements are met.

5. Yes; all four requirements are met.

6. Yes; all four requirements are met.

7. No; requirement #3 is not met. There are more than 2 possible outcomes.

8. Yes; all four requirements are met.

9. let W = guessing the wrong answer
        C = guessing the correct answer
   $P(W) = 4/5$, for each question
   $P(C) = 1/5$, for each question

   a. $P(WWC) = P(W_1 \text{ and } W_2 \text{ and } C_3)$
              $= P(W_1) \cdot P(W_2) \cdot P(C_3)$
              $= (4/5) \cdot (4/5) \cdot (1/5) = 16/125 = .128$
   b. There are 3 possible arrangements: WWC, WCW, CWW
      Following the pattern in part (a)
      $P(WWC) = P(W_1 \text{ and } W_2 \text{ and } C_3) = P(W_1) \cdot P(W_2) \cdot P(C_3) = (4/5) \cdot (4/5) \cdot (1/5) = 16/125$
      $P(WCW) = P(W_1 \text{ and } C_2 \text{ and } W_3) = P(W_1) \cdot P(C_2) \cdot P(W_3) = (4/5) \cdot (1/5) \cdot (4/5) = 16/125$
      $P(CWW) = P(C_1 \text{ and } W_2 \text{ and } W_3) = P(C_1) \cdot P(W_2) \cdot P(W_3) = (1/5) \cdot (4/5) \cdot (4/5) = 16/125$
   c. P(exactly one correct answer) = P(WWC or WCW or CWW)
                                     $= P(WWC) + P(WCW) + P(CWW)$
                                     $= 16/125 + 16/125 + 16/125 = 48/125 = .384$

10. let W = guessing the wrong answer
         C = guessing the correct answer
    $P(W) = 3/4$, for each question
    $P(C) = 1/4$, for each question
    a. $P(WWCCCC) = P(W_1 \text{ and } W_2 \text{ and } C_3 \text{ and } C_4 \text{ and } C_5 \text{ and } C_6)$
                  $= P(W_1) \cdot P(W_2) \cdot P(C_3) \cdot P(C_4) \cdot P(C_5) \cdot P(C_6)$
                  $= (3/4) \cdot (3/4) \cdot (1/4) \cdot (1/4) \cdot (1/4) \cdot (1/4) = 9/4096 = .00220$

b. There are $6!/(2!4!) = 15$ possible arrangements as follows. The probability for each arrangement will include the factor (3/4) two times and the factor (1/4) four times to give the result $9/4096 = .00220$ of part (a)

WWCCCC	CWWCCC	CCWWCC	CCCWWC	CCCCWW
WCWCCC	CWCWCC	CCWCWC	CCCWCW	
WCCWCC	CWCCWC	CCWCCW		
WCCCWC	CWCCCW			
WCCCCW				

c. P(exactly 4 correct answers) $= 15 \cdot (9/4096) = .0330$

11. From Table A-1 in the .01 column and the 2-0 row, .980.

12. From Table A-1 in the .01 column and the 7-2 row, .002.

13. From Table A-1 in the .95 column and the 4-3 row, .171.

14. From Table A-1 in the .99 column and the 6-5 row, .057.

15. From Table A-1 in the .95 column and the 10-4 row, $.000^+$.

16. From Table A-1 in the .05 column and the 11-7 row, $.000^+$.

NOTE: To use the binomial formula, one must identify 3 quantities: n,x,p. Table A-1, for example, requires only these 3 values to supply a probability. Since what the text calls "q" always equals 1-p, it can be so designated without introducing unnecessary notation [just as no special notation is utilized for the quantity n-x, even though it appears twice in the binomial formula]. This has the additional advantage of ensuring that the probabilities p and 1-p sum to 1.00 and protecting against an error in the separate calculation and/or identification of "q." In addition, reversing the order of (n-x)! and x! in the denominator of the $_nC_x$ coefficient term seems appropriate. That agrees with the $n!/(n_1!n_2!)$ logic of the "permutation rule when some objects are alike" for n_1 objects of one type and n_2 objects of another type, and that places the "x" and "n-x" in the same order in both the denominator of the coefficient term and the exponents. Such a natural ordering also leads to fewer errors. Accordingly, this manual expresses the binomial formula as

$P(x) = [n!/x!(n-x)!] \cdot p^x \cdot (1-p)^{n-x}$

17. $P(x) = [n!/x!(n-x)!] \cdot p^x \cdot (1-p)^{n-x}$
$P(x=4) = [6!/4!2!] \cdot (.55)^4 \cdot (.45)^2$
$= [15] \cdot (.55)^4 (.45)^2 = [15] \cdot (.0915) \cdot (.2025) = .2779$

IMPORTANT NOTE: The intermediate values of 15, .0915 and .2025 are given to help those with incorrect answers to identify the portion of the problem in which the mistake was made. This practice will be followed in most problems (i.e., not just binomial problems) throughout the manual. In practice, all calculations can be done in one step on the calculator. You may choose to (or be asked to) write down such intermediate values for your own (or the instructor's) benefit, but never round off in the middle of a problem. Do not write the values down on paper and then re-enter them in the calculator – use the memory to let the calculator remember with complete accuracy any intermediate values that will be used in subsequent calculations. In addition, always make certain that the quantity [n!/x!(n-x)!] is a whole number and that the final answer is between 0 and 1.

18. $P(x) = [n!/x!(n-x)!] \cdot p^x \cdot (1-p)^{n-x}$
$P(x=2) = [6!/2!4!] \cdot (.45)^2 \cdot (.55)^4$
$= [15] \cdot (.45)^2 \cdot (.55)^4 = .2780$

19. $P(x) = [n!/x!(n-x)!] \cdot p^x \cdot (1-p)^{n-x}$
    $P(x=3) = [8!/3!5!] \cdot (1/4)^4 \cdot (3/4)^6$
    $= [56] \cdot (.25)^3 \cdot (.75)^5 = .208$

20. $P(x) = [n!/x!(n-x)!] \cdot p^x \cdot (1-p)^{n-x}$
    $P(x=8) = [10!/8!2!] \cdot (1/3)^8 \cdot (2/3)^2$
    $= [45] \cdot (1/6561) \cdot (4/9) = .00305$

21. $P(x \geq 5) = P(x=5 \text{ or } x=6) = P(x=5) + P(x=6)$
    $= .3283 + .1428 = .4711$
    No; since $.4711 > .05$, this is not an unusual occurrence.

22. $P(x \leq 2) = P(x=0 \text{ or } x=1 \text{ or } x=2) = P(x=0) + P(x=1) + P(x=2)$
    $= .0005 + .0071 + .0462 = .0538.$
    No; since $.0538 > .05$, this is not an unusual occurrence.

23. $P(x > 1) = 1 - P(x \leq 1)$
    $= 1 - P(x=0 \text{ or } x=1)$
    $= 1 - [P(x=0) + P(x=1)]$
    $= 1 - [.0005 + .0071]$
    $= 1 - [.0076] = .9924$
    NOTE: This also could be found as $P(x > 1) = P(x=2 \text{ or } x=3 \text{ or } x=4 \text{ or } x=5 \text{ or } x=6)$. In general the manual will choose the most efficient technique for solving problems that may be approached in more than one way.
    Yes; since P(not having more than one on time) $= 1 - .9924 = .0076 < .05$, not having more than one on time would be an unusual occurrence.

24. $P(x \geq 1) = 1 - P(x=0)$
    $= 1 - .0005 = .9995$
    Yes; since P(not having at least one on time) $= 1 - .9995 = .0005 < .05$, not having at least one on time would be an unusual occurrence.

25. Let x = the number of men that are color blind.
    binomial problem: $n = 6$ and $p = .09$, use the binomial formula
    $P(x) = [n!/x!(n-x)!] \cdot p^x \cdot (1-p)^{n-x}$
    $P(x=2) = [6!/2!4!] \cdot (.09)^2 \cdot (.91)^4$
    $= [15] \cdot (.0081) \cdot (.6857) = .0833$

26. Let x = the number of defective bulbs.
    binomial problem: $n = 24$ and $p = .04$, use the binomial formula
    $P(x) = [n!/x!(n-x)!] \cdot p^x \cdot (1-p)^{n-x}$
    $P(\text{accept shipment}) = P(x \leq 1)$
    $= P(x=0) + P(x=1)$
    $= [24!/0!24!] \cdot (.04)^0 \cdot (.96)^{24} + [24!/1!23!] \cdot (.04)^1 \cdot (.96)^{23}$
    $= [1] \cdot (1) \cdot (.3754) + [24] \cdot (.04) \cdot (.3911)$
    $= .3754 + .3754 = .7508$

27. Let x = the number of taxpayers that are audited.
    binomial problem: $n = 5$ and $p = .01$, use Table A-1
    a. $P(x=3) = .000^+$
    b. $P(x \geq 3) = P(x=3) + P(x=4) + P(x=5)$
    $= .000^+ + .000^+ + .000^+ = .000^+$
    c. Since $.000^+ < .05$, "three or more are audited" is an unusual result and we conclude that factors other than chance are at work. It appears that either customers of the Hemingway Company are being targeted by the IRS for audits or that customers with

the types of returns that are often audited are selecting the Hemingway Company to do their returns.

NOTE: A classic scenario of this type is the hospital that has higher than average patient mortality. This can be due either to the care being below average or to the accepting of a higher than average proportion of more serious cases.

28. Let x = the number of wrong answers.
binomial problem: n = 10 and p = .15, use the binomial formula
  a. $P(x) = [n!/x!(n-x)!] \cdot p^x \cdot (1-p)^{n-x}$
  $P(x=1) = [10!/1!9!] \cdot (.15)^1 \cdot (.85)^9$
  $= [10] \cdot (.1500) \cdot (.2316) = .347$
  b. $P(x=0) = [10!/0!10!] \cdot (.15)^0 \cdot (.85)^{10}$
  $= [1] \cdot (1) \cdot (.1969) = .197$
  $P(x \le 1) = P(x=0) + P(x=1)$
  $= .197 + .347 = .544$
  c. No; since .544 > .05, "at most one wrong number" is not an unusual occurrence when the error rate is 15%.

29. Let x = the number of booked passengers that actually arrive.
binomial problem: n = 15 and p = .85, use the binomial formula
$P(x) = [n!/x!(n-x)!] \cdot p^x \cdot (1-p)^{n-x}$
$P(x=15) = [15!/15!0!] \cdot (.85)^{15} \cdot (.15)^0$
$= [1] \cdot (.0874) \cdot (1) = .0874$
No; the probability is not low enough to be of no concern – since .0874 > .05, not having enough seats is not an unusual event.

30. Let x = the number of Viagra users that experienced a headache.
binomial problem: n = 8 and p = .04, use the binomial formula
  a. $P(x) = [n!/x!(n-x)!] \cdot p^x \cdot (1-p)^{n-x}$
  $P(x=3) = [8!/3!5!] \cdot (.04)^3 \cdot (.96)^5$
  $= [56] \cdot (.000064) \cdot (.8154) = .00292$
  b. $P(x) = [n!/x!(n-x)!] \cdot p^x \cdot (1-p)^{n-x}$
  $P(x=8) = [8!/8!0!] \cdot (.04)^8 \cdot (.96)^0$
  $= [1] \cdot (.04)^8 (1) = 6.55 \times 10^{-12} = .00000000000655$
  c. Yes; if the 4% rate applied to Viagra users, there is almost no chance that all 8 would experience headaches.

31. Let x = the number of households tuned to *60 Minutes*.
binomial problem: n = 10 and p = .10, use Table A-1
  a. $P(x=0) = .107$
  b. $P(x \ge 1) = 1 - P(x=0)$
  $= 1 - .107 = .893$
  c. $P(x \le 1) = P(x=0) + P(x=1)$
  $= .107 + .268 = .375$
  d. No; since .375 > .05, it would not be unusual to find at most one household watching *60 Minutes* when that show had a 20% share of the market.

32. Let x = the number of special program students who graduated.
binomial problem: n = 10 and p = .94, use the binomial formula
$P(x) = [n!/x!(n-x)!] \cdot p^x \cdot (1-p)^{n-x}$
  a. $P(x \ge 9) = P(x=9) + P(x=10)$
  $= [10!/9!1!] \cdot (.94)^9 \cdot (.06)^1 + [10!/10!0!] \cdot (.94)^{10} \cdot (.06)^0$
  $= [10] \cdot (.5730) \cdot (.06) + [1] \cdot (.5386) \cdot (1)$
  $= .344 + .539 = .883$

b. $P(x=8) = [10!/8!2!] \cdot (.94)^8 \cdot (.06)^2$
$= [36] \cdot (.6096) \cdot (.0036) = .079$
$P(x \le 7) = 1 - P(x > 7)$
$= 1 - [P(x=8) + P(x=9) + P(x=10)]$
$= 1 - [.079 + .344 + .539]$
$= 1 - [.962] = .038$

Yes; since $P(x \le 7) = .038 < .05$, getting only 7 that graduated would be an unusual result.

33. Let x = the number of women hired.
binomial problem: n = 20 and p = .50, use the binomial formula
$P(x) = [n!/x!(n-x)!] \cdot p^x \cdot (1-p)^{n-x}$
$P(x \le 2) = P(x=0) + P(x=1) + P(x=2)$
$= [20!/0!20!] \cdot (.5)^0 \cdot (.5)^{20} + [20!/1!19!] \cdot (.5)^1 \cdot (.5)^{19} + [20!/2!18!] \cdot (.5)^2 \cdot (.5)^{18}$
$= [1] \cdot (1) \cdot (.00000095) + [20] \cdot (.5) \cdot (.00000191) + [190] \cdot (.25) \cdot (.00000381)$
$= .00000095 + .00001907 + .00018120 = .000201$
Yes, the small probability of this result occurring by chance when all applicants are otherwise equally qualified does support a charge of gender discrimination.

34. Let x = the number of jackpots hit.
binomial problem: n = 5 and p = 1/2000 = .0005, use the binomial formula
a. $P(x) = [n!/x!(n-x)!] \cdot p^x \cdot (1-p)^{n-x}$
$P(x=2) = [5!/2!3!] \cdot (.0005)^2 \cdot (.9995)^3$
$= [10] \cdot (.00000025) \cdot (.9985) = .000002496$
b. $P(x \ge 2) = 1 - [P(x=0) + P(x=1)]$
$= 1 - \{[5!/0!5!] \cdot (.0005)^0 \cdot (.9995)^5 + [5!/1!4!] \cdot (.0005)^1 \cdot (.9995)^4\}$
$= 1 - \{[1] \cdot (1) \cdot (.997502499) + [5] \cdot (.0005) \cdot (.9980015)\}$
$= 1 - \{.997502499 + .002495004\}$
$= 1 - \{.999997503\} = .000002497$
c. No; if the slot machine is functioning properly with P(jackpot) = 1/2000, then either the guest is not telling the truth or an extremely rare event as occurred.

35. The requested table is given in the .50 column of the second page of Table A-1 in the back of the book.
Let x = the number of girls in 12 births.
$P(x \ge 9) = P(x=9) + P(x=10) + P(x=11) + P(x=12)$
$= .054 + .016 + .003 + .000^+ = .073$
No; this is not evidence that the gender selection technique is effective. Since .073 > .05, getting 9 or more girls is not an unusual event and could occur by chance alone.

36. Let x = the number of selected persons that have so taken courses.
binomial: n = 5 and p = .57, use the binomial formula
$P(x) = [n!/x!(n-x)!] \cdot p^x \cdot (1-p)^{n-x}$
$P(x \le 1) = P(x=0) + P(x=1)$
$= [5!/0!0!] \cdot (.57)^0 \cdot (.43)^5 + [5!/1!0!] \cdot (.57)^1 \cdot (.43)^4$
$= [1] \cdot (1) \cdot (.0147) + [5] \cdot (.57) \cdot (.0342)$
$= .0147 + .0974 = .1121$
No; this is not evidence that the 57% rate is wrong. Since .1121 > .05, the described event is not unusual and could reasonably occur by chance alone when the rate is 57%.

37. Let x = the number of components tested to find 1st defect
geometric problem: p = .2, use the geometric formula
$P(x) = p \cdot (1-p)^{x-1}$
$P(x=7) = (.2) \cdot (.8)^6 = (.2) \cdot (.2621) = .0524$

38. Let x = the number of winning selections
A = 6 (winning numbers), B = 48 (losing numbers), n = 6 (selections)
Use the hypergeometric formula.
P(x) = [A!/(A-x)!x!]·[B!/(B-n+x)!(n-x)!] ÷ [(A+B)!/(A+B-n)!n!]
a. P(x=6) = [6!/0!6!]·[48!/48!0!] ÷ [54!/48!/6!]
= [1]·[1] ÷ [25,827,165] = .0000000387
b. P(x=5) = [6!/1!5!]·[48!/47!1!] ÷ [54!/48!/6!]
= [6]·[48] ÷ [25,827,165] = .0000112
c. P(x=3) = [6!/3!3!]·[48!/45!3!] ÷ [54!/48!/6!]
= [20]·[17296] ÷ [25,827,165] = .0134
d. P(x=0) = [6!/6!0!]·[48!/42!6!] ÷ [54!/48!/6!]
= [1]·[12,271,512] ÷ [25,827,165] = .475
NOTE: The formula is really $[_AC_x]·[_BC_{n-x}] ÷ [_{A+B}C_n]$ and comes from the methods of Chapter 3.

39. Extending the pattern to cover 6 types of outcomes, where $\Sigma x = n$ and $\Sigma p = 1$,
$P(x_1,x_2,x_3,x_4,x_5,x_6) = [n!/(x_1!x_2!x_3!x_4!x_5!x_6!)]·p_1^{x_1}·p_2^{x_2}·p_3^{x_3}·p_4^{x_4}·p_5^{x_5}·p_6^{x_6}$
n = 20
$p_1 = p_2 = p_3 = p_4 = p_5 = p_6 = 1/6$
$x_1 = 5, x_2 = 4, x_3 = 3, x_4 = 2, x_5 = 3, x_6 = 3$
Use the multinomial formula.
$P(x_1,x_2,x_3,x_4,x_5,x_6) = [n!/(x_1!x_2!x_3!x_4!x_5!x_6!)]·p_1^{x_1}·p_2^{x_2}·p_3^{x_3}·p_4^{x_4}·p_5^{x_5}·p_6^{x_6}$
$= [20!/(5!4!3!2!3!3!)]·(1/6)^5·(1/6)^4·(1/6)^3·(1/6)^2·(1/6)^3·(1/6)^3$
$= [20!/(5!4!3!2!3!3!)]·(1/6)^{20}$
$= [1.955·10^{12}]·(2.735·10^{-16}) = .000535$

40. let x = the number of major earthquakes per year
$P(x) = \mu^x·e^{-\mu}/x!$ with $\mu = 93/100 = .93$
a. $P(x=0) = (.93)^0·e^{-.93}/0! = (1)·(.3946)/1 = .3946$
b. $P(x=1) = (.93)^1·e^{-.93}/1! = (.93)·(.3946)/1 = .3669$
c. $P(x=2) = (.93)^2·e^{-.93}/2! = (.8649)·(.3946)/2 = .1706$
d. $P(x=3) = (.93)^3·e^{-.93}/3! = (.8044)·(.3946)/6 = .05289$
e. $P(x=4) = (.93)^4·e^{-.93}/4! = (.7481)·(.3946)/24 = .01230$
f. $P(x=5) = (.93)^5·e^{-.93}/5! = (.6957)·(.3946)/120 = .002287$
g. $P(x=6) = (.93)^6·e^{-.93}/6! = (.6470)·(.3946)/720 = .0003545$
h. $P(x=7) = (.93)^7·e^{-.93}/7! = (.6017)·(.3946)/5040 = .00004710$
NOTE: The following table summarizes the above calculations. Since it is a probability distribution, the probabilities must sum to 1.000 – or an error has been made.

x	P(x)
0	.3946
1	.3669
2	.1706
3	.0529
4	.0123
5	.0023
6	.0004
7	.0000+
8 or more	.0000+ (by subtraction)
	1.0000

4.4 Mean, Variance and Standard Deviation for the Binomial Distribution

1. $\mu = n{\cdot}p = (400){\cdot}(.2) = 80.0$
   $\sigma^2 = n{\cdot}p{\cdot}(1-p) = (400){\cdot}(.2){\cdot}(.8) = 64.0$; $\sigma = 8.0$
   minimum usual value $= \mu - 2\sigma = 80.0 - 2{\cdot}(8.0) = 64.0$
   maximum usual value $= \mu + 2\sigma = 80.0 + 2{\cdot}(8.0) = 96.0$

2. $\mu = n{\cdot}p = (250){\cdot}(.45) = 112.5$
   $\sigma^2 = n{\cdot}p{\cdot}(1-p) = (250){\cdot}(.45){\cdot}(.55) = 61.875$; $\sigma = 7.86$
   minimum usual value $= \mu - 2\sigma = 112.5 - 2{\cdot}(7.86) = 96.8$
   maximum usual value $= \mu + 2\sigma = 112.5 + 2{\cdot}(7.86) = 128.2$

3. $\mu = n{\cdot}p = (1984){\cdot}(3/4) = 1488.0$
   $\sigma^2 = n{\cdot}p{\cdot}(1-p) = (1984){\cdot}(3/4){\cdot}(1/4) = 372.0$; $\sigma = 19.3$
   minimum usual value $= \mu - 2\sigma = 1488.0 - 2{\cdot}(19.3) = 1449.4$
   maximum usual value $= \mu + 2\sigma = 1488.0 + 2{\cdot}(19.3) = 1526.6$

4. $\mu = n{\cdot}p = (767){\cdot}(1/6) = 127.83$
   $\sigma^2 = n{\cdot}p{\cdot}(1-p) = (767){\cdot}(1/6){\cdot}(5/6) = 106.53$; $\sigma = 10.32$
   minimum usual value $= \mu - 2\sigma = 127.83 - 2{\cdot}(10.32) = 107.2$
   maximum usual value $= \mu + 2\sigma = 127.83 + 2{\cdot}(10.32) = 148.5$

5. Let x = the number of correct answers.
   binomial problem: n = 10, p = .5
   a. $\mu = n{\cdot}p = (10){\cdot}(.5) = 5.0$
      $\sigma^2 = n{\cdot}p{\cdot}(1-p) = (10){\cdot}(.5){\cdot}(.5) = 2.50$; $\sigma = 1.6$
   b. maximum usual value $= \mu + 2\sigma = 5.0 + 2{\cdot}(1.6) = 8.2$
      No; since 7 is less than or equal to the maximum usual value, it would not be unusual
      for a student to pass by getting at least 7 correct answers.

6. let x = the number of correct answers
   binomial problem: n = 10, p = .2
   a. $\mu = n{\cdot}p = (10){\cdot}(.2) = 2.0$
      $\sigma^2 = n{\cdot}p{\cdot}(1-p) = (10){\cdot}(.2){\cdot}(.8) = 1.60$; $\sigma = 1.3$
   b. maximum usual value $= \mu + 2\sigma = 2.0 + 2{\cdot}(1.3) = 4.6$
      Yes; since 7 is greater than the maximum usual value, it would be unusual for a
      student to pass by getting at least 7 correct answers.

7. Let x = the number of wins.
   binomial problem: n = 100, p = 1/38
   a. $\mu = n{\cdot}p = (100){\cdot}(1/38) = 2.6$
      $\sigma^2 = n{\cdot}p{\cdot}(1-p) = (100){\cdot}(1/38){\cdot}(37/38) = 2.56$; $\sigma = 1.6$
   b. minimum usual value $= \mu - 2\sigma = 2.6 - 2{\cdot}(1.6) = -0.6$ [use 0, by practical constraints]
      No; since 0 is greater than or equal to the minimum usual value, it would not be unusual
      not to win once in the 100 trials.

8. Let x = the number of left-handers.
   binomial problem: n = 25, p = .1
   a. $\mu = n{\cdot}p = (25){\cdot}(.1) = 2.5$
      $\sigma^2 = n{\cdot}p{\cdot}(1-p) = (25){\cdot}(.1){\cdot}(.9) = 2.25$; $\sigma = 1.5$
   b. maximum usual value $= \mu + 2\sigma = 2.5 + 2{\cdot}(1.5) = 5.5$
      No; since 5 is less than or equal to the maximum usual value, it would not be unusual for
      a class of 25 students to include 5 left-handers.

9. Let x = the number of girls among the 15 births.
   binomial problem: n=15, p = .82

x	P(x)
0	.000+
1	.000+
2	.003
3	.014
4	.042
5	.092
6	.153
7	.196
8	.196
9	.153
10	.092
11	.042
12	.014
13	.003
14	.000+
15	.000+
	1.000

   a. The table at the right was constructed using the .50 column and the final group of values (for n=15) in Table A-1.
   b. μ = n·p = (15)·(.50) = 7.5
      σ^2 = n·p·(1-p) = (15)·(.50)·(.50) = 3.75; σ = 1.9
   c. minimum usual value = μ - 2σ = 7.5 - 2·(1.9) = 3.7
      maximum usual value = μ + 2σ = 7.5 + 2·(1.9) = 11.3
      No; since 10 is between the minimum and maximum usual values, it would not be unusual to get that many girls. NOTE: Since the problem doesn't specify whether the couples were trying to conceive boys or girls, both extremes need to be considered.

10. Let x = the number of letter r's per page.
    binomial problem: n = 2600, p = .077
    a. μ = n·p = (2600)·(.077) = 200.2
       σ^2 = n·p·(1-p) = (2600)·(.077)·(.923) = 184.78; σ = 13.6
    b. Unusual values are those outside $\mu \pm 2\cdot\sigma$
                         200.2 ± 2·(13.6)
                         200.2 ± 27.2
                         173.0 to 227.4
    No; since 175 is within the above limits it would not be considered an unusual result.

11. Let x = the number of customers filing complaints.
    binomial problem: n = 850, p = .032
    a. μ = n·p = (850)·(.032) = 27.2
       σ^2 = n·p·(1-p) = (850)·(.032)·(.968) = 26.33; σ = 5.1
    b. minimum usual value = μ - 2σ = 27.2 - 2·(5.1) = 17.0
       Yes; since 7 is less than the minimum usual value, it would be unusual to get that many complaints if the program had no effect and the rate were still 3.2%. This is sufficient evidence to conclude that the program is effective in lowering the rate of complaints.

12. Let x = the number of M&M's that are blue.
    binomial problem: n = 100, p = .10
    a. μ = n·p = (100)·(.10) = 10.0
       σ^2 = n·p·(1-p) = (100)·(.10)·(.90) = 9.0; σ = 3.0
    b. Unusual values are those outside $\mu \pm 2\cdot\sigma$
                              10.0 ± 2·(3.0)
                              10.0 ± 6.0
                              4.0 to 16.0
    No; since 5 is within the above limits it would not be considered an unusual result. No; it does not seem that the claimed rate of 10% is wrong.

13. Let x = the number that develop cancer.
    binomial problem: n = 420,000, p = .000340
    a. μ = n·p = (420,000)·(.000340) = 142.8
       σ^2 = n·p·(1-p) = (420,000)·(.000340)·(.999660) = 142.75; σ = 11.9
    b. Unusual values are those outside $\mu \pm 2\cdot\sigma$
                         142.8 ± 2·(11.9)
                         142.8 ± 23.8
                         119.0 to 166.6
    No; since 135 is within the above limits, it would not be considered an unusual result.
    c. These results do not support the publicized concern that cell phones are such a risk.

14. Let x = the number receiving the drug who experience flu symptoms
   binomial problem: n = 863, p = .019
   a. μ = n·p = (863)·(.019) = 16.4
      σ^2 = n·p·(1-p) = (863)·(.019)·(.981) = 16.09; σ = 4.0
   b. Unusual values are those outside $\mu \pm 2 \cdot \sigma$
$$16.4 \pm 2 \cdot (4.0)$$
$$16.4 \pm 8.0$$
$$8.4 \text{ to } 24.4$$
   No; since 19 is within these limits, it would not be considered an unusual result.
   c. No; these results do not suggest that persons receiving the drug experience flu symptoms
   any differently from persons not receiving the drug.

15. Let x = the number of adults who believe human cloning should not be allowed.
   a. (1012)·(.89) = 901
      NOTE: Actually, x/1012 rounds to 89% for 896≤x≤905.
   b. binomial problem: n = 1012, p = .50
      μ = n·p = (1012)·(.50) = 506.0
      σ^2 = n·p·(1-p) = (1012)·(.50)·(.50) = 253.0; σ = 15.9
   c. maximum usual value = $\mu + 2\sigma$ = 506.0 + 2·(15.9) = 537.8
      Yes; the results (at least 896 believe that human cloning should not be allowed) of the
      Gallup poll are unusually high if the assumed rate of 50% is true. Yes; this is evidence
      that the majority of adults believe that human cloning should not be allowed.

16. Let x = the number of 500 such NYC drivers that had an accident in the last year.
   a. (500)·(.42) = 210
      NOTE: Actually, x/210 rounds to 42% for 208≤x≤212.
   b. binomial problem: n = 500, p = .34
      μ = n·p = (500)·(.34) = 170.0
      σ^2 = n·p·(1-p) = (500)·(.34)·(.66) = 112.2; σ = 10.6
   c. maximum usual value = $\mu + 2\sigma$ = 170.0 + 2·(10.6) = 191.2
      Yes; the results (at least 208 with accidents) for the NYC drivers are unusually high if the
      34% rate for the general population applies. Yes; it appears that the higher rates for
      NYC drivers are justified.

17. Let x = the number of baby girls.
   binomial problem: n = 100, p = .5
   μ = n·p = (100)·(.5) = 50.0
   σ^2 = n·p·(1-p) = (100)·(.5)·(.5) = 25.0; σ = 5.0
   a. Yes: a probability histogram would reveal an approximately bell-shaped distribution.
      The most likely value is x=50, with the likelihoods decreasing symmetrically for x
      values smaller or larger than 50.
   b. Since 40 and 60 correspond to $\mu \pm 2 \cdot \sigma$, the empirical rule indicates that approximately
      95% of the time x will fall between 40 and 60.
   c. Since 35 and 65 correspond to $\mu \pm 3 \cdot \sigma$, the empirical rule indicates that approximately
      99.7% of the time x will fall between 35 and 65.
   d. Since 40 and 60 correspond to $\mu \pm 2 \cdot \sigma$, use Chebyshev's theorem with k=2. The
      portion of cases within k·σ of μ is at least 1 - $1/k^2$ = 1- 1/4 = 3/4 (i.e., at least 75%).
   NOTE: Parts (b) and (d) agree, since 95% is "at ;east 75%." Chebyshev's theorem applies
   to all distributions and must be more general; the empirical rule applies only to bell-shaped
   distributions and can be more specific.

18. NOTE: Because mathematical formulation of this problem involves complicated algebra
   that does not promote better understanding of the concepts involved, use a trial-and-error
   approach using Table A-1. The procedure given below may not be the most efficient, but it
   is easy to follow and promotes better understanding of the concepts involved.
   Let x = the number of edible pizzas.

binomial problem: n is unknown, p = .8, we want $P(x \geq 5) \geq .99$

for n=5, $P(x \geq 5) = P(x=5)$
                    $= .328$

for n=6, $P(x \geq 5) = P(x=5) + P(x=6)$
                    $= .393 + .262 = .655$

for n=7, $P(x \geq 5) = P(x=5) + P(x=6) + P(x=7)$
                    $= .275 + .367 + .210 = .852$

for n=8, $P(x \geq 5) = P(x=5) + P(x=6) + P(x=7) + P(x=8)$
                    $= .147 + .294 + .336 + .168 = .945$

for n=9, $P(x \geq 5) = P(x=5) + P(x=6) + P(x=7) + P(x=8) + P(x=9)$
                    $= .066 + .176 + .302 + .302 + .134 = .980$

for n=10, $P(x \geq 5) = P(x=5) + P(x=6) + P(x=7) + P(x=8) + P(x=9) + P(x=10)$
                    $= .026 + .088 + .201 + .302 + .268 + .107 = .992$

The minimum number of pizzas necessary to be at least 99% sure that there will be 5 edible pizzas available is n = 10.

Review Exercises

1. a. A random variable is a characteristic that assumes a single value (usually a numerical value), determined by chance, for each outcome of an experiment.

    b. A probability distribution is a statement of the possible values a random variable can assume and the probability associated with each of those values. To be valid it must be true for each value x in the distribution that $0 \leq P(x) \leq 1$ and that $\Sigma P(x) = 1$.

    c. Yes, the given table is a valid probability distribution because it meets the definition and conditions in part (b) above.

    NOTE: The following table summarizes the calculations for parts (d) and (e).

x	P(x)	x·P(x)	x^2	x^2P(x)
0	.08	0	0	0
1	.05	.05	1	.05
2	.10	.20	4	.40
3	.13	.39	9	1.17
4	.15	.60	16	2.40
5	.21	1.05	25	5.25
6	.09	.54	26	3.24
7	.19	1.33	49	9.31
	1.00	4.16		21.82

    d. $\mu = \Sigma x \cdot P(x) = 4.16$, rounded to 4.2

    e. $\sigma^2 = \Sigma x^2 \cdot P(x) - \mu^2 = 21.82 - (4.16)^2 = 4.5144$; $\sigma = 2.1247$, rounded to 2.1

    f. No; since $P(x=0) = .08 > .05$.

2. Let x = the number of TV's tuned to *West Wing*.
    binomial problem: n = 20 and p = .15, use the binomial formula

    a. $E(x) = \mu = n \cdot p = (20) \cdot (.15) = 3.0$

    b. $\mu = n \cdot p = (20) \cdot (.15) = 3.0$

    c. $\sigma^2 = n \cdot p \cdot (1-p) = (20) \cdot (.15) \cdot (.85) = 2.55$; $\sigma = 1.6$

    d. $P(x) = [n!/x!(n-x)!] \cdot p^x \cdot (1-p)^{n-x}$
       $P(x=5) = [20!/5!15!] \cdot (.15)^5 \cdot (.85)^{15}$
                $= [15504] \cdot (.0000759) \cdot (.0874) = .103$

    e. approach #1: minimum usual value = $\mu - 2\sigma = 3.0 - 2 \cdot (1.6) = -0.2$
       No; since 0 is not less than the minimum usual value, it would not be unusual to find that 0 sets are tuned to *West Wing*.
       approach #2: $P(x=5) = [20!/0!20!] \cdot (.15)^0 \cdot (.85)^{20} = (1) \cdot (1) \cdot (.0388) = .0388$
       Yes; since $.0388 < .05$, it would be unusual to find that 0 sets are tuned to *West Wing*.

resolution: Both approaches are guidelines, and not hard and fast rules. Approach #1 best applies when the probability distribution is approximately bell-shaped and the underlying question is whether it is considered unusual to get a result as extreme as or more extreme than the one under consideration. Approach #2 best applies when the underlying question is about one particular result only, often because that result is the lower or upper limit of the probability distribution. In this instance, follow approach #2.

3. Let x = the number of companies that test for drug abuse.
   binomial problem: n = 10 and p = .80, use Table A-1
   a. $P(x=5) = .026$
   b. $P(x \geq 5) = P(x=5) + P(x=6) + P(x=7) + P(x=8) + P(x=9) + P(x=10)$
      $= .026 + .088 + .201 + .302 + .268 + .107 = .992$
   c. $\mu = n \cdot p = (10) \cdot (.80) = 8.0$
      $\sigma^2 = n \cdot p \cdot (1-p) = (10) \cdot (.80) \cdot (.20) = 1.60; \ \sigma = 1.3$
   d. Unusual values are those outside $\mu \pm 2 \cdot \sigma$
      $$8.0 \pm 2 \cdot (1.3)$$
      $$8.0 \pm 2.6$$
      $$5.4 \text{ to } 10.6$$
   No; since 6 is within these limits, it would not be unusual to find that 6 of the 10 companies test for substance abuse.

4. Let x = the number of workers fired for inability to get along with others.
   binomial problem: n = 5 and p = .17, use the binomial formula
   $P(x) = [n!/x!(n-x)!] \cdot p^x \cdot (1-p)^{n-x}$
   a. $P(x=4) = [5!/4!1!] \cdot (.17)^4 \cdot (.83)^1 = (5) \cdot (.000835) \cdot (.83) = .00347$
      $P(x=5) = [5!/5!0!] \cdot (.17)^5 \cdot (.83)^0 = (1) \cdot (.000142) \cdot (1) = .000142$
      $P(x \geq 4) = P(x=4) + P(x=5)$
      $= .00347 + .00014 = .00361$
   b. Yes; since $.00361 < .05$, $x \geq 4$ would be an unusual result for a company with the standard rate of 17%.

Cumulative Review Exercises

1. a. The table below at the left was used to calculate the mean and standard deviation.

x	f	f·x	f·x²
0	47	0	0
1	3	3	3
2	1	2	4
3	0	0	0
4	3	12	48
5	11	55	275
6	3	18	108
7	3	21	147
8	1	8	64
9	1	9	81
	73	128	730

x	r.f.
0	.644
1	.041
2	.014
3	.000
4	.041
5	.151
6	.041
7	.041
8	.014
9	.014
	1.000

$\bar{x} = [\Sigma(f \cdot x)]/[\Sigma f] = 128/73 = 1.8$
$s^2 = \{[\Sigma f] \cdot [\Sigma(f \cdot x^2)] - [\Sigma(f \cdot x)]^2\}/\{[(\Sigma f)] \cdot [(\Sigma f) - 1]\}$
  $= [(73) \cdot (730) - (128)^2]/[(73) \cdot (72)]$
  $= 36906/5256 = 7.022$
$s = 2.6$

   b. The table is given above at the right and was constructed using $r.f. = f/(\Sigma f) = f/70$.

c. The first two columns of the table below constitute the requested probability distribution.
The other columns were added to calculate the mean and the standard deviation.

x	P(x)	x·P(x)	x^2	x^2P(x)
0	.1	0	0	0
1	.1	.1	1	.1
2	.1	.2	4	.4
3	.1	.3	9	.9
4	.1	.4	16	1.6
5	.1	.5	25	2.5
6	.1	.6	36	3.6
7	.1	.7	49	4.9
8	.1	.8	64	6.4
9	.1	.9	81	8.1
	1	4.5		28.5

$\mu = \Sigma x \cdot P(x)$
$= 4.5$
$\sigma^2 = \Sigma x^2 \cdot P(x) - \mu^2$
$= 28.5 - (4.5)^2$
$= 8.25$
$\sigma = 2.8723$, rounded to 2.9

d. The presence of so many 0's make it clear that the last digits do not represent a random sample. Factors other than accurate measurement (which, like social security numbers and other such data, would represent random final digits) determined the recorded distances.

2. Let x = the number of such cars that fail the test.
binomial problem: n = 20 and p = .01, use the binomial formula
a. $E(x) = \mu = n \cdot p = (20) \cdot (.01) = 0.2$
b. $\mu = n \cdot p = (20) \cdot (.01) = 0.2$
$\sigma^2 = n \cdot p \cdot (1-p) = (20) \cdot (.01) \cdot (.99) = .198$; $\sigma = 0.4$
c. $P(x) = [n!/x!(n-x)!] \cdot p^x \cdot (1-p)^{n-x}$
$P(x=0) = [20!/0!20!] \cdot (.01)^0 \cdot (.99)^{20} = (1) \cdot (1) \cdot (.818) = .818$
$P(x \geq 1) = 1 - P(x=0)$
$= 1 - .818 = .182$
d. Unusual values are those outside $\mu \pm 2 \cdot \sigma$
$0.2 \pm 2 \cdot (0.4)$
0.2 ± 0.8
-0.6 to 1.0
Yes; since 3 is outside these limits, it would be considered an unusual result.
e. Let F = a randomly selected car fails the test.
$P(F) = .01$, for each selection
$P(F_1 \text{ and } F_2) = P(F_1) \cdot P(F_2)$, for independent events
$= (.01) \cdot (.01)$
$= .0001$

Chapter 5

Normal Probability Distributions

5-2 The Standard Normal Distribution

1. The height of the rectangle is .5. Probability corresponds to area, and the area of a rectangle is (width)·(height).
    $P(x < 50.3)$ = (width)·(height)

    $\qquad\qquad$ = (50.3 - 50.0)·(.5)
    $\qquad\qquad$ = (.3)·(.5)
    $\qquad\qquad$ = .15

2. The height of the rectangle is .5. Probability corresponds to area, and the area of a rectangle is (width)·(height).
    $P(x > 51.0)$ = (width)·(height)

    $\qquad\qquad$ = (52.0-51.0)·(.5)
    $\qquad\qquad$ = (1.0)·(.5)
    $\qquad\qquad$ = .50

3. The height of the rectangle is .5. Probability corresponds to area, and the area of a rectangle is (width)·(height).
    $P(50.5 < x < 50.8)$ = (width)·(height)

    $\qquad\qquad\qquad$ = (50.8-50.5)·(.5)
    $\qquad\qquad\qquad$ = (.3)·(.5)
    $\qquad\qquad\qquad$ = .15

4. The height of the rectangle is .5. Probability corresponds to area, and the area of a rectangle is (width)·(height).
    $P(50.5 < x < 51.8)$ = (width)·(height)

    $\qquad\qquad\qquad$ = (51.8-50.5)·(.5)
    $\qquad\qquad\qquad$ = (1.3)·(.5)
    $\qquad\qquad\qquad$ = .65

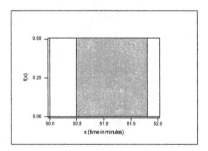

5. The height of the rectangle is 1/6. Probability corresponds to area, and the area of a rectangle is (width)·(height).
    $P(x > 10)$ = (width)·(height)

    $\qquad\qquad$ = (12-10)·(1/6)
    $\qquad\qquad$ = (2)·(1/6)
    $\qquad\qquad$ = .333

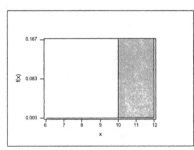

6.   The height of the rectangle is 1/6. Probability corresponds to area, and the area of a rectangle is (width)·(height).
P(x < 11) = (width)·(height)
= (11-6)·(1/6)
= (5)·(1/6)
= .833

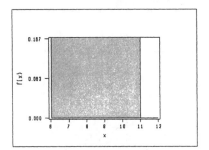

7.   The height of the rectangle is 1/6. Probability corresponds to area, and the area of a rectangle is (width)·(height).
P(7 < x < 10) = (width)·(height)
= (10-7)·(1/6)
= (3)·(1/6)
= .5

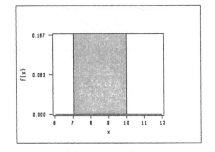

8.   The height of the rectangle is 1/6. Probability corresponds to area, and the area of a rectangle is (width)·(height).
P(6.5 < x < 8) = (width)·(height)
= (8-6.5)·(1/6)
= (1.5)·(1/6)
= .250

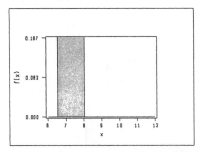

NOTE: The sketch is the key to exercises 9-28. It tells whether to subtract two Table A-2 probabilities, to subtract a Table A-2 probability from 1.0, etc. For the remainder of chapter 5, THE ACCOMPANYING SKETCHES ARE NOT TO SCALE and are intended only as aides to help the reader understand how to use the tabled values to answers the questions. In addition, the probability of any single point in a continuous distribution is zero – i.e., P(x=a) = 0 for any single point a. For normal distributions, therefore, this manual ignores P(x=a) and uses P(x<a) = 1 - P(x>a).

9.   P(z<-.25) = .4013

10.   P(z<-2.75) = .0030

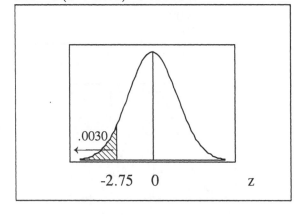

11.   P(z < .25) = .5987

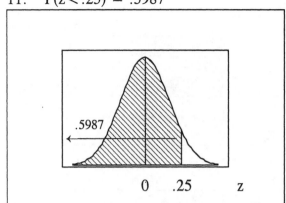

14.   P(z > 1.96)
       = 1 - P(z < 1.96)
       = 1 - .9750
       = .0250

12.   P(z < 2.75) = .9970

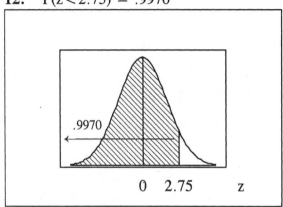

15.   P(z > -2.33)
       = 1 - P(z < -2.33)
       = 1 - .0099
       = .9901

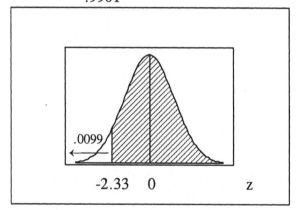

13.   P(z > 2.33)
       = 1 - P(z < 2.33)
       = 1 - .9901
       = .0099

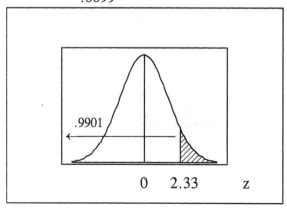

16.   P(z > -1.96)
       = 1 - P(z < -1.96)
       = 1 - .0250
       = .9750

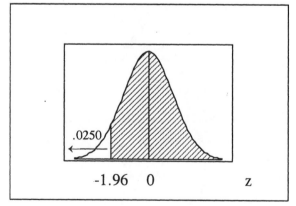

17. P(.50 < z < 1.50)
    = P(z < 1.50) - P(z < .50)
    = .9332 - .6915
    = .2417

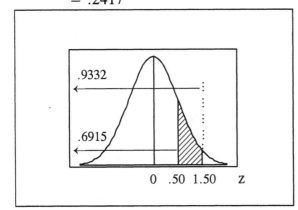

20. P(2.00 < z < 2.34)
    = P(z < 2.34) - P(z < 2.00)
    = .9904 - .9772
    = .0132

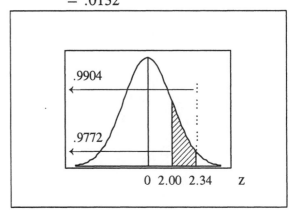

18. P(1.50 < z < 2.50)
    = P(z < 2.50) - P(z < 1.50)
    = .9938 - .9332
    = .0606

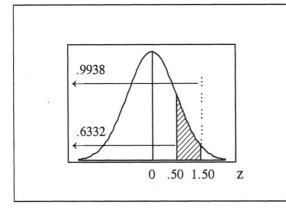

21. P(-2.67 < z < 1.28)
    = P(z < 1.28) - P(z < -2.67)
    = .8997 - .0038
    = .8959

19. P(-2.00 < z < -1.00)
    = P(z < -1.00) - P(z < -2.00)
    = .1587 - .0228
    = .1359

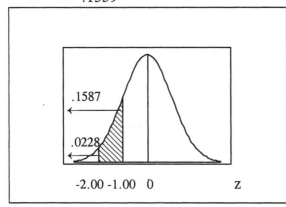

22. P(-1.18 < z < 2.15)
    = P(z < 2.15) - P(z < -1.18)
    = .9842 - .1190
    = .8652

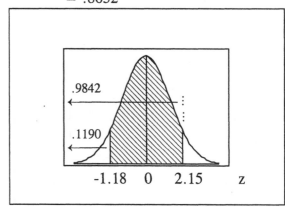

23. $P(-.52 < z < 3.75)$
       $= P(z < 3.75) - P(z < -.52)$
       $= .9999 - .3015$
       $= .6984$

26. $P(z < -3.61) = .0001$

24. $P(-3.88 < z < 1.07)$
       $= P(z < 1.07) - P(z < -3.88)$
       $= .8577 - .0001$
       $= .8576$

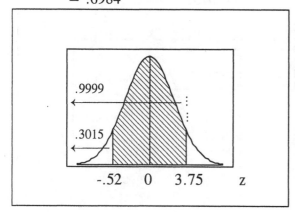

27. $P(z > 0)$
       $= 1 - P(z < 0)$
       $= 1 - .5000$
       $= .5000$

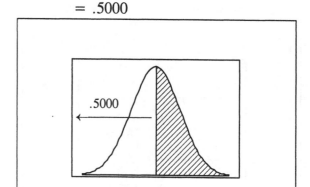

25. $P(z > 3.57)$
       $= 1 - P(z < 3.57)$
       $= 1 - .9999$
       $= .0001$

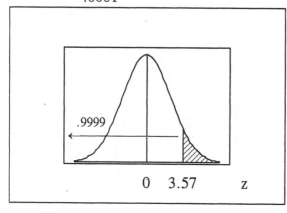

28. $P(z < 0) = .5000$

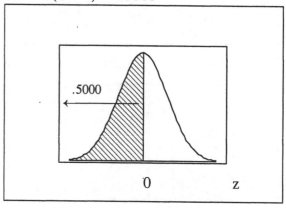

29.   P(-1.00 < z < 1.00)
      = P(z < 1.00) - P(z < -1.00)
      = .8413 - .1587
      = .6826 or 68.26%

32.   P(-3.50 < z < 3.50)
      = P(z < 3.50) - P(z < -3.50)
      = .9999 - .0001
      = .9998 or 99.98%

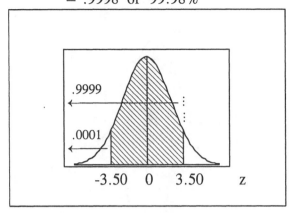

30.   P(-2.00 < z < 2.00)
      = P(z < 2.00) - P(z < -2.00)
      = .9772 - .0228
      = .9544 or 95.44%

33.   P(-1.96 < z < 1.96)
      = P(z < 1.96) - P(z < -1.96)
      = .9750 - .0250
      = .9500

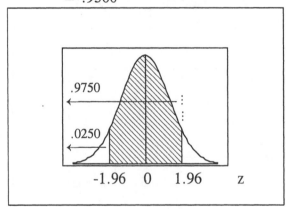

31.   P(-3.00 < z < 3.00)
      = P(z < 3.00) - P(z < -3.00)
      = .9987 - .0013
      = .9974 or 99.74%

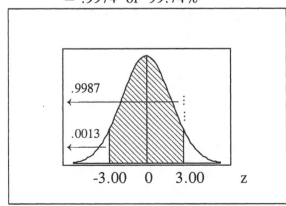

34.   P(z < 1.645) = .9500

35. $P(z > -2.575)$
$= 1 - P(z < -2.575)$
$= 1 - .0050$
$= .9950$

36. $P(1.96 < z < 2.33)$
$= P(z < 2.33) - P(z < 1.96)$
$= .9901 - .9750$
$= .0151$

NOTE: The sketch is the key to exercises 37-40. It tells what probability (i.e., cumulative area) to look up when reading Table A-2 "backwards." It also provides a check against gross errors by indicating at a glance whether a z score is above or below 0.

37.   For P_{90}, the cumulative area is .9000. The closest entry is .8997, for which $z = 1.28$.

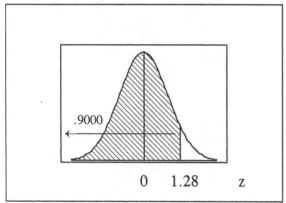

39.   For the lowest 5%, the cumulative area is .0500 – indicated by an asterisk, for which $z = -1.645$.

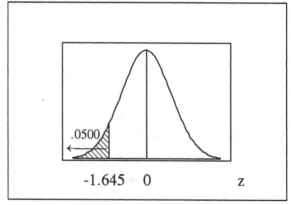

38.   For P_{20}, the cumulative area is .2000. The closest entry is .2005, for which $z = -.84$.

40.   For the highest and lowest 3%, the cumulative areas are .9700 and .0003. The closest entries are .9699 and .0301, for which $z = 1.88$ and -1.88.

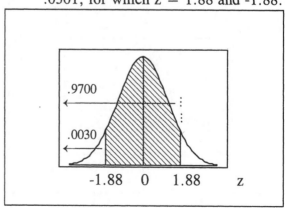

41. Rewrite each of the given statements in terms of z, recalling that z is the number of standard deviations a score is from the mean.

a. P(-1.00 < z < 1.00)
     = P(z < 1.00) - P(z < -1.00)
     = .8413 - .1587
     = .6826   or   68.26%

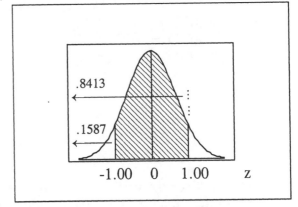

b. P(-1.96 < z < 1.96)
     = P(z < 1.96) - P(z < -1.96)
     = .9750 - .0250
     = .9500   or   95.00%

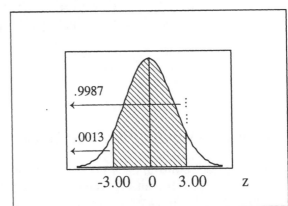

c. P(-3.00 < z < 3.00)
     = P(z < 3.00) - P(z < -3.00)
     = .9987 - .0013
     = .9974   or   99.74%

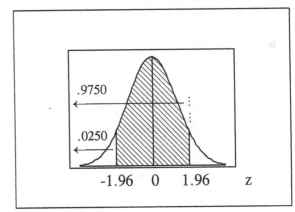

d. P(-1.00 < z < 2.00)
     = P(z < 2.00) - P(z < -1.00)
     = .9772 - .1587
     = .8185   or   81.85%

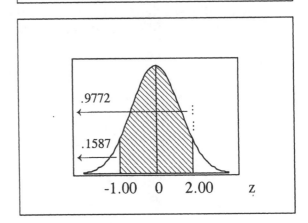

e. P(z < -2.00 or z > 2.00)
   = P(z < -2.00) + P(z > 2.00)
   = P(z < -2.00) + [1 - P(z < 2.00)]
   = .0228 + [1 - .9772]
   = .0228 + .0228
   = .0456

42. **NOTE:** Since the vertical axis gives the height of the figure above an x value and not the probability of an x value, avoid confusion by using the label f(x) instead of P(x). It is correct from the figure to say f(5) = c, for example, but not P(x=5) = c.
   a. Since the area of a triangle is (½)·(base)·(height) and ΣP(x) =1,
      (½)·(5-0)·c + (½)·(10-5)· = 1
              2.5c + 2.5c = 1
                      5c = 1
                       c = .20
   b. Since 3 is 3/5 of the way from the left end to the peak, f(3) = (3/5)·(.20) = .12.
      P(0 < x < 3) = (½)·(base)·(height)
                   = (½)·(3)·(.12)
                   = .18
   c. Since 2 is 2/5 of the way from the left end to the peak, f(2) = (2/5)·(.20) = .08.
      Since 9 is 1/5 of the way from the left end to the peak, f(9) = (1/5)·(.20) = .04.
      P(2 < x < 9) = 1 - P(x < 2) - P(x > 9)
                   = 1 - (½)·(base)·(height) - (½)·(base)·(height)
                   = 1 - (½)·(2)·(.08) - (½)·(1)·(.04)
                   = 1 - .08 -.02
                   = 1 - .10
                   = .90

5-3 Applications of Normal Distributions

NOTE: In each nonstandard normal distribution, x scores are converted to z scores using the formula z = (x-μ)/σ and rounded to two decimal places. For "backwards" problems, solving the preceding formula for x yields x = μ + zσ. The area (cumulative probability) given in Table A-2 will be designated by A. As in the previous section, drawing and labeling the sketch is the key to successful completion of the exercises.

1. μ = 100
   σ = 15
   P(x < 115)
      = P(z < 1.00)
      = .8413

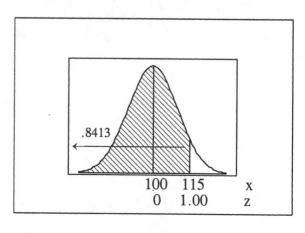

2. $\mu = 100$
$\sigma = 15$
$P(x > 131.5)$
$\quad = P(z > 2.10)$
$\quad = 1 - P(z < 2.10)$
$\quad = 1 - .9821$
$\quad = .0179$

3. $\mu = 100$
$\sigma = 15$
$P(90 < x < 110)$
$\quad = P(-.67 < z < .67)$
$\quad = P(z < .67) - P(z < -.67)$
$\quad = .7486 - .2514$
$\quad = .4972$

4. $\mu = 100$
$\sigma = 15$
$P(110 < x < 120)$
$\quad = P(.67 < z < 1.33)$
$\quad = P(z < 1.33) - P(z < .67)$
$\quad = .9082 - .7486$
$\quad = .1596$

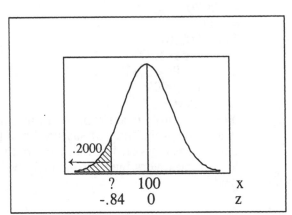

5. $\mu = 100$
$\sigma = 15$
For P_{20}, $A = .2000$ [.2005] and $z = -.84$.
$x = \mu + z\sigma$
$\quad = 100 + (-.84)(15)$
$\quad = 100 - 12.6$
$\quad = 87.4$

6. $\mu = 100$
$\sigma = 15$
For P_{80}, A = .8000 [.7995] and z = .84.
$x = \mu + z\sigma$
$\quad = 100 + (.84)(15)$
$\quad = 100 + 12.6$
$\quad = 112.6$

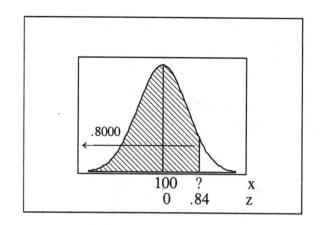

7. $\mu = 100$
$\sigma = 15$
For the top 15%,
$\quad$ A = .8500 [.8508] and z = 1.04.
$x = \mu + z\sigma$
$\quad = 100 + (1.04)(15)$
$\quad = 100 + 15.6$
$\quad = 115.6$

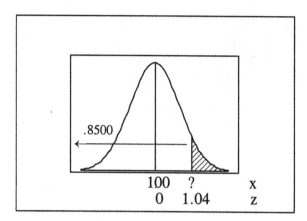

8. $\mu = 100$
$\sigma = 15$
For the top 55%,
$\quad$ A = .4500 [.4483] and z = -.13.
$x = \mu + z\sigma$
$\quad = 100 + (-.13)(15)$
$\quad = 100 - 1.95$
$\quad = 98.05$

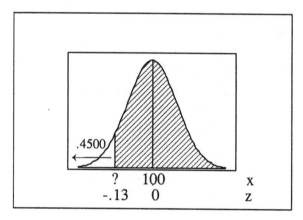

9. $\mu = 98.20$
$\sigma = .62$
a. $P(x > 100.6)$
$\quad = P(z > 3.87)$
$\quad = 1 - P(< 3.87)$
$\quad = 1 - .9999$
$\quad = .0001$
Yes; the cutoff is appropriate in that there is a small probability of saying that a healthy person has a fever, but many people with low grade fevers may erroneously be labeled healthy.

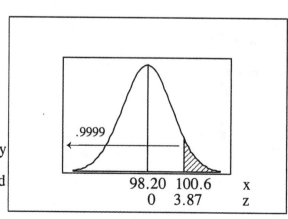

b. For the top 5%, A=.9500 and z=1.645.
   $x = \mu + z\sigma$
   $ = 98.20 + (1.645)(.62)$
   $ = 98.20 + 1.02$
   $ = 99.22$

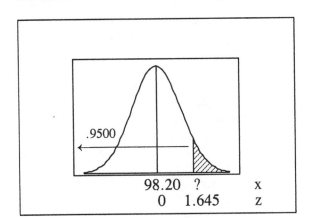

10. $\mu = 268$
$\sigma = 15$
a. P(x>308)
   $= P(z>2.67)$
   $= 1 - P(z<2.67)$
   $= 1 - .9962$
   $= .0038$
The result suggests an unusual event has occurred – but certainly not an impossible one, as about 38 of every 10,000 pregnancies can be expected to last as long.

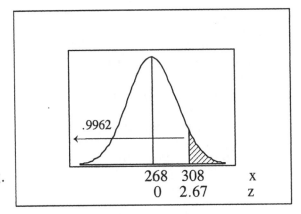

b. For the lowest 4%,
   A=.0400 [.0401] and z = -1.75.
   $x = \mu + z\sigma$
   $ = 268 + (-1.75)(15)$
   $ = 268 - 26$
   $ = 242$

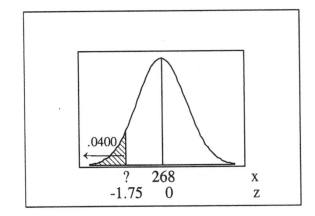

11. $\mu = 998$
$\sigma = 202$
a. P(x<1100)
   $= P(z<.50)$
   $= .6915$ or 69.15%

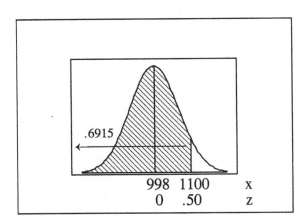

b. For the top 40%,
    A = .6000 [.5987] and z = .25.
$x = \mu + z\sigma$
    $= 998 + (.25)(202)$
    $= 998 + 50.5$
    $= 1048.5$
The minimum required score would change
each year, and it could not be determined
until all the test results were in. In addition,
there could be problems because the
applicants might feel they were competing
against each other rather than a standard.

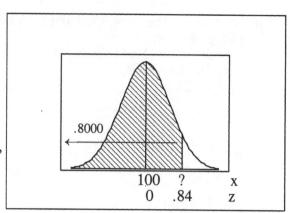

12. $\mu = 6.0$
    $\sigma = 1.0$
    For the smallest 2.5%, A = .0250 and z = -1.96.
    For the largest 2.5%, A = .9750 and z = 1.96.
    $x_S = \mu + z\sigma$
        $= 6.0 + (-1.96)(1.0)$
        $= 6.0 - 1.96$
        $= 4.04$, rounded to 4.0
    $x_L = \mu + z\sigma$
        $= 6.0 + (1.96)(1.0)$
        $= 6.0 + 1.96$
        $= 7.96$, rounded to 8.0

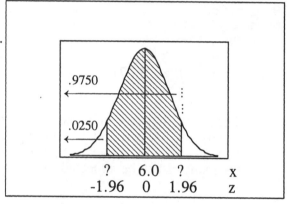

13. $\mu = 8.2$
    $\sigma = 1.1$
    a. $P(x < 5.0)$
        $= P(z < -2.91)$
        $= .0018$

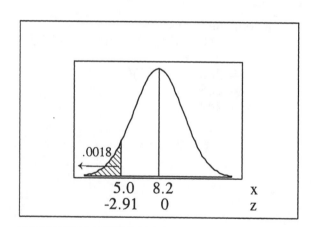

b. For the shortest 1%,
    A = .0100 [.0099] and z = -2.33.
    $x = \mu + z\sigma$
        $= 8.2 + (-2.33)(1.1)$
        $= 8.2 - 2.6$
        $= 5.6$ years
For a "nicer" figure, consider a warranty
of 5.5 years = 66 months [for which
$P(x < 5.5) < P(x < 5.6) = .01$].

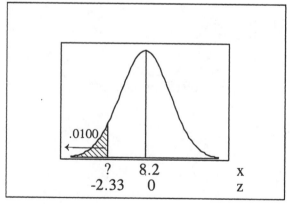

14. $\mu = 7.1$
$\sigma = 1.4$
a. $P(x < 8.0)$
$= P(z < .64)$
$= .7389$

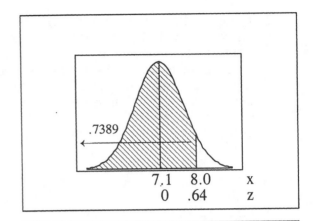

b. For the lowest 2%,
A = .0200 [.0202] and z = -2.05
$x = \mu + z\sigma$
$= 7.1 + (-2.05)(1.4)$
$= 7.1 - 2.87$
$= 4.23$, rounded to 4.2
For a "nicer" figure, consider a warranty
of 50 months = 4.17 years [for which
$P(x < 4.17) < P(x < 4.2) = .02$].

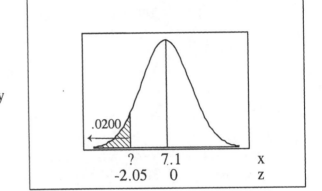

15. $\mu = .91470$
$\sigma = .03691$
a. $P(x < .88925)$
$= P(z < -.69)$
$= .2451$ or 24.51%, close to 25%

b. For the lowest 25%,
A = .2500 [.2514] and z = -.67.
$x = \mu + z\sigma$
$= .91470 + (-.67)(.03691)$
$= .91470 - .02473$
$= .88997$, close to .88925

NOTE: Comparing the results using the normal distribution in parts (a) and (b) above to the
actual values is not quite fair for two reasons.

1. There are differences in precision. While the weights in the problem were measured to the nearest .00001 gram, percentiles are stated to the whole percent (i.e., the nearest .01) and using the closest entry in Table A-2 limits the accuracy to 3 digits (since the z scores are accurate to the nearest 0.01). A more appropriate comparison uses 2 digits to see that 25% = 25% in part (a) and 3 digits to see that .890 ≈ .889 in part (b).

2. The normal distribution is continuous, but the actual data is discrete. Since the 25th percentile for n=100 scores is $(x_{25}+x_{26})/2$, it might be more appropriate to use A=.2550 instead of A=.2500 in any comparisons. Adjustments to handle discrepancies between continuous and discrete variables are covered in section 5-6.

16. μ = .816822
σ = .007507

a. P(x > .8250)
  = P(z > 1.09)
  = 1 - P(z < 1.09)
  = 1 - .8621
  = .1379

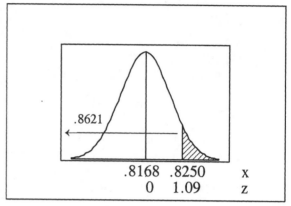

b. For the bottom 2.5%, A=.0250 & z=-1.96.
For the top 2.5%, A=.9750 & z=1.96.

$x_B = \mu + z\sigma$
  = .816822 + (-1.96)(.007507)
  = .816822 - .014714
  = .80211

$x_T = \mu + z\sigma$
  = .816822 + (1.96)(.007507)
  = .816822 + .014714
  = .82154

17. μ = 63.6
σ = 2.5

P(x > 70)
  = P(z > 2.56)
  = 1 - P(z < 2.56)
  = 1 - .9948
  = .0052 or .52%

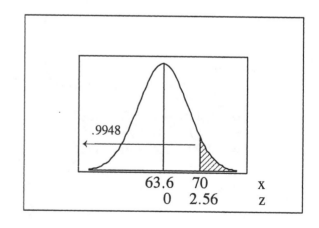

18. $\mu = 63.6$
$\sigma = 2.5$
$P(58 < x < 80)$
    $= P(-2.24 < z < 6.56)$
    $= P(z < 6.56) - P(z < -2.24)$
    $= .9999 - .0125$
    $= .9874$ or 98.74%
No; only 1.26% are too short or too tall.

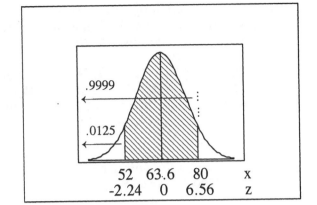

19. $\mu = 63.6$
$\sigma = 2.5$
$P(66.5 < x < 71.5)$
    $= P(1.16 < z < 3.16)$
    $= P(z < 3.16) - P(z < 1.16)$
    $= .9992 - .8770$
    $= .1222$
The percentage meeting the requirement is 12.22%. Yes; the Rockettes are taller than the general population of women.

20. $\mu = 63.6$
$\sigma = 2.5$
For the shortest 20%,
    $A = .2000 \ [.2005]$ and $z = -.84$.
For the tallest 20%,
    $A = ..8000 \ [.7995]$ and $z = .84$.
$x_S = \mu + z\sigma$
    $= 63.6 + (-.84)(2.5)$
    $= 63.6 - 2.1$
    $= 61.5$
$x_T = \mu + z\sigma$
    $= 63.6 + (.84)(2.5)$
    $= 63.6 + 2.1$
    $= 65.7$

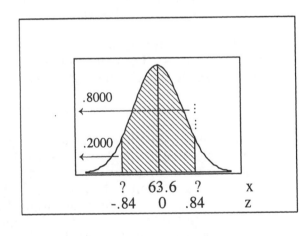

21. normal distribution with $\mu = 143$ lbs and $\sigma = 29$ lbs
a. The z scores are always unit-free. Because the numerator and the denominator of the fraction $z = (x-\mu)/\sigma$ have the same units, the units will divide out.
b. For a population of size N, $\mu = \Sigma x/N$ and $\sigma^2 = \Sigma(x-\mu)^2/N$.
   As shown below, $\mu_z = 0$ and $\sigma_z = 1$ will be true for *any* set of z scores.
   $\Sigma z = \Sigma[(x-\mu)/\sigma] = (1/\sigma) \cdot [\Sigma(x-\mu)]$
              $= (1/\sigma) \cdot [\Sigma x - \Sigma\mu] = (1/\sigma) \cdot [N\mu - N\mu] = (1/\sigma) \cdot 0 = 0$
   $\Sigma z^2 = \Sigma[(x-\mu)/\sigma]^2 = (1/\sigma^2) \cdot [\Sigma(x-\mu)^2] = (1/\sigma^2) \cdot [N\sigma^2] = N$
   $\mu_z = (\Sigma z)/N = 0/N = 0$
   $\sigma_z^2 = \Sigma(z-\mu_z)^2/N = \Sigma(z-0)^2/N = \Sigma z^2/N = N/N = 1; \sigma_z = \sqrt{1} = 1$
   Since rescaling the scores will not change the basic shape of the distribution, the z scores will still have a normal distribution.

c. For a population of size N, $\mu = \Sigma x/N$ and $\sigma^2 = \Sigma(x-\mu)^2/N$.
As shown below, multiplying each value by a constant multiplies the mean and the standard deviation by that constant.

Let $y = k \cdot x$

$\mu_y = \Sigma y/N = [\Sigma(k \cdot x)]/N = [k \cdot (\Sigma x)]/N = k \cdot [(\Sigma x)/N] = k \cdot \mu_x$

$\sigma_y^2 = \Sigma[y - \mu_y]^2/N = \Sigma[k \cdot x - k \cdot \mu_x]^2/N = k^2 \cdot \Sigma[x-\mu_x]^2/N = k^2 \cdot \sigma_x^2; \; \sigma_y = k \cdot \sigma_x$

Since changing from pounds to kilograms multiplies each weight by .4536,

$\mu = (.4536)(143) = 64.9$ kg

$\sigma = (.4536)(29) = 13.2$ kg

22. normal distribution with $\mu = 100$ and $\sigma = 15$
a. $P(x > 105) = P(z > .33) = 1 - P(z < .33) = 1 - .6293 = .3707$
b. $P(x > 105) = P_C(x > 105.5) = P(z > .36) = 1 - P(z < .37) = 1 - .6443 = .3557$
c. There is a difference of $.3707 - .3557 = .015$, an error of $.015/.3557 = 4.2\%$ when the correction is not used.

5-4   Sampling Distributions and Estimators

1. No; while the long run average of the values of the sample proportion equals the population proportion, sampling variability produces a distribution of sample proportions. The value of any one sample proportion is a member of that sampling distribution, but not necessarily equal to its long run average.

2. It is the distribution of the sample means from all possible samples of size 12. If the book has 300 pages, for example, there would be $_{300}C_{12} = 300!/(288!12!) = 8.88 \times 10^{20}$ possible samples of size 12. The value 5.08 is one of those 8.88×10^{20} values, whose long rung average is equal to the true value for all 300 pages.

3. No; the histogram from one sample reflects the shape of the population distribution of individual scores. The shape of the sampling distribution of sample means is not necessarily the same as the shape of the population distribution of individual scores.

4. a. The 10% is a statistic, because it was calculated from a sample and not from the entire population.
   b. The sampling distribution of which this value is a part consists of the sample proportions from all possible samples of size 1015 from the population.
   c. Yes; as the sample size increases, the sampling variability decreases – so that any one value is more likely to be closer to the true population value. For a sample of size n=1, the sampling distribution is the original population and the sampling variance is the same as the population variance. If the sample is the entire population, there is only one possible sample and the sampling "distribution" is a single value with variance zero. As the sample size increases from 1 to the population size, the sampling variance decreases from the original population variance to zero.

5. For the original population,
$\mu = \Sigma x/N = (10+6+5)/3 = 21/3 = 7$.
a. The 9 equally likely samples and their means are given at the immediate right.
b. Each of the 9 means has probability 1/9. The sampling distribution, a list of the means and the total probability of each, is given at the far right
c. $\mu_{\bar{x}} = \Sigma \bar{x} \cdot P(\bar{x}) = 63/9 = 7$.
d. Yes. Yes, the sample mean is an unbiased estimator of the population mean.

sample	$\bar{x}$
5,5	5.0
5,6	5.5
5,10	7.5
6,5	5.5
6,6	6.0
6,10	8.0
10,5	7.5
10,6	8.0
10,10	10.0
	63.0

$\bar{x}$	$P(\bar{x})$	$\bar{x} \cdot P(\bar{x})$
5.0	1/9	5/9
5.5	2/9	11/9
6.0	1/9	6/9
7.5	2/9	15/9
8.0	2/9	16/9
10.0	1/9	10/9
	9/9	63/9

6. For the original population,
$\mu = \Sigma x/N = (1+11+9+3)/4 = 24/4 = 6$.

a. The 16 equally likely samples and their means are given at the immediate right.

b. Each of the 16 means has probability 1/16. The sampling distribution, a list of the means and the total probability of each, is given at the far right

c. $\mu_{\bar{x}} = \Sigma\bar{x}\cdot P(\bar{x}) = 96/16 = 6$

d. Yes. Yes, the sample mean is an unbiased estimator of the population mean.

sample	$\bar{x}$
1,1	1
1,3	2
1,9	5
1,11	6
3,1	2
3,3	3
3,9	6
3,11	7
9,1	5
9,3	6
9,9	9
9,11	10
11,1	6
11,3	7
11,9	10
11,11	11
	96

$\bar{x}$	$P(\bar{x})$	$\bar{x}\cdot P(\bar{x})$
1	1/16	1/16
2	2/16	4/16
3	1/16	3/16
5	2/16	10/16
6	4/16	24/16
7	2/16	14/16
9	1/16	9/16
10	2/16	20/16
11	1/16	11/16
	16/16	96/16

7. For the original population,
$\mu = \Sigma x/N$
$= (85+79+82+73+78)/5$
$= 397/5 = 79.4$

a. The 25 equally likely samples and their means are given at the immediate right.

b. Each of the 25 means has probability 1/25. The sampling distribution, a list of the means and the total probability of each, is given at the far right

c. $\mu_{\bar{x}} = \Sigma\bar{x}\cdot P(\bar{x}) = 1985/25 = 79.4$

d. Yes. Yes, the sample mean is an unbiased estimator of the population mean.

sample	$\bar{x}$
73,73	73.0
73,78	75.5
73,79	76.0
73,82	77.5
73,85	79.0
78,73	75.5
78,78	78.0
78,79	78.5
78,82	80.0
78,85	81.5
79,73	76.0
79,78	78.5
79,79	79.0
79,82	80.5
79,85	82.0
82,73	77.5
82,78	80.0
82,79	80.5
82,82	82.0
82,85	83.5
85,73	79.0

$\bar{x}$	$P(\bar{x})$	$\bar{x}\cdot P(\bar{x})$
73.0	1/25	73/25
75.5	2/25	151/25
76.0	2/25	152/25
77.5	2/25	155/25
78.0	1/25	78/25
78.5	2/25	157/25
79.0	3/25	237/25
80.0	2/25	160/25
80.5	2/25	161/25
81.5	2/25	163/25
82.0	3/25	246/25
83.5	2/25	167/25
85.0	1/25	85/25
	25/25	1985/25

sample	$\bar{x}$
85,78	81.5
85,79	82.0
85,82	83.5
85,85	85.0
	1985.0

8. For the original population,
$\mu = \Sigma x/N$
$= (62+46+68+64+57)/5$
$= 297/5 = 59.4$

a. The 25 equally likely samples and their means are given at the immediate right.

b. Each of the 25 means has probability 1/25. The sampling distribution, a list of the means and the total probability of each, is given at the far right

c. $\mu_{\bar{x}} = \Sigma\bar{x}\cdot P(\bar{x}) = 1485/25 = 59.4$

d. Yes. Yes, the sample mean is an unbiased estimator of the population mean.

sample	$\bar{x}$
46,46	46.0
46,57	51.5
46,62	54.0
46,64	55.0
46,68	57.0
57,46	51.5
57,57	57.0
57,62	59.5
57,64	60.5
57,68	62.5
62,46	54.0
62,57	59.5
62,62	62.0
62,64	63.0
62,68	65.0
64,46	55.0
64,57	60.5
64,62	63.0
64,64	64.0
64,68	66.0
68,46	57.0

$\bar{x}$	$P(\bar{x})$	$\bar{x}\cdot P(\bar{x})$
46.0	1/25	46/25
51.5	2/25	103/25
54.0	2/25	108/25
55.0	2/25	110/25
57.0	3/25	171/25
59.5	2/25	119/25
60.5	2/25	121/25
62.0	1/25	62/25
62.5	2/25	125/25
63.0	2/25	126/25
64.0	1/25	64/25
65.0	2/25	130/25
66.0	2/25	132/25
68.0	1/25	68/25
	25/25	1485/25

sample	$\bar{x}$
68,57	62.5
68,62	65.0
68,64	66.0
68,68	68.0
	1485.0

9. For the original population, the proportion of females is $p = 3/4$.
   a. Selecting with replacement, there are $4^2 = 16$ equally likely samples.
      Let x = the number of females per sample.
      binomial problem: $n = 2$ and $p = 3/4$, use the binomial formula
      $$P(x) = [n!/x!(n-x)!] \cdot p^x \cdot (1-p)^{n-x}$$
      $$P(x=0) = [2!/0!2!] \cdot (3/4)^0 \cdot (1/4)^2 = [1] \cdot (1) \cdot (1/16) = 1/16$$
      $$P(x=1) = [2!/1!1!] \cdot (3/4)^1 \cdot (1/4)^1 = [2] \cdot (3/4) \cdot (1/4) = 6/16$$
      $$P(x=2) = [2!/2!0!] \cdot (3/4)^2 \cdot (1/4)^0 = [1] \cdot (9/16) \cdot (1) = 9/16$$
      This means that of the 16 samples, there are
      1 with $\hat{p} = 0/2 = 0$ [namely, MM]
      6 with $\hat{p} = 1/2 = .50$ [namely, MA MB MC AM BM CM]
      9 with $\hat{p} = 2/2 = 1.00$ [namely, AA AB AC BA BB BC CA CB CC]
   b. The sampling distribution, a list of the sample proportions and the probability
      of each, is as follows.

$\hat{p}$	$P(\hat{p})$	$\hat{p} \cdot P(\hat{p})$
0.00	1/16	0/16
0.50	6/16	3/16
1.00	9/16	9/16
	16/16	12/16

   c. $\mu_{\hat{p}} = \Sigma \hat{p} \cdot P(\hat{p}) = 12/16 = 3/4$
   d. Yes. Yes, the sample proportion is an unbiased estimator of the population proportion.

10. For the original population, the proportion of defects is $p = 2/5$.
   a. Selecting with replacement, there are $5^2 = 25$ equally likely samples.
      Let x = the number of defects per sample.
      binomial problem: $n = 2$ and $p = 2/5$, use the binomial formula
      $$P(x) = [n!/x!(n-x)!] \cdot p^x \cdot (1-p)^{n-x}$$
      $$P(x=0) = [2!/0!2!] \cdot (2/5)^0 \cdot (3/5)^2 = [1] \cdot (1) \cdot (9/25) = 9/25$$
      $$P(x=1) = [2!/1!1!] \cdot (2/5)^1 \cdot (3/5)^1 = [2] \cdot (2/5) \cdot (3/5) = 12/25$$
      $$P(x=2) = [2!/2!0!] \cdot (2/5)^2 \cdot (3/5)^0 = [1] \cdot (4/25) \cdot (1) = 4/25$$
      This means that of the 25 samples, there are
      9 with $\hat{p} = 0/2 = 0$
      12 with $\hat{p} = 1/2 = .50$
      4 with $\hat{p} = 2/2 = 1.00$
   b. The sampling distribution, a list of the sample proportions and the probability
      of each, is as follows.

$\hat{p}$	$P(\hat{p})$	$\hat{p} \cdot P(\hat{p})$
0.00	9/25	0/25
0.50	12/25	6/25
1.00	4/25	4/25
	25/25	10/25

   c. $\mu_{\hat{p}} = \Sigma \hat{p} \cdot P(\hat{p}) = 10/25 = 2/5$
   d. Yes. Yes, the sample proportion is an unbiased estimator of the population proportion.

11. For the original population, the proportion of Democrats is $10/13 = .769$.
   a. One procedure is as follows. Generate a list of random numbers, find their remainders
      when divided by 13, let the 10 remainders 0-9 correspond to the 10 Democrats and let the
      3 remainders 10-12 correspond to the 3 Republicans. So that each remainder has the
      same chance to occur, limit the usable random numbers to a whole multiple of 13. Using
      the $7 \times 13 = 91$ two-digit numbers from 00 to 90 and discarding all others, for example,
      allows each remainder 7 chances to appear among the usable random numbers. Applying
      this procedure to the first two digits of each 5-digit sequence in the list of random
      numbers for the exercises in section 3-6 yields the following.
      46 gives remainder 7, a Democrat
      99 is not usable
      72 gives remainder 7, a Democrat
      44 gives remainder 5, a Democrat
      86 gives remainder 8, a Democrat
      00 gives remainder 0, a Democrat

b. The proportion of Democrats in the sample in part (a) is 5/5 = 1.00.

c. The proportion in part (b) is a statistic, because it was calculated from a sample.

d. No; the above sample proportion does not equal the true population proportion of .769. No; samples of size n=5 only produce sample proportions of 0,.20,.40,.60,.80 or 1.00.

e. The sample proportion is an unbiased estimator of the population proportion. If all possible 13^5 = 371,293 samples were listed, the mean of those sample proportions would equal the true population proportion.

12. For the original population, the proportion of senators from Maine is 2/3.
Label the senators ME1, ME2 and TX. Selecting without replacement there are 3·2 = 6 equally likely possible samples given at the left below.

sample	$\hat{p}$
ME1,ME2	2/2 = 1.00
ME1,TX	1/2 = .50
ME2,ME1	2/2 = 1.00
ME2,TX	1/2 = .50
TX,ME1	1/2 = .50
TX,ME2	1/2 = .50

$\hat{p}$	$P(\hat{p})$	$\hat{p} \cdot P(\hat{p})$
0.50	4/6	2/6
1.00	2/6	2/6
	6/6	4/6

The sampling distribution given at the right above verifies that $\mu_{\hat{p}} = \Sigma\hat{p}\cdot P(\hat{p}) = 4/6 = 2/3$, which equal to the population proportion.

13. The population mean is $\mu = \Sigma x/N = (62+46+68+64+57) = 297/5 = 59.4$.

a. All possible samples of size n=2 form a population of $N=_5C_2=10$ members as follows.

sample	$\overline{x}$	$\overline{x}-\mu_{\overline{x}}$	$(\overline{x}-\mu_{\overline{x}})^2$
46-57	51.5	-7.9	62.41
46-62	54.0	-5.4	29.16
46-64	55.0	-4.4	19.36
46-68	57.0	-2.4	5.76
57-62	59.5	.1	.01
57-64	60.5	1.1	1.21
57-68	62.5	3.1	9.61
62-64	63.0	3.6	12.96
62-68	65.0	5.6	31.36
64-68	66.0	6.6	43.56
	594.0	0	215.40

$\mu_{\overline{x}} = \Sigma\overline{x}/N = 594.0/10 = 59.4$

$\sigma_{\overline{x}}^2 = \Sigma(\overline{x}-\mu_{\overline{x}})^2/N = 215.40/10 = 21.540$
$\sigma_{\overline{x}} = 4.64$

b. All possible samples of size n=3 form a population of $N=_5C_3=10$ members as follows.

sample	$\overline{x}$	$\overline{x}-\mu_{\overline{x}}$	$(\overline{x}-\mu_{\overline{x}})^2$
46-57-62	55.00	-4.40	19.36
46-57-64	55.67	-3.73	13.94
46-57-68	57.00	-2.40	5.76
46-62-64	57.33	-2.07	4.27
46-62-68	58.67	-.73	.54
46-64-68	59.33	-.07	.00
57-62-64	61.00	1.60	2.56
57-62-68	62.33	2.93	8.60
57-64-68	63.00	3.60	12.96
62-64-68	64.67	5.27	27.74
	594.00	0	95.73

$\mu_{\overline{x}} = \Sigma\overline{x}/N = 594.00/10 = 59.4$

$\sigma_{\overline{x}}^2 = \Sigma(\overline{x}-\mu_{\overline{x}})^2/N = 95.73/10 = 9/573$
$\sigma_{\overline{x}} = 3.09$

c. All possible samples of size n=4 form a population of $N=_5C_4=5$ members as follows.

sample	$\overline{x}$	$\overline{x}-\mu_{\overline{x}}$	$(\overline{x}-\mu_{\overline{x}})^2$
46-57-62-64	57.25	-2.15	4.6225
46-57-62-68	58.25	-1.15	1.3225
46-57-64-68	58.75	-.65	.4225
46-62-64-68	60.00	.60	.3600
57-62-64-68	62.75	3.35	11.2225
	297.00	0	17.9500

$\mu_{\overline{x}} = \Sigma\overline{x}/N = 297.00/5 = 59.4$

$\sigma_{\overline{x}}^2 = \Sigma(\overline{x}-\mu_{\overline{x}})^2/N = 17.9500/5 = 3.5900$
$\sigma_{\overline{x}} = 1.89$

d. Yes; each of the above sampling distributions has a mean equal to the population mean.

e. As the sample size increases, the variation of the sampling distribution decreases.

14. The MAD of the population is 1.56, as illustrated by the following table.

x	$|x-\overline{x}|$	
1	5/3	$\overline{x} = \Sigma x/N = 8/3$
2	2/3	$MAD = \Sigma |x-\overline{x}|/N$
5	7/3	$= (14/3)/3 = 14/9 = 1.56$
8	14/3	

The sampling distribution of the 9 possible equally likely sample MAD's has a mean of .89, as illustrated by the following tables.

sample	x	$|x-\overline{x}|$'s	MAD
1,1	1.0	0,0	0
1,2	1.5	.5,.5	.5
1,5	3.0	2,2	2.0
2,1	1.5	.5,.5	.5
2,2	2.0	0,0	0
2,5	3.5	1.5,1.5	1.5
5,1	3.0	2,2	2.0
5,2	3.5	1.5,1.5	1.5
5,5	5.0	0,0	0

MAD	P(MAD)	MAD·P(MAD)
0	3/9	0/9
.5	2/9	1/9
1.5	2/9	3/9
2.0	2/9	4/9
	9/9	8/9

$\mu_{MAD} = \Sigma MAD \cdot P(MAD)$
$= 8/9 = .89$

The sample MAD is not a good estimator of the population MAD.

15. The 27 equally likely samples of size n=3 are listed below, followed by their medians. The sampling distribution of the medians is given at the right.

m	P(m)	m·P(m)
1	7/27	7/27
2	13/27	26/27
5	7/27	35/27
	27/27	68/27

```
111-1  121-1  151-1  211-1  221-2  251-2  511-1  521-2  551-5
112-1  122-2  152-2  212-2  222-2  252-2  512-2  522-2  552-5
115-1  125-2  155-5  215-2  225-2  255-5  515-5  525-5  555-5
```

The means for the above samples are as follows. The sampling distribution for the means is given at the right.

$\overline{x}$	$P(\overline{x})$	$\overline{x} \cdot P(\overline{x})$
3/3	1/27	3/81
4/3	3/27	12/81
5/3	3/27	15/81
6/3	1/27	6/81
7/3	3/27	21/81
8/3	6/27	48/81
9/3	3/27	27/81
11/3	3/27	33/81
12/3	3/27	36/81
15/3	1/27	15/81
	27/27	216/81

```
3/3   4/3   7/3   4/3   5/3   8/3   7/3   8/3   11/3
4/3   5/3   8/3   5/3   6/3   9/3   8/3   9/3   12/3
7/3   8/3   11/3  8/3   9/3   12/3  11/3  12/3  15/3
```

$\mu_m = \Sigma m \cdot P(m) = 68/27 = 2.52$
$\mu_{\overline{x}} = \Sigma \overline{x} \cdot P(\overline{x}) = 216/81 = 2.67$

Since $\mu = 8/3 = 2.67$, the sample mean is a good estimator for the population mean, but the sample median is not. The sampling distributions indicate that

5-5 The Central Limit Theorem

NOTE: When using individual scores (i.e., making a statement about one x score from the original distribution), convert x to z using the mean and standard deviation of the x's and $z = (x-\mu)/\sigma$. When using a sample of n scores (i.e., making a statement about), convert $\overline{x}$ to z using the mean and standard deviation of the $\overline{x}$'s and $z = (\overline{x}-\mu_{\overline{x}})/\sigma_{\overline{x}}$.

IMPORTANT NOTE: After calculating $\sigma_{\overline{x}}$, STORE IT in the calculator to recall it with total accuracy whenever it is needed in subsequent calculations. DO NOT write it down on paper rounded off (even to several decimal places) and then re-enter it in the calculator whenever it is needed. This avoids both round-off errors and recopying errors

1. a. normal distribution
$\mu = 172$
$\sigma = 29$
$P(x < 167)$
$= P(z < -.17)$
$= .4325$

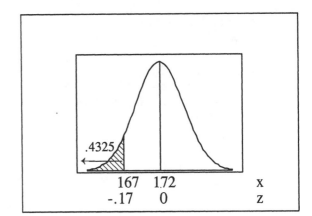

b. normal distribution,
since the original distribution is so
$\mu_{\bar{x}} = \mu = 172$
$\sigma_{\bar{x}} = \sigma/\sqrt{n} = 29/\sqrt{36} = 4.833$
$P(\bar{x} < 167)$
$= P(z < -1.03)$
$= .1515$

NOTE: Remember that the figures are for illustrative purposes, as an aid to solving the problem, and are not to scale. In scaled drawings, the shaded area would be very large (almost ½ the figure) in part 1(a) and very small in part 1(b).

2. a. normal distribution
$\mu = 172$
$\sigma = 29$
$P(x > 180)$
$= P(z > .28)$
$= 1 - P(z < .28)$
$= 1 - .6103$
$= .3897$

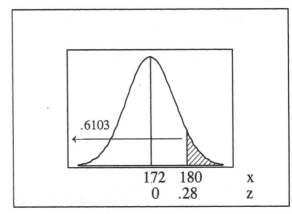

b. normal distribution,
since the original distribution is so
$\mu_{\bar{x}} = \mu = 172$
$\sigma_{\bar{x}} = \sigma/\sqrt{n} = 29/\sqrt{100} = 2.9$
$P(\bar{x} > 180)$
$= P(z > 2.76)$
$= 1 - P(z < 2.76)$
$= 1 - .9971$
$= .0029$

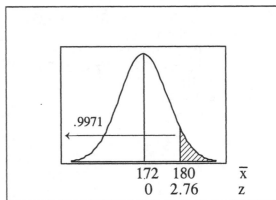

3. a. normal distribution
$\mu = 172$
$\sigma = 29$
$P(170 < x < 175)$
$= P(-.07 < z < .10)$
$= P(z < .10) - P(z < -.07)$
$= .5398 - .4721$
$= .0677$

b. normal distribution,
   since the original distribution is so
$\mu_{\bar{x}} = \mu = 172$
$\sigma_{\bar{x}} = \sigma/\sqrt{n} = 29/\sqrt{64} = 3.625$
$P(170 < \bar{x} < 175)$
$= P(-.55 < z < .83)$
$= P(z < .83) - P(z < -.55)$
$= .7967 - .2912$
$= .5055$

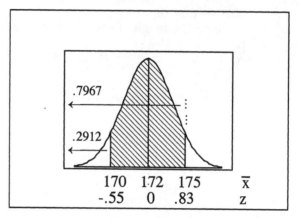

4. a. normal distribution
$\mu = 172$
$\sigma = 29$
$P(100 < x < 165)$
$= P(-2.48 < z < -.24)$
$= P(z < -.24) - P(z < -2.48)$
$= .4052 - .0066$
$= .3986$

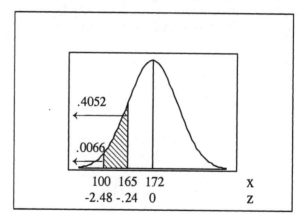

b. normal distribution,
   since the original distribution is so
$\mu_{\bar{x}} = \mu = 172$
$\sigma_{\bar{x}} = \sigma/\sqrt{n} = 29/\sqrt{81} = 3.222$
$P(100 < \bar{x} < 165)$
$= P(-22.34 < z < -2.17)$
$= P(z < -2.17) - P(z < -22.34)$
$= .1050 - .0001$
$= .0149$

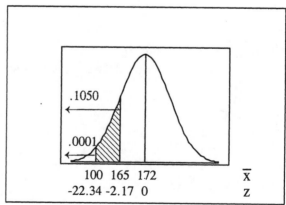

5. a. normal distribution,
    since the original distribution is so
    $\mu_{\bar{x}} = \mu = 172$
    $\sigma_{\bar{x}} = \sigma/\sqrt{n} = 29/\sqrt{25} = 5.8$
    $P(\bar{x} > 160)$
       $= P(z > -2.07)$
       $= 1 - P(z < -2.07)$
       $= 1 - .0192$
       $= .9808$

  b. When the original distribution is normal,
    the sampling distribution of the $\bar{x}$'s is
    normal regardless of the sample size.

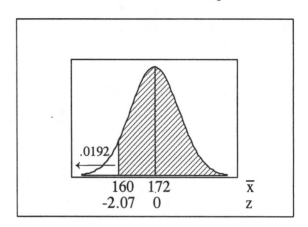

6. a. normal distribution,
    since the original distribution is so
    $\mu_{\bar{x}} = \mu = 172$
    $\sigma_{\bar{x}} = \sigma/\sqrt{n} = 29/\sqrt{4} = 14.5$
    $P(160 < \bar{x} < 180)$
       $= P(-.83 < z < .55)$
       $= P(z < .55) - P(z < -.83)$
       $= .7088 - .2033$
       $= .5055$

  b. When the original distribution is normal,
    the sampling distribution of the $\bar{x}$'s is
    normal regardless of the sample size.

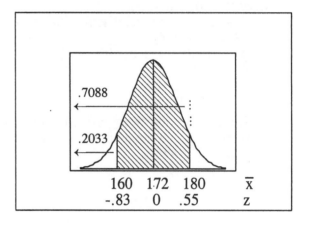

7. a. normal distribution
    $\mu = 143$
    $\sigma = 29$
    $P(140 < x < 211)$
       $= P(-.10 < z < 2.34)$
       $= P(z < 2.34) - P(z < -.10)$
       $= .9904 - .4602$
       $= .5302$

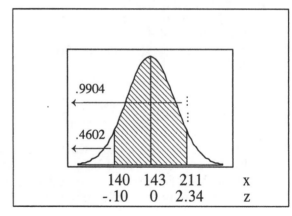

  b. normal distribution,
    since the original distribution is so
    $\mu_{\bar{x}} = \mu = 143$
    $\sigma_{\bar{x}} = \sigma/\sqrt{n} = 29/\sqrt{36} = 4.833$
    $P(140 < \bar{x} < 211)$
       $= P(-.62 < z < 14.07)$
       $= P(z < 14.07) - P(z < -.62)$
       $= .9999 - .2676$
       $= .7323$

  c. The information from part (a) is more
    relevant, since the seat will be occupied by
    one woman at a time.

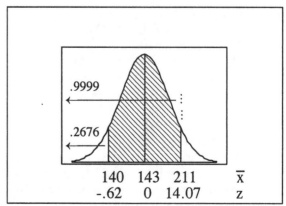

8. a. normal distribution
   $\mu = 6.0$
   $\sigma = 1.0$
   $P(x < 6.2)$
      $= P(z < .20)$
      $= .5793$

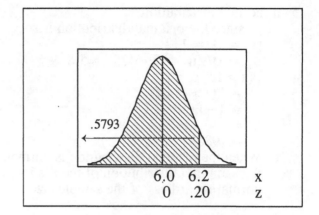

  b. normal distribution,
      since the original distribution is so
   $\mu_{\bar{x}} = \mu = 6.0$
   $\sigma_{\bar{x}} = \sigma/\sqrt{n} = 1.0/\sqrt{100} = .10$
   $P(\bar{x} < 6.2)$
      $= P(z < 2.00)$
      $= .9772$

  c. The information from part (a) is more
   relevant, since the helmets will be worn by
   one man at a time.

9. a. normal distribution,
      since the original distribution is so
   $\mu_{\bar{x}} = \mu = 14.4$
   $\sigma_{\bar{x}} = \sigma/\sqrt{n} = 1.0/\sqrt{2} = .707$
   $P(\bar{x} > 16.0)$
      $= P(z > 2.26)$
      $= 1 - P(z < 2.26)$
      $= 1 - .9881$
      $= .0119$

  b. No. Yes; even if all the seats were occupied
   by 2 men, there would be a problem only
   about 1% of the time. In practice, most
   men probably sit with a female or a child.

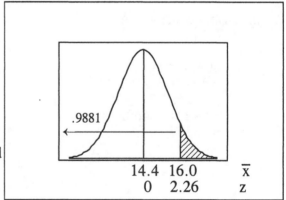

10. normal distribution,
      by the Central Limit Theorem
   $\mu_{\bar{x}} = \mu = .500$
   $\sigma_{\bar{x}} = \sigma/\sqrt{n} = .289/\sqrt{100} = .0289$
   $P(\bar{x} > .57)$
      $= P(z > 2.42)$
      $= 1 - P(z < 2.42)$
      $= 1 - .9922$
      $= .0078$

  b. Yes; since $.0078 < .05$, generating such
   random numbers would be considered an
   unusual event for a properly working
   random number generator.

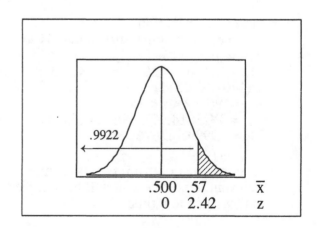

11. a. normal distribution,
       by the Central Limit Theorem
       $\mu_{\bar{x}} = \mu = 12.00$
       $\sigma_{\bar{x}} = \sigma/\sqrt{n} = .11/\sqrt{36} = .0183$
       $P(\bar{x} \geq 12.19)$
          $= P(z \geq 10.36)$
          $= 1 - P(z < 10.36)$
          $= 1 - .9999$
          $= .0001$
    b. No; if $\mu = 12$, then an extremely rare event
       has occurred. No; there is no cheating,
       since the actual amount is more than the
       advertised amount.

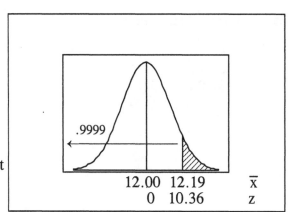

12. a. normal distribution
       $\mu = 100$
       $\sigma = 15$
       $P(x > 133)$
          $= P(z > 2.20)$
          $= .1 - P(z < 2.20)$
          $= 1 - .9861$
          $= .0139$

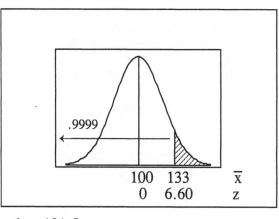

    b. normal distribution,
       since the original distribution is so
       $\mu_{\bar{x}} = \mu = 100$
       $\sigma_{\bar{x}} = \sigma/\sqrt{n} = 15/\sqrt{9} = 5.0$
       $P(\bar{x} > 133)$
          $= P(z > 6.60)$
          $= 1 - P(z < 6.60)$
          $= 1 - .9999$
          $= .0001$
    c. No; if the mean is 133, all we know is that
       the scores were clustered around 133.
       Some scores could have been considerably
       higher, and others considerably lower – in
       particular, some scores could have been lower than 131.5.

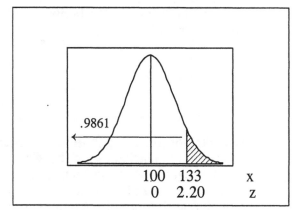

13. a. normal distribution,
       by the Central Limit Theorem
       $\mu_{\bar{x}} = \mu = 8.2$
       $\sigma_{\bar{x}} = \sigma/\sqrt{n} = 1.1/\sqrt{50} = .156$
       $P(\bar{x} \leq 7.8)$
          $= P(z \leq -2.57)$
          $= .0051$
    b. Yes; it appears that the TV sets sold by the
       Portland Electronics store are of less than
       average quality.

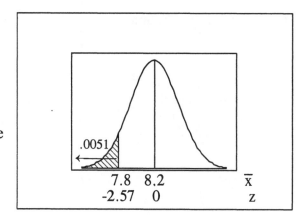

14. a. normal distribution

$\mu = 114.8$

$\sigma = 13.1$

$P(x > 140)$

$\quad = P(z > 1.92)$

$\quad = 1 - P(z < 1.92)$

$\quad = 1 - .9726$

$\quad = .0274$

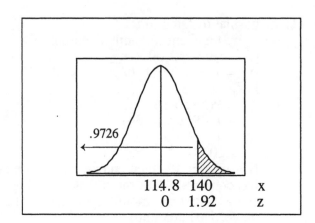

b. normal distribution,

since the original distribution is so

$\mu_{\bar{x}} = \mu = 114.8$

$\sigma_{\bar{x}} = \sigma/\sqrt{n} = 13.1/\sqrt{4} = 6.55$

$P(\bar{x} > 140)$

$\quad = P(z > 3.85)$

$\quad = 1 - P(z < 3.85)$

$\quad = 1 - .9999$

$\quad = .0001$

c. When the original distribution is normal, the sampling distribution of the $\bar{x}$'s is normal regardless of the sample size.

d. No; the mean can be less than 140 even though one or more of the values is greater than 140.

15. a. normal distribution,

by the Central Limit Theorem

$\mu_{\bar{x}} = \mu = .941$

$\sigma_{\bar{x}} = \sigma/\sqrt{n} = .313/\sqrt{40} = .0495$

$P(\bar{x} \le .882)$

$\quad = P(z < -1.19)$

$\quad = .1170$

b. No; since $.1170 > .05$, getting such a mean under the previous conditions would not be considered unusual.

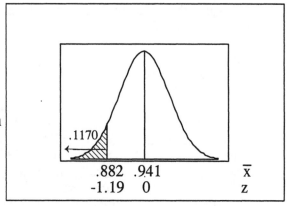

16. a. normal distribution

$\mu = 509$

$\sigma = 112$

$P(x \ge 590)$

$\quad = P(z \ge .72)$

$\quad = 1 - P(z < .72)$

$\quad = 1 - .7642$

$\quad = .2358$

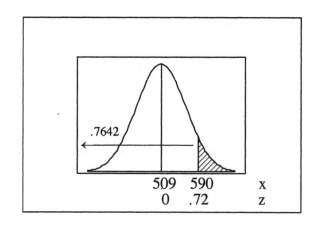

b. normal distribution,
   since the original distribution is so
   $\mu_{\bar{x}} = \mu = 509$
   $\sigma_{\bar{x}} = \sigma/\sqrt{n} = 112/\sqrt{16} = 28$
   $P(\bar{x} \geq 590)$
      $= P(z \geq 2.89)$
      $= 1 - P(z < 2.89)$
      $= 1 - .9981$
      $= .0019$

c. When the original distribution is normal, the sampling distribution of the $\bar{x}$'s is normal regardless of the sample size.

d. Yes; since $.0019 < .05$ by quite a bit, there is strong evidence to support the claim that the course is effective – assuming, as stated, that the 16 participants were truly a random sample (and not self-selected or otherwise chosen in some biased manner).

17. normal distribution,
    since the original distribution is so
    $\mu_{\bar{x}} = \mu = 27.44$
    $\sigma_{\bar{x}} = \sigma/\sqrt{n} = 12.46/\sqrt{4872} = .179$
    $P(\bar{x} > 27.88)$
       $= P(z > 2.46)$
       $= 1 - P(z < 2.46)$
       $= 1 - .9931$
       $= .0069$

    The system is currently acceptable and can expect to be overloaded only $(.0069)(52) = .36$ weeks a year -- or about once every three years.

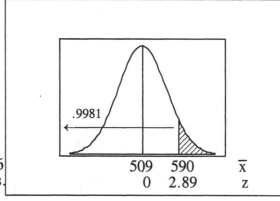

18. $\mu = .9147$
    $\sigma = .0369$

    a. This cannot be answered without knowing the shape of the distribution.
       NOTE: If the weights of the M&M's are normally distributed, then Table A-2 can be used and $P(x > .9085) = P(z > -.17)$
                                     $= 1 - P(z < -.17)$
                                     $= 1 - .4325$
                                     $= .5675.$

    b. normal distribution,
       by the Central Limit Theorem
       $\mu_{\bar{x}} = \mu = .9147$
       $\sigma_{\bar{x}} = \sigma/\sqrt{n} = .0369/\sqrt{1498} = .000953$
       $P(\bar{x} \geq .9085)$
          $= P(z \geq -6.50)$
          $= 1 - P(z < -6.50)$
          $= 1 - .0001$
          $= .9999$

    c. Yes; the company is providing at least the amount claimed on the label with almost absolute certainty.

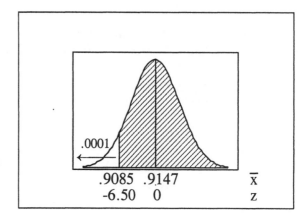

19. normal distribution,
    since the original distribution is so
    $\mu_{\bar{x}} = \mu = 172$
    $\sigma_{\bar{x}} = \sigma/\sqrt{n} = 29/\sqrt{16} = 7.25$
    This is a "backwards" normal problem,
    with A = .9760 and z = 1.96.
    $\bar{x} = \mu_{\bar{x}} + z\sigma_{\bar{x}}$
    $= 172 + (1.96)(7.25)$
    $= 172 + 14.21$
    $= 186.21$
    For 16 men, the total weight is
    (16)(186.21) = 2979 lbs.

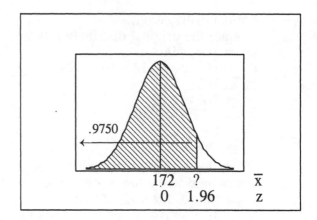

20. a. normal distribution,
    since the original distribution is so
    $\mu_{\bar{x}} = \mu = 14.4$
    $\sigma_{\bar{x}} = \sigma/\sqrt{n} = 1.0/\sqrt{18} = .236$
    This is a "backwards" normal problem,
    with A = .9760 and z = 1.96.
    $\bar{x} = \mu_{\bar{x}} + z\sigma_{\bar{x}}$
    $= 14.4 + (1.96)(.236)$
    $= 14.4 + .46$
    $= 14.86$
    For 18 men, the total width is
    (18)(14.86) = 267.5 in.

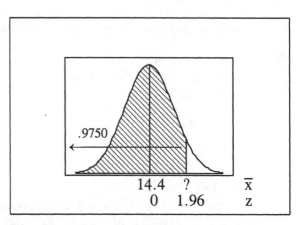

   b. The 14.4 inch figure applies to the general male population, not to football players (who
   would tend to be larger than normal anyway) wearing pads. Furthermore, the
   calculations in part (a) do not consider any spacing between the players.

21. normal distribution, since the original distribution is so
    NOTE: Since 8/120 = .0667 > .05, use the finite population correction factor
    $\mu_{\bar{x}} = \mu = 143$
    $\sigma_{\bar{x}} = [\sigma/\sqrt{n}]\cdot\sqrt{(N-n)/(N-1)}$
    $= [29/\sqrt{8}]\cdot\sqrt{(120-8)/(120-1)}$
    $= [29/\sqrt{8}]\cdot\sqrt{(112)/(119)}$
    $= 9.947$
   a. A total weight of 1300 for 8 women
      corresponds to $\bar{x} = 1300/8 = 162.5$.
      $P(\bar{x} \le 162.5)$
      $= P(z \le 1.96)$
      $= .9750$

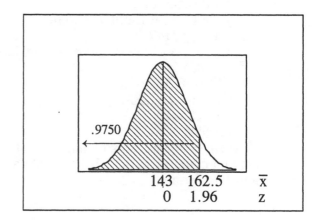

b. normal distribution,
   since the original distribution is so
$\mu_{\bar{x}} = \mu = 143$
$\sigma_{\bar{x}} = 9.947$ (as calculated above)
This is a "backwards" normal problem,
   with A = .9900 [.9901] and z=2.33.
$\bar{x} = \mu_{\bar{x}} + z\sigma_{\bar{x}}$
   $= 143 + (2.33)(9.947)$
   $= 143 + 23.18$
   $= 166.18$
For 8 women, the total weight is
   $(8)(166.18) = 1329$ lbs.

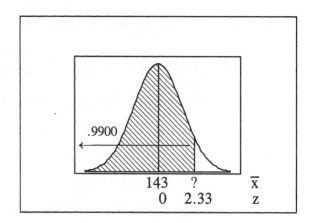

22. a.

x	x−μ	(x−μ)²
2	−6	36
3	−5	25
6	−2	4
8	0	0
11	3	9
18	10	100
48	0	174

$\mu = (\Sigma x)/N = 48/6 = 8$

$\sigma^2 = \Sigma(x-\mu)^2/N = 174/6 = 29$

$\sigma = 5.385$

b. and c.

sample	x̄	x̄−μ_x̄	(x̄−μ_x̄)²
2,3	2.5	−5.5	30.25
2,6	4.0	−4.0	16.00
2,8	5.0	−3.0	9.00
2,11	6.5	−1.5	2.25
2,18	10.0	2.0	4.00
3,6	4.5	−3.5	12.25
3,8	5.5	−2.5	6.25
3,11	7.0	−1.0	1.00
3,18	10.5	2.5	6.25
6,8	7.0	−1.0	1.00
6,11	8.5	.5	.25
6,18	12.0	4.0	16.00
8,11	9.5	1.5	2.25
8,18	13.0	5.0	25.00
11,18	14.5	6.5	42.25
	120.0	0.0	174.00

d. Refer to the 15 x̄ values and the two "extra" columns in the table for parts (b) and (c).

$\mu_{\bar{x}} = \Sigma\bar{x}/15 = 120/15 = 8$
$\sigma_{\bar{x}}^2 = \Sigma(\bar{x}-\mu_{\bar{x}})^2/15 = 174/15 = 11.6$
$\sigma_{\bar{x}} = \sqrt{11.6} = 3.406$

e. $\mu = 8 = \mu_{\bar{x}}$
   $[\sigma/\sqrt{n}]\cdot\sqrt{(N-n)/(N-1)} = [5.385/\sqrt{2}]\cdot\sqrt{(6-2)/(6-1)} = 3.406 = \sigma_{\bar{x}}$

23. normal distribution,
   by the Central Limit Theorem
$\mu_{\bar{x}} = \mu = .500$
$\sigma_{\bar{x}} = \sigma/\sqrt{n} = .289/\sqrt{100} = .0289$
$P(.499 < \bar{x} < .501)$
   $= P(-.03 < z < .03)$
   $= P(z < .03) - P(z < -.03)$
   $= .5120 - .4880$
   $= .0240$

Since .0240 < .05, the event is "unusual" in
that the sample mean will not fall within those
narrow limits very often. Since the probability
of getting a result "as extreme or more extreme" would be very close to ½ (whether the
sample mean was less than or greater than $\mu = .5000$), the event is not of the "extreme" sort
that leads one to question the assumptions associated with the procedure. The key idea is
the difference between "unusual in the sense of rare" and "unusual in the sense of extreme."
Since there are so many possible results, the probability of any one them (even the most
"normal" ones) occurring is small.

5-6 Normal as Approximation to Binomial

NOTE: As in the previous sections, P(E) represents the probability of an event E; this manual uses $P_c(E)$ to represent the probability of an event E with the continuity correction applied.

1. the area to the right of 15.5; in symbols, $P(x>15) = P_c(x>15.5)$

2. the area to the right of 23.5; in symbols, $P(x \geq 24) = P_c(x>23.5)$

3. the area to the left of 99.5; in symbols, $P(x<100) = P_c(x<99.5)$

4. the area from 26.5 to 27.5; in symbols, $P(x=57) = P_c(26.5<x<27.5)$

5. the area to the left of 4.5; in symbols, $P(x \leq 4) = P_c(x<4.5)$

6. the area from 14.5 to 20.5; in symbols, $P(15 \leq x \leq 20) = P_c(14.5<x<20.5)$

7. the area from 7.5 to 10.5; in symbols, $P(8 \leq x \leq 10) = P_c(7.5<x<10.5)$

8. the area from 2.5 to 3.5; in symbols, $P(x=3) = P_c(2.5<x<3.5)$

IMPORTANT NOTE: As in the previous sections, store σ in the calculator so that it may be recalled with complete accuracy whenever it is needed in subsequent calculations.

9. binomial: n = 14 and p = .50
   a. from Table A-1, P(x=9) = .122
   b. normal approximation appropriate since
      np = 14(.50) = 7 $\geq$ 5
      n(1-p) = 14(.50) = 7 $\geq$ 5
      μ = np = 14(.50) = 7
      $\sigma = \sqrt{np(1-p)} = \sqrt{14(.50)(.50)} = 1.871$
      P(x=9)
         $= P_c(8.5<x<9.5)$
         $= P(.80<z<1.34)$
         $= P(z<1.34) - P(z<.80)$
         $= .9099 - .7881$
         $= .1218$

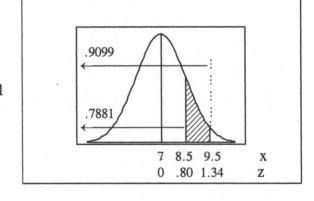

10. binomial: n = 12 and p = .80
    a. from Table A-1, P(x=7) = .053
    b. normal approximation <u>not</u> appropriate since
       n(1-p) = 12(.20) = 2.4 < 5

11. binomial: n = 15 and p = .90
    a. from Table A-1, P(x $\geq$ 14) = P(x=14) + P(x=15)
                                    = .343 + .206
                                    = .549
    b. normal approximation <u>not</u> appropriate since n(1-p) = 15(.10) = 1.5 < 5

12. binomial: n = 13 and p = .40
    a. from Table A-1,
       P(x<3) = P(x=0) + P(x=1) + P(x=2)
              = .001 + .011 + .045
              = .057

b. normal approximation appropriate since
$$np = 13(.40) = 5.2 \geq 5$$
$$n(1-p) = 13(.60) = 7.8 \geq 5$$
$$\mu = np = 13(.40) = 5.2$$
$$\sigma = \sqrt{np(1-p)} = \sqrt{13(.40)(.60)} = 1.766$$
$$P(x < 3)$$
$$= P_c(x < 2.5)$$
$$= P(z < -1.53)$$
$$= .0630$$

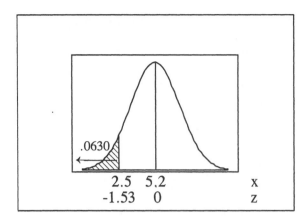

13. let x = the number of girls born
binomial: n = 100 and p = .50
normal approximation appropriate since
$$np = 100(.50) = 50 \geq 5$$
$$n(1-p) = 100(.50) = 50 \geq 5$$
$$\mu = np = 100(.50) = 50$$
$$\sigma = \sqrt{np(1-p)} = \sqrt{100(.50)(.50)} = 5.000$$
$$P(x > 55)$$
$$= P_c(x > 55.5)$$
$$= P(z > 1.10)$$
$$= 1 - P(z < 1.10)$$
$$= 1 - .8643$$
$$= .1357$$

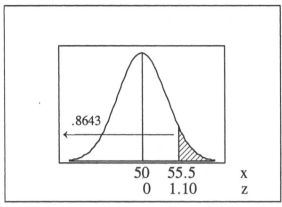

No; since .1357 > .05, it is not unusual to get more than 55 girls in 100 births.

14. let x = the number of girls born
binomial: n = 100 and p = .50
normal approximation appropriate since
$$np = 100(.50) = 50 \geq 5$$
$$n(1-p) = 100(.50) = 50 \geq 5$$
$$\mu = np = 100(.50) = 50$$
$$\sigma = \sqrt{np(1-p)} = \sqrt{100(.50)(.50)} = 5.000$$
$$P(x \geq 65)$$
$$= P_c(x > 64.5)$$
$$= P(z > 2.90)$$
$$= 1 - P(z < 2.90)$$
$$= 1 - .9981$$
$$= .0019$$

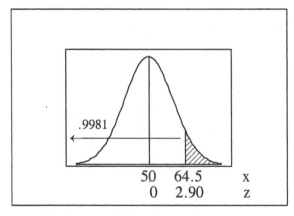

Yes: since .0019 < .05, it is unusual to get at least 65 girls in 100 births.

15. let x = the number of correct responses
binomial: n = 100 and p = .50
normal approximation appropriate since
$$np = 100(.50) = 50 \geq 5$$
$$n(1-p) = 100(.50) = 50 \geq 5$$
$$\mu = np = 100(.50) = 50$$
$$\sigma = \sqrt{np(1-p)} = \sqrt{100(.50)(.50)} = 5.000$$
$$P(x \geq 60)$$
$$= P_c(x > 59.5)$$
$$= P(z > 1.90)$$
$$= 1 - P(z < 1.90)$$
$$= 1 - .9713$$
$$= .0287$$

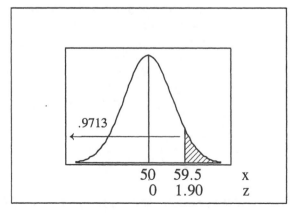

No; the probability of passing by chance is small – since .0287 < .05, it would be unusual.

16. let x = the number of correct responses
binomial: n = 25 and p = .2
normal approximation appropriate since
$\quad$ np = 25(.2) = 5 ≥ 5
$\quad$ n(1-p) = 25(.8) = 20 ≥ 5
μ = np = 25(.2) = 5
σ = $\sqrt{np(1-p)}$ = $\sqrt{25(.2)(.8)}$ = 2.000
P(3 ≤ x ≤ 10)
$\quad$ = P_c(2.5 < x < 10.5)
$\quad$ = P(-1.25 < z < 2.75)
$\quad$ = P(z < 2.75) - P(z < -1.25)
$\quad$ = .9970 - .1056
$\quad$ = .8914

17. let x = the number with yellow pods
binomial: n = 580 and p = .25
normal approximation appropriate since
$\quad$ np = 580(.25) = 145 ≥ 5
$\quad$ n(1-p) = 580(.75) = 435 ≥ 5
μ = np = 580(.25) = 145
σ = $\sqrt{np(1-p)}$ = $\sqrt{580(.25)(.75)}$ = 10.428
P(x ≥ 152)
$\quad$ = P_c(x > 151.5)
$\quad$ = P(z > .62)
$\quad$ = 1 - P(z < .62)
$\quad$ = 1 - .7324
$\quad$ = .2676

No; such as result would not be unusual when the true proportion is 25%.

18. let x = the number experiencing flu symptoms
binomial: n = 863 and p = .019
normal approximation appropriate since
$\quad$ np = 863(.019) = 16.397 ≥ 5
$\quad$ n(1-p) = 863(.981) = 846.603 ≥ 5
μ = np = 863(.019) = 16.397
σ = $\sqrt{np(1-p)}$ = $\sqrt{863(.019)(.981)}$ = 4.011
P(x ≥ 19)
$\quad$ = P_c(x > 18.5)
$\quad$ = P(z > .52)
$\quad$ = 1 - P(z < .52)
$\quad$ = 1 - .6985 = .3015

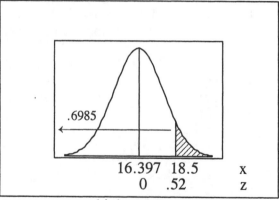

Those taking the drug do not appear to have flu symptoms at a higher than normal rate.

19. let x = the number of color blind men
binomial: n = 600 and p = .09
normal approximation appropriate since
$\quad$ np = 600(.09) = 54 ≥ 5
$\quad$ n(1-p) = 600(.91) = 546 ≥ 5
μ = np = 600(.09) = 54
σ = $\sqrt{np(1-p)}$ = $\sqrt{600(.09)(.91)}$ = 7.010
P(x ≥ 50)
$\quad$ = P_c(x > 49.5)
$\quad$ = P(z > -.64)
$\quad$ = 1 - P(z < -.64)
$\quad$ = 1 - .2611 = .7389

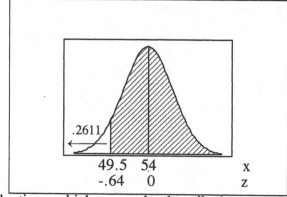

No; they will get the desired number about 3/4 of the time, which cannot be described as "very confident."

20. let x = the number developing cancer
binomial: n = 420,000 and p = .000340
normal approximation appropriate since
$\quad$ np = 420,000(.000340) = 142.8 ≥ 5
$\quad$ n(1-p) = 420,000(.999660) = 419,857.2 ≥ 5
μ = np = 420,000(.000340) = 142.8
$\sigma = \sqrt{np(1-p)} = \sqrt{420,000(.000340)(.999660)}$
$\qquad\qquad = 11.949$
P(x ≤ 135)
$\quad = P_c(x < 135.5)$
$\quad = P(z < -.61)$
$\quad = .2709$

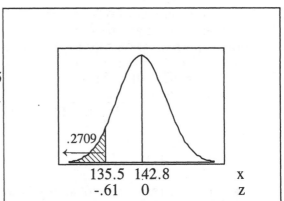

The results suggest that finding "135 or fewer cancer cases" is not an unusual event, and so the cancer rate among cell phone uses appears not to differ significantly from that of the general population.
NOTE: To test the media claim that cell phone usage is associated with a higher rate, one should calculate the probability of finding "135 or more cancer cases."

21. let x = the number of booked arrivals
binomial: n = 400 and p = .85
normal approximation appropriate since
$\quad$ np = 400(.85) = 340 ≥ 5
$\quad$ n(1-p) = 400(.15) = 60 ≥ 5
μ = np = 400(.85) = 340
$\sigma = \sqrt{np(1-p)} = \sqrt{400(.85)(.15)} = 7.141$
P(x > 350)
$\quad = P_c(x > 350.5)$
$\quad = P(z > 1.47)$
$\quad = 1 - P(z < 1.47)$
$\quad = 1 - .9292$
$\quad = .0708$

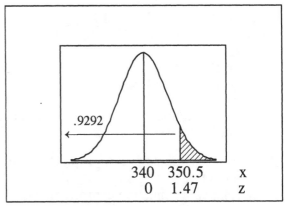

Yes; the airline would probably be willing to allow overbooking to occur 7% of the time (i.e., about 1 in every 14 flights) in order to fly with fewer empty seats.

22. let x = the number that arrive on time
binomial: n = 40 and p = .723
normal approximation appropriate since
$\quad$ np = 40(.723) = 28.92 ≥ 5
$\quad$ n(1-p) = 40(.277) = 11.08 ≥ 5
μ = np = 40(.723) = 28.92
$\sigma = \sqrt{np(1-p)} = \sqrt{40(.723)(.277)} = 2.830$
P(x ≤ 19)
$\quad = P_c(x < 19.5)$
$\quad = P(z < -3.33)$
$\quad = .0004$
Yes; since .0004 < .05, getting 19 or fewer on-time flights would be an unusual event.

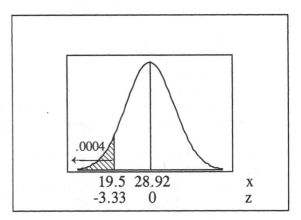

23. let x = the number of women hired
    binomial: n = 62 and p = .50
    normal approximation appropriate since
        np = 62(.50) = 31 ≥ 5
        n(1-p) = 62(.50) = 31 ≥ 5
    μ = np = 62(.50) = 31
    σ = $\sqrt{np(1-p)}$ = $\sqrt{62(.50)(.50)}$ = 3.937
    P(x≤21)
        = P_c(x<21.5)
        = P(z<-2.41)
        = .0080
    Yes; since the resulting probability is so small,
    it does support a charge of such discrimination.

24. let x = the number of blue M&M's
    binomial: n = 100 and p = .10
    normal approximation appropriate since
        np = 100(.10) = 10 ≥ 5
        n(1-p) = 100(.90) = 90 ≥ 5
    μ = np = 100(.10) = 10
    σ = $\sqrt{np(1-p)}$ = $\sqrt{100(.10)(.90)}$ = 3.000
    P(x≤5)
        = P_c(x<5.5)
        = P(z<-1.50)
        = .0668
    No; since .0668 > .05, it is not very unusual
    to get 5 or fewer blue M&M's among 100.

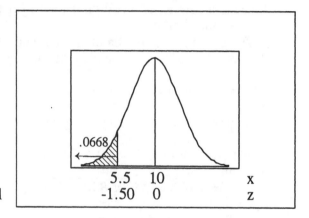

25. let x = the number with group O blood
    binomial: n = 400 and p = .45
    normal approximation appropriate since
        np = 400(.45) = 180 ≥ 5
        n(1-p) = 400(.55) = 220 ≥ 5
    μ = np = 400(.45) = 180
    σ = $\sqrt{np(1-p)}$ = $\sqrt{400(.45)(.55)}$ = 9.950
    P(x≥177)
        = P_c(x>176.5)
        = P(z>-.35)
        = 1 - P(z<-.35)
        = 1 - .3632 = .6368
    Yes; the pool is "likely" to be sufficient, but it
    wouldn't be unusual for it not to be sufficient either.

26. let x = the number of defects found
    binomial: n = 50 and p = .10
    normal approximation appropriate since
        np = 50(.10) = 5 ≥ 5
        n(1-p) = 50(.90) = 45 ≥ 5
    μ = np = 50(.10) = 5
    σ = $\sqrt{np(1-p)}$ = $\sqrt{50(.10)(.90)}$ = 2.12
    P(x≥2)
        = P_c(x>1.5)
        = P(z>-1.65)
        = 1 - P(z<-1.65)
        = 1 - .0495 = .9505
    Yes; it will do so about 95% of the time.

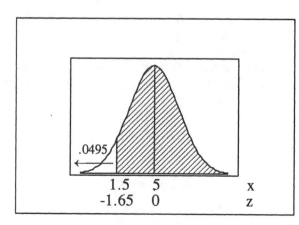

27. let x = the number of accidents in the group
    binomial: n = 500 and p = .34
    normal approximation appropriate since
        np = 500(.34) = 170 ≥ 5
        n(1-p) = 500(.66) = 330 ≥ 5
    μ = np = 500(.34) = 170
    σ = √np(1-p) = √500(.34)(.66) = 10.592
    A 40% accident rate implies
        x = 500(.40) = 200.
    P(x≥200)
        = P_c(x > 199.5)
        = P(z > 2.79)
        = 1 - P(z < 2.79)
        = 1 - .9974
        = .0026

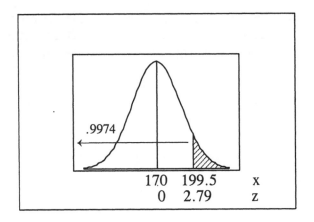

    Yes; either a very unusual sample occurred, or the true NYC rate us higher than 34%.
    NOTE: The number of in the survey that had accidents last year was not given. Any
    198≤x≤202 rounds to 40%. The conclusion will be the same for any value within those
    limits.

28. let x = the number opposed to human cloning
    binomial: n = 1012 and p = .50
    normal approximation appropriate since
        np = 1012(.50) = 506 ≥ 5
        n(1-p) = 1012(.50) = 506 ≥ 5
    μ = np = 1012(.50) = 506
    σ = √np(1-p) = √1012(.50)(.50) = 15.906
    An 89% opposition rate implies
        x = 1012(.89) = 901
    P(x≥901)
        = P_c(x > 900.5)
        = P(z > 24.80)
        = 1 - P(z < 24.80)
        = 1 - .9999
        = .0001

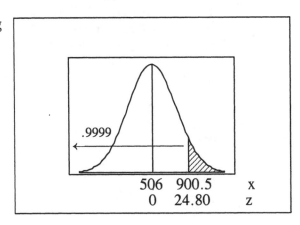

    Yes; this is strong evidence that the majority of the population opposes human cloning.
    NOTE: The number of in the survey that opposed human cloning was not given. Any
    896≤x≤905 rounds to 89%. The conclusion will be the same for any value within those
    limits.

29. let x = the number of times Marc wins $35
    binomial: n = 200 and p = 1/38
    normal approximation appropriate since
        np = 200(1/38) = 5.26 ≥ 5
        n(1-p) = 200(37/38) = 194.76 ≥ 5
    μ = np = 200(1/38) = 5.26
    σ = √np(1-p) = √200(1/38)(37/38) = 2.264
    Marc needs at least 6 $35 wins for a profit.
        P(x≥6)
            = P_c(x > 5.5)
            = P(z > .10)
            = 1 - P(z < .10)
            = 1 - .5398
            = .4602

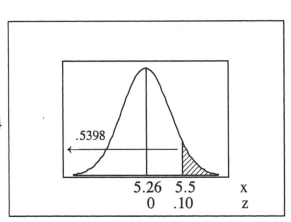

30. This is a two-step problem. Use the normal distribution to find the probability a set lasts more than 10 years, and then use that probability as p in a binomial problem with n=250.

let t = time (in years) of TV life before
   replacement
normal: $\mu = 8.2$ and $\sigma = 1.1$
$P(t > 10.0)$
   $= P(z > 1.64)$
   $= 1 - P(z < 1.64)$
   $= 1 - .9495$
   $= .0505$

let x = the number of TV's with t > 10
binomial: n = 250 and p = .0505
normal approximation appropriate since
   np = 250(.0505) = 12.625 ≥ 5
   n(1-p) = 250(.9495) = 237.375 ≥ 5
$\mu = np = 250(.0505) = 12.625$
$\sigma = \sqrt{np(1-p)} = \sqrt{250(.0505)(.9495)} = 3.462$
$P(x \geq 15)$
   $= P_c(x > 14.5)$
   $= P(z > .54)$
   $= 1 - P(z < .54)$
   $= 1 - .7054$
   $= .2946$

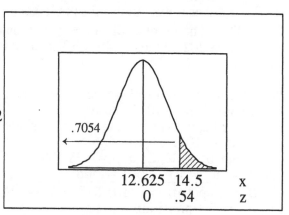

Review Exercises

1. a. normal distribution
   $\mu = 3420$
   $\sigma = 495$
   $P(x < 2200)$
      $= P(z < -2.46)$
      $= .0069 \text{ or } .69\%$

   For 900 births, we expect
      $(.0069)(900) \approx 6$ to be at risk.

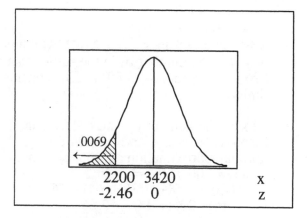

b. For the lowest 2%,
   A=.0200 [.0202] and z =-2.05
   $x = \mu + z\sigma$
   $= 3420 + (-2.05)(495)$
   $= 3420 - 1015$
   $= 2405$

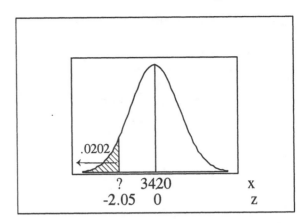

c. normal distribution,
   since the original distribution is so
   $\mu_{\bar{x}} = \mu = 3420$
   $\sigma_{\bar{x}} = \sigma/\sqrt{n} = 495/\sqrt{16} = 123.75$
   $P(\bar{x} > 3700)$
   $= P(z > 2.26)$
   $= 1 - P(z < 2.26)$
   $= 1 - .9881$
   $= .0019$

d. normal distribution,
   since the original distribution is so
   $\mu_{\bar{x}} = \mu = 3420$
   $\sigma_{\bar{x}} = \sigma/\sqrt{n} = 495/\sqrt{49} = 70.714$
   $P(3300 < \bar{x} < 3700)$
   $= P(-1.70 < z < 3.96)$
   $= P(z < 3.96) - P(z < -1.70)$
   $= .9999 - .0446$
   $= .9553$

2. let x = the number of offspring with blue eyes
   binomial: n = 100 and p = .25
   normal approximation appropriate since
   np = 100(.25) = 25 ≥ 5
   n(1-p) = 100(.75) = 75 ≥ 5
   $\mu = np = 100(.25) = 25$
   $\sigma = \sqrt{np(1-p)} = \sqrt{100(.25)(.75)} = 4.330$
   $P(x \le 19)$
   $= P_c(x < 19.5)$
   $= P(z < -1.27)$
   $= .1020$
   No; since .1020 > .05, it is not very unusual
   to get 19 or fewer such offspring among 100.

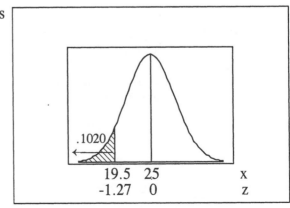

3. a. normal distribution
   $\mu = 69.0$
   $\sigma = 2.8$
   $P(64 < x < 78)$
   $= P(-1.79 < z < 3.21)$
   $= P(z < 3.21) - P(z < -1.79)$
   $= .9993 - .0367$
   $= .9626$

   b. For the shortest 2%,
      $A = .0200$ [.0202] and $z = -2.05$.
   $x = \mu + z\sigma$
      $= 69.0 + (-2.05)(2.8)$
      $= 69.0 - 5.7$
      $= 63.3$
   For the tallest 2%,
      $A = .9800$ [.9798] and $z = 2.05$.
   $x = \mu + z\sigma$
      $= 69.0 + (2.05)(2.8)$
      $= 6.90 + 5.7$
      $= 74.7$
   The new minimum and maximum
   requirements would be 63.3 inches and 74.7 inches respectively.

   c. normal distribution,
      since the original distribution is so
   $\mu_{\bar{x}} = \mu = 69.0$
   $\sigma_{\bar{x}} = \sigma/\sqrt{n} = 2.8/\sqrt{64} = .350$
   $P(\bar{x} > 68.0)$
      $= P(z > -2.86)$
      $= 1 - P(z < -2.86)$
      $= 1 - .0021$
      $= .9979$

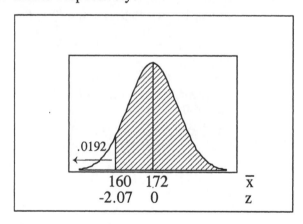

4. Probability corresponds to area. The
   calculations at the right verify that the
   height is 2.5 from 11.8 to 12.2. Since
   there is no probability outside those limits,
   the height outside those limits is 0.

   total area = 1
   (width)(height) = 1
   (12.2 - 11.8)(height) = 1
   .4(height) = 1
   height = 1/.4 = 2.5

a. P(x < 12.0) = (width)(height)
    = (12.0-11.8)(2.5)
    = (.2)(2.5)
    = .50

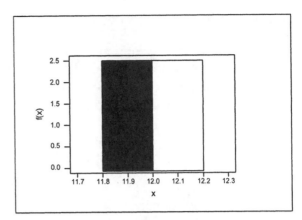

b. P(11.2 < x < 12.7) = P(11.2 < x < 11.8) + P(11.8 < x < 12.2) + P(12.2 < x < 12.7)
    = (width)(height) + (width)(height) + (width)(height)
    = (11.8 - 11.2)(0) + (12.2 - 11.8)(2.5) + (12.7 - 12.2)(0)
    = (.6)(0) + (.4)(2.5) + (.5)(0)
    = 0 + 1 + 0
    = 1, a certainty

c. P(x > 12.2) = (width)(height)
    = (width)·0
    = 0, an impossibility

d. P(11.9 < x < 12.0) = (width)(height)
    = 12.0 - 11.9)(2.5)
    = (.1)(2.5)
    = .25

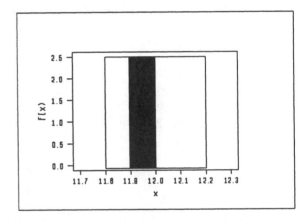

5. a. Since n=100, the Central Limit Theorem guarantees that the sampling distribution of the means of different samples will be normal – regardless of the shape of the original distribution.
   b. $\sigma_{\bar{x}} = \sigma/\sqrt{n} = 512/\sqrt{100} = 51.2$ lb
   c. Let x = the number who voted in the last election.
       binomial: n = 1200 and p = ?
   For each per person define the variable y as follows:
       y = 1 if the person voted
       y = 0 if the person did not vote.
   The sample proportion x/n is really a sample mean, since x/n = Σy/n. Since n=1200, the Central Limit Theorem guarantees that the sampling distribution will be normal – regardless of the shape of the original distribution.

Cumulative Review Exercises

1. The n=8 ordered scores are: 55 59 62 63 66 66 66 67
    summary values: $\Sigma x = 504$, $\Sigma x^2 = 31,876$
    a. $\bar{x} = (\Sigma x)/n = (504)/8 = 63.0$ mm
    b. $\tilde{x} = (63 + 66)/2 = 64.5$ mm
    c. M = 66 mm
    d. $s^2 = [n(\Sigma x^2) - (\Sigma x)^2]/[n(n-1)]$
        $= [8(31,876) - (504)^2]/[8(7)]$
        $= 992/56$
        $= 17.714$
        $s = 4.209$ rounded to 4.2 mm
    e. $z = (x-\bar{x})/s$
        $z_{59} = (59 - 63.0)/4.209 = -.95$
    f. r.f. of scores greater than 59 is 6/8 = .75 = 75%
    g. normal: $\mu = 63.0$ and $\sigma = 4.299$
        $P(x > 59) = P(z > -.95)$
        $= 1 - P(z < .95)$
        $= 1 - .1711$
        $= .8289$ or 82.89%
    h. Ratio, since distances between scores are meaningful and there is a natural zero.
    i. Continuous, since length can be any value on a continuum.

2. a. Let L = a person is left-handed.
        P(L) = .10, for each random selection
        $P(L_1 \text{ and } L_2 \text{ and } L_3) = P(L_1) \cdot P(L_2) \cdot P(L_3) = (.10) \cdot (.10) \cdot (.10) = .001$
    b. Let N = a person is not left-handed
        P(N) = .90, for each random selection
        P(at least one left-hander) = 1 - P(no left-handers)
        $= 1 - P(N_1 \text{ and } N_2 \text{ and } N_3)$
        $= 1 - P(N_1) \cdot P(N_2) \cdot P(N_3)$
        $= 1 - (.90) \cdot (.90) \cdot (.90)$
        $= 1 - .729$
        $= .271$
    c. binomial: n = 3 and p = P(left-hander) = .10
        normal approximation <u>not</u> appropriate since
        np = 3(.10) = 0.3 < 5
    d. binomial: n = 50 and p = .10
        $\mu = np = 50(.10) = 5$
    e. binomial: <u>n = 50 and p = .10</u>
        $\sigma = \sqrt{np(1-p)} = \sqrt{50(.10)(.90)} = 2.121$
    f. An unusual score is one that is more than 2 standard deviations from the mean.
        $z = (x-\mu)/\sigma$
        $z_8 = (8-5)/2.212$
        $= 1.41.$
        Since 8 is 1.41 standard deviations from the mean, it would <u>not</u> be an unusual score.

Chapter 6

Estimates and Sample Sizes

6-2 Estimating a Population Proportion

IMPORTANT NOTE: When calculating confidence intervals using the formula

$$\hat{p} \pm E$$
$$\hat{p} \pm z_{\alpha/2}\sqrt{\hat{p}\hat{q}/n}$$

do not round off in the middle of the problem. This may be accomplished conveniently on most calculators having a memory as follows.

(1) Calculate $\hat{p}$ = x/n and STORE the value
(2) Calculate E as 1 - RECALL = * RECALL = ÷ n = √ * $z_{\alpha/2}$ =
(3) With the value of E showing on the display, the upper confidence limit is calculated by + RECALL.
(4) With the value of the upper confidence limit showing on the display, the lower confidence limit is calculated by - RECALL ± + RECALL

You must become familiar with your own calculator. [Do your homework using the same type of calculator you will be using for the exams.] The above procedure works on most calculators; make certain you understand why it works and verify whether it works on your calculator. If it does not seem to work on your calculator, or if your calculator has more than one memory so that you can STORE both $\hat{p}$ and E at the same time, ask your instructor for assistance.

NOTE: It should be true that $0 \le \hat{p} \le 1$ and that E ≤ .5 [usually, much less than .5]. If such is not the case, an error has been made.

1. For .99 confidence, α = 1-.99 = .01 and $\alpha/2$ = .01/2 = .005.
   For the upper .005, A = .9950 and z = 2.575.
   $z_{\alpha/2}$ = $z_{.005}$ = 2.575

2. For .90 confidence, α = 1-.90 = .10 and $\alpha/2$ = .10/2 = .05.
   For the upper .05, A = .9500 and z = 1.645.
   $z_{\alpha/2}$ = $z_{.05}$ = 1.645

3. For .98 confidence, α = 1-.98 = .02 and $\alpha/2$ = .02/2 = .01.
   For the upper .01, A = .9900 [.9901] and z = 2.33.
   $z_{\alpha/2}$ = $z_{.01}$ = 2.33

4. For .92 confidence, α = 1-.92 = .08 and $\alpha/2$ = .08/2 = .04.
   For the upper .04, A = .9600 [.9599] and z = 1.75.
   $z_{\alpha/2}$ = $z_{.04}$ = 1.75

5. Let L = the lower confidence limit; U = the upper confidence limit.
   $\hat{p}$ = (L + U)/2 = (.220 + .280)/2 = .500/2 = .250
   E = (U - L)/2 = (.280 - .220)/2 = .060/2 = .030
   The interval can be expressed as .250 ± .030.

6. Let L = the lower confidence limit; U = the upper confidence limit.
   $\hat{p}$ = (L + U)/2 = (.456 + .496)/2 = .952/2 = .476
   E = (U - L)/2 = (.496 - .456)/2 = .040/2 = .020
   The interval can be expressed as .476 ± .020.

7. Let L = the lower confidence limit; U = the upper confidence limit.
   $\hat{p}$ = (L + U)/2 = (.604 + .704)/2 = 1.308/2 = .654
   E = (U - L)/2 = (.704 - .604)/2 = .100/2 = .050
   The interval can be expressed as .654 $\pm$ .050.

8. Let L = the lower confidence limit; U = the upper confidence limit.
   L = $\hat{p}$ - E = .742 - .030 = .712
   U = $\hat{p}$ + E = .742 + .030 = .772
   The interval can be expressed as .712 < p < .772.

9. Let L = the lower confidence limit; U = the upper confidence limit.
   $\hat{p}$ = (L + U)/2 = (.444 + .484)/2 = .928/2 = .464
   E = (U - L)/2 = (.484 - .444)/2 = .040/2 = .020

10. Let L = the lower confidence limit; U = the upper confidence limit.
   $\hat{p}$ = (L + U)/2 = (.278 + .338)/2 = .616/2 = .308
   E = (U - L)/2 = (.338 - .278)/2 = .060/2 = .030

11. Let L = the lower confidence limit; U = the upper confidence limit.
   $\hat{p}$ = (L + U)/2 = (.632 + .678)/2 = 1.310/2 = .655
   E = (U - L)/2 = (.678 - .632)/2 = .046/2 = .023

12. Let L = the lower confidence limit; U = the upper confidence limit.
   $\hat{p}$ = (L + U)/2 = (.887 + .927)/2 = 1.814/2 = .907
   E = (U - L)/2 = (.927 - .887)/2 = .040/2 = .020

13. α = .05 and $\hat{p}$ = x/n = 200/800 = .25
   E = $z_{.025}\sqrt{\hat{p}\hat{q}/n}$ = $1.960\sqrt{(.25)(.75)/800}$ = .0300

14. α = .01 and $\hat{p}$ = x/n = 400/1200 = .33
   E = $z_{.005}\sqrt{\hat{p}\hat{q}/n}$ = $2.575\sqrt{(.33)(.67)/1200}$ = .0350

15. α = .01 and $\hat{p}$ = x/n = [450/1000] = .45
   E = $z_{.005}\sqrt{\hat{p}\hat{q}/n}$ = $2.575\sqrt{(.45)(.55)/1000}$ = .0405

16. α = .05 and $\hat{p}$ = x/n = [400/500] = .80
   E = $z_{.025}\sqrt{\hat{p}\hat{q}/n}$ = $1.96\sqrt{(.80)(.20)/500}$ = .0351

17. α = .05 and $\hat{p}$ = x/n = 300/400 = .750
   $\hat{p} \pm z_{.025}\sqrt{\hat{p}\hat{q}/n}$
   $.750 \pm 1.96\sqrt{(.750)(.250)/400}$
   .750 $\pm$ .042
   .708 < p < .792

18. α = .01 and $\hat{p}$ = x/n = 200/1200 = .1667
   $\hat{p} \pm z_{.005}\sqrt{\hat{p}\hat{q}/n}$
   $.1667 \pm 2.575\sqrt{(.1667)(.8333)/1200}$
   .1667 $\pm$ .0277
   .139 < p < .194

19. α = .02 and $\hat{p}$ = x/n = 176/1655 = .1063
   $\hat{p} \pm z_{.01}\sqrt{\hat{p}\hat{q}/n}$
   $.1063 \pm 2.33\sqrt{(.1063)(.8937)/1655}$
   .1063 $\pm$ .0177
   .089 < p < .124

20. $\alpha = .10$ and $\hat{p} = x/n = 1776/2001 = .8876$
$\hat{p} \pm z_{.05}\sqrt{\hat{p}\hat{q}/n}$
$.8876 \pm 1.645\sqrt{(.8876)(.1124)/2001}$
$.8876 \pm .0116$
$.176 < p < .899$

21. $\hat{p}$ unknown, use $\hat{p} = .5$
$n = [(z_{.005})^2\hat{p}\hat{q}]/E^2 = [(2.575)^2(.5)(.5)]/(.060)^2 = 460.46$, rounded up to 461

22. $\hat{p}$ unknown, use $\hat{p} = .5$
$n = [(z_{.025})^2\hat{p}\hat{q}]/E^2 = [(1.96)^2(.5)(.5)]/(.038)^2 = 665.10$, rounded up to 666

23. $\hat{p} = .15$
$n = [(z_{.025})^2\hat{p}\hat{q}]/E^2 = [(1.96)^2(.185)(.815)]/(.05)^2 = 231.69$, rounded up to 232

24. $\hat{p} = .33$
$n = [(z_{.05})^2\hat{p}\hat{q}]/E^2 = [(1.645)^2(.08)(.92)]/(.03)^2 = 221.29$, rounded up to 222

25. a. We are 95% certain that the interval from 4.891% to 5.308% contains the true percentage of 18-20 year old males who drove within the last month while impaired from alcohol.
    b. Yes, since any rate greater than 0% presents a risk to society and is preventable.
    c. The upper confidence interval limit of 5.308% would be a responsible conservative estimate.

26. a. We are 99% certain that the interval from 93.053% to 94.926% contains the true percentage of U.S. households having telephones.
    b. Based on the preceding result, pollsters should not be too concerned about results from surveys conducted by telephone if (1) proper techniques are used and (2) issues that would elicit differing responses from phone and non-phone households are not at stake. Proper techniques involve follow up of non-responses (due to work schedules, etc.), making certain the appropriate person in the household (and not just whoever answers the phone, etc.) is responding, etc. Issues involving agricultural policies, for example, would miss the opinions of the Amish (who are primarily involved in farming and do not have phones for religious reasons). And issues involving welfare policies might under-survey those using such services (since multiple poverty-level families tend to share housing units and have only one phone among them). In general, however, one can probably assume that those households with phones would be the households most likely to buy, use or be familiar with the subject of the survey.

27. NOTE: This problem is limited to whole percent accuracy. Any x value from 293 (293/1025 = .2859) to 302 (302/1025 = .2946) gives a $\hat{p}$ that rounds to the given 29%. Since the exact value of x was not given, three decimal accuracy is not possible.
    a. $\hat{p} = x/n = [297.25/1025] = .29 = 29\%$
    b. $\hat{p} \pm z_{.005}\sqrt{\hat{p}\hat{q}/n}$
       $.29 \pm 2.575\sqrt{(.29)(.71)/1025}$
       $.29 \pm .04$
       $.25 < p < .33$
       $25\% < p < 33\%$
    c. The upper confidence interval limit of 33% would be a responsible estimate for determining the maximum impact.

28. **NOTE:** This problem is limited to whole percent accuracy. Any x value from 317 (317/491 = .6456) to 321 (321/491 = .6538) gives a $\hat{p}$ that rounds to the given 65%. Since the exact value of x was not given, three decimal accuracy is not possible.
    a. $\hat{p} = x/n = [319.15/491] = .65 = 65\%$

   b. $\hat{p} \pm z_{.025}\sqrt{\hat{p}\hat{q}/n}$
     .65 $\pm$ 1.96$\sqrt{(.65)(.35)/491}$
     .65 $\pm$ .04
     .61 < p < .69
     61% < p < 69%
   c. Yes; since the interval in which we have 95% confidence is entirely above 50%.

29. a. α = .05 and $\hat{p}$ = x/n = 152/(152+428) = 152/580 = .262
     $\hat{p} \pm z_{.025}\sqrt{\hat{p}\hat{q}/n}$
     .262 $\pm$ 1.96$\sqrt{(.262)(.738)/580}$
     .262 $\pm$ .036
     .226 < p < .298
     22.6% < p < 29.8%
   b. No; since the confidence interval includes 25%, there is no contradiction.

30. a. α = .01 and $\hat{p}$ = x/n = 701/1002 = .700
     $\hat{p} \pm z_{.005}\sqrt{\hat{p}\hat{q}/n}$
     .700 $\pm$ 2.575$\sqrt{(.700)(.300)/1002}$
     .700 $\pm$ .037
     .662 < p < .737
   b. No; since the confidence interval does not include 61%, the survey results are not consistent with the actual voter turnout.

31. a. α = .01 and $\hat{p}$ = x/n = 7/221 = .032
     NOTE: Since $\hat{p}$ = x/n = 3.2% was given, we may assume x = $\hat{p}\cdot$n = .032·221 = 7. No other integer value x/221 rounds to .032.
     $\hat{p} \pm z_{.005}\sqrt{\hat{p}\hat{q}/n}$
     .032 $\pm$ 2.575$\sqrt{(.032)(.968)/221}$
     .032 $\pm$ .030
     .00134 < p < .0620
     0.134% < p < 6.20%
   b. Since 1.8% is within the interval in part (a), it cannot be ruled out as the correct value for the true proportion of Ziac users that experience dizziness. The test does not provide evidence that Ziac users experience any more dizziness than non-users – i.e., the test does not provide evidence that dizziness is an adverse reaction to Ziac.

32. a. α = .02 and $\hat{p}$ = x/n = 144/785 = .183
     NOTE: Since $\hat{p}$ = x/n = 18.3% was given, we may assume x = $\hat{p}\cdot$n = .183·785 = 144. No other integer value x/785 rounds to .183.
     $\hat{p} \pm z_{.01}\sqrt{\hat{p}\hat{q}/n}$
     .183 $\pm$ 2.33$\sqrt{(.183)(.817)/785}$
     .183 $\pm$ .032
     .151 < p < .216
     15.1% < p < 21.6%
   b. Yes; since 27% is not within the interval in part (a), it is not a reasonable possibility for the true smoking rate of those with four years of college.

33. $\hat{p}$ unknown, use $\hat{p}$ = .50
   n = $[(z_{.005})^2\hat{p}\hat{q}]/E^2$ = $[(2.575)^2(.50)(.50)]/(.02)^2$ = 4144.14, rounded up to 4145

34. a. $\hat{p}$ unknown, use $\hat{p}$ = .5
     n = $[(z_{.005})^2\hat{p}\hat{q}]/E^2$ = $[(2.575)^2(.5)(.5)]/(.025)^2$ = 2652.25, rounded up to 2653
   b. $\hat{p}$ = .15
     n = $[(z_{.005})^2\hat{p}\hat{q}]/E^2$ = $[(2.575)^2(.15)(.85)]/(.025)^2$ = 1352.65, rounded up to 1353

c. In general, results from a self-selected sample are not valid. It is not appropriate to assume that those who choose to respond will be representative of the general population. In this instance it would not be unreasonable to think that right-handed golfers would tend to ignore the survey as unimportant, while left-handed golfers would be more likely to call in to "stand up" for themselves – in which case the results would over-estimate the proportion of golfers that are left-handed.

35. a. $\hat{p} = .86$
$n = [(z_{.03})^2 \hat{p}\hat{q}]/E^2 = [(1.88)^2(.86)(.14)]/(.03)^2 = 472.82$, rounded up to 473
b. $\hat{p}$ unknown, use $\hat{p} = .5$
$n = [(z_{.03})^2 \hat{p}\hat{q}]/E^2 = [(1.88)^2(.5)(.5)]/(.03)^2 = 981.78$, rounded up to 982
c. In general, results from a self-selected sample are not valid. It is not appropriate to assume that those who choose to respond will be representative of the general population.

36. a. $\hat{p} = .07$
$n = [(z_{.025})^2 \hat{p}\hat{q}]/E^2 = [(1.96)^2(.07)(.93)]/(.03)^2 = 277.88$, rounded up to 278
b. $\hat{p}$ unknown, use $\hat{p} = .5$
$n = [(z_{.025})^2 \hat{p}\hat{q}]/E^2 = [(1.96)^2(.5)(.5)]/(.03)^2 = 1067.11$, rounded up to 1068

37. a. $\alpha = .10$ and $\hat{p} = x/n = 7/80 = .0875$
$\hat{p} \pm z_{.01}\sqrt{\hat{p}\hat{q}/n}$
$.0875 \pm 1.645\sqrt{(.0875)(.9125)/80}$
$.0875 \pm .0520$
$.036 < p < .139$
b. $\hat{p} = .0875$
$n = [(z_{.02})^2 \hat{p}\hat{q}]/E^2 = [(2.05)^2(.0875)(.9125)]/(.03)^2 = 372.83$, rounded up to 373
c. Yes; since $0.25\% = .0025$ is not in within the confidence interval in part (a), we may safely conclude that women have a lower rate of red/green color blindness than men do.

38. **NOTE:** This problem is limited to whole percent accuracy. Any x value between 780 ($780/4000 = .1950$) and 820 ($820/4000 = .2050$) gives a $\hat{p}$ that rounds to the given 20%. Since the exact value of x was not given, three decimal accuracy is not possible.
a. $\alpha = .03$ and $\hat{p} = x/n = [800/4000] = .20$
$\hat{p} \pm z_{.015}\sqrt{\hat{p}\hat{q}/n}$
$.20 \pm 2.17\sqrt{(.20)(.80)/4000}$
$.20 \pm .01$
$.19 < p < .21$
b. $\hat{p}$ unknown, use $\hat{p} = .5$
$n = [(z_{.005})^2 \hat{p}\hat{q}]/E^2 = [(2.575)^2(.5)(.5)]/(.005)^2 = 66306.25$, rounded up to 66307
c. Yes; since $11\% = .11$ is not in within the confidence interval in part (a), we may safely conclude that 60 Minutes had a greater share of the audience than the wrestling special did. No; exposing professional wrestling was probably not necessary.
d. In general, results from a self-selected sample are not valid. It is not appropriate to assume that those who choose to respond will be representative of the general population.

39. a. $\alpha = .05$ and $\hat{p} = x/n = 135/420000 = .000321$
$\hat{p} \pm z_{.025}\sqrt{\hat{p}\hat{q}/n}$
$.000321 \pm 1.96\sqrt{(.000321)(.999679)/420000}$
$.000321 \pm .000054$
$.000267 < p < .000376$
$.0267\% < p < .0376\%$
b. No; since the confidence interval includes .0340%, the results are consistent with those for the general population.

40. **NOTE:** This problem is limited to tenth of a percent accuracy. Any x value from 434 (434/8411 = .05160) to 441 (441/8411 = .05243) gives a $\hat{p}$ that rounds to the given 5.2%. Since the exact value of x was not given, four decimal accuracy is not possible.

   a. $\alpha = .05$ and $\hat{p} = x/n = [437.372/8411] = .052$

      $\hat{p} \pm z_{.025}\sqrt{\hat{p}\hat{q}/n}$

      $.052 \pm 1.96\sqrt{(.052)(.948)/8411}$

      $.052 \pm .005$

      $.047 < p < .057$

      $4.7\% < p < 5.7\%$

   b. Yes; since the confidence intervals do not overlap, the death rates appear to differ substantially. The occurrence of an explosion or fire on the ground increases the death rate significantly.

   c. Use 5.7%, the reasonable upper limit for the true percentage of pilot deaths in all crash landings.

41. a. $\alpha = .05$ and $\hat{p} = x/n = 6/123 = .0488$

      $\hat{p} \pm z_{.025}\sqrt{\hat{p}\hat{q}/n}$

      $.0488 \pm 1.96\sqrt{(.0488)(.9512)/123}$

      $.0488 \pm .0381$

      $.0107 < p < .0868$

      $1.07\% < p < 8.68\%$

   b. $\alpha = .05$ and $\hat{p} = x/n = 811/1115 = .727$

      $\hat{p} \pm z_{.025}\sqrt{\hat{p}\hat{q}/n}$

      $.727 \pm 1.96\sqrt{(.727)(.273)/1115}$

      $.727 \pm .026$

      $.701 < p < .753$

      $70.1\% < p < 75.3\%$

   c. Yes; the confidence intervals do not overlap. About 72.7% of the hunters in general wear orange. If wearing orange is unrelated to some other event involving hunters (e.g., eating eggs for breakfast), we expect about 72.7% of the hunters involved in that event to wear orange. If being mistaken for game is unrelated to wearing orange, we expect about 72.7% of those mistaken for game to be wearing orange. Since the proportion of hunters mistaken for game while wearing orange is significantly less, wearing orange appears to lessen the chances of being mistaken for game.

     NOTE: While the true percentage who actually wear orange is likely less than the percentage who say they routinely wear orange [see exercise #30 for a comparable situation], the differences here are too great to be explained away in that manner.

42. **NOTE:** All parts of this problem are limited to whole percent accuracy. For n=651, more than one value for x rounds to the given $\hat{p}$ values of 94% and 75%. Since the exact value of x was not given, three decimal accuracy is not possible.

   a. $\alpha = .10$ and $\hat{p} = x/n = [611.94/651] = .94 = 94\%$

      $\hat{p} \pm z_{.05}\sqrt{\hat{p}\hat{q}/n}$

      $.94 \pm 1.645\sqrt{(.94)(.06)/651}$

      $.94 \pm .02$

      $.92 < p < .96$

      $92\% < p < 96\%$

   b. $\alpha = .10$ and $\hat{p} = x/n = [488.25/651] = .75 = 75\%$

      $\hat{p} \pm z_{.05}\sqrt{\hat{p}\hat{q}/n}$

      $.75 \pm 1.645\sqrt{(.75)(.25)/651}$

      $.75 \pm .03$

      $.72 < p < .78$

      $72\% < p < 78\%$

   c. Yes; since the confidence intervals do not overlap, we may infer that the true percentage is higher for sloppy dressing than for unstylish dressing.

43. $\alpha = .05$ and $\hat{p} = x/n = 21/100 = .210$
$\hat{p} \pm z_{.025}\sqrt{\hat{p}\hat{q}/n}$
$.210 \pm 1.960\sqrt{(.210)(.790)/100}$
$.210 \pm .080$
$.130 < p < .290$
$13.0\% < p < 29.0\%$
Yes; this result is consistent with the 20% rate reported by the candy maker.

44. a. $\alpha = .05$ and $\hat{p} = x/n = 28/50 = .560$
$\hat{p} \pm z_{.025}\sqrt{\hat{p}\hat{q}/n}$
$.560 \pm 1.96\sqrt{(.560)(.440)/50}$
$.560 \pm .138$
$.422 < p < .698$
$42.2\% < p < 69.8\%$
   b. $\alpha = .05$ and $\hat{p} = x/n = 25/50 = .500$
$\hat{p} \pm z_{.025}\sqrt{\hat{p}\hat{q}/n}$
$.500 \pm 1.96\sqrt{(.500)(.500)/50}$
$.500 \pm .139$
$.361 < p < .639$
$36.1\% < p < 63.9\%$
   c. No; since the confidence intervals have considerable overlap, there is no significant difference between the two population percentages. The two percentages could be equal.
   d. The analysis presented in parts (a) and (b) considers only the presence of tobacco or alcohol usage, and ignores the length of the usage. [Even an analysis that considers the length of the usage fails to consider the nature of the usage – i.e., whether the product is presented as a positive or negative factor.]

45. For n=829, any x value from 419 [419/829 = .5054] to 426 [426/829 = .5138] rounds to 51%. The two confidence intervals associated with those extreme possibilities are as follows.
$\alpha = .05$ and $\hat{p} = x/n = 419/829 = .505$
$\hat{p} \pm z_{.025}\sqrt{\hat{p}\hat{q}/n}$
$.505 \pm 1.96\sqrt{(.505)(.495)/829}$
$.505 \pm .034$
$.471 < p < .539$
$\alpha = .05$ and $\hat{p} = x/n = 426/829 = .514$
$\hat{p} \pm z_{.025}\sqrt{\hat{p}\hat{q}/n}$
$.514 \pm 1.96\sqrt{(.514)(.486)/829}$
$.514 \pm .034$
$.480 < p < .548$
While the results do not differ substantially from the $.476 < p < .544$ given in the text using $\hat{p} = .51$, they do illustrate the folly of giving an interval with 3 decimal "accuracy" when the original problem was stated to the nearest percent. In truth, even the second decimal is not certain – as the two intervals above round to $.47 < p < .54$ and $.48 < p < .55$.

46. $\hat{p}$ unknown, use $\hat{p} = .5$
$n = [N\hat{p}\hat{q}(z_{.005})^2]/[\hat{p}\hat{q}(z_{.005})^2 + (N-1)E^2]$
$= [(10000)(.5)(.5)(2.575)^2]/[(.5)(.5)(2.575)^2 + (9999)(.005)^2]$
$= [16576.56]/[1.907631] = 8689.61$, rounded up to 8690

47. $\alpha = .05$ and $\hat{p} = x/n = 630/750 = .840$
$\hat{p} - z_{.05}\sqrt{\hat{p}\hat{q}/n}$
$.840 - 1.645\sqrt{(.840)(.160)/750}$
$.840 - .022$
$.818 < p$
The interval is expressed as $p > .818$. The desired figure is 81.8%

48. $\alpha = .05$ and $\hat{p} = x/n = 3/8 = .375$

$\hat{p} \pm z_{.025}\sqrt{\hat{p}\hat{q}/n}$

$.375 \pm 1.96\sqrt{(.375)(.625)/8}$

$.375 \pm .335$

$.040 < p < .710$

Yes; the results are "reasonably close" – being shifted down 4.5% from the true interval $.085 < p < .755$ – but depending on the context such an error could be serious.

6-3 Estimating a Population Mean: σ Known

1. For .98 confidence, $\alpha = 1-.98 = .02$ and $\alpha/2 = .02/2 = .01$. For the upper .01, $A = .9900$ [.9901] and $z = 2.33$.
   $z_{\alpha/2} = z_{.01} = 2.33$

2. For .95 confidence, $\alpha = 1-.95 = .05$ and $\alpha/2 = .05/2 = .025$. For the upper .025, $A = .9750$ and $z = 1.96$.
   $z_{\alpha/2} = z_{.025} = 1.96$

3. For .96 confidence, $\alpha = 1-.96 = .04$ and $\alpha/2 = .04/2 = .02$. For the upper .02, $A = .9800$ [.9798] and $z = 2.05$.
   $z_{\alpha/2} = z_{.02} = 2.05$

4. For .995 confidence, $\alpha = 1-.995 = .005$ and $\alpha/2 = .005/2 = .0025$. For the upper .0025, $A = .9975$ and $z = 2.81$.
   $z_{\alpha/2} = z_{.0025} = 2.81$

5. Yes, if the sample is a simple random sample.

6. No, because σ is not known.

7. Yes, if the sample is a simple random sample.

8. No, because σ is not known.

NOTE: When the sample mean is given (i.e., not calculated from raw data), the accuracy with which $\bar{x}$ is reported determines the accuracy for the endpoints of the confidence interval.

9. $\alpha = .05$, $\alpha/2 = .025$, $z_{.025} = 1.96$
   a. $E = z_{.025} \cdot \sigma/\sqrt{n}$
      $= 1.96 \cdot (12,345)/\sqrt{100}$
      $= 2419.62$ dollars
   b. $\bar{x} \pm E$
      $95,000 \pm 2,420$
      $92,580 < \mu < 97,420$ (dollars)

10. $\alpha = .01$, $\alpha/2 = .005$, $z_{.005} = 2.575$
    a. $E = z_{.005} \cdot \sigma/\sqrt{n}$
       $= 2.575 \cdot (4.6)/\sqrt{50}$
       $= 1.68$ years
    b. $\bar{x} \pm E$
       80.5 ± 1.7
       $78.8 < \mu < 82.2$ (years)

11. $\alpha = .10$, $\alpha/2 = .05$, $z_{.05} = 1.645$
    a. $E = z_{.05} \cdot \sigma/\sqrt{n}$
       $= 1.645 \cdot (2.50)/\sqrt{25}$
       $= .8225$ seconds
    b. $\bar{x} \pm E$
       $5.24 \pm .82$
       $4.42 < \mu < 6.06$ (seconds)

12. $\alpha = .05$, $\alpha/2 = .025$, $z_{.025} = 1.96$

   a. $E = z_{.025} \cdot \sigma/\sqrt{n}$

       $= 1.96 \cdot (9900)/\sqrt{28}$

       $= 3667.01$ dollars

   b. $\bar{x} \pm E$

       $45,678 \pm 3,667$

       $42,011 < \mu < 49,345$ (dollars)

13. $n = [z_{.025} \cdot \sigma/E]^2 = [1.96 \cdot (500)/125]^2 = 61.47$, rounded up to 62

14. $n = [z_{.005} \cdot \sigma/E]^2 = [2.575 \cdot (15)/3]^2 = 165.77$, rounded up to 166

15. $n = [z_{.05} \cdot \sigma/E]^2 = [1.645 \cdot (48)/5]^2 = 249.38$, rounded up to 250

16. $n = [z_{.03} \cdot \sigma/E]^2 = [1.88 \cdot (9877)/500]^2 = 1379.20$, rounded up to 1380

17. $\bar{x} = 318.1$

18. $262.09 < \mu < 374.11$

19. First find the value of E as follows.

             width $= 2 \cdot E$

   $374.11 - 262.09 = 2 \cdot E$

        $112.02 = 2 \cdot E$

         $56.01 = E$

   Then use $\bar{x}$ and E to give the interval as: 318.1 ± 56.01

20. We have 95% confidence that the interval from 262.09 to 374.11 contains μ, the true value of the population mean.

21. $\bar{x} \pm z_{.025} \cdot \sigma/\sqrt{n}$

   $30.4 \pm 1.96 \cdot (1.7)/\sqrt{61}$

   30.4 ± 0.4

   $30.0 < \mu < 30.8$

   It is unrealistic to know the value of σ.

22. $\bar{x} \pm z_{.005} \cdot \sigma/\sqrt{n}$

   $182.9 \pm 2.575 \cdot (121.8)/\sqrt{54}$

   182.9 ± 42.7

   $140.2 < \mu < 225.6$

   It is unrealistic to know the value of σ.

23. $\bar{x} \pm z_{.05} \cdot \sigma/\sqrt{n}$

   $172.5 \pm 1.645 \cdot (119.5)/\sqrt{40}$

   172.5 ± 31.1

   $141.4 < \mu < 203.6$

   It is unrealistic to know the value of σ.

24. $\bar{x} \pm z_{.005} \cdot \sigma/\sqrt{n}$

   $40.6 \pm 2.575 \cdot (1.6)/\sqrt{100}$

   40.6 ± 0.4

   $40.2 < \mu < 41.0$

   It is unrealistic to know the value of σ.

25. $n = [z_{.025} \cdot \sigma/E]^2 = [1.96 \cdot (15)/2]^2 = 216.09$, rounded up to 217

26. $n = [z_{.005} \cdot \sigma/E]^2 = [2.575 \cdot (.068)/.025]^2 = 49.06$, rounded up to 50

27. $n = [z_{.025} \cdot \sigma/E]^2 = [1.96 \cdot (6250)/500]^2 = 600.25$, rounded up to 601

28. $n = [z_{.02} \cdot \sigma/E]^2 = [2.05 \cdot (112.2)/15]^2 = 235.13$, rounded up to 236

29. Using the range rule of thumb, $\sigma \approx$ (range)/4 $= (70,000-12,000)/4 = 58,000/4 = 14,500$.

    $n = [z_{.025} \cdot \sigma/E]^2 = [1.96 \cdot (14,500)/100]^2 = 80,769.64$, rounded up to 80,770

   No, this sample size is not practical. Of the three terms in the formula for n, $z_{\alpha/2}$ and E are set by the expectations of the researcher while σ is determined by the variable under consideration and not under control of the researcher. Either lower the level confidence (which will make $z_{\alpha/2}$ less than 1.96, thus decreasing n) or increase the margin of error (which will make E larger than 100, thus decreasing n).

30. Answers will vary, but a reasonable estimate for the minimum and maximum ages of college textbooks in use might be 0 years and 10 years respectively.
Using the range rule of thumb, $\sigma \approx$ (range)$/4 = (10-0)/4 = 10/4 = 2.5$.
$n = [z_{.05} \cdot \sigma/E]^2 = [1.645 \cdot (2.5)/.25]^2 = 270.60$, rounded up to 271

31. The minimum and maximum values in the data set are 56 and 96 respectively.
Using the range rule of thumb, $\sigma \approx$ (range)$/4 = (96-56)/4 = 40/4 = 10$ and
$n = [z_{.025} \cdot \sigma/E]^2 = [1.96 \cdot (10)/2]^2 = 96.04$, rounded up to 97.
Using the sample standard deviation for the male pulse values [11.297] to estimate σ,
$n = [z_{.025} \cdot \sigma/E]^2 = [1.96 \cdot (11.297)/2]^2 = 122.56$, rounded up to 123.
The two values are relatively close. Since s (which considers all the data) is a better estimator for σ than R/4 (which is based entirely on the extreme values), the sample size of 123 should be preferred.

32. The minimum and maximum values in the data set are 41 and 102 respectively.
Using the range rule of thumb, $\sigma \approx$ (range)$/4 = (102-41)/4 = 61/4 = 15.25$ and
$n = [z_{.025} \cdot \sigma/E]^2 = [1.96 \cdot (15.25)/3]^2 = 99.26$, rounded up to 100.
Using the sample standard deviation of the female diastolic values [11.626] to estimate σ,
$n = [z_{.025} \cdot \sigma/E]^2 = [1.96 \cdot (11.626)/3]^2 = 57.69$, rounded up to 58.
The two values seem significantly different. Since s (which considers all the data) is a better estimator for σ than R/4 (which is based entirely on the extreme values), the sample size of 58 should be preferred.

33. $\bar{x} \pm [z_{.025} \cdot \sigma/\sqrt{n}] \cdot \sqrt{(N-n)/(N-1)}$
$110 \pm [1.96 \cdot (15)/\sqrt{35}] \cdot \sqrt{(250-35)/(250-1)}$
$110 \pm [4.9695] \cdot [.9292]$
110 ± 4.617
$105 < \mu < 115$

34. From exercise #25, $\alpha = .05$ and $E = 2$ and $\sigma = 15$. Use $N = 200$ to find n as follows.
$n = N\sigma^2(z_{.025})^2/[(N-1)E^2 + \sigma^2(z_{.025})^2]$
$= 200 \cdot (15)^2(1.96)^2/[(200-1)(2)^2 + (15)^2(1.96)^2]$
$= 172872/[1660.36] = 104.12$, rounded up to 105

6-4 Estimating a Population Mean: σ Not Known

IMPORTANT NOTE: This manual uses the following conventions.
(1) The designation "df" stands for "degrees of freedom."
(2) Since the t value depends on both the degrees of freedom and the probability lying beyond it, double subscripts are used to identify points on t distributions. The t distribution with 15 degrees of freedom and .025 beyond it, for example, is designated $t_{15,.025} = 2.132$.
(3) Always use the closest entry in Table A-3. When the desired df is exactly halfway between the two nearest tabled values, be conservative and choose the one with the lower df.
(4) As the degrees of freedom increase, the t distribution approaches the standard normal distribution – and the "large" row of the t table actually gives z values. Consequently, the z scores for certain "popular" α and $\alpha/2$ values may be found by reading Table A-3 "frontwards" instead of reading Table A-2 "backwards." This is not only easier but also more accurate, since Table A-3 includes one more decimal place. Note, for example, that $t_{large,.05} = 1.645 = z_{.05}$ (as found from the z table) and $t_{large,.01} = 2.326 = z_{.01}$ (more accurate than the 2.33 as found from the z table). The manual uses this technique from this point on. [That $t_{large,.005} = 2.576 \neq 2.575 = z_{.005}$ is discrepancy caused by using different mathematical approximation techniques to construct the tables, and not a true difference. The manual will continue to use $z_{.005} = 2.575$.]

1. σ unknown and population approximately normal:
   If the sample is a simple random sample, use t.
   n = 5; df = 4
   α = .05; α/2 = .025
   $t_{4,.025}$ = 2.776

2. σ unknown and population approximately normal:
   If the sample is a simple random sample, use t.
   n = 10; df = 9
   α = .05; α/2 = .025
   $t_{9,.025}$ = 2.262

3. σ known and the population is not approximately normal
   Since n < 30, neither the z distribution nor the t distribution applies.

4. σ known and n > 30:
   If the sample is a simple random sample, use z.
   α = .01; α/2 = .005
   $z_{.005}$ = 2.575

5. σ unknown and population approximately normal:
   If the sample is a simple random sample, use t.
   n = 92; df = 91 [90]
   α = .10; α/2 = .05
   $t_{91,.05}$ = 1.662

6. σ known and the population is not approximately normal:
   Since n < 30, neither the z distribution nor the t distribution applies.

7. σ known and population approximately normal:
   If the sample is a simple random sample, use z.
   α = .02; α/2 = .01
   $z_{.01}$ = 2.236

8. σ unknown and population approximately normal:
   If the sample is a simple random sample, use t.
   n = 37; df = 36
   α = .02; α/2 = .01
   $t_{36,.01}$ = 2.434

9. α = .05, α/2 = .025; n = 15, df = 14
   a. E = $t_{14,.025} \cdot s/\sqrt{n}$
      = 2.145·(108)/$\sqrt{15}$
      = 59.8

   b. $\bar{x} \pm E$
      496 ± 60
      436 < μ < 556

10. α = .01, α/2 = .005; n = 32, df = 31
    a. E = $t_{31,.005} \cdot s/\sqrt{n}$
       = 2.744·(.70)/$\sqrt{32}$
       = .3396 (inches)

    b. $\bar{x} \pm E$
       14.50 ± .34
       14.16 < μ < 14.84 (inches)

11. 112.84 < μ < 121.56
    We are 95% confident that the interval from 112.84 to 121.56 contains μ, the true value of the population mean.

12. 77.297 < μ < 80.453
    We are 99% confident that the interval from 77.297 to 80.453 contains μ, the true value of the population mean.

13. σ unknown and distribution approximately normal, use t
$\bar{x} \pm t_{11,.025} \cdot s/\sqrt{n}$
$26,227 \pm 2.201 \cdot (15,873)/\sqrt{12}$
$26,227 \pm 10,085$
$16,142 < \mu < 36,312$ (dollars)
We are 95% certain that the interval from $16,142 to $36,312 contains the true mean repair cost for repairing Dodge Vipers under the specified conditions.

14. a. σ unknown and distribution approximately normal, use t
$\bar{x} \pm t_{19,.005} \cdot s/\sqrt{n}$
$9004 \pm 2.861 \cdot (5629)/\sqrt{20}$
9004 ± 3601
$5,403 < \mu < 12,605$ (dollars)
 b. The upper confidence limit of $12,605 would be a reasonable high-end estimate for the long-run average hospital costs of such accident victims.

15. a. σ unknown and n > 30, use t
$\bar{x} \pm t_{30,.005} \cdot s/\sqrt{n}$
$-.419 \pm 2.750 \cdot (3.704)/\sqrt{31}$
$-.419 \pm 1.829$
$-2.248 < \mu < 1.410$ (°F)
 b. Yes, the confidence interval includes 0. No; since the confidence interval includes 0, the true difference could be 0 – i.e., there is not evidence to conclude the three-day forecasts are too high or too low.

16. a. σ unknown and distribution approximately normal, use t
$\bar{x} \pm t_{19,.005} \cdot s/\sqrt{n}$
$4.4 \pm 2.861 \cdot (4.2)/\sqrt{20}$
4.4 ± 2.7
$1.7 < \mu < 7.1$ (inches)
 b. No, the confidence interval does not include 0. Yes; since the confidence interval lies entirely above 0, it supports the claim that women tend to marry men who are taller than themselves.
 NOTE: In truth, the above interval in part (a) and conclusion in part (b) is not necessarily valid for all women who marry – but only for the population of women from which the sample was taken (viz., women who had children and were presumably within some age range determined by the details of the survey).

17. preliminary values: $n = 7$, $\Sigma x = .85$, $\Sigma x^2 = .1123$
$\bar{x} = (\Sigma x)/n = (.85)/7 = .121$
$s^2 = [n(\Sigma x^2) - (\Sigma x)^2]/[n(n-1)] = [7(.1123) - (.85)^2]/[7(6)] = .00151$
$s = .039$

σ unknown (and assuming the distribution is approximately normal), use t
$\bar{x} \pm t_{6,.01} \cdot s/\sqrt{n}$
$.121 \pm 3.143 \cdot (.039)/\sqrt{7}$
$.121 \pm .046$
$.075 < \mu < .168$ (grams/mile)
No; since the confidence interval includes values greater than .165, there is a reasonable possibility that the requirement is not being met.

18. preliminary values: $n = 6$, $\Sigma x = 9.23$, $\Sigma x^2 = 32.5197$
$\bar{x} = (\Sigma x)/n = (0.23)/6 = 1.538$
$s^2 = [n(\Sigma x^2) - (\Sigma x)^2]/[n(n-1)] = [6(32.5197) - (9.23)^2]/[6(5)] = 3.664$
$s = 1.914$

σ unknown (and assuming the distribution is approximately normal), use t

$\bar{x} \pm t_{5,.025}/\sqrt{n}$
$1.538 \pm 2.571\cdot(1.914)/\sqrt{6}$
1.538 ± 2.009
$-.471 < \mu < 3.547$ (micrograms/cubic meter)
Yes; the fact that 4 of the 5 sample values are below $\bar{x}$ raises a question about whether the data meets the requirement that the underlying population distribution is normal.

19. a. σ unknown (and assuming the distribution is approximately normal), use t
$\bar{x} \pm t_{9,.025}\cdot s/\sqrt{n}$
$175 \pm 2.262\cdot(15)/\sqrt{10}$
175 ± 11
$164 < \mu < 186$ (beats per minute)
   b. σ unknown (and assuming the distribution is approximately normal), use t
$\bar{x} \pm t_{9,.025}\cdot s/\sqrt{n}$
$124 \pm 2.262\cdot(18)/\sqrt{10}$
124 ± 13
$111 < \mu < 137$ (beats per minute)
   c. The maximum likely value for the true mean heart rate for hand-shovelers, 186.
   d. Since the two confidence intervals do not overlap, there is evidence that hand-shovelers experience significantly higher heart rates than those using electric snow blowers.

20. a. σ unknown and n > 30, use t
$\bar{x} \pm t_{39,.025}\cdot s/\sqrt{n}$
$69.4 \pm 2.024\cdot(11.3)/\sqrt{40}$
69.4 ± 3.6
$65.8 < \mu < 73.0$ (beats per minute)
   b. σ unknown and n > 30, use t
$\bar{x} \pm t_{39,.025}\cdot s/\sqrt{n}$
$76.3 \pm 2.024\cdot(12.5)/\sqrt{40}$
76.3 ± 4.0
$72.3 < \mu < 80.3$ (beats per minute)
   c. No; since the two confidence intervals overlap, we cannot conclude that the population means for males and females are difference – both populations could have the same mean, some value in the region of the overlap.

21. <u>4000 BC</u>   <u>150 AD</u>
n = 12   n = 12
$\Sigma x = 1544$ $\Sigma x = 1600$
$\Sigma x^2 = 198898$ $\Sigma x^2 = 213610$
$\bar{x} = (\Sigma x)/n = (1544)/12 = 128.67$ $\bar{x} = (\Sigma x)/n = (1600)/12 = 133.33$
$s^2 = [n(\Sigma x^2) - (\Sigma x)^2]/[n(n-1)]$ $s^2 = [n(\Sigma x^2) - (\Sigma x)^2]/[n(n-1)]$
$\quad = [12(198898) - (1544)^2]/[12(11)]$ $\quad = [12(213610) - (1600)^2]/[12(11)]$
$\quad = 21.515$ $\quad = 25.152$
s = 4.638   s = 5.015

σ unknown (and assuming normality), use t σ unknown (and assuming normality), use t
$\bar{x} \pm t_{11,.025}\cdot s/\sqrt{n}$ $\bar{x} \pm t_{11,.025}\cdot s/\sqrt{n}$
$128.67 \pm 2.201\cdot(4.638)/\sqrt{12}$ $133.33 \pm 2.201\cdot(5.015)/\sqrt{12}$
128.67 ± 2.95 133.33 ± 3.19
$125.7 < \mu < 131.6$ $130.1 < \mu < 136.5$

Since the two 95% confidence intervals overlap, the two samples could from populations with the same mean. This is not evidence to conclude that the head sizes have changed. NOTE: The level of confidence was not specified. While 95% is the standard level of confidence when no specific value is given, it is possible that using less than 95% confidence would shorten the intervals to the point where there is no overlap.

22. <u>males</u>

$n = 50$

$\Sigma x = 2054.9$

$\Sigma x^2 = 84562.23$

$\bar{x} = (\Sigma x)/n = (2054.9)/50 = 41.098$

$s^2 = [n(\Sigma x^2) - (\Sigma x)^2]/[n(n-1)]$
$= [50(84562.23) - (2054.9)^2]/[50(49)]$
$= 2.244$

$s = 1.498$

σ unknown and $n > 30$, use t

$\bar{x} \pm t_{49,.025} \cdot s/\sqrt{n}$

$41.098 \pm 2.009 \cdot (1.498)/\sqrt{50}$

$41.098 \pm .426$

$40.67 < \mu < 41.52$ (cm)

<u>females</u>

$n = 50$

$\Sigma x = 2002.4$

$\Sigma x^2 = 80323.82$

$\bar{x} = (\Sigma x)/n = (2002.4)/50 = 40.048$

$s^2 = [n(\Sigma x^2) - (\Sigma x)^2]/[n(n-1)]$
$= [50(80323.82) - (2002.4)^2]/[50(49)]$
$= 2.688$

$s = 1.639$

σ unknown and $n > 30$, use t

$\bar{x} \pm t_{49,.025} \cdot s/\sqrt{n}$

$40.048 \pm 2.009 \cdot (1.639)/\sqrt{50}$

$40.048 \pm .466$

$39.58 < \mu < 40.51$ (cm)

Since the two 95% confidence intervals do not overlap, the two samples appear to have come from populations with different means. This is evidence to conclude that the males have larger head circumferences.

NOTE: The level of confidence was not specified. While 95% is the standard level of confidence when no specific value is given, it is possible that using more than 95% confidence would lengthen the intervals to the point where they overlap.

23. a. preliminary values: $n = 36$, $\Sigma x = 29.6677$, $\Sigma x^2 = 24.45037155$

$\bar{x} = (\Sigma x)/n = (29.6677)/36 = .82410$

$s^2 = [n(\Sigma x^2) - (\Sigma x)^2]/[n(n-1)] = [36(24.45037155) - (29.6677)^2]/[36(35)] = .00003249$

$s = .005700$

σ unknown and $n > 30$, use t

$\bar{x} \pm t_{35,.025} \cdot s/\sqrt{n}$

$.82410 \pm 2.032 \cdot (.005700)/\sqrt{36}$

$.82410 \pm .00193$

$.82217 < \mu < .82603$ (lbs)

b. preliminary values: $n = 36$, $\Sigma x = 28.2189$, $\Sigma x^2 = 22.12028574$

$\bar{x} = (\Sigma x)/n = (28.2189)/36 = .78386$

$s^2 = [n(\Sigma x^2) - (\Sigma x)^2]/[n(n-1)] = [36(22.12028574) - (28.2189)^2]/[36(35)] = .00001900$

$s = .004359$

σ unknown and $n > 30$, use t

$\bar{x} \pm t_{35,.025} \cdot s/\sqrt{n}$

$.78386 \pm 2.032 \cdot (.004359)/\sqrt{36}$

$.78386 \pm .00148$

$.78238 < \mu < .78533$ (lbs)

c. The confidence intervals do not overlap. Cans of diet Pepsi weigh significantly less than cans of regular Pepsi.

24. a. preliminary values: $n = 40$, $\Sigma x = 1039.9$, $\Sigma x^2 = 27493.83$

$\bar{x} = (\Sigma x)/n = (1039.9)/40 = 25.9975$

$s^2 = [n(\Sigma x^2) - (\Sigma x)^2]/[n(n-1)] = [40(27493.83) - (1039.9)^2]/[40(39)] = 11.7700$

$s = 3.431$

σ unknown and $n > 30$, use t

$\bar{x} \pm t_{39,.005} \cdot s/\sqrt{n}$

$25.9975 \pm 2.712 \cdot (3.431)/\sqrt{40}$

25.9975 ± 1.4711

$24.53 < \mu < 27.47$

b. preliminary values: $n = 40$, $\Sigma x = 1029.6$, $\Sigma x^2 = 27984.46$

$\bar{x} = (\Sigma x)/n = (1029.6)/40 = 25.7400$

$s^2 = [n(\Sigma x^2) - (\Sigma x)^2]/[n(n-1)] = [40(27984.46) - (1029.6)^2]/[40(39)] = 38.0143$

s = 6.166
σ unknown and n > 30, use t
$\bar{x} \pm t_{39,.005} \cdot s/\sqrt{n}$
25.7400 ± 2.712·(6.166)/$\sqrt{40}$
25.7400 ± 2.6438
23.10 < μ < 28.38

c. The confidence intervals overlap – in fact, the interval for the males is completely contained within the interval for the females. No, men do not appear to have a mean body mass index that is greater than the mean body mass index of women. If there are any body mass index differences, it may be that the female values are more variable.

25. preliminary values: n = 7, Σx = 60.79, Σx² = 3600.1087
$\bar{x} = (\Sigma x)/n = (60.79)/7 = 8.684$
$s^2 = [n(\Sigma x^2) - (\Sigma x)^2]/[n(n-1)] = [7(3600.1087) - (60.79)^2]/[7(6)] = 512.0318$
s = 22.628

σ unknown (and assuming the distribution is approximately normal), use t
$\bar{x} \pm t_{6,.025} \cdot s/\sqrt{n}$
8.684 ± 2.447·(22.628)/$\sqrt{7}$
8.684 ± 20.928
-12.244 < μ < 29.613 (grams/mile)
This is considerably different from the .075 < μ < .168 interval of exercise #17. Confidence intervals appear to be very sensitive to outliers. Outliers found in sample data should be examined for two reasons: (1) to determine whether they are errors, (2) to determine whether their presence in small samples indicates that the data fail to meet the normal distribution requirement.

26. For any α, the z value is smaller than the corresponding t value (although the difference decreases as n increases). This creates a smaller E and a narrower confidence interval than one is entitled to – i.e., it does not take into consideration the extra uncertainty created by using the sample s instead of the true population σ.

6-5 Estimating a Population Variance

1. $\chi_L^2 = \chi_{15,.975}^2 = 6.262$; $\chi_R^2 = \chi_{15,.025}^2 = 27.488$

2. $\chi_L^2 = \chi_{50,.975}^2 = 32.357$; $\chi_R^2 = \chi_{50,.025}^2 = 71.420$

3. $\chi_L^2 = \chi_{79,.995}^2 = 51.172$; $\chi_R^2 = \chi_{79,.005}^2 = 116.321$
NOTE: Use df = 80, the closest entry.

4. $\chi_L^2 = \chi_{39,.95}^2 = 26.509$; $\chi_R^2 = \chi_{39,.05}^2 = 55.758$

5.　　$(n-1)s^2/\chi_{19,.025}^2 < \sigma^2 < (n-1)s^2/\chi_{19,.975}^2$
$(19)(12345)^2/32.852 < \sigma^2 < (19)(12345)^2/8.907$
88,140,188 < σ² < 325,090,544
9,388 < σ < 18,030 (dollars)

6.　　$(n-1)s^2/\chi_{26,.005}^2 < \sigma^2 < (n-1)s^2/\chi_{26,.995}^2$
$(26)(4.6)^2/48.920 < \sigma^2 < (26)(4.6)^2/11.160$
12.246 < σ² < 49.297
3.4 < σ < 7.0 (years)

7. $(n-1)s^2/\chi^2_{29,.05} < \sigma^2 < (n-1)s^2/\chi^2_{29,.95}$
$(29)(2.50^2/42.557 < \sigma^2 < (29)(2.50^2/17.708$
$4.2590 < \sigma^2 < 10.2355$
$2.06 < \sigma < 3.20$ (seconds)

8. $(n-1)s^2/\chi^2_{50,.025} < \sigma^2 < (n-1)s^2/\chi^2_{50,.975}$
$(50)(9900)^2/71.420 < \sigma^2 < (50)(9900)^2/32.357$
$68,615,234 < \sigma^2 < 151,451,000$
$8,283 < \sigma < 12,307$ (dollars)

9. From the upper right section of Table 6-2, n = 191.

10. From the upper right section of Table 6-2, n = 20.

11. From the lower left section of Table 6-2, n = 133,448.
No, for most applications this is not a practical sample size.

12. From the upper left section of Table 6-2, n = 210.

NOTE: When raw scores are available, $\overline{x}$ and s should be calculated as the primary descriptive statistics -- but use the unrounded value of s^2 in the confidence interval formula. In addition, always make certain that the confidence interval for σ includes the calculated value of s.

13. $(n-1)s^2/\chi^2_{11,.025} < \sigma^2 < (n-1)s^2/\chi^2_{11,.975}$
$(11)(15873)^2/21.920 < \sigma^2 < (11)(15873)^2/3.816$
$126,435,831 < \sigma^2 < 726,277,101$
$11,244 < \sigma < 26,950$ (dollars)
We are 95% confident that the interval from \$11,244 to \$26,950 contains σ, the true standard deviation for the repair amounts of all such cars.

14. summary information
n = 18 $\overline{x}$ = 3787.0
Σx = 68,166 s^2 = 3066.82
Σx^2 = 258,196,778   s = 55.4
       $(n-1)s^2/\chi^2_{17,.005} < \sigma^2 < (n-1)s^2/\chi^2_{17,.995}$
$(17)(3066.82)/35.718 < \sigma^2 < (17)(3066.82)/5.697$
$1459.65 < \sigma^2 < 9151.47$
$38.2 < \sigma < 95.7$ (mL)
No; the interval indicates 99% confidence that $\sigma > 30$.

15. summary information
n = 6 $\overline{x}$ = 1.538
Σx = 9.23 s^2 = 3.664
Σx^2 = 32.5197   s = 1.914
     $(n-1)s^2/\chi^2_{5,.025} < \sigma^2 < (n-1)s^2/\chi^2_{5,.975}$
$(5)(3.664)/12.833 < \sigma^2 < (5)(3.664)/.831$
$1.4276 < \sigma^2 < 22.0468$
$1.195 < \sigma < 4.695$ (micrograms/cubic meter)
Yes; the fact that 4 of the 5 sample values are below $\overline{x}$ raises a question about whether the data meets the requirement that the underlying population distribution is normal.

16. summary information

n = 12 $\overline{x}$ = 3.504
Σx = 42.05 s^2 = .011899
Σx^2 = 147.4811   s = .109

$$(n-1)s^2/\chi^2_{11,.025} < \sigma^2 < (n-1)s^2/\chi^2_{11,.975}$$
$$(11)(.011899)/21.920 < \sigma^2 < (11)(.011899)/3.816$$
$$.006 < \sigma^2 < .034$$
$$.077 < \sigma < .185 \ (oz)$$

Yes; he is in trouble. Since .06 is below the above confidence interval, we can be 95% confident that the population standard deviation is greater than .06.

17. a. $(n-1)s^2/\chi^2_{9,.025} < \sigma^2 < (n-1)s^2/\chi^2_{9,.975}$
$$(9)(15)^2/19.023 < \sigma^2 < (9)(15)^2/2.700$$
$$106.5 < \sigma^2 < 750.0$$
$$10 < \sigma < 27 \ (beats \ per \ minute)$$
b. $(n-1)s^2/\chi^2_{9,.025} < \sigma^2 < (n-1)s^2/\chi^2_{9,.975}$
$$(9)(18)^2/19.023 < \sigma^2 < (9)(18)^2/2.700$$
$$153.3 < \sigma^2 < 1080.0$$
$$12 < \sigma < 33 \ (beats \ per \ minute)$$
c. No; the two groups do not appear to differ much in variation.

18. a. $(n-1)s^2/\chi^2_{39,.025} < \sigma^2 < (n-1)s^2/\chi^2_{9,.975}$
$$(39)(11.3)^2/59.342 < \sigma^2 < (39)(11.3)^2/24.433$$
$$83.919 < \sigma^2 < 203.819$$
$$9.2 < \sigma < 14.3 \ (beats \ per \ minute)$$
b. $(n-1)s^2/\chi^2_{39,.025} < \sigma^2 < (n-1)s^2/\chi^2_{39,.975}$
$$(39)(12.5)^2/59.342 < \sigma^2 < (39)(12.5)^2/24.433$$
$$102.689 < \sigma^2 < 249.407$$
$$10.1 < \sigma < 15.8 \ (beats \ per \ minute)$$
c. No; the two groups do not appear to differ much in variation.

19. a. summary information

n = 10 $\overline{x}$ = 7.15
Σx = 71.5 s^2 = .2272
Σx^2 = 513.27   s = .48

$$(n-1)s^2/\chi^2_{9,.025} < \sigma^2 < (n-1)s^2/\chi^2_{9,.975}$$
$$(9)(.2272)/19.023 < \sigma^2 < (9)(.2272)/2.700$$
$$.1075 < \sigma^2 < .7573$$
$$.33 < \sigma < .87 \ (minutes)$$

b. summary information

n = 10 $\overline{x}$ = 7.15
Σx = 71.5 s^2 = 3.3183
Σx^2 = 541.09   s = 1.82

$$(n-1)s^2/\chi^2_{9,.025} < \sigma^2 < (n-1)s^2/\chi^2_{9,.975}$$
$$(9)(3.3183)/19.023 < \sigma^2 < (9)(3.3183)/2.700$$
$$1.5699 < \sigma^2 < 11.0610$$
$$1.25 < \sigma < 3.33 \ (minutes)$$

c. Yes, there is a difference. The multiple line system exhibits more variability among the waiting times. The greater consistency among the single line waiting times seems fairer to the customers and more professional.

20. a. summary information

$n = 40$ $\bar{x} = 26.00$
$\Sigma x = 1039.9$ $s^2 = 11.7700$
$\Sigma x^2 = 27493.83$ $s = 3.431$

$(n-1)s^2/\chi^2_{39,.005} < \sigma^2 < (n-1)s^2/\chi^2_{39,.995}$
$(39)(11.7700)/66.766 < \sigma^2 < (39)(11.7700)/20.707$
$6.8752 < \sigma^2 < 22.1679$
$2.62 < \sigma < 4.71$ (minutes)

b. summary information

$n = 40$ $\bar{x} = 25.74$
$\Sigma x = 1029.6$ $s^2 = 38.0143$
$\Sigma x^2 = 27984.46$ $s = 6.166$

$(n-1)s^2/\chi^2_{39,.005} < \sigma^2 < (n-1)s^2/\chi^2_{39,.995}$
$(39)(38.0143)/66.766 < \sigma^2 < (39)(38.0143)/20.707$

$22.2053 < \sigma^2 < 71.5969$
$4.71 < \sigma < 8.46$ (minutes)

c. Yes; since the confidence intervals do not overlap, there is a difference – just barely at the 99% confidence level, but more obviously for lower confidence levels. This is evidence that there is more variation in body mass index among females than among males.

21. a. The given interval $2.8 < \sigma < 6.0$
$$7.84 < \sigma^2 < 36.00$$
and the usual calculations $(n-1)s^2/\chi^2_{19,\alpha/2} < \sigma^2 < (n-1)s^2/\chi^2_{19,1-\alpha/2}$
$$(19)(3.8)^2/\chi^2_{19,\alpha/2} < \sigma^2 < (19)(3.8)^2/\chi^2_{19,1-\alpha/2}$$
$$274.36/\chi^2_{19,\alpha/2} < \sigma^2 < 274.36/\chi^2_{19,1-\alpha/2}$$

imply that $7.84 = 274.37/\chi^2_{19,\alpha/2}$ and $36.00 = 274.36/\chi^2_{19,1-\alpha/2}$

$\quad\quad \chi^2_{19,\alpha/2} = 274.36/7.84$ $\quad\quad\quad\quad \chi^2_{19,1-\alpha/2} = 274.36/36.00$
$\quad\quad\quad\quad = 34.99$ $\quad\quad\quad\quad\quad\quad\quad\quad = 7.62$

The closest entries in Table A-4 are $\chi^2_{19,\alpha/2} = 34.805$ and $\chi^2_{19,1-\alpha/2} = 7.633$
which imply $\quad\quad\quad\quad\quad\quad\quad\quad \alpha/2 = .01$ $\quad\quad 1 - \alpha/2 = .99$
$\quad\quad\quad\quad\quad\quad\quad\quad\quad\quad\quad\quad \alpha = .02$ $\quad\quad\quad\quad \alpha/2 = .01$
$\quad\quad\quad\quad\quad\quad\quad\quad\quad\quad\quad\quad\quad\quad\quad\quad\quad\quad\quad\quad \alpha = .02$

The level of confidence is therefore is $1-\alpha = 98\%$.

b. $(n-1)s^2/\chi^2_{11,.025} < \sigma^2 < (n-1)s^2/\chi^2_{11,.975}$

using the lower endpoint $\quad\quad$ OR $\quad\quad$ using the upper endpoint
$(11)s^2/21.920 = (19.1)^2$ $\quad\quad\quad\quad\quad$ $(11)s^2/3.816 = (45.8)^2$
$\quad\quad s^2 = 726.97$ $\quad\quad\quad\quad\quad\quad\quad\quad s^2 = 727.69$
$\quad\quad s = 27.0$ $\quad\quad\quad\quad\quad\quad\quad\quad\quad s = 27.0$

22. $\chi^2 = \frac{1}{2}[\pm z_{.025} + \sqrt{2 \cdot df - 1}\,]^2$
$\quad\quad = \frac{1}{2}[\pm 1.960 + \sqrt{2 \cdot (771) - 1}\,]^2$
$\quad\quad = \frac{1}{2}[\pm 1.960 + 39.256]^2$
$\quad\quad = \frac{1}{2}[37.296]^2 \quad\quad$ or $\quad\quad \frac{1}{2}[41.216]^2$
$\quad\quad = 695.48 \quad\quad\quad\quad$ or $\quad\quad 849.36$

$\quad (n-1)s^2/\chi^2_{771,.025} < \sigma^2 < (n-1)s^2/\chi^2_{771,.975}$
$(771)(2.8)^2/849.36 < \sigma^2 < (771)(2.8)^2/695.48$
$\quad\quad\quad 7.117 < \sigma^2 < 8.691$
$\quad\quad\quad\quad 2.7 < \sigma < 2.9$ (inches)

Review Exercises

1. a. $\hat{p} = x/n = 111/1233 = .0900 = 9.00\%$
   b. $\hat{p} \pm z_{.05}\sqrt{\hat{p}\hat{q}/n}$
      $.0900 \pm 1.96\sqrt{(.0900)(.9100)/1233}$
      $.0900 \pm .0160$
      $.0740 < p < .1060$
      $7.40\% < p < 10.60\%$
   c. $\hat{p}$ unknown, use $\hat{p} = .5$
      $n = [(z_{.005})^2\hat{p}\hat{q}]/E^2 = [(2.575)^2(.5)(.5)]/(.025)^2 = 2652.25$, rounded up to 2653

2. a. σ unknown and population normal, use t
      $\bar{x} \pm t_{24,.025} \cdot s/\sqrt{n}$
      $7.01 \pm 2.064 \cdot 3.741/\sqrt{25}$
      7.01 ± 1.54
      $5.47 < \mu < 8.55$ (years)
   b. $(n-1)s^2/\chi^2_{24,.025} < \sigma^2 < (n-1)s^2/\chi^2_{24,.975}$
      $(24)(3.74)^2/39.364 < \sigma^2 < (24)(3.74)^2/12.401$
            $8.528 < \sigma^2 < 27.071$
             $2.92 < \sigma < 5.20$ (years)
   c. $n = [z_{.005} \cdot \sigma/E]^2 = [2.575 \cdot (3.74)/.25]^2 = 1483.94$, rounded up to 1484
   d. No; those who purchased a General Motors car are not necessarily representative of all car owners.

3. a. $\hat{p} = x/n = 308/611 = .504 = 50.4\%$
   b. $\hat{p} \pm z_{.01}\sqrt{\hat{p}\hat{q}/n}$
      $.5041 \pm 2.326\sqrt{(.5041)(.4959)/611}$
      $.5041 \pm .0470$
      $.4570 < p < .5511$
      $45.7\% < p < 55.1\%$
   c. No; since 43% is not within the confidence interval, the survey results are not consistent with the facts. People might not want to admit they voted for a losing candidate, especially if the winner is turning out to be a good president. [If the winner is turning out to be a bad president, the percentage in the survey who said they voted for the winner might actually be lower than the true value.]

4. a. summary information
      $n = 12$ $\bar{x} = 6.500$
      $\Sigma x = 78.0$ $s^2 = 5.9945$
      $\Sigma x^2 = 572.94$ $s = 2.448$
      σ unknown (and assuming normality), use t
      $\bar{x} \pm t_{11,.025} \cdot s/\sqrt{n}$
      $6.500 \pm 2.201 \cdot (2.448)/\sqrt{12}$
      6.500 ± 1.556
      $4.94 < \mu < 8.06$
   b. summary information
      $n = 12$ $\bar{x} = 5.075$
      $\Sigma x = 60.9$ $s^2 = 1.3639$
      $\Sigma x^2 = 324.07$ $s = 1.168$
      σ unknown (and assuming normality), use t
      $\bar{x} \pm t_{11,.025} \cdot s/\sqrt{n}$
      $5.075 \pm 2.201 \cdot (1.168)/\sqrt{12}$
      5.075 ± 0.742
      $4.33 < \mu < 5.82$

c. summary information

$n = 12$	$\bar{x} = 8.433$
$\Sigma x = 101.2$	$s^2 = 4.0333$
$\Sigma x^2 = 897.82$	$s = 2.008$

σ unknown (and assuming normality), use t

$\bar{x} \pm t_{11,.025} \cdot s/\sqrt{n}$

$8.433 \pm 2.201 \cdot (2.008)/\sqrt{12}$

8.433 ± 1.276

$7.16 < \mu < 8.71$

d. The mean grade-level rating appears to be significantly higher for Tolstoy than for Clancy or Rowling.

5. $n = [z_{.05} \cdot \sigma/E]^2 = [1.645 \cdot (2.45)/.5]^2 = 64.97$, rounded up to 65

6. $(n-1)s^2/\chi^2_{11,.025} < \sigma^2 < (n-1)s^2/\chi^2_{11,.975}$

$\qquad (11)(1.17)^2/21.920 < \sigma^2 < (11)(1.17)^2/3.816$

$\qquad\qquad\qquad .687 < \sigma^2 < 3.946$

$\qquad\qquad\qquad\quad .83 < \sigma < 1.99$

7. $\hat{p}$ unknown, use $\hat{p} = .5$

$n = [(z_{.015})^2 \hat{p}\hat{q}]/E^2 = [(2.17)^2(.5)(.5)]/(.02)^2 = 2943.06$, rounded up to 2944

8. $\hat{p} = .93$

$n = [(z_{.01})^2 \hat{p}\hat{q}]/E^2 = [(2.326)^2(.93)(.07)]/(.04)^2 = 220.32$, rounded up to 221

Cumulative Review Exercises

1. Begin by making a stem-and-leaf plot and calculating summary statistics.

10 | 5	
11 |	$n = 9$
11 | 599	$\Sigma x = 1089$
12 | 3	$\Sigma x^2 = 132223$
12 | 5788	

a. $\bar{x} = (\Sigma x)/n = (1089)/9 = 121.0$ lbs

b. $\tilde{x} = 123.0$ lbs

c. $M = 119, 128$ (bi-modal)

d. m.r. $= (105 + 128)/2 = 116.5$ lbs

e. $R = 128 - 105 = 23$ lbs

f. $s^2 = [n(\Sigma x^2) - (\Sigma x)^2]/[n(n-1)]$

$\qquad = [9(132223) - (1089)^2]/[9(8)]$

$\qquad = 56.75$ lbs^2

g. $s = 7.5$ lbs

h. for $Q_1 = P_{25}$, $L = (25/100)(9) = 2.25$, round up to 3

$\qquad Q_1 = x_3 = 119$ lbs

i. for $Q_2 = P_{50}$, $L = (50/100)(9) = 4.50$, round up to 5

$\qquad Q_2 = x_5 = 123$ lbs

j. for $Q_3 = P_{75}$, $L = (75/100)(9) = 6.75$, round up to 7

$\qquad Q_3 = x_7 = 127$ lbs

k. ratio, since differences are consistent and there is a meaningful zero

l. The boxplot is at the right.

m. σ unknown (and assuming normality), use t
$\bar{x} \pm t_{8,.005} \cdot s/\sqrt{n}$
$121.0 \pm 3.355 \cdot 7.5/\sqrt{9}$
121.0 ± 8.4
$112.6 < \mu < 129.4$ (lbs)

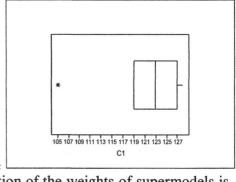

NOTE: Since both the stem-and-leaf plot and the boxplot indicate that the weights do not appear to come from a normal population, the methods of the chapter are not appropriate. It appears the distribution of the weights of supermodels is truncated at some upper limit and skewed to the left. Even though the confidence intervals for μ and σ should not be constructed, the intervals in part (m) above and part (n) below are given as a review of the techniques.

n. $(n-1)s^2/\chi^2_{8,.005} < \sigma^2 < (n-1)s^2/\chi^2_{8,.995}$
    $(8)(56.75)/21.955 < \sigma^2 < (8)(56.75)/1.344$
        $20.68 < \sigma^2 < 337.80$
        $4.5 < \sigma < 18.4$ (lbs)

o. E = 2 and α = .01
$n = [z_{.005} \cdot \sigma/E]^2$
$= [2.575 \cdot 7.5/2]^2 = 94.07$, rounded up to 95

p. For the general female population, an unusually low weight would be one below 85 lbs (i.e., more than 2σ below μ). Individually, none of the supermodels has an unusually low weight. As a group, however, they are each well below the general population mean weight and appear to weigh substantially less than the general population – as evidenced by their mean weight as given by the point estimate in part (a) and the interval estimate in part (m).

2. a. binomial: n = 200 and p = .25
    a normal approximation is appropriate since
        $np = 200(.25) = 50 \geq 5$
        $n(1-p) = 200(.75) = 150 \geq 5$
    use $\mu = np = 200(.25) = 50$
        $\sigma = \sqrt{n(p)(1-p)} = \sqrt{200(.25)(.75)}$
        $= 6.214$
    $P(x \geq 65)$
        $= P_c(x > 64.5)$
        $= P(z > 2.37)$
        $= 1 - P(z < 2.37)$
        $= 1 - .9911$
        $= .0089$

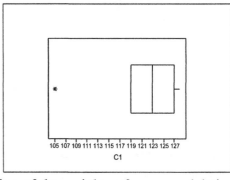

b. $\hat{p} = 65/200 = .325$
    $\alpha = .05$
    $\hat{p} \pm z_{.025}\sqrt{\hat{p}\hat{q}/n}$
    $.325 \pm 1.960\sqrt{(.325)(.675)/200}$
    $.325 \pm .065$
    $.260 < p < .390$

c. No; the expert's value of .25 does not seem correct for two reasons.
    From part (a): if the expert is correct, then the probability of getting the sample obtained is very small – less than 1%.
    From part (b): according to the sample obtained, there is 95% confidence that the interval from .26 to .39 includes the true value – that is, there is 95% confidence that the value is not .25.

Chapter 7

Hypothesis Testing

7-2 Basics of Hypothesis testing

1. There is not sufficient evidence to support the claim. Under the assumption that the claim is not true, having 26 girls among 50 babies is the type of result you expect to occur.

2. There is sufficient evidence to support the claim. Under the assumption that the claim is not true, having 49 girls among 50 babies would be a very rare event. Therefore the assumption that the claim is not true is probably not correct.

3. There is sufficient evidence to support the claim. Under the assumption that the claim is not true, having 475 of 500 persons like pizza would be a rare event. Therefore the assumption that the claim is not true is probably not correct.

4. There is not sufficient evidence to support the claim. Under the assumption that the claim is not true, having $s = 14.99$ is the type of result you would expect to occur.

5. original statement: $\mu > 50,000$ (does not contain the equality; must be H_1)
    competing idea: $\mu \leq 50,000$
    H_o: $\mu = 50,000$
    H_1: $\mu > 50,000$

6. original statement: $\mu \geq 110$
    competing idea: $\mu < 100$ (does not contain the equality; must be H_1)
    H_o: $\mu = 110$
    H_1: $\mu < 110$

7. original statement: $p > .5$ (does not contain the equality; must be H_1)
    competing idea: $p \leq .5$
    H_o: $p = .5$
    H_1: $p > .5$

8. original statement: $p \neq .70$ (does not contain the equality; must be H_1)
    competing idea: $p = .70$
    H_o: $p = .70$
    H_1: $p \neq .70$

9. original statement: $\sigma < 2.8$ (does not contain the equality; must be H_1)
    competing idea: $\sigma \geq 2.8$
    H_o: $\sigma = 2.8$
    H_1: $\sigma < 2.8$

10. original statement: $p = .24$
    competing idea: $p \neq .24$ (does not contain the equality; must be H_1)
    H_o: $p = .24$
    H_1: $p \neq .24$

11. original statement: $\mu \geq 12$
   competing idea: $\mu < 12$ (does not contain the equality; must be H_1)
    H_o: $\mu = 12$
    H_1: $\mu < 12$

12. original statement: $\sigma > 3000$ (does not contain the equality; must be H_1)
   competing idea: $\sigma \leq 3000$
    H_o: $\sigma = 3000$
    H_1: $\sigma > 3000$

NOTE: Recall that z_α is the z with α <u>above</u> it. By the symmetry of the normal distribution, the z with α <u>below</u> it is $z_{1-\alpha} = -z_\alpha$.

13. Two-tailed test; place $\alpha/2$ in each tail.
   Use $A = 1-\alpha/2 = 1-.0250 = .9750$ and $z = 1.96$.
   critical values are $\pm z_{\alpha/2} = \pm z_{.025} = \pm 1.96$

14. Two-tailed test; place $\alpha/2$ in each tail.
   Use $A = 1-\alpha/2 = 1-.0050 = .9950$ and $z = 2.575$.
   critical values are $\pm z_{\alpha/2} = \pm z_{.005} = \pm 2.575$

15. Right-tailed test; place α in the upper tail.
   Use $A = 1-\alpha = 1-.0100 = .9900$ [closest entry $= .9901$] and $z = 2.33$.
   critical value is $+z_\alpha = +z_{.01} = +2.33$ [or 2.326 from the "large" row of the t table]

16. Left-tailed test; place α in the lower tail.
   Use $A = \alpha = .0500$ and $z = -1.645$.
   critical value is $z_{1-\alpha} = -z_\alpha = -z_{.05} = -1.645$

17. Two-tailed test; place $\alpha/2$ in each tail.
   Use $A = 1-\alpha/2 = 1-.0500 = .9500$ and $z = 1.645$.
   critical values are $\pm z_{\alpha/2} = \pm z_{.05} = \pm 1.645$

18. Right-tailed test; place α in the upper tail.
   Use $A = 1-\alpha = 1-.1000 = .9000$ [closest entry $= .8997$] and $z = 1.28$.
   critical value is $z_\alpha = z_{.10} = 1.28$ [or 1.282 from the "large" row of the t table]

19. Left-tailed test; place α in the lower tail.
   Use $A = \alpha = .0200$ [closest entry $= .0202$] and $z = -2.05$.
   critical value is $-z_\alpha = -z_{.02} = -2.05$

20. Two-tailed test; place $\alpha/2$ in each tail.
   Use $A = 1-\alpha/2 = 1-.0025 = .9975$ and $z = 2.81$.
   critical value is $\pm z_\alpha = \pm z_{.0025} = \pm 2.81$

21. $\hat{p} = x/n = x/1025 = .29$
   $z_{\hat{p}} = (\hat{p} - p)/\sqrt{pq/n} = (.29-.50)/\sqrt{(.50)(.50)/1025} = -.21/.0156 = -13.45$

22. $\hat{p} = x/n = x/580 = .262$
   $z_{\hat{p}} = (\hat{p} - p)/\sqrt{pq/n} = (.262-.25)/\sqrt{(.25)(.75)/580} = .012/.0180 = .67$

23. $\hat{p} = x/n = x/400 = .290$
   $z_{\hat{p}} = (\hat{p} - p)/\sqrt{pq/n} = (.290-.25)/\sqrt{(.25)(.75)/400} = .04/.0217 = 1.85$

24. $\hat{p} = x/n = x/800 = .12$
   $z_{\hat{p}} = (\hat{p} - p)/\sqrt{pq/n} = (.12-.103)/\sqrt{(.103)(.897)/800} = .017/.0107 = 1.58$

25.　P-value $= P(z > .55)$
　　　　　　　$= 1 - P(z < .55)$
　　　　　　　$= 1 - .7088$
　　　　　　　$= .2912$

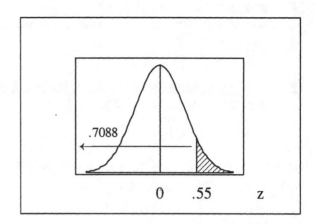

26.　P-value $= P(z < -1.72)$
　　　　　　　$= .0427$

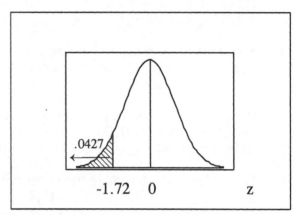

27.　P-value $= 2 \cdot P(z > 1.95)$
　　　　　　　$= 2 \cdot [1 - P(z < 1.95)]$
　　　　　　　$= 2 \cdot [1 - .9744]$
　　　　　　　$= 2 \cdot [.0256]$
　　　　　　　$= .0512$

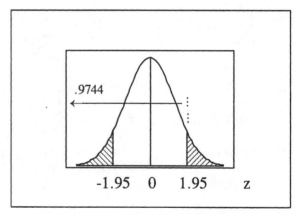

28.　P-value $= 2 \cdot P(z < -1.63)$
　　　　　　　$= 2 \cdot (.0516)$
　　　　　　　$= .1032$

29.　P-value = P(z > 1.97)
　　　　　　 = 1 - P(z < 1.97)
　　　　　　 = 1 - .9756
　　　　　　 = .0244

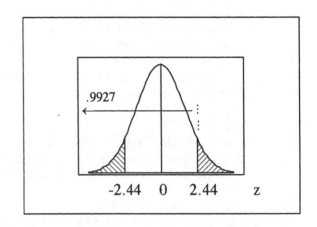

30.　P-value = 2 ·P(z > 2.44)
　　　　　　 = 2 ·[1 - P(z < 2.44)]
　　　　　　 = 2 ·[1 - .9927]
　　　　　　 = 2 ·[.0073]
　　　　　　 = .0146

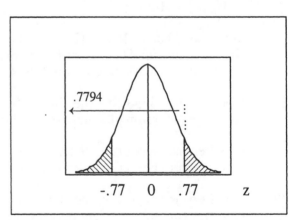

31.　P-value = 2 ·P(z > .77)
　　　　　　 = 2 ·[1 - P(z < .77)]
　　　　　　 = 2 ·[1 - .7794]
　　　　　　 = 2 ·[.2206]
　　　　　　 = .4412

32.　P-value = P(z < -1.90)
　　　　　　 = .0287

33.   original claim: $p > .5$ (does not contain the equality; must be H_1)
       competing idea: $p \leq .5$
           H_o: $p = .5$
           H_1: $p > .5$
       initial conclusion: Reject H_o.
       final conclusion: There is sufficient evidence to support the claim that the proportion of
           married women is greater than .5.

34.   original claim: $p < .27$ (does not contain the equality; must be H_1)
       competing idea: $p \geq .27$
           H_o: $p = .27$
           H_1: $p < .27$
       initial conclusion: Reject H_o.
       final conclusion: There is sufficient evidence to support the claim that the proportion of
           college graduates that smoke is less than .27.

35.   original claim: $p \neq .038$ (does not contain the equality; must be H_1)
       competing idea: $p = .038$
           H_o: $p = .038$
           H_1: $p \neq .038$
       initial conclusion: Fail to reject H_o.
       final conclusion: There is not sufficient evidence to support the claim that the proportion of
           commercial aviation crashes that are fatal is different from .038.

36.   original claim: $p = .10$
       competing idea: $p \neq .10$ (does not contain the equality; must be H_1)
           H_o: $p = .10$
           H_1: $p \neq .10$
       initial conclusion: Reject H_o.
       final conclusion: There is sufficient evidence to reject the claim that the proportion of
           M&M's that are blue is equal to .10.

37.   type I error: supporting the claim $p > .5$ when $p = .5$ is true
       type II error: failing to support the claim $p > .5$ when $p > .5$ is true

38.   type I error: supporting the claim $p < .27$ when $p = .27$ is true
       type II error: failing to support the claim $p < .27$ when $p < .27$ is true

39.   type I error: supporting the claim $p \neq .038$ when $p = .038$ is true
       type II error: failing to support the claim $p \neq ,038$ when $p \neq .038$ is true

40.   type I error: rejecting the claim $p = .10$ when $p = .10$ is true
       type II error: failing to reject the claim $p = .10$ when $p \neq .10$ is true

41. $\hat{p} = x/n = x/491 = .27$
       $z_{\hat{p}} = (\hat{p} - p)/\sqrt{pq/n} = (.27-.50)/\sqrt{(.50)(.50)/491} = -.23/.0226 = -10.19$
       P-value $= P(z > -10.19) = 1 - (z < -10.19) = 1 - .0001 = .9999$
       The claim is that $p > .5$. Only $\hat{p}$ values so much larger than .5 that they are unlikely to
       occur by chance if $p = .5$ is true give statistical support to the claim. A $\hat{p}$ smaller than .5
       does not give any support to the claim.

42.   Not necessarily. Rejection at the .05 level of significance means the result was among the
       most extreme 5% of the possible results, but not necessarily among the most extreme 1%
       of the possible results as required for rejection at the .01 level of significance.

43.   Prefer .01, the lowest of the given values. The P-value is the probability of getting by
      chance alone less than or equal to the number of defects observed if the old rate is still in
      effect. The lower the P-value, the less likely your results could have occurred by chance
      alone – and the more likely your new process truly reduces the rate of defects.

44.   No, since the claim that $p = .10$ must be the null hypothesis. The two possible conclusions
      in a statistical hypothesis test are "reject the null hypothesis" or "fail to reject the null
      hypothesis" – but failing to reject to reject a claim merely means there was not enough
      evidence to discredit it, not necessarily that the data supported it.
      NOTE: In general, a statistical hypothesis test never <u>proves</u> anything – it merely provides
      a conclusion with a certain level of confidence attached. So long as the entire population
      is not examined, there will always be a certain probability of making an error because an
      unusual sample occurs.

45.   Mathematically, in order for α to equal 0 the magnitude of the critical value would have to
      be infinite. Practically, the only way never to make a type I error is to always fail to reject
      H_o. From either perspective, the only way to achieve $\alpha = 0$ is to never reject H_o no
      matter how extreme the sample data might be.

46.   The basic test of hypothesis is given below
      and illustrated by the figure at the right.
      H_o: $p = .5$
      H_1: $p < .5$
      $\alpha = .05$
      C.R. $z < -z_{.05} = -1.645$

      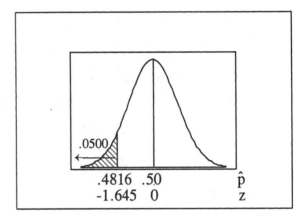

      The $\hat{p}$ corresponding to $z = -1.645$ is found
      by solving $z_{\hat{p}} = (\hat{p} - p)/\sqrt{pq/n}$ for $\hat{p}$ as
      follows.
      $\hat{p} = p + z_{\hat{p}} \cdot \sqrt{pq/n}$
      $= .5 + (-1.645) \cdot \sqrt{(.5)(.5)/1998}$
      $= .5 + (-1.645) \cdot (.0112)$
      $= .5 - .0184$
      $= .4816$

   a. $\beta = $ P(not rejecting $H_o | H_o$ is false)
      $= $ P($\hat{p} > .4816 | p = .45$)
      $= $ P($z > 2.84$)
      $= 1 - $ P($z < 2.84$)
      $= 1 - .9977$
      $= .0023$

      The z corresponding to $\hat{p} = .4816$ is
      found as follows.
      $z_{\hat{p}} = (\hat{p} - p)/\sqrt{pq/n}$
      $= (.4816 - .45)/\sqrt{(.45)(.55)/1998}$
      $= (.0316)/(.0111)$
      $= 2.84$

   b. In this particular scenario,
      the power is given by $1 - \beta = 1 - .0023 = .9977$.
      In general,
      $\beta = $ P(failing to reject $H_o | H_o$ is false)
      $1 - \beta = $ P(rejecting $H_o | H_o$ is false)

7-3 Testing a Claim about a Proportion

NOTE: To reinforce the concept that all z scores are standardized rescalings obtained by subtracting the mean and dividing by the standard deviation, the manual uses the "usual" z formula written to apply to $\hat{p}$'s
$$z_{\hat{p}} = (\hat{p} - \mu_{\hat{p}})/\sigma_{\hat{p}}.$$
When the normal approximation to the binomial applies, the $\hat{p}$'s are normally distributed
with $\mu_{\hat{p}} = p$ and $\sigma_{\hat{p}} = \sqrt{pq/n}$.
And so the formula for the z statistic may also be written as
$$z_{\hat{p}} = (\hat{p} - p)/\sqrt{pq/n} .$$

1. a. $z_{\hat{p}} = (\hat{p} - \mu_{\hat{p}})/\sigma_{\hat{p}} = (\hat{p} - p)/\sqrt{pq/n} = (.2494 - .25)/\sqrt{(.25)(.75)/8023} = -.0006/.0048$
   b. $z = \pm 1.96$ $= -.12$
   c. P-value $= 2 \cdot P(z < -.12) = 2 \cdot (.4522) = .9044$
   d. Do not reject H_o; there is not sufficient evidence to conclude $p \neq .25$.
   e. No, the hypothesis test will either "reject" or "fail to reject" the claim that a population parameter is equal to a specified value.

2. a. $z_{\hat{p}} = (\hat{p} - \mu_{\hat{p}})/\sigma_{\hat{p}} = (\hat{p} - p)/\sqrt{pq/n} = (.62 - .50)/\sqrt{(.50)(.50)/1087} = .12/.0152 = 7.91$
   b. $z = 1.645$
   c. P-value $= P(z > 7.91) = 1 - P(z < 7.91) = 1 - .9999 = .0001$
   d. Reject H_o; there is sufficient evidence to conclude $p > .50$.
   e. No, the value of the test statistic is influenced by the sample size. While the difference between 62% and 50% is highly significant for this relatively large sample of size n=1087, that difference may not be significant for smaller samples – i.e., for smaller samples, that difference might reasonably occur by chance even when p=50% is true.

3. original claim: $p < .62$
   $\hat{p} = x/n = x/2500 = .60$
   H_o: $p = .62$
   H_1: $p < .62$
   $\alpha = .01$
   C.R. $z < -z_{.01} = -2.326$
   calculations:
   $z_{\hat{p}} = (\hat{p} - \mu_{\hat{p}})/\sigma_{\hat{p}}$
   $= (.60 - .62)/\sqrt{(.62)(.38)/2500}$
   $= -.02/.00971$
   $= -2.06$

   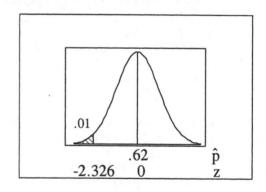

   P-value $= P(z < -2.06) = .0197$
   conclusion:
   Do not reject H_o; there is not sufficient evidence to conclude that $p < .62$.
   If the data came from self-selected voluntary respondents, the test is not valid.

4. original claim: $p = .30$
   $\hat{p} = x/n = x/109,857 = .291$
   H_o: $p = .30$
   H_1: $p \neq .30$
   $\alpha = .01$
   C.R. $z < -z_{.005} = -2.575$
   $z > z_{.005} = 2.575$
   calculations:
   $z_{\hat{p}} = (\hat{p} - \mu_{\hat{p}})/\sigma_{\hat{p}}$
   $= (.291 - .30)/\sqrt{(.30)(.70)/109,857}$
   $= -.009/.00138$
   $= -6.51$

P-value $= 2 \cdot P(z < -6.51) = 2 \cdot (.0001) = .0002$
conclusion:
    Reject H_o; there is sufficient evidence reject the claim that $p = .30$ and to conclude that $p \neq .30$ (in fact, that $p < .30$).
Even though 29.1% is so close to 30%, the sample size was so large that it was able to distinguish between those values. In general, a very large sample allows one to make precise conclusions.

5. original claim: $p > .15$
    $\hat{p} = x/n = 149/880 = .169$
    H_o: $p = .15$
    H_1: $p > .15$
    $\alpha = .05$
    C.R. $z > z_{.05} = 1.645$
    calculations:
        $z_{\hat{p}} = (\hat{p} - \mu_{\hat{p}})/\sigma_{\hat{p}}$
        $= (.169 - .15)/\sqrt{(.15)(.85)/880}$
        $= .019/.0120$
        $= 1.60$

    P-value $= P(z > 1.60) = 1 - P(z < 1.60) = 1 - .9452 = .0548$
conclusion:
    Do not reject H_o; there is not sufficient evidence to conclude that $p > .15$.
No; since technology and the use of technology is changing so rapidly, any figures from 1997 would no longer be valid today. [By the time you are reading this, e-mail could be so common that essentially 100% of the households use it -- or it could have been replaced by something newer and be so out-dated that essentially 0% of the households still use it!]

6. original claim: $p > .35$
    $\hat{p} = x/n = 4019/4276 = .940$
    H_o: $p = .35$
    H_1: $p > .35$
    $\alpha = .01$
    C.R. $z > z_{.01} = 2.326$
    calculations:
        $z_{\hat{p}} = (\hat{p} - \mu_{\hat{p}})/\sigma_{\hat{p}}$
        $= (.940 - .35)/\sqrt{(.35)(.65)/4276}$
        $= .590/.00729$
        $= 80.87$

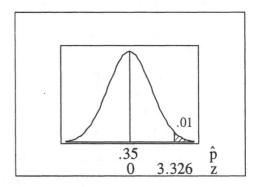

    P-value $= P(z > 80.87) = 1 - P(z < 80.87) = 1 - .9999 = .0001$
conclusion:
    Reject H_o; there is sufficient evidence to conclude that $p > .35$.
Yes; what appears to be obvious supporting information really is statistically significant evidence.

7. original claim: $p > .50$
    $\hat{p} = x/n = x/829 = .51$
    H_o: $p = .50$
    H_1: $p > .50$
    $\alpha = .10$
    C.R. $z > z_{.10} = 1.282$
    calculations:
        $z_{\hat{p}} = (\hat{p} - \mu_{\hat{p}})/\sigma_{\hat{p}}$
        $= (.51 - .50)/\sqrt{(.50)(.50)/829}$
        $= .01/.0174$
        $= .58$

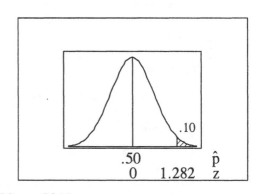

        P-value $= P(z > .58) = 1 - P(z < .58) = 1 - .7190 = .2810$

conclusion:
    Do not reject H_o; there is not sufficient evidence to conclude that $p > .50$.
No; since there are state and regional differences (in both circumstances and opinions) the conclusions reached for any one state can not be generalized to the country as a whole.

8. original claim: $p < .10$
    $\hat{p} = x/n = x/1012 = .09$
    H_o: $p = .10$
    H_1: $p < .10$
    $\alpha = .05$
    C.R. $z < -z_{.05} = -1.645$
    calculations:
        $z_{\hat{p}} = (\hat{p} - \mu_{\hat{p}})/\sigma_{\hat{p}}$
           $= (.09 - .10)/\sqrt{(.10)(.90)/1012}$
           $= -.01/.00943$
           $= -1.06$
    P-value $= P(z < -1.06) = .1446$

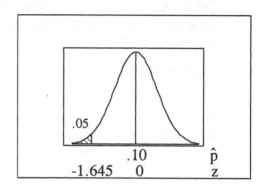

conclusion:
    Do not reject H_o; there is not sufficient evidence to conclude that $p < .10$.
If a newspaper ran such a headline, it would be doing so with P(error) $= .1446$ – for even when p equals 10%, there is a 14.46% of getting results as "convincing" as those above.

9. original claim: $p = .01$
    $\hat{p} = x/n = 20/1234 = .016$
    H_o: $p = .01$
    H_1: $p \neq .01$
    $\alpha = .05$
    C.R. $z < -z_{.025} = -1.96$
        $z > z_{.025} = 1.96$
    calculations:
        $z_{\hat{p}} = (\hat{p} - \mu_{\hat{p}})/\sigma_{\hat{p}}$
           $= (.016 - .01)/\sqrt{(.01)(.99)/1234}$
           $= .006/.00283$
           $= 2.19$

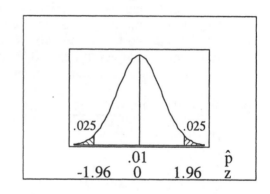

    P-value $= 2 \cdot P(z > 2.19) = 2 \cdot [1 - P(z < 2.19)] = 2 \cdot [1 - .9857] = 2 \cdot [.0143] = .0286$
conclusion:
    Reject H_o; there is sufficient evidence reject the claim that $p = .01$ and to conclude that $p \neq .01$ (in fact, that $p > .01$).
No; based on these results, consumers appear to be subjected to more overcharges than under the old pre-scanner system.

10. original claim: $p < .058$
    $\hat{p} = x/n = 58/1520 = .038$
    H_o: $p = .058$
    H_1: $p < .058$
    $\alpha = .01$
    C.R. $z < -z_{.01} = -2.326$
    calculations:
        $z_{\hat{p}} = (\hat{p} - \mu_{\hat{p}})/\sigma_{\hat{p}}$
           $= (.038 - .058)/\sqrt{(.058)(.942)/1520}$
           $= -.020/.00600$
           $= -3.31$

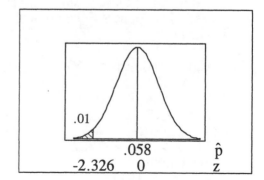

    P-value $= P(z < -3.31) = .0005$
conclusion:
    Reject H_o; there is sufficient evidence to conclude that $p < .058$
Yes, the result suggests that fewer job applicants now use drugs.

11. original claim: $p > .610$
$\hat{p} = x/n = 2231/3581 = .623$
H_o: $p = .610$
H_1: $p > .610$
$\alpha = .05$
C.R. $z > z_{.05} = 1.645$
calculations:
$z_{\hat{p}} = (\hat{p} - \mu_{\hat{p}})/\sigma_{\hat{p}}$
$= (.623 - .610)/\sqrt{(.610)(.390)/3581}$
$= .013/.00815$
$= 1.60$
P-value $= P(z > 1.60) = 1 - P(z < 1.60) = 1 - .9452 = .0548$
conclusion:
Do not reject H_o; there is not sufficient evidence to conclude that $p > .610$.

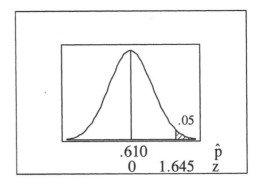

12. original claim: $p > .019$
$\hat{p} = x/n = 19/863 = .022$
H_o: $p = .019$
H_1: $p > .019$
$\alpha = .01$
C.R. $z > z_{.01} = 2.326$
calculations:
$z_{\hat{p}} = (\hat{p} - \mu_{\hat{p}})/\sigma_{\hat{p}}$
$= (.022 - .019)/\sqrt{(.019)(.981)/863}$
$= .003/.00465$
$= .65$
P-value $= P(z > .65) = 1 - P(z < .65) = 1 - .7422 = .2578$
conclusion:
Do not reject H_o; there is not sufficient evidence to conclude that $p > .019$.
No, flu symptoms do not appear to be an adverse reaction of the treatment.

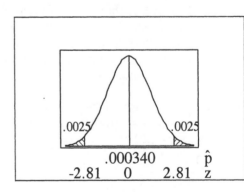

13. original claim: $p = .000340$
$\hat{p} = x/n = 135/420,095 = .000321$
H_o: $p = .000340$
H_1: $p \ne .000340$
$\alpha = .005$
C.R. $z < -z_{.0025} = -2.81$
$z > z_{.0025} = 2.81$
calculations:
$z_{\hat{p}} = (\hat{p} - \mu_{\hat{p}})/\sigma_{\hat{p}}$
$= (.000321 - .000340)/\sqrt{\dfrac{(.000340)(.999660)}{420,095}}$
$= -.000019/.0000284$
$= -.66$
P-value $= 2 \cdot P(z < -.66) = 2 \cdot (.2546) = .5092$
conclusion:
Do not reject H_o; there is not sufficient evidence reject the claim that $p = .000340$.
No; based on these results, cell phone users have no reason for such concern.

14. original claim: $p > .50$
  $\hat{p} = x/n = 39/(39+32) = 39/71 = .549$
  $H_0\colon p = .50$
  $H_1\colon p > .50$
  $\alpha = .10$
  C.R. $z > z_{.10} = 1.282$
  calculations:

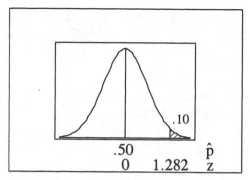

  $z_{\hat{p}} = (\hat{p} - \mu_{\hat{p}})/\sigma_{\hat{p}}$
  $\qquad = (.549 - .50)/\sqrt{(.50)(.50)/71}$
  $\qquad = .049/.0593$
  $\qquad = .83$
  P-value $= P(z > .83) = 1 - P(z < .83) = 1 - .7967 = .2033$
  conclusion:
  Do not reject H_0; there is not sufficient evidence to conclude that $p > .50$.
  Not necessarily. To test whether the therapy is effective, the results need to be compared
  to those of a control group – i.e., a group that tried to quit smoking without the therapy.

15. original claim: $p < .27$
  $\hat{p} = x/n = 144/785 = .183$
  $H_0\colon p = .27$
  $H_1\colon p < .27$
  $\alpha = .01$
  C.R. $z < -z_{.01} = -2.326$
  calculations:

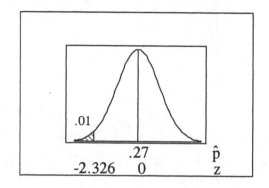

  $z_{\hat{p}} = (\hat{p} - \mu_{\hat{p}})/\sigma_{\hat{p}}$
  $\qquad = (.183 - .27)/\sqrt{(.27)(.73)/785}$
  $\qquad = -.087/.0158$
  $\qquad = -5.46$
  P-value $= P(z < -5.46) = .0001$
  conclusion:
  Reject H_0; there is sufficient evidence to conclude that $p < .27$.
  Since not smoking is the better decision from both a health and a financial perspective, one
  would expect it to be the choice of the better decision-makers – and presumably the
  additional education college graduates have makes them better decision-makers than the
  general population.

16. original claim: $p > .20$
  $\hat{p} = x/n = 1024/(1024+3836) = 1024/4860 = .21$
  $H_0\colon p = .20$
  $H_1\colon p > .20$
  $\alpha = .025$
  C.R. $z > z_{.025} = 1.96$
  calculations:

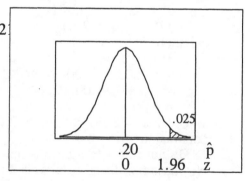

  $z_{\hat{p}} = (\hat{p} - \mu_{\hat{p}})/\sigma_{\hat{p}}$
  $\qquad = (.211 - .20)/\sqrt{(.20)(.80)/4860}$
  $\qquad = .011/.00574$
  $\qquad = 1.86$
  P-value $= P(z > 1.86) = 1 - P(z < 1.86) = 1 - .9686 = .0314$
  conclusion:
  Do not reject H_0; there is not sufficient evidence to conclude that $p > .20$.
  Argue that even though $\hat{p} = .211$ happens to be greater than 20%, that is not enough
  evidence to be 97.5% certain that the true population proportion is greater than 20%.

17.   original claim: $p > .75$
      $\hat{p} = x/n = x/500 = .91$
      H_0: $p = .75$
      H_1: $p > .75$
      $\alpha = .01$
      C.R. $z > z_{.01} = 2.326$
      calculations:

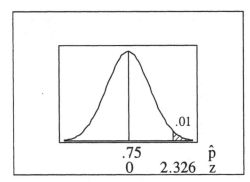

$$z_{\hat{p}} = (\hat{p} - \mu_{\hat{p}})/\sigma_{\hat{p}}$$
$$= (.91 - .75)/\sqrt{(.75)(.25)/500}$$
$$= .16/.0194$$
$$= 8.26$$

    P-value = $P(z > 8.26) = 7.22 \times 10^{-17} = .0000000000000000722$ [from TI-83 Plus]
conclusion:
    Reject H_0; there is sufficient evidence to conclude that $p > .75$.
The TI-83 Plus values agree with those calculated above. Yes; based on these sample
results, the funding will be approved.

18.   original claim: $p < .50$
      $\hat{p} = x/n = x/1998 = .48$
      H_0: $p = .50$
      H_1: $p < .50$
      $\alpha = .05$
      C.R. $z < -z_{.05} = -1.645$
      calculations:

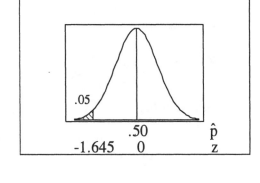

$$z_{\hat{p}} = (\hat{p} - \mu_{\hat{p}})/\sigma_{\hat{p}}$$
$$= (.48 - .50)/\sqrt{(.50)(.50)/1998}$$
$$= -.02/.0112$$
$$= -1.79$$

    P-value = $P(z < -1.79) = .0367$
conclusion:
    Reject H_0; there is sufficient evidence to conclude that $p < .50$.
The TI-83 Plus values agree with those calculated above. Yes; based on these sample
results, the executive's claim is supported.

19.   There are 100 M&M candies listed in Data Set 19, and 5 of them are blue.
      original claim: $p = .10$
      $\hat{p} = x/n = 5/100 = .05$
      H_0: $p = .10$
      H_1: $p \neq .10$
      $\alpha = .05$ [assumed]
      C.R. $z < -z_{.025} = -1.96$
          $z > z_{.025} = 1.96$
      calculations:

$$z_{\hat{p}} = (\hat{p} - \mu_{\hat{p}})/\sigma_{\hat{p}}$$
$$= (.05 - .10)/\sqrt{(.10)(.90)/100}$$
$$= -.05/.03$$
$$= -1.67$$

    P-value = $2 \cdot P(z < -1.67) = 2 \cdot (.0475) = .0950$
conclusion:
    Do not reject H_0; there is not sufficient evidence reject the claim that $p = .10$.

20.   There are 50 movies listed in Data Set 7; 16 of them show no [0 seconds] alcohol or tobacco use, 34 show some use of alcohol or tobacco (or both).
original claim: p > .50
$\hat{p}$ = x/n = 34/50 = .68
H_o: p = .50
H_1: p > .50
α = .05
C.R. z > $z_{.05}$ = 1.645
calculations:
$z_{\hat{p}}$ = ($\hat{p}$ - $\mu_{\hat{p}}$)/$\sigma_{\hat{p}}$
   = (.68 - .50)/$\sqrt{(.50)(.50)/50}$
   = .18/.0707
   = 2.55

P-value = P(z>2.55) = 1 - P(z<2.55) = 1 - .9946 = .0054
conclusion:
Reject H_o; there is sufficient evidence to conclude that p > .50.

21.   original claim: p = .10
$\hat{p}$ = x/n = 119/1000 = .119
H_o: p = .10
H_1: p ≠ .10
α = .05
C.R. z < -$z_{.025}$ = -1.96
      z > $z_{.025}$ = 1.96
calculations:
$z_{\hat{p}}$ = ($\hat{p}$ - $\mu_{\hat{p}}$)/$\sigma_{\hat{p}}$
   = (.119 - .10)/$\sqrt{(.10)(.90)/1000}$
   = .019/.00949
   = 2.00

P-value = 2·P(z>2.00) = 2·[1 - P(z<2.00)] = 2·[1 - .9772] = 2·[.0228] = .0456
conclusion:
Reject H_o; there is sufficient evidence reject the claim that p = .10 and conclude that p ≠ .10 (in fact, that p > .10).

a. As seen above, the traditional method leads to rejection of the claim that p=.10 because the calculated z=2.00 is greater than the critical value of 1.96.
b. As seen above, the P-value method leads to rejection of the claim that p=.10 because the calculated P-value=.0456 is less than the level of significance of .05.
c. α = .05 and $\hat{p}$ = x/n = 119/1000 = .119
   $\hat{p} \pm z_{.025}\sqrt{\hat{p}\hat{q}/n}$
   .119 $\pm$ 1.96$\sqrt{(.119)(.881)/1000}$
   .119 $\pm$ .020
   .099 < p < .139
Since .10 is inside the confidence interval, this suggests that p=.10 is a reasonable claim that should not be rejected.
d. The traditional method and the P-value method are mathematically equivalent and will always agree. As seen by this example, the confidence interval method does not always lead to the same conclusion as the other two methods.

22.   There are 50 movies listed in Data Set 7; 16 of them show no [0 seconds] alcohol or tobacco use, 34 show some use of alcohol or tobacco (or both).
original claim: p > .50
$\hat{p}$ = x/n = 34/50 = .68
The test of hypothesis considers the probability of obtaining a result as extreme as or more extreme than the one obtained. In this problem, that would be P(x≥34) = P_c(x>33.5). The value of the sample proportion corrected for continuity is therefore
$\hat{p}$ = x/n = 33.5/50 = .67.

H_o: p = .50
H_1: p > .50
α = .05
C.R. z > $z_{.05}$ = 1.645
calculations:
 $z_{\hat{p}}$ = $(\hat{p} - \mu_{\hat{p}})/\sigma_{\hat{p}}$
  = $(.67 - .50)/\sqrt{(.50)(.50)/50}$
  = .17/.0707
  = 2.40
 P-value = P(z > 2.40)
  = 1 - P(z < 2.40) = 1 - .9918 = .0082

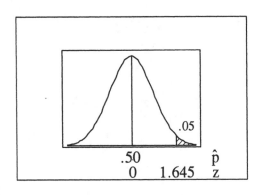

conclusion:
 Reject H_o; there is sufficient evidence to conclude that p > .50.
The calculated test statistic is slightly smaller than the 2.55 in exercise #20, and so the P-value is slightly larger than the .0054 in exercise #20. The change is minor and does not affect the conclusion.

23. The basic test of hypothesis is given below and illustrated by the figure at the right.
  H_o: p = .5
  H_1: p > .5
  α = .05
  C.R. z > $z_{.05}$ = 1.645

  The $\hat{p}$ corresponding to z = 1.645 is found
   by solving $z_{\hat{p}}$ = $(\hat{p} - p)/\sqrt{pq/n}$ for $\hat{p}$ as
   follows.
   $\hat{p}$ = p + $z_{\hat{p}} \cdot \sqrt{pq/n}$
    = .5 + 1.645$\cdot\sqrt{(.5)(.5)/50}$
    = .5 + 1.645$\cdot$(.0707)
    = .5 + .1163
    = .6163

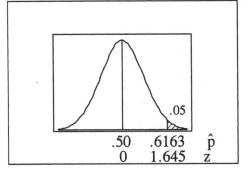

  β = P(not rejecting H_o | H_o is false)
   = P($\hat{p}$ < .6163 | p = .45)
   = P(z < 2.36)
   = .9909

  The z corresponding to $\hat{p}$ = .6163 is
   found as follows.
   $z_{\hat{p}}$ = $(\hat{p} - p)/\sqrt{pq/n}$
    = $(.6163 - .45)/\sqrt{(.45)(.55)/50}$
    = (.1663)/(.0704)
    = 2.36

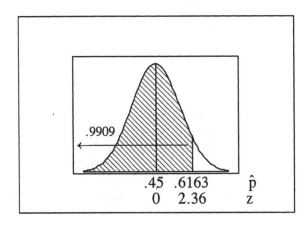

7-4 Testing a Claim about a Mean: σ Known

1. Yes, since σ is known and the original population is normally distributed.

2. No, since σ is unknown.

3. No, since σ is unknown.

4. Yes, since σ is known and n > 30.

5. original claim: $\mu > 118$
    $\bar{x} = 120$
    $H_o: \mu = 118$
    $H_1: \mu > 118$
    $\alpha = .05$
    C.R. $z > z_{.05} = 1.645$
    calculations:
    $z_{\bar{x}} = (\bar{x} - \mu)/\sigma_{\bar{x}}$
    $= (120 - 118)/(12\sqrt{50})$
    $= 2/1.697$
    $= 1.18$
    P-value $= P(z > 1.18) = 1 - P(z < 1.18) = 1 - .8810 = .1190$
    conclusion:
    Do not reject H_o; there is not sufficient evidence to conclude that $\mu > 118$.

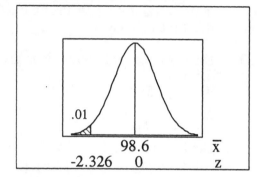

6. original claim: $\mu < 98.6$
    $\bar{x} = 98.20$
    $H_o: \mu = 98.6$
    $H_1: \mu < 98.6$
    $\alpha = .01$
    C.R. $z < -z_{.01} = -2.326$
    calculations:
    $z_{\bar{x}} = (\bar{x} - \mu)/\sigma_{\bar{x}}$
    $= (98.20 - 98.6)/(.62/\sqrt{106})$
    $= -.40/.0602 = -6.64$

    P-value $= P(z < -6.64) = .0001$
    conclusion:
    Reject H_o; there is sufficient evidence to conclude that $\mu < 98.6$.

7. original claim: $\mu = 5.00$
    $\bar{x} = 5.25$
    $H_o: \mu = 5.00$
    $H_1: \mu \neq 5.00$
    $\alpha = .01$
    C.R. $z < -z_{.005} = -2.575$
    $z > z_{.005} = 2.575$
    calculations:
    $z_{\bar{x}} = (\bar{x} - \mu)/\sigma_{\bar{x}}$
    $= (5.25 - 5.00)/(2.50/\sqrt{80})$
    $= .25/.2795 = .89$
    P-value $= 2 \cdot P(z > .89) = 2 \cdot [1 - P(z < .89)] = 2 \cdot [1 - .8133] = 2 \cdot [.1867] = .3734$
    conclusion:
    Do not reject H_o; there is not sufficient evidence reject the claim that $\mu = .10$.

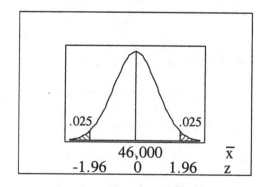

8. original claim: $\mu = 46,000$
    $\bar{x} = 45,678$
    $H_o: \mu = 46,000$
    $H_1: \mu \neq 46,000$
    $\alpha = .05$
    C.R. $z < -z_{.025} = -1.96$
    $z > z_{.025} = 1.96$
    calculations:
    $z_{\bar{x}} = (\bar{x} - \mu)/\sigma_{\bar{x}}$
    $= (45,678 - 46,000)/(9900/\sqrt{65})$
    $= -322/1227.944 = -.26$
    P-value $= 2 \cdot P(z < -.26) = 2 \cdot (.3974) = .7948$

conclusion:
    Do not reject H_o; there is not sufficient evidence reject the claim that $\mu = 46{,}000$.

9.   original claim: $\mu > 30.0$
        $\bar{x} = 30.4$
    H_o: $\mu = 30.0$
    H_1: $\mu > 30.0$
    $\alpha = .05$
    C.R. $z > z_{.05} = 1.645$
    calculations:
        $z_{\bar{x}} = (\bar{x} - \mu)/\sigma_{\bar{x}}$
            $= (30.4 - 30.0)/(1.7/\sqrt{61})$
            $= .4/.218$
            $= 1.84$
        P-value $= P(z > 1.84) = 1 - P(z < 1.84) = 1 - .9671 = .0329$
    conclusion:
        Reject H_o; there is sufficient evidence to conclude that $\mu > 30.0$.

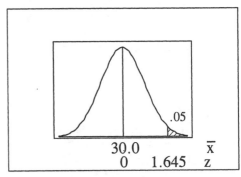

10.   original claim: $\mu < 200$
        $\bar{x} = 182.9$
    H_o: $\mu = 200$
    H_1: $\mu < 200$
    $\alpha = .10$
    C.R. $z < -z_{.10} = -1.282$
    calculations:
        $z_{\bar{x}} = (\bar{x} - \mu)/\sigma_{\bar{x}}$
            $= (182.9 - 200)/(121.8/\sqrt{54})$
            $= -17.1/16.575 = -1.03$
        P-value $= P(z < -1.03) = .1515$
    conclusion:
        Do not reject H_o; there is not sufficient evidence to conclude that $\mu < 200$.

11.   original claim: $\mu = 200.0$
        $\bar{x} = 172.5$
    H_o: $\mu = 200.0$
    H_1: $\mu \neq 200.0$
    $\alpha = .01$
    C.R. $z < -z_{.005} = -2.575$
        $z > z_{.005} = 2.575$
    calculations:
        $z_{\bar{x}} = (\bar{x} - \mu)/\sigma_{\bar{x}}$
            $= (172.5 - 200.0)/(119.5/\sqrt{40})$
            $= -27.5/18.895 = -1.46$
        P-value $= 2 \cdot P(z < -1.46) = 2 \cdot (.0721) = .1442$
    conclusion:
        Do not reject H_o; there is not sufficient evidence reject the claim that $\mu = 200.0$.

12.   original claim: $\mu = 40.0$; $\bar{x} = 40.6$
    H_o: $\mu = 40.0$
    H_1: $\mu \neq 40.0$
    $\alpha = .05$
    C.R. $z < -z_{.025} = -1.96$
        $z > z_{.025} = 1.96$
    calculations:
        $z_{\bar{x}} = (\bar{x} - \mu)/\sigma_{\bar{x}}$
            $= (40.6 - 40.0)/(1.6/\sqrt{100})$
            $= .6/.16 = 3.75$

P-value = $2 \cdot P(z > 3.75) = 2 \cdot [1 - P(z < 3.75)] = 2 \cdot [1 - .9999] = 2 \cdot (.0001) = .0002$
conclusion:
  Reject H_o; there is sufficient evidence reject the claim that $\mu = 40.0$ and conclude that $\mu \neq 40.0$ (in fact, that $\mu > 40.0$).

13. original claim: $\mu \neq .9085$
       $\overline{x} = .91470$
   H_o: $\mu = .9085$
   H_1: $\mu \neq .9085$
   $\alpha = .05$ [assumed]
   C.R. $z < -z_{.025} = -1.96$
          $z > z_{.025} = 1.96$
   calculations:
       $z_{\overline{x}} = (\overline{x} - \mu)/\sigma_{\overline{x}}$
           $= (.91470 - .9085)/(.03691/\sqrt{100})$
           $= .0062/.003691$
           $= 1.68$

   P-value = $2 \cdot P(z > 1.68) = 2 \cdot [1 - P(z < 1.68)] = 2 \cdot [1 - .9535] = 2 \cdot (.0465) = .0930$
conclusion:
  Do not reject H_o; there is not sufficient evidence to conclude that $\mu \neq .9085$
Both the calculated z and the P-value agree with the Minitab output. No; since $\overline{x} > .9085$, it appears that any deviance is in favor of the consumer. No; since the company presumably figures its costs based on what is actually produced rather than on what is advertised, they are not losing money by making the candy slightly heavier than necessary.

14. original claim: $\mu = 4.50$
       $\overline{x} = 1.753$
   H_o: $\mu = 4.50$
   H_1: $\mu \neq 4.50$
   $\alpha = .05$
   C.R. $z < -z_{.025} = -1.96$
          $z > z_{.025} = 1.96$
   calculations:
       $z_{\overline{x}} = (\overline{x} - \mu)/\sigma_{\overline{x}}$
           $= (1.753 - 4.50)/(2.87/\sqrt{73})$
           $= -2.747/.3359$
           $= -8.18$

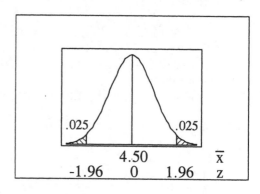

   P-value = $2 \cdot P(z < -8.18) = 2 \cdot (.0001) = .0002$
conclusion:
  Reject H_o; there is sufficient evidence reject the claim that $\mu = 4.50$ and conclude that $\mu \neq 4.50$ (in fact, that $\mu < 4.50$).
Both the calculated z and the P-value agree with the Minitab output. No; it appears that the distances were not accurately measured.

15. original claim: $\mu = 0$
       $\overline{x} = -.419$
   H_o: $\mu = 0$
   H_1: $\mu \neq 0$
   $\alpha = .05$ [assumed]
   C.R. $z < -z_{.025} = -1.96$
          $z > z_{.025} = 1.96$
   calculations:
       $z_{\overline{x}} = (\overline{x} - \mu)/\sigma_{\overline{x}}$
           $= (-.419 - 0)/(3.704/\sqrt{31})$
           $= -.419/.6653$
           $= -.63$

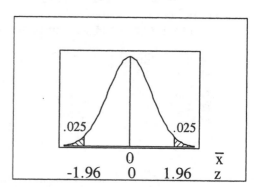

P-value = $2 \cdot P(z < -.63) = 2 \cdot (.2643) = .5286$
conclusion:
   Do not reject H_o; there is not sufficient evidence reject the claim that $\mu = 0$.
Both the calculated z and the P-value agree with the TI-83 Plus output. The mean difference does not appear to be significantly different form 0. This suggests that the 3-day forecast high temperatures are correct <u>on the average</u> – but that does not necessarily instill confidence in any one single prediction, as the $\sigma = 3.7$ suggests that it's not unusual for the predictions to be off by $2 \cdot (3.7) = 7.4$ degrees in either direction.

16. original claim: $\mu < 281.81$
    $\bar{x} = 267.11$
    H_o: $\mu = 281.81$
    H_1: $\mu < 281.81$
    $\alpha = .01$
    C.R. $z < -z_{.01} = -2.326$
    calculations:

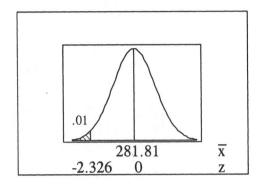

      $z_{\bar{x}} = (\bar{x} - \mu)/\sigma_{\bar{x}}$
         $= (267.11 - 281.81)/(22.11/\sqrt{175})$
         $= -14.7/1.6714$
         $= -8.80$
    P-value = $P(z < -8.80) = .0001$
conclusion:
   Reject H_o; there is sufficient evidence to conclude that $\mu < 281.81$.
Both the caluclated z and the P-value agree with the TI-83 Plus output. Yes, the thinner cans do appear to have a mean axial load less than 281.82 lbs.

17. a. It is unrealistic that the value of σ would be known.
   b. original claim: $\mu \neq 98.6$; $\bar{x} = 98.20$
     H_o: $\mu = 98.6$
     H_1: $\mu \neq 98.6$
     $\alpha = .05$
     C.R. $z < -z_{.025} = -1.96$
        $z > z_{.025} = 1.96$
     calculations:
      $z_{\bar{x}} = (\bar{x} - \mu)/\sigma_{\bar{x}}$
      $-1.96 < (98.20 - 98.6)/(\sigma/\sqrt{106})$
        $\sigma < (98.20 - 98.6)/(-1.96/\sqrt{106})$
        $\sigma < (-.4)/(-.1904)$
        $\sigma < 2.101$; The largest possible standard deviation is 2.10
   c. No; if $s = .62$ for $n = 106$ sample values, it seems unlikely that the true value of σ in this particular instance would be greater than 2.10. The assumption that $\sigma = .62$ seems appropriate in that the conclusion would be the same for any other value reasonably close to .62.

18. original claim: $\mu = 100$; $\bar{x} = 103.6$
   H_o: $\mu = 100$
   H_1: $\mu \neq 100$
   $\alpha = .01$
   C.R. $z < -z_{.005} = -2.575$
      $z > z_{.005} = 2.575$
   calculations:

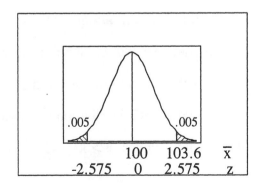

     $z_{\bar{x}} = (\bar{x} - \mu)/\sigma_{\bar{x}}$
     $2.575 < (103.6 - 100)/(\sigma/\sqrt{62})$
       $\sigma < (103.6 - 100)/(2.575/\sqrt{62})$
       $\sigma < 3.6/.327$
       $\sigma < 11.008$; The largest possible standard deviation is 11.0.

19.   original claim: $\mu \neq 98.6$
H_o: $\mu = 98.6$
H_1: $\mu \neq 98.6$
$\alpha = .05$
C.R. $z < -z_{.025} = -1.960$
$\quad\ z > z_{.025} = 1.960$

in terms of $\overline{x}$, as seen by the calculations below,
C.R. $\overline{x} < 98.482$
$\quad\ \overline{x} > 98.718$

calculations:
$$z_{\overline{x}} = (\overline{x} - \mu)/\sigma_{\overline{x}} \qquad\qquad z_{\overline{x}} = (\overline{x} - \mu)/\sigma_{\overline{x}}$$
$$-1.960 = (\overline{x} - 98.6)/(.62/\sqrt{106}) \qquad 1.960 = (\overline{x} - 98.6)/(.62/\sqrt{106})$$
$$\overline{x} = 98.482 \qquad\qquad\qquad\quad \overline{x} = 98.718$$

a. $\beta = P(98.482 < \overline{x} < 98.718 \mid \mu = 98.7)$
$\quad = P(-3.62 < z < .30)$
$\quad = P(z < .30) - P(z < -3.62)$

$\quad = .6179 - .0001$
$\quad = .6178$

b. $\beta = P(98.482 < \overline{x} < 98.718 \mid \mu = 98.4)$
$\quad = P(1.36 < z < 5.28)$
$\quad = P(5.28 < z < 1.36)$
$\quad = .9999 - .9131$
$\quad = .0868$

7-5 Testing a Claim about a Mean: σ Not Known

1. σ unknown and distribution approximately normal, use t

2.   distribution not normal and $n \leq 30$, neither

3. σ known and distribution approximately normal, use z

4. σ unknown and $n > 30$, use t

5. $t_{11,.01} = 2.718 < 2.998 < 3.106 = t_{11,.005}$
    $.01 > $ P-value $ < .005$
    $.005 < $ P-value $ < .01$

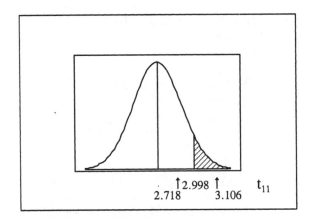

6. $-t_{11,.10} = -1.363 < -.855$
    $.10 < $ P-value
    P-value $ > .10$

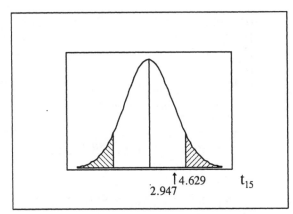

7. $t_{15,.005} = 2.947 < 4.629$
    $.005 > \frac{1}{2}$(P-value)
    P-value $ < .01$

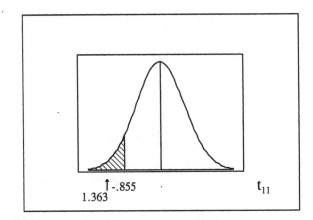

8. $t_{8,.05} = -1.860 < -1.577 < -1.397 = -t_{8,.10}$
    $.05 < \frac{1}{2}$(P-value) $ < .10$
    $.10 < $ P-value $ < .20$

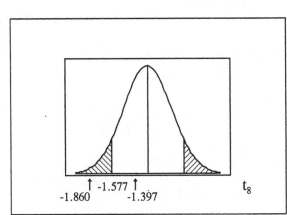

9.   original claim: $\mu > 118$
     H_o: $\mu = 118$
     H_1: $\mu > 118$
     $\alpha = .05$
     C.R. $t > t_{19,.05} = 1.729$
     calculations:
        $t_{\bar{x}} = (\bar{x} - \mu)/s_{\bar{x}}$
             $= (120 - 118)/(12\sqrt{20})$
             $= 2/2.683$
             $= .745$
        P-value $= P(t_{19} > .745) > .10$
     conclusion:
        Do not reject H_o; there is not sufficient evidence to conclude that $\mu > 118$.

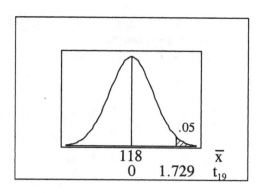

10. original claim: $\mu < 98.6$
     H_o: $\mu = 98.6$
     H_1: $\mu < 98.6$
     $\alpha = .01$
     C.R. $t < -t_{34,.01} = -2.441$
     calculations:
        $t_{\bar{x}} = (\bar{x} - \mu)/s_{\bar{x}}$
             $= (98.20 - 98.6)/(.62/\sqrt{35})$
             $= -.40/.1047$
             $= -3.817$
        P-value $= P(t_{34} < -3.817) < .005$
     conclusion:
        Reject H_o; there is sufficient evidence to conclude that $\mu < 98.6$.

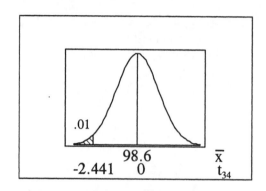

11. original claim: $\mu = 5.00$
     H_o: $\mu = 5.00$
     H_1: $\mu \neq 5.00$
     $\alpha = .01$
     C.R. $t < -t_{80,.005} = -2.639$
          $t > t_{80,.005} = 2.639$
     calculations:
        $t_{\bar{x}} = (\bar{x} - \mu)/t_{\bar{x}}$
             $= (5.25 - 5.00)/(2.50/\sqrt{81})$
             $= .25/.2778$
             $= .900$
        P-value $= 2 \cdot P(t_{80} > .900) > .20$
     conclusion:
        Do not reject H_o; there is not sufficient evidence reject the claim that $\mu = .10$.

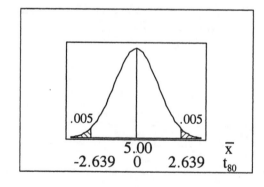

12. original claim: $\mu = 46,000$
     H_o: $\mu = 46,000$
     H_1: $\mu \neq 46,000$
     $\alpha = .05$
     C.R. $t < -t_{26,.025} = -2.056$
          $t > t_{26,.025} = 2.056$
     calculations:
        $t_{\bar{x}} = (\bar{x} - \mu)/s_{\bar{x}}$
             $= (45,678 - 46,000)/(9900/\sqrt{27})$
             $= -322/1905.256 = -.169$
        P-value $= 2 \cdot P(t_{26} < -.169) > .20$
     conclusion:
        Do not reject H_o; there is not sufficient evidence reject the claim that $\mu = 46,000$.

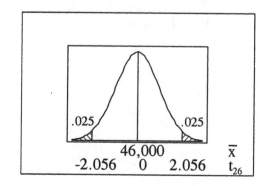

13.   original claim: $\mu > 4$
     H_o: $\mu = 4$
     H_1: $\mu > 4$
     $\alpha = .05$
     C.R. $t > t_{11,.05} = 1.796$
     calculations:
     $\quad t_{\bar{x}} = (\bar{x} - \mu)/s_{\bar{x}}$
     $\quad\quad = (5.075 - 4)/(1.168/\sqrt{12})$
     $\quad\quad = 1.075/.337$
     $\quad\quad = 3.188$
     $\quad$ P-value $= P(t_{11} > 3.188) < .005$
     conclusion:
     $\quad$ Reject H_o; there is sufficient evidence to conclude that $\mu > 4$.
     Yes; based on this sample, the teachers will use the book.

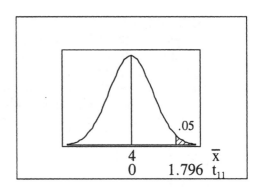

14.   original claim: $\mu < .3$
     H_o: $\mu = .3$
     H_1: $\mu < .3$
     $\alpha = .05$
     C.R. $t < -t_{15,.05} = -1.753$
     calculations:
     $\quad t_{\bar{x}} = (\bar{x} - \mu)/s_{\bar{x}}$
     $\quad\quad = (.295 - .3)/(.168/\sqrt{16})$
     $\quad\quad = -.005/.042$
     $\quad\quad = -.119$
     $\quad$ P-value $= P(t_{15} < -.119) > .10$
     conclusion:
     $\quad$ Do not reject H_o; there is not sufficient evidence to conclude that $\mu < .3$.

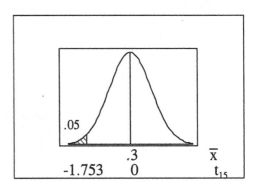

15.   original claim: $\mu \neq 0$
     H_o: $\mu = 0$
     H_1: $\mu \neq 0$
     $\alpha = .05$
     C.R. $t < -t_{30,.025} = -2.042$
     $\quad\quad t > t_{30,.025} = 2.042$
     calculations:
     $\quad t_{\bar{x}} = (\bar{x} - \mu)/s_{\bar{x}}$
     $\quad\quad = (-.419 - 0)/(3.704/\sqrt{31})$
     $\quad\quad = -.419/.665$
     $\quad\quad = -.630$
     $\quad$ P-value $= 2 \cdot P(t_{30} < -.630) > .20$
     conclusion:
     $\quad$ Do not reject H_o; there is not sufficient evidence to reject the claim that $\mu = 0$.
     Yes; based on this result, the forecasts do seem to be reasonably accurate.

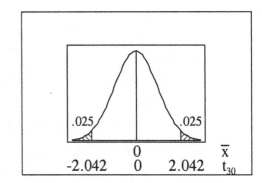

16.   original claim: $\mu > 0$
     H_o: $\mu = 0$
     H_1: $\mu > 0$
     $\alpha = .01$
     C.R. $t > t_{19,.01} = 2.539$
     calculations:
     $\quad t_{\bar{x}} = (\bar{x} - \mu)/s_{\bar{x}}$
     $\quad\quad = (4.4 - 0)/(4.2/\sqrt{20})$
     $\quad\quad = 4.4/.939$
     $\quad\quad = 4.685$
     $\quad$ P-value $= P(t_{19} > 4.685) < .005$

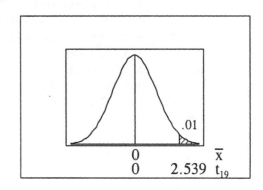

conclusion:
    Reject H_o; there is sufficient evidence to conclude that $\mu > 0$.
Yes; the results support the claim that women tend to marry men taller than themselves.
NOTE: Since the women were not selected at random from among all married women, the results do not apply to the general population of married women. The women in the survey were those who had children (presumably by choice) – and most likely whose children were in a certain age range, which places them in a certain age range.

17.   original claim: $\mu = 0$
    H_o: $\mu = 0$
    H_1: $\mu \neq 0$
    $\alpha = .01$
    C.R. $t < -t_{39,.005} = -2.712$
        $t > t_{39,.005} = 2.712$
    calculations:
        $t_{\bar{x}} = (\bar{x} - \mu)/s_{\bar{x}}$
            $= (117.3 - 0)/(185.0/\sqrt{40})$
            $= 117.3/29.251$
            $= 4.010$
        P-value $= 2 \cdot P(t_{39} > 4.010) < .01$

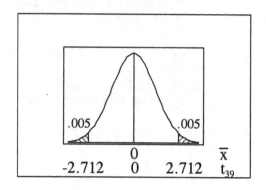

conclusion:
    Reject H_o; there is sufficient evidence to reject the claim that $\mu = 0$ and to conclude that $\mu \neq 0$ (in fact, that $\mu > 0$).
One conclude that on the average, people's wrist watches tend to be almost two minutes fast – which is probably by deliberate choice.

18.   original claim: $\mu < 75$
    H_o: $\mu = 75$
    H_1: $\mu < 75$
    $\alpha = .05$ [assumed]
    C.R. $t < -t_{15,.05} = -1.753$
    calculations:
        $t_{\bar{x}} = (\bar{x} - \mu)/s_{\bar{x}}$
            $= (70.41 - 75)/(19.70/\sqrt{16})$
            $= -4.59/4.925$
            $= -.932$
        P-value $= P(t_{15} < -.932) > .10$

conclusion:
    Do not reject H_o; there is not sufficient evidence to conclude that $\mu < 75$.
Since the sample mean was less than 75, these are certainly not results that would cause one to reject the college's claim. But since the sample mean was not far enough below 75 to rule out getting such a result by chance alone when $\mu < 75$ is not true, there is not enough evidence to conclude with 95% certainty that the college's claim is correct.
NOTE: It is possible that the student and the college are using two different definitions of "the mean price of a textbook." The student appears to have selected at random from among the available titles, regardless of the quantities sold. The college may be basing their claim on the total paid for textbooks divided by the number of books sold – which would be a weighted average. Suppose, for example, the college offers only two classes – a large one of 95 students with a textbook that costs $10, and a small one of 5 students with a textbook that costs $100. If each student buys the text, what would you consider "the mean price of a textbook" that semester? Is it $(10+100)/2 = 55, or is it $(950+500)/100 = $1450/100 = 14.50?

19.   original claim: $\mu > 69.5$
H_o: $\mu = 69.5$
H_1: $\mu > 69.5$
$\alpha = .05$
C.R. $t > t_{34,.05} = 1.691$
calculations:
$t_{\bar{x}} = (\bar{x} - \mu)/s_{\bar{x}}$
$= (73.4 - 69.5)/(8.7/\sqrt{35})$
$= 3.9/1.471$
$= 2.652$
$.005 < $ P-value $= P(t_{34} > 2.652) < .01$

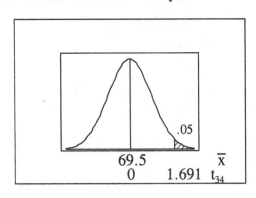

conclusion:
    Reject H_o; there is sufficient evidence to conclude that $\mu > 69.5$.
Yes, it does appear that male symphony conductors live longer than males form the general population – but in one sense that is like saying "male centenarians live longer than males from the general population." Male conductors should not be compared to "males from the general population" – but to "males from general population who have reached, say, age 35." Males who die in their teens, for example, are included in the general male population but (since we have no foreknowledge about what vocation they might have chosen had they lived) not in the population of male symphony orchestra conductors.

20.   original claim: $\mu \neq 92.84$
H_o: $\mu = 92.84$
H_1: $\mu \neq 92.84$
$\alpha = .05$
C.R. $t < -t_{39,.025} = -2.024$
$t > t_{39,.025} = 2.024$
calculations:
$t_{\bar{x}} = (\bar{x} - \mu)/s_{\bar{x}}$
$= (92.67 - 92.84)/(1.79/\sqrt{40})$
$= -.17/.283$
$= -.601$
P-value $= 2 \cdot P(t_{39} < -.601) > .20$

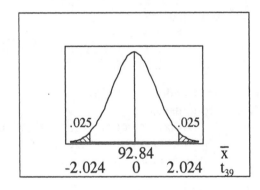

conclusion:
    Do not reject H_o; there is not sufficient evidence to conclude that $\mu \neq 98.24$.
No, it does not appear that the new baseballs are significantly different in this respect.

21.   original claim: $\mu < 1000$
H_o: $\mu = 1000$
H_1: $\mu < 1000$
$\alpha = .05$ [assumed]
C.R. $t < -t_{4,.05} = -2.132$
calculations:
$t_{\bar{x}} = (\bar{x} - \mu)/s_{\bar{x}}$
$= (767 - 1000)/(285/\sqrt{5})$
$= -233/127.46$
$= -1.828$
P-value $= .071$

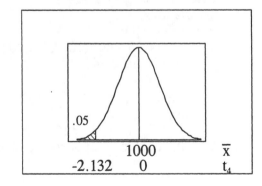

conclusion:
    Do not reject H_o; there is not sufficient evidence to conclude that $\mu < 1000$.
No; while the sample mean was less than $1000, the company cannot be 95% certain that the population mean is less than that amount.

22. original claim: $\mu > 420$
H_o: $\mu = 420$
H_1: $\mu > 420$
$\alpha = .05$ [assumed]
C.R. t > $t_{14,.05}$ = 1.761
calculations:
$t_{\bar{x}} = (\bar{x} - \mu)/s_{\bar{x}}$
$\quad = (442.2 - 420)/(44.0/\sqrt{15})$
$\quad = 22.2/11.361$
$\quad = 1.954$
P-value = .035
conclusion:
Reject H_o; there is sufficient evidence to conclude that $\mu > 420$.
Yes, appears (at the .05 level of significance) that the modifications improved reliability.

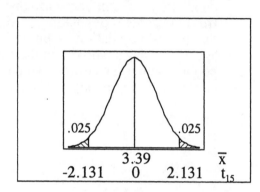

23. original claim: $\mu = 3.39$
H_o: $\mu = 3.39$
H_1: $\mu \neq 3.39$
$\alpha = .05$ [assumed]
C.R. t < -$t_{15,.025}$ = -2.131
$\quad$ t > $t_{15,.025}$ = 2.131
calculations:
$t_{\bar{x}} = (\bar{x} - \mu)/s_{\bar{x}}$
$\quad = (3.675 - 3.39)/(.6573/\sqrt{16})$
$\quad = .285/.1643$
$\quad = 1.734$
P-value = .1034
conclusion:
Do not reject H_o; there is not sufficient evidence to conclude that $\mu \neq 3.39$.
No; based on these results the supplement does not appear to have a significant effect on birth weight.

24. original claim: $\mu > 60$
H_o: $\mu = 60$
H_1: $\mu > 60$
$\alpha = .05$ [assumed]
C.R. t > $t_{19,.05}$ = 1.729
calculations:
$t_{\bar{x}} = (\bar{x} - \mu)/s_{\bar{x}}$
$\quad = (74.35 - 60)/(10.038/\sqrt{20})$
$\quad = 14.35/2.2446$
$\quad = 6.393$
P-value = 1.968×10^{-6} = .000001968
conclusion:
Reject H_o; there is sufficient evidence to conclude that $\mu > 60$.
Yes, the evidence supports the claim that the mean student rate is greater than 60.

25.   summary statistics: $n = 6$, $\Sigma x = 9.23$, $\Sigma x^2 = 32.5197$, $\overline{x} = 1.538$, $s = 1.914$
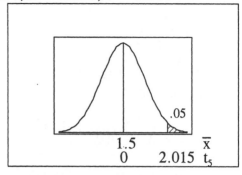
original claim: $\mu > 1.5$
H_0: $\mu = 1.5$
H_1: $\mu > 1.5$
$\alpha = .05$
C.R. $t > t_{5,.05} = 2.015$
calculations:
    $t_{\overline{x}} = (\overline{x} - \mu)/s_{\overline{x}}$
       $= (1.538 - 1.5)/(1.914/\sqrt{6})$
       $= .0383/.78147$
       $= .049$

    P-value $= P(t_5 > .049) > .10$
conclusion:
    Do not reject H_0; there is not sufficient evidence to conclude that $\mu > 1.5$.
Yes; since 5 of the 6 values are below the sample mean, there is reason to doubt that the population values are normally distributed.

26.   summary statistics: $n = 21$, $\Sigma x = 84$, $\Sigma x^2 = 430$, $\overline{x} = 4.000$, $s = 2.1679$
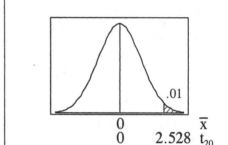
original claim: $\mu > 0$
H_0: $\mu = 0$
H_1: $\mu > 0$
$\alpha = .01$
C.R. $t > t_{20,.01} = 2.528$
calculations:
    $t_{\overline{x}} = (\overline{x} - \mu)/s_{\overline{x}}$
       $= (4.000 - 0)/(2.1679/\sqrt{21})$
       $= 4.000/.4731$
       $= 8.455$

    P-value $= P(t_{20} > 8.455) < .005$
conclusion:
    Reject H_0; there is sufficient evidence to conclude that $\mu > 0$.
Yes, the treatment appears to be effective.

27.   summary statistics: $n = 23$, $\Sigma x = 241.27$, $\Sigma x^2 = 2536.5762$, $\overline{x} = 10.490$ $s = .507$

original claim: $\mu < 10.5$
H_0: $\mu = 10.5$
H_1: $\mu < 10.5$
$\alpha = .05$ [assumed]
C.R. $t < -t_{22,.05} = -1.717$
calculations:
    $t_{\overline{x}} = (\overline{x} - \mu)/s_{\overline{x}}$
       $= (10.490 - 10.5)/(.507/\sqrt{23})$
       $= -.01/.1057$
       $= -.095$
    P-value $= P(t_{22} < -.095) > .10$
conclusion:
    Do not reject H_0; there is not sufficient evidence to conclude that $\mu < 10.5$.
The precision of the numbers changed from 1 to 2 decimal accuracy, presumably as improved technology produced more accurate timing devices. The test does not consider the sequential nature of the data, and would give the same results no matter what the order of the data. Because the test fails to consider the significant order effect, it only summarizes the past and cannot accurately project into the future. No; the test does not address the issue about future times being close to 10.5, and such a conclusion would not be valid.

28.   summary statistics: $n = 10$, $\Sigma x = 433.0$, $\Sigma x^2 = 18,878.90$, $\bar{x} = 43.3$, $s = 3.801$
original claim: $\mu > 40$
H_o: $\mu = 40$
H_1: $\mu > 40$
$\alpha = .01$
C.R. $t > t_{9,.01} = 2.821$
calculations:
$$t_{\bar{x}} = (\bar{x} - \mu)/s_{\bar{x}}$$
$$= (43.3 - 40)/(3.801/\sqrt{10})$$
$$= 3.3/1.202$$
$$= 2.746$$
$.01 < \text{P-value} = P(t_9 > 2.746) < .025$
conclusion:
Do not reject H_o; there is not sufficient evidence to conclude that $\mu > 40$.

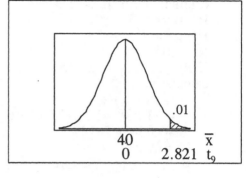

29.   summary statistics: $n = 12$, $\Sigma x = 78.0$, $\Sigma x^2 = 572.94$, $\bar{x} = 6.50$, $s = 2.448$
original claim: $\mu > 6$
H_o: $\mu = 6$
H_1: $\mu > 6$
$\alpha = .05$ [assumed]
C.R. $t > t_{11,.05} = 1.796$
calculations:
$$t_{\bar{x}} = (\bar{x} - \mu)/s_{\bar{x}}$$
$$= (6.50 - 6)/(2.448/\sqrt{12})$$
$$= .50/.7068$$
$$= .707$$
P-value $= P(t_{11} > .707) > .10$
conclusion:
Do not reject H_o; there is not sufficient evidence to conclude that $\mu > 6$.
While the sample mean is above 6, the teacher cannot be 95% certain that the population
mean is above 6.

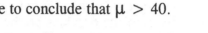

30.   Of the 50 films, 28 show the use of tobacco and are included in the sample.
summary statistics: $n = 28$, $\Sigma x = 2872$, $\Sigma x^2 = 694,918$, $\bar{x} = 102.57$, $s = 121.77$
original claim: $\mu = 120$ seconds
H_o: $\mu = 120$
H_1: $\mu \neq 120$
$\alpha = .05$ [assumed]
C.R. $t < -t_{27,.025} = -2.052$
         $t > t_{27,.025} = 2.052$
calculations:
$$t_{\bar{x}} = (\bar{x} - \mu)/s_{\bar{x}}$$
$$= (102.57 - 120)/(121.77/\sqrt{28})$$
$$= -17.429/23.012$$
$$= -.757$$
P-value $= 2 \cdot P(t_{27} < -.757) > .20$
conclusion:
Do not reject H_o; there is not sufficient evidence to conclude that $\mu \neq 120$.
Whether the claim is deceptive depends on what is meant by "given the sample data."
Considering the sample mean, the claim is not deceptive. If $\mu = 120$, one would not expect
to find $\bar{x} = 120$ in every sample – but values relatively near 120. The above $\bar{x} = 102.57$ is
near enough that we expect values that far or farther from 120 more than 20% of the time
when $\mu = 120$ is true. The claim could be considered deceptive, however, in that it refers
to "movies that show the use of tobacco" without indicating whether that is 1% or 75% of
the population – and most casual readers will mentally generalize the 2 minute figure to
include all films [instead of the approximately 56% suggested by the data].

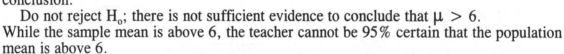

31.   summary statistics: n = 36, Σx = 439.0, Σx^2 = 5353.82, $\overline{x}$ = 12.194, s = .1145
original claim: $\mu > 12$
H_o: $\mu = 12$
H_1: $\mu > 12$
$\alpha = .01$
C.R. $t > t_{35,.01} = 2.441$
calculations:
$t_{\overline{x}} = (\overline{x} - \mu)/s_{\overline{x}}$
$= (12.194 - 12)/(.1145/\sqrt{36})$
$= .1944/.01908$
$= 10.189$

P-value $= P(t_{35} > 10.189) < .005$
conclusion:
Reject H_o; there is sufficient evidence to conclude that $\mu > 12$.
While the population mean appears to be above 12, the volume should not be reduced
unless the standard deviation can be lowered. If $\mu \approx 12.194$ and $\sigma \approx .1145$ as the data
suggests, then the limits $\mu \pm 2\sigma$ for "usual" occurrences already include values below 12 –
i.e., it would not be unusual to get a can with less than 12 ounces. Reducing the volume
would further increase the number of sub-standard cans, possibly to the point of serious
legal or public relations problems.

32.   summary statistics: n = 16, Σx = 104.8, Σx^2 = 724.74, $\overline{x}$ = 6.55, s = 1.598
original claim: $\mu > 6$
H_o: $\mu = 6$
H_1: $\mu > 6$
$\alpha = .05$ [assumed]
C.R. $t > t_{15,.05} = 1.753$
calculations:
$t_{\overline{x}} = (\overline{x} - \mu)/s_{\overline{x}}$
$= (6.55 - 6)/(1.598/\sqrt{16})$
$= .55/.39947$
$= 1.377$

$.05 < $ P-value $= P(t_{15} > 1.377) < .10$
conclusion:
Do not reject H_o; there is not sufficient evidence to conclude that $\mu > 6$.
No, we cannot be 95% certain that cereal has excessive sodium content.

33.   The P-value is changed. The summary values n, $\overline{x}$ and s do not change. The standard
error of the mean, which is $s_{\overline{x}} = s/\sqrt{n}$, does not change. The calculated t, which is
$t_{\overline{x}} = (\overline{x} - \mu)/s_{\overline{x}}$, does not change. Since the test is now two-tailed, the P-value doubles and
is now $2 \cdot P(t_{14} > 1.954) = 2 \cdot (.035) = .070$. In this instance, changing the P-value
changes the conclusion and (at the assumed .05 level of significance) there is not enough
evidence to reject H_o:$\mu = 420$.

34.   Because the z distribution has less spread than a t distribution, $z_\alpha < t_\alpha$ for any α. Since a
smaller z score (in absolute value) is needed to reject H_o, rejection is more likely with z
than with t.

35.   The new test of hypothesis is given below. In this instance the presence of a drastic outlier
outlier drastically changed the summery statistics but did not have much of an impact on
the overall test of hypothesis. In general, however, the effects of an outlier can be
substantial. One could argue that the effect is not so great in this exercise because the
original test already involved an outlier: by the $\overline{x} \pm s$ standard, 5.40 is an "unusual" result
– and it is so much larger than the others that it is the only value above $\overline{x}$.

summary statistics: $n=6$, $\Sigma x = 543.83$, $\Sigma x^2 = 291,603.3597$, $\overline{x} = 90.638$, $s = 220.142$

original claim: $\mu > 1.5$

$H_o: \mu = 1.5$

$H_1: \mu > 1.5$

$\alpha = .05$

C.R. $t > t_{5,.05} = 2.015$

calculations:

$\quad t_{\overline{x}} = (\overline{x} - \mu)/s_{\overline{x}}$

$\qquad = (90.638 - 1.5)/(220.142/\sqrt{6})$

$\qquad = 89.138/89.872$

$\qquad = .992$

$\quad$ P-value $= P(t_5 > .992) > .10$

conclusion:

$\quad$ Do not reject H_o; there is not sufficient evidence to conclude that $\mu > 1.5$.

36. $A = z_{.05} \cdot [8 \cdot df + 3)/(8 \cdot df + 1)]$

$\qquad = 1.645 \cdot [8 \cdot 9 + 3)/(8 \cdot 9 + 1)]$

$\qquad = 1.645 \cdot [75/73]$

$\qquad = 1.690$

$t = \sqrt{df \cdot (e^{A \cdot A/df} - 1)}$

$\quad = \sqrt{9 \cdot (e^{(1.960)(1.960)/9} - 1)}$

$\quad = \sqrt{9 \cdot (e^{.317} - 1)}$

$\quad = \sqrt{9 \cdot (.3735)}$

$\quad = 1.833$

This agrees exactly with $t_{9,.05} = 1.833$ given in Table A-3.

37. original claim: $\mu > 40$

$H_o: \mu = 40$

$H_1: \mu > 40$

$\alpha = .01$

C.R. $t > t_{9,.01} = 2.821$

calculations:

$\qquad t_{\overline{x}} = (\overline{x} - \mu)/s_{\overline{x}}$

$\quad 2.821 = (\overline{x} - 40)/(3.801/\sqrt{10})$

$\quad 3.390 = \overline{x} - 40$

$\qquad \overline{x} = 43.3899$

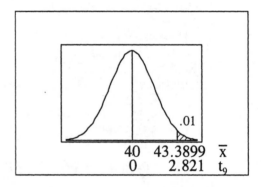

$\beta = P(\text{failing to reject } H_o | H_o \text{ is false})$

$\quad = P(\overline{x} < 43.3899 | \mu = 45.0518)$

$\quad = P(t_9 < -1.383)$

$\quad = .10 \ [\text{since } -t_{9,.10} = -1.383]$

in the above calculation of β,

$\quad t_{\overline{x}} = (\overline{x} - \mu)/s_{\overline{x}}$

$\qquad = (43.3899 - 45.0518)/(3.801/\sqrt{10})$

$\qquad = -1.6619/1.202$

$\qquad = -1.383$

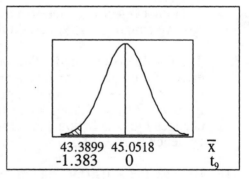

7-6 Testing a Claim about a Standard Deviation or Variance

NOTE: Following the pattern used with the z and t distributions, this manual uses the closest entry from Table A-4 for χ^2 as if it were the precise value necessary and does not use interpolation. This procedure sacrifices very little accuracy – and even interpolation does not yield precise values. When extreme accuracy is needed in practice, statisticians refer either to more accurate tables or to computer-produced values.

ADDITIONAL NOTE: The χ^2 distribution depends upon n, and it "bunches up" around df = n-1. In addition, the formula $\chi^2 = (n-1)s^2/\sigma^2$ used in the calculations contains df = n-1. When the exact df needed in the problem does not appear in the table and the closest χ^2 value is used to determine the critical region, some instructors recommend using the same df in the calculations that were used to determine the C.R. This manual typically uses the closest entry to determine the C.R. and the n from the problem in the calculations, even though this introduces a slight discrepancy.

1. H_o: $\sigma = 15$
     H_1: $\sigma \neq 15$
     $\alpha = .05$
     C.R. $\chi^2 < \chi^2_{19,.975} = 8.907$
          $\chi^2 > \chi^2_{19,.025} = 32.852$
     calculations:
          $\chi^2 = (n-1)s^2/\sigma^2$
              $= (19)(10)^2/(15)^2$
              $= 8.444$
          $.02 < $ P-value $< .05$

     conclusion:
          Reject H_o; there is sufficient evidence to conclude that $\sigma \neq 15$ (in fact, that $\sigma < 15$).

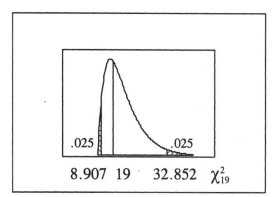

GRAPHICS NOTE: To illustrate χ^2 tests of hypotheses, this manual uses a "generic" figure, resembling a chi-squared distribution with approximately 4 degrees of freedom – chi-squared distributions with 1 and 2 degrees of freedom actually have no upper limit and approach the y axis asymptotically, while chi-squared distributions with more than 30 degrees of freedom are essentially symmetric and normal-looking. The expected value of the chi-squared distribution is the degrees of freedom for the problem, typically n-1. Since the distribution is positively skewed, this manual indicates that value slightly to the right of the figure's "peak." Loosely speaking, the distribution "bunches up" around the degrees of freedom.

2. H_o: $\sigma = 12$
     H_1: $\sigma > 12$
     $\alpha = .01$
     C.R. $\chi^2 > \chi^2_{4,.01} = 13.277$
     calculations:
          $\chi^2 = (n-1)s^2/\sigma^2$
              $= (4)(18)^2/(12)^2$
              $= 9.000$
          $.05 < $ P-value $< .10$

     conclusion:
          Do not reject H_o; there is not sufficient evidence to conclude that $\sigma > 12$.

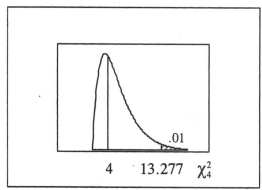

3. H_o: $\sigma = 50$
     H_1: $\sigma < 50$
     $\alpha = .01$
     C.R. $\chi^2 < \chi^2_{29,.99} = 14.257$
     calculations:
          $\chi^2 = (n-1)s^2/\sigma^2$
              $= (29)(30)^2/(50)^2$
              $= 10.440$
          P-value $< .005$

     conclusion:
          Reject H_o; there is sufficient evidence to conclude that $\sigma < 50$.

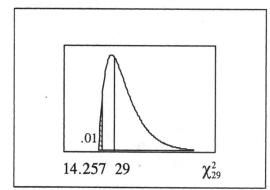

4. H_o: $\sigma = 4$
    H_1: $\sigma \neq 4$
    $\alpha = .05$
    C.R. $\chi^2 < \chi^2_{80,.975} = 57.153$
         $\chi^2 > \chi^2_{80,.025} = 106.629$
    calculations:
        $\chi^2 = (n-1)s^2/\sigma^2$
           $= (80)(4.7)^2/(4)^2$
           $= 110.450$
       $.02 < $ P-value $ < .05$
    conclusion:

    Reject H_o; there is sufficient evidence to conclude that $\sigma \neq 4$ (in fact, that $\sigma > 4$).

5. original claim: $\sigma > .04$
    H_o: $\sigma = .04$
    H_1: $\sigma > .04$
    $\alpha = .01$
    C.R. $\chi^2 > \chi^2_{39,.01} = 63.691$
    calculations:
        $\chi^2 = (n-1)s^2/\sigma^2$
           $= (39)(.31)^2/(.04)^2$
           $= 2342.4375$
       P-value $< .005$

    conclusion:
    Reject H_o; there is sufficient evidence to conclude that $\sigma > .04$.
Peanut M&M's vary more than plain M&M's since lack of uniformity in peanut sizes introduces a significant additional source of variation. Plain M&M's are produced to specifications with little variation from piece to piece. Peanut M&M's start with a peanut – not produced to specifications, but occurring with varying sizes. After rejecting very large and very small peanuts, there is still more variation than in a controlled process.

6. original claim: $\sigma < .0005$
    H_o: $\sigma = .0005$
    H_1: $\sigma < .0005$
    $\alpha = .05$
    C.R. $\chi^2 < \chi^2_{11,.95} = 4.575$
    calculations:
        $\chi^2 = (n-1)s^2/\sigma^2$
           $= (11)(.00047)^2/(.0005)^2$
           $= 9.7196$
       $.10 < $ P-value $ < .90$
    conclusion:

    Do not reject H_o; there is not sufficient evidence to conclude that $\sigma < .00047$.

7. original claim: $\sigma \neq 43.7$
    H_o: $\sigma = 43.7$
    H_1: $\sigma \neq 43.7$
    $\alpha = .05$
    C.R. $\chi^2 < \chi^2_{80,.975} = 57.153$
         $\chi^2 > \chi^2_{80,.025} = 106.629$
    calculations:
        $\chi^2 = (n-1)s^2/\sigma^2$
           $= (80)(52.3)^2/(43.7)^2$
           $= 114.586$
     $.01 < $ P-value $ < .02$

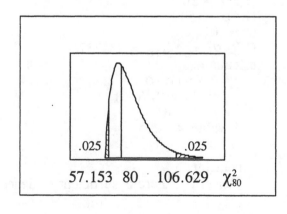

conclusion:
    Reject H_o; there is sufficient evidence to conclude that $\sigma \neq 43.7$ (in fact, that $\sigma > 43.7$). Since it appears that the standard deviation has increased, the new production method seems to be worse (at least so far as product consistency is concerned) than the old one.

8. original claim: $\sigma < 14.1$
    H_o: $\sigma = 14.1$
    H_1: $\sigma < 14.1$
    $\alpha = .01$
    C.R. $\chi^2 < \chi^2_{26,.99} = 12.198$
    calculations:
        $\chi^2 = (n-1)s^2/\sigma^2$
        $= (26)(9.3)^2/(14.1)^2$
        $= 11.311$
        $.005 < \text{P-value} < .01$

conclusion:
    Reject H_o; there is sufficient evidence to conclude that $\sigma < 14.1$.
No; a lower standard deviation does not suggest that the current class is doing better, but that they are more similar to each other and show less variation. The standard deviation speaks only about the spread of the scores and not their location.

9. original claim: $\sigma < 6.2$
    H_o: $\sigma = 6.2$
    H_1: $\sigma < 6.2$
    $\alpha = .05$
    C.R. $\chi^2 < \chi^2_{24,.95} = 13.848$
    calculations:
        $\chi^2 = (n-1)s^2/\sigma^2$
        $= (24)(3.8)^2/(6.2)^2$
        $= 9.016$
        $\text{P-value} < .005$

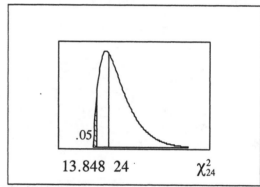

conclusion:
    Reject H_o; there is sufficient evidence to conclude that $\sigma < 6.2$.
Customers prefer waiting times with less variation because eliminating very long or very short waits depending only on which line is chosen creates a more predictable and more professional business climate. No; the smaller variability does not mean a smaller mean time.

10. original claim: $\sigma < 2.11$
    H_o: $\sigma = 2.11$
    H_1: $\sigma < 2.11$
    $\alpha = .005$
    C.R. $\chi^2 < \chi^2_{105,.005} = 67.328$
    calculations:
        $\chi^2 = (n-1)s^2/\sigma^2$
        $= (105)(.62)^2/(2.11)^2$
        $= 9.066$
        $\text{P-value} < .005$

conclusion:
    Reject H_o; there is sufficient evidence to conclude that $\sigma < 2.11$.
It appears we can be very confident that $\sigma < 2.11$ and that the previous conclusion about the mean is valid.

NOTE: When dealing with raw data, use the calculated value of s^2 directly in the formula $\chi^2 = (n-1)s^2/\sigma^2$. It is good to take the square root to find the value of s to see whether it is larger or smaller than the hypothesized σ, but do not introduce unnecessary rounding errors by entering the value for s and then squaring it.

11.   summary statistics: $n = 9$, $\Sigma x = 1089$, $\Sigma x^2 = 132223$, $\bar{x} = 121.0$, $s^2 = 56.75$
original claim: $\sigma < 29$
H_o: $\sigma = 29$
H_1: $\sigma < 29$
$\alpha = .01$
C.R. $\chi^2 < \chi^2_{8,.99} = 1.646$
calculations:
$\quad \chi^2 = (n-1)s^2/\sigma^2$
$\qquad = (8)(56.75)/(29)^2$
$\qquad = .540$
P-value $< .005$

conclusion:
   Reject H_o; there is sufficient evidence to conclude that $\sigma < 29$.

12.   summary statistics: $n = 18$, $\Sigma x = 1259.0$, $\Sigma x^2 = 88084.00$, $\bar{x} = 69.944$, $s^2 = 1.408$
original claim: $\sigma < 2.5$
H_o: $\sigma = 2.5$
H_1: $\sigma < 2.5$
$\alpha = .05$
C.R. $\chi^2 < \chi^2_{17,.95} = 8.672$
calculations:
$\quad \chi^2 = (n-1)s^2/\sigma^2$
$\qquad = (17)(1.408)/(2.5)^2$
$\qquad = 3.831$
P-value $< .005$

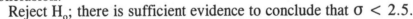

conclusion:
   Reject H_o; there is sufficient evidence to conclude that $\sigma < 2.5$.

13.   Usually we use the closest table entry – or, when the desired df is exactly halfway between the closest two tabled values, we act conservatively and choose the smaller df. For this exercise only (and related exercise #17), use interpolation to estimate
$\quad \chi^2_{35,.95} = (18.493 + 26.509)/2 = 22.501$.
summary statistics: $n = 36$, $\Sigma x = 442.5000$, $\Sigma x^2 = 5439.35004672$
$\quad \bar{x} = 12.2917$, $s^2 = .008216$ [$s = .0907$]
original claim: $\sigma < .10$
H_o: $\sigma = .10$
H_1: $\sigma < .10$
$\alpha = .05$
C.R. $\chi^2 < \chi^2_{35,.95} = 22.501$
calculations:
$\quad \chi^2 = (n-1)s^2/\sigma^2$
$\qquad = (35)(.008216)/(.10)^2$
$\qquad = 28.755$
$.10 <$ P-value $< .90$

conclusion:
   Do not reject H_o; there is not sufficient evidence to conclude that $\sigma < .10$.
If the mean is less than 12 ounces, then the company is guilty of cheating the consumers.
If the mean is greater than 12 ounces but the standard deviation is high, there still may be a significant number of individual cans containing less than 12 ounces.

14. summary statistics: $n = 40$, $\Sigma x = 4432$, $\Sigma x^2 = 502,488$, $\overline{x} = 111.0$, $s^2 = 292.882$
original claim: $\sigma = 23.4$
H_o: $\sigma = 23.4$
H_1: $\sigma \neq 23.4$
$\alpha = .05$ [assumed]
C.R. $\chi^2 < \chi^2_{39,.975} = 24.433$
　　$\chi^2 > \chi^2_{39,.025} = 59.342$
calculations:
　$\chi^2 = (n-1)s^2/\sigma^2$
　　$= (39)(292.882)/(23.4)^2$
　　$= 20.861$
　$.01 < $ P-value $ < .02$

conclusion:
　Reject H_o; there is sufficient evidence to conclude that $\sigma \neq 23.4$ (in fact, that $\sigma < 23.4$).

15. summary statistics: $n = 40$, $\Sigma x = 6902.0$, $\Sigma x^2 = 1,217,971.76$
　　$\overline{x} = 172.55$, $s^2 = 693.119$ [$s = 26.327$]
original claim: $\sigma = 28.7$
H_o: $\sigma = 28.7$
H_1: $\sigma \neq 28.7$
$\alpha = .05$
C.R. $\chi^2 < \chi^2_{39,.975} = 24.433$
　　$\chi^2 > \chi^2_{39,.025} = 59.342$
calculations:
　$\chi^2 = (n-1)s^2/\sigma^2$
　　$= (39)(693.110)/(28.7)^2$
　　$= 32.818$
　P-value $> .20$
conclusion:
　Do not reject H_o; there is not sufficient evidence to conclude that $\sigma \neq 28.7$.
Underestimating the variation in the weight could lead to designing an elevator that
handled the average expected weight per load, but that had a relatively high risk of being
overloaded.

16. summary statistics: $n = 40$, $\Sigma x = 2527.8$, $\Sigma x^2 = 160,037.38$, $\overline{x} = 63.195$, $s^2 = 7.5413$
original claim: $\sigma = 2.52$
H_o: $\sigma = 2.52$
H_1: $\sigma \neq 2.52$
$\alpha = .05$
C.R. $\chi^2 < \chi^2_{39,.975} = 24.433$
　　$\chi^2 > \chi^2_{39,.025} = 59.342$
calculations:
　$\chi^2 = (n-1)s^2/\sigma^2$
　　$= (39)(7.5413)/(2.52)^2$
　　$= 46.148$
　P-value $> .20$
conclusion:
　Do not reject H_o; there is not sufficient evidence to conclude that $\sigma \neq 2.52$.
Underestimating the variation in height could lead to designing car seats unsuitable for too
many women at the extremes – i.e., the proportion of women too short or to tall for the
seat could be unacceptably large.

17. Usually we use the closest table entry – or, when the desired df is exactly halfway between
the closest two tabled values, we act conservatively and choose the smaller df. For this
exercise only (and related exercise #13), use interpolation to estimate
　$\chi^2_{35,.95} = (18.493 + 26.509)/2 = 22.501$.

original claim: $\sigma < .10$
H_o: $\sigma = .10$
H_1: $\sigma < .10$
$\alpha = .05$
C.R. $\chi^2 < \chi^2_{35,.95} = 22.501$
calculations:
$$(n-1)s^2/\sigma^2 < 22.501$$
$$(35)s^2/(.10)^2 < 22.501$$
$$s^2 < .006428$$
$$s < .0802$$
The largest s that would lead to rejection of
H_o (and support of $\sigma < .10$) is $s = .08$

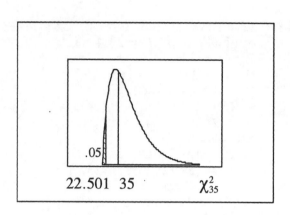

18.   a. lower $\chi^2 = \frac{1}{2}(-z_{.025} + \sqrt{2 \cdot df - 1}\,)^2$
$$= \frac{1}{2}(-1.96 + \sqrt{2 \cdot (100) - 1}\,)^2$$
$$= \frac{1}{2}(-1.96 + \sqrt{199}\,)^2$$
$$= \frac{1}{2}(147.543)$$
$$= 73.7722 \quad [\text{compare to } \chi^2_{100,.975} = 74.222 \text{ from Table A-4}]$$
upper $\chi^2 = \frac{1}{2}(z_{.025} + \sqrt{2 \cdot df - 1}\,)^2$
$$= \frac{1}{2}(1.96 + \sqrt{2 \cdot (100) - 1}\,)^2$$
$$= \frac{1}{2}(1.96 + \sqrt{199}\,)^2$$
$$= \frac{1}{2}(258.140)$$
$$= 129.070 \quad [\text{compare to } \chi^2_{100,.025} = 129.561 \text{ from Table A-4}]$$
b. lower $\chi^2 = \frac{1}{2}(-z_{.025} + \sqrt{2 \cdot df - 1}\,)^2$ upper $\chi^2 = \frac{1}{2}(z_{.025} + \sqrt{2 \cdot df - 1}\,)^2$
$= \frac{1}{2}(-1.96 + \sqrt{2 \cdot (149) - 1}\,)^2$ $= \frac{1}{2}(1.96 + \sqrt{2 \cdot (149) - 1}\,)^2$
$= \frac{1}{2}(-1.96 + \sqrt{297}\,)^2$ $= \frac{1}{2}(1.96 + \sqrt{297}\,)^2$
$= \frac{1}{2}(233.286)$ $= \frac{1}{2}(368.398)$
$= 116.643$ $= 184.199$

19.   a. lower $\chi^2 = df \cdot [1 - 2/(9 \cdot df) - z_{.025}\sqrt{2/(9 \cdot df)}\,]^3$
$$= 100 \cdot [1 - 2/(9 \cdot 100) - 1.96\sqrt{2/(9 \cdot 100)}\,]^3$$
$$= 100 \cdot [.9054]^3$$
$$= 74.216 \quad [\text{compare to } \chi^2_{100,.975} = 74.222 \text{ from Table A-4}]$$
upper $\chi^2 = df \cdot [1 - 2/(9 \cdot df) + z_{.025}\sqrt{2/(9 \cdot df)}\,]^3$
$$= 100 \cdot [1 - 2/(9 \cdot 100) + 1.96\sqrt{2/(9 \cdot 100)}\,]^3$$
$$= 100 \cdot [1.0902]^3$$
$$= 129.565 \quad [\text{compare to } \chi^2_{100,.025} = 129.561 \text{ from Table A-4}]$$
b. lower $\chi^2 = df \cdot [1 - 2/(9 \cdot df) - z_{.025}\sqrt{2/(9 \cdot df)}\,]^3$
$$= 149 \cdot [1 - 2/(9 \cdot 149) - 1.96\sqrt{2/(9 \cdot 149)}\,]^3$$
$$= 149 \cdot [.9228]^3$$
$$= 117.093$$
upper $\chi^2 = df \cdot [1 - 2/(9 \cdot df) - z_{.025}\sqrt{2/(9 \cdot df)}\,]^3$
$$= 149 \cdot [1 - 2/(9 \cdot 149) - 1.96\sqrt{2/(9 \cdot 149)}\,]^3$$
$$= 149 \cdot [1.0742]^3$$
$$= 184.690$$

20. Yes, although the effect may not be "dramatic" if the sample is extremely large. Because this section tests the "spread" of scores, and by definition an outlier is one that is "spread" away from the others, the presence of an outlier directly affects the property being measured and tested.

21.   a. If there are disproportionately more 0's and 5's, there would be an overabundance of digits less than 6 – i.e., at the lower end of the scale. This would reduce the mean to something less than 4.5 and (since most of the digits are bunched within these narrower limits) reduce the standard deviation to less than 3.

     b. If H_o were true and $\sigma = 3$, we would expect a uniform distribution of digits; if H_1 were true and $\sigma < 3$, we would expect a distribution of digits that peaks at 0 and/or 5 and is positively skewed. In either case, the data would not be coming from a normal distribution – which is one of the assumptions of the test.

22.   original claim: $\sigma < 6.2$

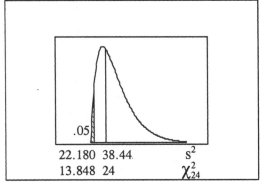

H_o: $\sigma = 6.2$
H_1: $\sigma < 6.2$
$\alpha = .05$
C.R. $\chi^2 < \chi^2_{24,.95} = 13.848$
calculations:

$$\chi^2 = (n-1)s^2/\sigma^2$$
$$13.848 = (24)s^2/(6.2)^2$$
$$532.317 = (24)s^2$$
$$22.180 = s^2$$

In terms of s^2, then, the expected value of the sampling distribution is $(6.2)^2 = 38.44$ critical region is $s^2 < 22.180$.

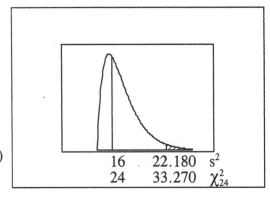

$$\beta = P(\text{not rejecting } H_o | H_o \text{ is false})$$
$$= P(s^2 > 22.180 | \sigma = 4)$$
$$= P(\chi^2_{24} > 33.270)$$
$$= .10 \text{ [from Table A-4,}$$
$$\text{closest entry } = 33.196]$$

The above value was obtained as follows:
If $\sigma = 4$ is true, the sampling distribution
at the right applies and $\chi^2 = (n-1)s^2/\sigma^2$
$$= (24)(22.180)/(16)$$
$$= 33.270$$

Review Exercises

1.   a. No; because the sample consisted only of those who chose to reply, the respondents are not necessarily representative of the general population.

     b. No; While the 0.2 lb loss is statistically significant, it is not of practical significance. In truth, there is essentially no chance that any H_o is <u>exactly</u> true to an infinite number of decimal places – and so given a large enough sample, virtually any H_o will be rejected. When the sample is so large that it is able to detect minute differences of no useful value, some statisticians call this "an insignificant significant difference."

     c. Choose .001, the smallest of the suggested P-values. This corresponds to the smallest chance that such results could have occurred by chance alone, and hence gives the most support to the conclusion that the cure was effective.

     d. Do not reject H_o: $\mu = 12$, there is not sufficient evidence to conclude that $\mu > 12$.

     e. "...rejecting the null hypothesis when it is true."

2. a. original claim: $\mu < 10,000 \Rightarrow H_o: \mu = 10,000$ and $H_1: \mu < 10,000$
       asks about μ, with σ unknown and $n > 30$: use the t distribution [with df $= 749$]
    b. original claim: $\sigma > 1.8 \Rightarrow H_o: \sigma = 1.8$ and $H_1: \sigma < 1.8$
       asks about σ: assuming the population is approximately normal, use the χ^2 distribution
    c. original claim: $p > .50 \Rightarrow H_o: p = .50$ and $H_1: p > .50$
       asks about p, with $np \geq 5$ and $n(1-p) \geq 5$: use the z distribution
    d. original claim: $\mu = 100 \Rightarrow H_o: \mu = 100$ and $H_1: \mu \neq 100$
       asks about μ, with σ known and $n > 30$: use the z distribution

3. a. original claim: $\mu = 100$
       $\overline{x} = 98.4$
       $H_o: \mu = 100$
       $H_1: \mu \neq 100$
       $\alpha = .10$
       C.R. $z < -z_{.05} = -1.645$
       $\quad z > z_{.05} = 1.645$
       calculations:
       $\quad z_{\overline{x}} = (\overline{x} - \mu)/\sigma_{\overline{x}}$
       $\quad\quad = (98.4 - 100)/(15/\sqrt{50})$
       $\quad\quad = -1.6/2.121 = -.75$
       P-value $= 2 \cdot P(z < -.75) = 2 \cdot (.2266) = .4532$
       conclusion:
       Do not reject H_o; there is not sufficient evidence reject the claim that $\mu = 100$.

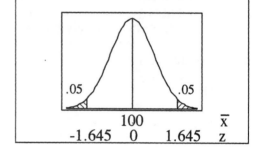

    b. original claim: $\mu = 100$
       $H_o: \mu = 100$
       $H_1: \mu \neq 100$
       $\alpha = .10$
       C.R. $t < -t_{49,.05} = -1.676$
       $\quad t > t_{49,.05} = 1.676$
       calculations:
       $\quad t_{\overline{x}} = (\overline{x} - \mu)/s_{\overline{x}}$
       $\quad\quad = (98.4 - 100)/(16.3/\sqrt{50})$
       $\quad\quad = -1.6/2.305 = -.694$
       P-value $> .20$
       conclusion:
       Do not reject H_o; there is not sufficient evidence to reject the claim that $\mu = 100$.

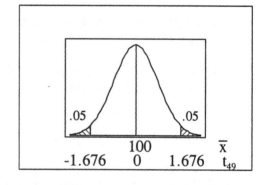

    c. original claim: $\sigma = 15$
       $H_o: \sigma = 15$
       $H_1: \sigma \neq 15$
       $\alpha = .10$
       C.R. $\chi^2 < \chi^2_{49,.95} = 34.764$
       $\quad \chi^2 > \chi^2_{49,.05} = 67.505$
       calculations:
       $\quad \chi^2 = (n-1)s^2/\sigma^2$
       $\quad\quad = (49)(16.3)^2/(15)^2$
       $\quad\quad = 57.861$
       P-value $> .20$
       conclusion:
       Do not reject H_o; there is not sufficient evidence to reject the claim that $\sigma = 15$.

    d. Yes; based on the preceding results, the random number generator appears to be
       working correctly.

4. original claim: $p < .50$
    $\hat{p} = x/n = x/150 = .44$
    H_o: $p = .50$
    H_1: $p < .50$
    $\alpha = .05$
    C.R. $z < -z_{.05} = -1.645$
    calculations:
    $\quad z_{\hat{p}} = (\hat{p} - \mu_{\hat{p}})/\sigma_{\hat{p}}$
    $\qquad = (.44 - .50)/\sqrt{(.50)(.50)/150}$
    $\qquad = -.06/.0408 = -1.47$
    $\quad$ P-value $= P(z < -1.47) = .0708$
    conclusion:
    $\quad$ Do not reject H_o; there is not sufficient evidence to conclude that $p < .50$.

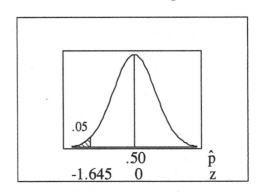

5. original claim: $\mu = 5.670$
    H_o: $\mu = 5.670$
    H_1: $\mu \neq 5.670$
    $\alpha = .01$
    C.R. $t < -t_{49,.005} = -2.678$
    $\qquad t > t_{49,.005} = 2.678$
    calculations:
    $\quad t_{\bar{x}} = (\bar{x} - \mu)/s_{\bar{x}}$
    $\qquad = (5.622 - 5.670)/(.068/\sqrt{50})$
    $\qquad = -.048/.009617 = -4.991$
    $\quad$ P-value $< .01$
    conclusion:
    $\quad$ Reject H_o; there is sufficient evidence to reject the claim that $\mu = 5.670$ and conclude
    that $\mu \neq 5.670$ (in fact, that $\mu < 5.670$).
    The quarters may have had a mean weight of 5.670 g when they were minted, but wear
    from being in circulation will reduce the weight of coins.

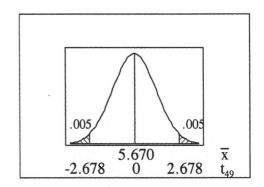

6. There are $n=5$ blue M%M's listed in Data Set 19.
    original claim: $\mu \geq .9085$
    H_o: $\mu = .9085$
    H_1: $\mu < .9085$
    $\alpha = .05$
    C.R. $t < -t_{4,.05} = -2.132$
    calculations:
    $\quad t_{\bar{x}} = (\bar{x} - \mu)/s_{\bar{x}}$
    $\qquad = (.9014 - .9085)/(.0573/\sqrt{5})$
    $\qquad = -.0071/.0256 = -.277$
    $\quad$ P-value $> .10$
    conclusion:
    $\quad$ Do not reject H_o; there is not sufficient evidence to reject the claim that $\mu \geq .9085$.
    No, this result does not provide evidence of such a discrepancy.

7. original claim: $p < .10$
    $\hat{p} = x/n = 111/1233 = .090$
    H_o: $p = .10$
    H_1: $p < .10$
    $\alpha = .05$
    C.R. $z < -z_{.05} = -1.645$
    calculations:
    $\quad z_{\hat{p}} = (\hat{p} - \mu_{\hat{p}})/\sigma_{\hat{p}}$
    $\qquad = (.090 - .10)/\sqrt{(.10)(.90)/1233}$
    $\qquad = -.010/.00854 = -1.17$

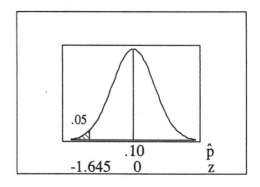

P-value = $P(z < -1.17)$ = .1210

conclusion:

Do not reject H_o; there is not sufficient evidence to conclude that $p < .10$. She can use that claim if she is willing to run a 12.10% risk of being wrong.

8. original claim: $p = .43$
    $\hat{p} = x/n = 308/611 = .504$
    H_o: $p = .43$
    H_1: $p \ne .43$
    $\alpha = .04$
    C.R. $z < -z_{.02} = -2.05$
    $\quad\quad z > z_{.02} = 2.05$
    calculations:
    $\quad z_{\hat{p}} = (\hat{p} - \mu_{\hat{p}})/\sigma_{\hat{p}}$
    $\quad\quad = (.0504 - .43)/\sqrt{(.43)(.57)/611}$
    $\quad\quad = .074/.0200$
    $\quad\quad = 3.70$

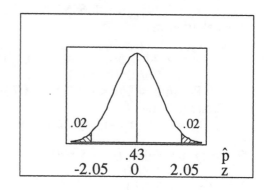

P-value = $2 \cdot P(z > 3.70)$ = $2 \cdot [1 - P(z < 3.70)]$ = $2 \cdot [1 - .9999]$ = $2 \cdot [.0001]$ = .0002

conclusion:

Reject H_o; there is sufficient evidence to reject the claim that $p = .43$ and conclude that $p \ne .43$ (in fact, that $p > .43$).

The result indicates that the proportion who say they voted for the winner is greater than proportion that actually did so vote. It appears that people are not responding honestly to the question – and this should raise a concern about the honesty of respondents in general, in situations where there is no independent reliable knowledge about the true value.

9. original claim: $\mu < 12$
    H_o: $\mu = 12$
    H_1: $\mu < 12$
    $\alpha = .05$ [assumed]
    C.R. $t < -t_{23,.05} = -1.714$
    calculations:
    $\quad t_{\bar{x}} = (\bar{x} - \mu)/s_{\bar{x}}$
    $\quad\quad = (11.4 - 12)/(.62/\sqrt{24})$
    $\quad\quad = -.6/.1266 = -4.741$
    $\quad$ P-value $< .005$
    conclusion:

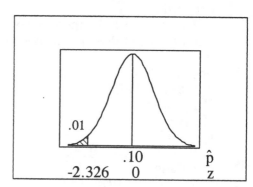

Reject H_o; there is sufficient evidence to conclude that $\mu < 12$.

No; assuming that proper random sampling techniques were used, his claim that the sample is too small to be meaningful is not valid. The t distribution adjusts for the various sample sizes to produce a valid test for any sample size n.

10. original claim: $p < .10$
    $\hat{p} = x/n = x/1248 = .08$
    H_o: $p = .10$
    H_1: $p < .10$
    $\alpha = .01$
    C.R. $z < -z_{.01} = -2.326$
    calculations:
    $\quad z_{\hat{p}} = (\hat{p} - \mu_{\hat{p}})/\sigma_{\hat{p}}$
    $\quad\quad = (.08 - .10)/\sqrt{(.10)(.90)/1248}$
    $\quad\quad = -.02/.00849 = -2.36$
    $\quad$ P-value = $P(z < -2.36) = .0091$
    conclusion:

Reject H_o; there is sufficient evidence to conclude that $p < .10$.

Yes; based on this result, the phrase "almost 1 out of 10" is justified. While "almost" is not well-defined, 10% is the closest round number to 8%. The test indicates we are confident that p < .10, but does not specify how much less.

NOTE: x=(.08)(1248)=99.84; any 94≤x≤106 rounds to 8%. Using the upper possibility $\hat{p}$ = x/n = 106/1248 = .0849 $z_{\hat{p}}$ = -1.774, which is not enough evidence to reject H_o: p=.10. This not only supports the opinion that "almost 1 out of 10" is justified, but it also shows how sensitive tests may be to rounding procedures – and that in this case the results are actually not reported with sufficient accuracy to conduct the test.

11. original claim: σ < .15
H_o: σ = .15
H_1: σ < .15
α = .05
C.R. χ^2 < $\chi^2_{70,.95}$ = 51.739
calculations:
χ^2 = (n-1)s^2/σ^2
    = (70)$(.12)^2$/$(.15)^2$
    = 44.800
.005 < P-value < .01

conclusion:
    Reject H_o; there is sufficient evidence to conclude that σ < .15.
Yes; assuming the costs and any other factors do not suggest otherwise, the company should consider purchasing the machine.

12. summary statistics: n = 70, Σx = 251.023, Σx^2 = 900.557440, $\bar{x}$ = 3.586, s = .0740
original claim: μ = 3.5
H_o: μ = 3.5
H_1: μ ≠ 3.5
α = .05 [assumed]
C.R. t < -$t_{69,.025}$ = -1.994
    t > $t_{69,.025}$ = 1.994
calculations:
$t_{\bar{x}}$ = ($\bar{x}$ - μ)/$s_{\bar{x}}$
    = (3.586 - 3.5)/(.0740/$\sqrt{70}$)
    = .086/.008849
    = 9.724
P-value < .01
conclusion:
    Reject H_o; there is sufficient evidence to reject the claim that μ = 3.5 and conclude that μ ≠ 3.5 (in fact, that μ > 3.5).
It appears the true mean weight is greater that the 3.5 g claimed on the label.

Cumulative Review Exercises

1. scores in order of magnitude: .018 .0268 .0281 .0320 .0440 .0524 .161 .175 .176
summary statistics: n = 9, Σx = .7133, Σx^2 = .09505961
a. $\bar{x}$ = (Σx)/n = .7133/9 = .0793
b. $\tilde{x}$ = .044
c. s^2 = [n(Σx^2) - $(\Sigma x)^2$]/[n(n-1)] = [9(.09505961) - $(.7133)^2$]/[9(8)] = .004816
    s = .0694
d. s^2 = .004816
e. R = .176 - .018 = .158

f. $\bar{x} = \pm t_{8,.025}s_{\bar{x}}$
   .0793 $\pm$ 2.306·(.0694/$\sqrt{9}$)
   .0793 $\pm$ .0533
   .0259 < μ < .1326

g. original claim: μ < .16

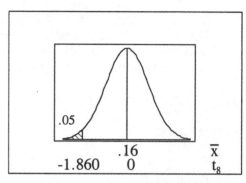

   H_0: μ = .16
   H_1: μ < .16
   α = .05
   C.R. t < -$t_{8,.05}$ = -1.860
   calculations:
   $t_{\bar{x}}$ = ($\bar{x}$ - μ)/$s_{\bar{x}}$
   = (.0793 - .16)/(.0694/$\sqrt{9}$)
   = -.0807/.0231 = -3.491
   P-value < .005
   conclusion:
   Reject H_0; there is sufficient evidence to conclude that μ < .16.

h. Yes; the values were listed in chronological order, and there seems to be a decreasing trend over time.

2.   a. normal distribution
   μ = 496
   σ = 108
   P(x > 500)
   = P(z > .04)
   = 1 - P(z < .04)
   = 1 - .5160
   = .4840

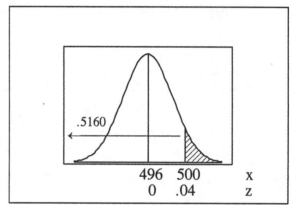

   b. let A = a selected score is above 500
   P(A) = .4840, for each selection
   $P(A_1$ and A_2 and A_3 and A_4 and $A_5)$
   = $P(A_1)$·$P(A_2)$·$P(A_3)$·$P(A_4)$·$P(A_5)$
   = $(.4840)^5$ = .0266

   c. normal distribution,
   since the original distribution is so
   $\mu_{\bar{x}}$ = μ = 496
   $\sigma_{\bar{x}}$ = $\sigma/\sqrt{n}$ = 108/$\sqrt{5}$ = 48.30
   P($\bar{x}$ > 500)
   = P(z > .08)
   = 1 - P(z < .08)
   = 1 - .5319
   = .4681

   d. For P_{90}, A = .9000 [.8997] and z = 1.28.
   [or, $z_{.10}$ = $t_{large,.10}$ = 1.282]
   x = μ + z·σ
   = 496 + (1.282)(108)
   = 496 + 138
   = 634

Chapter 8

Inferences from Two Samples

8-2 Inferences about Two Proportions

NOTE: To be consistent with the notation of the previous chapters, reinforcing the patterns and concepts presented there, the manual uses the "usual" z formula written to apply to $\hat{p}_1 - \hat{p}_2$'s:

$$z_{\hat{p}_1 - \hat{p}_2} = (\hat{p}_1 - \hat{p}_2 - \mu_{\hat{p}_1 - \hat{p}_2})/\sigma_{\hat{p}_1 - \hat{p}_2}$$

with $\mu_{\hat{p}_1 - \hat{p}_2} = p_1 - p_2$ and $\sigma_{\hat{p}_1 - \hat{p}_2} = \sqrt{\overline{p} \cdot \overline{q}/n_1 + \overline{p} \cdot \overline{q}/n_2}$ [when H_o includes $p_1 = p_2$]

where $\overline{p} = (x_1 + x_2)/(n_1 + n_2)$

And so the formula for the z statistic may also be written as

$$z_{\hat{p}_1 - \hat{p}_2} = ((\hat{p}_1 - \hat{p}_2) - (p_1 - p_2))/\sqrt{\overline{p} \cdot \overline{q}/n_1 + \overline{p} \cdot \overline{q}/n_2}$$

1. $x = \hat{p} \cdot n = .81 \cdot 37 = 29.97$, rounded to 30

2. $x = \hat{p} \cdot n = .63 \cdot 240 = 151.2$, rounded to 151 [although 152/240 also rounds to 63%]

3. $x = \hat{p} \cdot n = .289 \cdot 294 = 84.966$, rounded to 85

4. $x = \hat{p} \cdot n = .24 \cdot 205 = 49.2$, rounded to 49 [although 50/205 also rounds to 24%]

5. $\hat{p}_1 = x_1/n_1 = 192/436 = .440$ $\hat{p}_2 = x_2/n_2 = 40/121 = .331$
    $\hat{p}_1 - \hat{p}_2 = .440 - .331 = .110$
    a. $\overline{p} = (x_1 + x_2)/(n_1 + n_2) = (192 + 40)/(436 + 121) = 232/557 = .417$
    b. $z_{\hat{p}_1 - \hat{p}_2} = (\hat{p}_1 - \hat{p}_2 - \mu_{\hat{p}_1 - \hat{p}_2})/\sigma_{\hat{p}_1 - \hat{p}_2}$
       $= (.110 - 0)/\sqrt{(.417)(.583)/436 + (.417)(.583)/121}$
       $= .100/.0507 = 2.17$
    c. $\pm z_{.025} = \pm 1.960$
    d. P-value $= 2 \cdot P(z > 2.17) = 2 \cdot [1 - P(z < 2.17)] = 2 \cdot [1 - .9850] = 2 \cdot [.0150] = .0300$

NOTE: Since $\overline{p}$ is the weighted average of $\hat{p}_1$ and $\hat{p}_2$, it must always fall between those two values. If it does not, then an error has been made that must be corrected before proceeding. Calculation of $\sigma_{\hat{p}_1 - \hat{p}_2} = \sqrt{\overline{p} \cdot \overline{q}/n_1 + \overline{p} \cdot \overline{q}/n_2}$ can be accomplished with no round-off loss on most calculators by calculating $\overline{p}$ and proceeding as follows: STORE 1-RECALL = * RECALL = STORE RECALL ÷ n_1 + RECALL ÷ n_2 = $\sqrt{}$. The quantity $\sigma_{\hat{p}_1 - \hat{p}_2}$ may then be STORED for future use. Each calculator is different -- learn how your calculator works, and do the homework on the same calculator you will use for the exam. If you have any questions about performing/storing calculations on your calculator, check with your instructor or class assistant.

6. $\hat{p}_1 = x_1/n_1 = 101/10239 = .00986$ $\hat{p}_2 = x_2/n_2 = 56/9877 = .00567$
    $\hat{p}_1 - \hat{p}_2 = .00986 - .00567 = .00419$
    a. $\overline{p} = (x_1 + x_2)/(n_1 + n_2) = (101 + 56)/(10239 + 9877) = 157/20116 = .00780$
    b. $z_{\hat{p}_1 - \hat{p}_2} = (\hat{p}_1 - \hat{p}_2 - \mu_{\hat{p}_1 - \hat{p}_2})/\sigma_{\hat{p}_1 - \hat{p}_2}$
       $= (.00419 - 0)/\sqrt{(.00780)(.99220)/10239 + (.00780)(.99220)/9877}$
       $= .00419/.00124 = 3.38$
    c. $\pm z_{.025} = \pm 1.960$
    d. P-value $= 2 \cdot P(z > 3.38) = 2 \cdot [1 - P(z < 3.38)] = 2 \cdot [1 - .9996] = 2 \cdot [.0004] = .0008$

7. Let the employees be group 1.
    original claim: $p_1 - p_2 > 0$
    $\hat{p}_1 = x_1/n_1 = 192/436 = .440$
    $\hat{p}_2 = x_2/n_2 = 40/121 = .331$
    $\hat{p}_1 - \hat{p}_2 = .440 - .331 = .110$
    $\bar{p} = (x_1 + x_2)/(n_1 + n_2)$
    $\quad = (192 + 40)/(436 + 121)$
    $\quad = 232/557 = .417$
    H_o: $p_1 - p_2 = 0$
    H_1: $p_1 - p_2 > 0$
    $\alpha = .05$
    C.R. $z > z_{.05} = 1.645$
    calculations:

$z_{\hat{p}1-\hat{p}2} = (\hat{p}_1 - \hat{p}_2 - \mu_{\hat{p}1-\hat{p}2})/\sigma_{\hat{p}1-\hat{p}2}$
$\quad = (.110 - 0)/\sqrt{(.417)(.583)/436 + (.417)(.583)/121}$
$\quad = .110/.0507 = 2.17$
P-value $= P(z > 2.17) = 1 - P(z < 2.17) = 1 - .9850 = .0150$
conclusion:
    Reject H_o; there is sufficient evidence to conclude that $p_1 - p_2 > 0$.

8. Refer to the data and calculations in exercise #7.
    $(\hat{p}_1 - \hat{p}_2) \pm z_{.05}\sqrt{\hat{p}_1\hat{q}_1/n_1 + \hat{p}_2\hat{q}_2/n_2}$
    $.1098 \pm 1.645 \cdot \sqrt{(.440)(.560)/436 + (.331)(.669)/121}$
    $.1098 \pm .0805$
    $.029 < p_1 - p_2 < .190$
    Yes; since the interval does not contain zero, there is a significant difference between the employees and their bosses.

9. Let the women with low activity be group 1.
    $\hat{p}_1 = x_1/n_1 = 101/10239 = .00986$ $\qquad$ $\hat{p}_2 = x_2/n_2 = 56/9877 = .00567$
    $\hat{p}_1 - \hat{p}_2 = .00986 - .00567 = .00419$
    $(\hat{p}_1 - \hat{p}_2) \pm z_{.05}\sqrt{\hat{p}_1\hat{q}_1/n_1 + \hat{p}_2\hat{q}_2/n_2}$
    $.00419 \pm 1.645 \cdot \sqrt{(.00986)(.99014)/10239 + (.00567)(.99433)/9877}$
    $.00419 \pm .00203$
    $.00216 < p_1 - p_2 < .00623$
    Yes; since the confidence interval does not include 0, there does seem to be a significant difference – and that physical activity corresponds to a lower rate of the disease. Whether the difference is "substantial" is subjective, as the difference is only about 0.4%.

10. Refer to the data and calculations in exercise #9.
    original claim: $p_1 - p_2 > 0$
    $\bar{p} = (x_1 + x_2)/(n_1 + n_2)$
    $\quad = (101 + 56)/(10239 + 9877)$
    $\quad = 157/20116 = .00780$
    H_o: $p_1 - p_2 = 0$
    H_1: $p_1 - p_2 > 0$
    $\alpha = .05$
    C.R. $z > z_{.05} = 1.645$
    calculations:

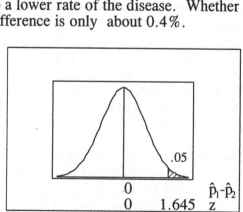

$z_{\hat{p}1-\hat{p}2} = (\hat{p}_1 - \hat{p}_2 - \mu_{\hat{p}1-\hat{p}2})/\sigma_{\hat{p}1-\hat{p}2}$
$\quad = (.00419 - 0)/\sqrt{(.00780)(.99220)/10239 + (.00780)(.99220)/9877}$
$\quad = .00419/.00124 = 3.38$
P-value $= P(z > 3.38) = 1 - P(z < 3.38) = 1 - .9996 = .0004$
conclusion:
    Reject H_o; there is sufficient evidence to conclude that $p_1 - p_2 > 0$.

11. Let the 2000 season be group 1.
     original claim: $p_1 - p_2 = 0$
     $\hat{p}_1 = x_1/n_1 = 83/247 = .336$
     $\hat{p}_2 = x_2/n_2 = 89/258 = .345$
     $\hat{p}_1 - \hat{p}_2 = .336 - .345 = -.00893$
     $\bar{p} = (x_1 + x_2)/(n_1 + n_2)$
     $= (83 + 89)/(247 + 258)$
     $= 172/505 = .341$
     H_o: $p_1 - p_2 = 0$
     H_1: $p_1 - p_2 \neq 0$
     $\alpha = .05$ [assumed]
     C.R. $z < -z_{.025} = -1.96$
     $z > z_{.025} = 1.96$
     calculations:

     $z_{\hat{p}1-\hat{p}2} = (\hat{p}_1 - \hat{p}_2 - \mu_{\hat{p}1-\hat{p}2})/\sigma_{\hat{p}1-\hat{p}2}$
     $= (-.00893 - 0)/\sqrt{(.341)(.659)/247 + (.341)(.659)/258}$
     $= -.00893/.0422 = -.21$
     P-value $= 2 \cdot P(z < -.21) = 2 \cdot (.4168) = .8336$
     conclusion:
     Do not reject H_o; there is not sufficient evidence to reject the claim that $p_1 - p_2 = 0$.
     Yes, the reversal rate appears to be the same for both years.

12. Let the employees of hospitals with the smoking ban be group 1.
     original claim: $p_1 - p_2 = 0$
     $\hat{p}_1 = x_1/n_1 = 56/843 = .0664$
     $\hat{p}_2 = x_2/n_2 = 27/703 = .0384$
     $\hat{p}_1 - \hat{p}_2 = .0664 - .0384 = .0280$
     $\bar{p} = (x_1 + x_2)/(n_1 + n_2)$
     $= (56 + 27)/(843 + 703)$
     $= 83/1546 = .0537$
     H_o: $p_1 - p_2 = 0$
     H_1: $p_1 - p_2 \neq 0$
     $\alpha = .05$
     C.R. $z < -z_{.025} = -1.96$
     $z > z_{.025} = 1.96$
     calculations:

     $z_{\hat{p}1-\hat{p}2} = (\hat{p}_1 - \hat{p}_2 - \mu_{\hat{p}1-\hat{p}2})/\sigma_{\hat{p}1-\hat{p}2}$
     $= (.0280 - 0)/\sqrt{(.0537)(.9463)/843 + (.0537)(.9463)/703}$
     $= .0280/.0115 = 2.43$
     P-value $= 2 \cdot P(z > 2.43) = 2 \cdot [1 - P(z < 2.43)] = 2 \cdot [1 - .9925] = 2 \cdot [.0075] = .0150$
     conclusion:
     Reject H_o; there is sufficient evidence to reject the claim that $p_1 - p_2 = 0$ and conclude
     that $p_1 - p_2 \neq 0$ (in fact, that $p_1 - p_2 > 0$).
     Since the calculated $z = 2.43 < z_{.005} < 2.575$ [and the calculated P-value $= .0150 > .01$], the
     difference is not significant at the .01 level of significance. Even though one cannot be
     99% certain, it does appear that the ban had an effect on the smoking quit rate.

13. Let those who received the vaccine be group 1.
     original claim: $p_1 - p_2 < 0$
     $\hat{p}_1 = x_1/n_1 = 14/1070 = .013$
     $\hat{p}_2 = x_2/n_2 = 95/532 = .179$
     $\hat{p}_1 - \hat{p}_2 = .013 - .179 = -.165$
     $\bar{p} = (x_1 + x_2)/(n_1 + n_2)$
     $= (14 + 95)/(1070 + 532)$
     $= 109/1602 = .068$

H_o: $p_1 - p_2 = 0$
H_1: $p_1 - p_2 < 0$
$\alpha = .05$ [assumed]
C.R. z < $-z_{.05}$ = -1.645

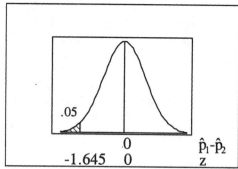

calculations:

$z_{\hat{p}_1 - \hat{p}_2} = (\hat{p}_1 - \hat{p}_2 - \mu_{\hat{p}_1 - \hat{p}_2})/\sigma_{\hat{p}_1 - \hat{p}_2}$
$= (-.165 - 0)/\sqrt{(.068)(.932)/1070 + (.068)(.932)/532}$
$= -.165/.0134 = -12.39$
P-value = P(z < -12.39) = .0001

conclusion:
   Reject H_o; there is sufficient evidence to conclude that $p_1 - p_2 < 0$.

14. Let the men group 1.
   a. original claim: $p_1 - p_2 > 0$
      $\hat{p}_1 = x_1/n_1 = 45/500 = .09000$
      $\hat{p}_2 = x_2/n_2 = 6/2100 = .00286$
      $\hat{p}_1 - \hat{p}_2 = .09000 - .00286 = .08714$
      $\bar{p} = (x_1 + x_2)/(n_1 + n_2)$
         $= (45 + 6)/(500 + 2100)$
         $= 51/2600 = .0196$

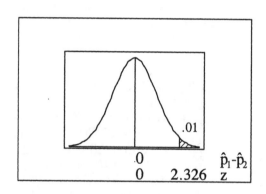

   H_o: $p_1 - p_2 = 0$
   H_1: $p_1 - p_2 > 0$
   $\alpha = .01$
   C.R. z > $z_{.01}$ = 2.326
   calculations:

   $z_{\hat{p}_1 - \hat{p}_2} = (\hat{p}_1 - \hat{p}_2 - \mu_{\hat{p}_1 - \hat{p}_2})/\sigma_{\hat{p}_1 - \hat{p}_2}$
      $= (.08714 - 0)/\sqrt{(.0196)(.9804)/500 + (.0196)(.9804)/2100}$
      $= .08714/.00690 = 12.63$
   P-value = P(z > 12.63) = 1 - P(z < 12.63) = 1 - .9999 = .0001
   conclusion:
      Reject H_o; there is sufficient evidence to conclude that $p_1 - p_2 > 0$.
   b. $(\hat{p}_1 - \hat{p}_2) \pm z_{.01}\sqrt{\hat{p}_1\hat{q}_1/n_1 + \hat{p}_2\hat{q}_2/n_2}$
      $.08714 \pm 2.326 \cdot \sqrt{(.09)(.91)/500 + (.00286)(.99714)/2100}$
      $.08714 \pm .02989$
      $.057 < p_1 - p_2 < .117$
      Yes; the interval does not contain zero, indicating a significant difference between the two groups.
   c. The proportion of women with this form of color blindness is very small. In general, the sample should be large enough to guarantee the occurrence of some persons with the desired characteristic so that a meaningful point estimate can be obtained. In particular, in order to use the normal approximation it must be true that $n_2 p_2 \geq 5$ – i.e., if p $\approx$ .003 we need $n_2 \geq 5/(.003) = 1667$.

15. Let those not wearing seat belts be group 1.
   original claim: $p_1 - p_2 > 0$
      $\hat{p}_1 = x_1/n_1 = 50/290 = .1724$
      $\hat{p}_2 = x_2/n_2 = 16/123 = .1301$
      $\hat{p}_1 - \hat{p}_2 = .1724 - .1301 = .0423$
      $\bar{p} = (x_1 + x_2)/(n_1 + n_2) = (50 + 16)/(290 + 123) = 66/413 = .160$

H_o: p_1-p_2 = 0
H_1: p_1-p_2 > 0
α = .05
C.R. z > $z_{.05}$ = 1.645

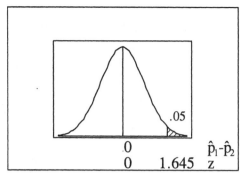

calculations:
$z_{\hat{p}_1-\hat{p}_2}$ = $(\hat{p}_1-\hat{p}_2 - \mu_{\hat{p}_1-\hat{p}_2})/\sigma_{\hat{p}_1-\hat{p}_2}$
        = (.0423 - 0)/$\sqrt{(.160)(.840)/290 + (.160)(.840)/123}$
        = .0423/.0394 = 1.07
P-value = P(z > 1.07) = 1 - P(z < 1.07) = 1 - .8577 = .1423
conclusion:
Do not reject H_o; there is not sufficient evidence to conclude that p_1-p_2 > 0.
Based on these results, no specific action should be taken.
NOTE: This test involves only children who were hospitalized – and perhaps a greater percentage of children wearing seat belts avoided being hospitalized in the first place.

16. Let the convicted arsonists be group 1.
original claim: p_1-p_2 > 0
    $\hat{p}_1$ = x_1/n_1 = 50/(50 + 43) = 50/93 = .538
    $\hat{p}_2$ = x_2/n_2 = 63/(63 + 144) = 63/207 = .304
    $\hat{p}_1$-$\hat{p}_2$ = .538 - .304 = .233
    $\bar{p}$ = $(x_1 + x_2)/(n_1 + n_2)$
       = (50 + 63)/(93 + 207)
       = 113/300 = .377

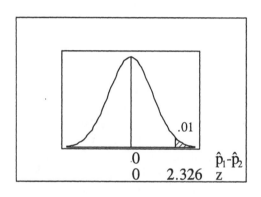

H_o: p_1-p_2 = 0
H_1: p_1-p_2 > 0
α = .01
C.R. z > $z_{.01}$ = 2.326
calculations:
$z_{\hat{p}_1-\hat{p}_2}$ = $(\hat{p}_1-\hat{p}_2 - \mu_{\hat{p}_1-\hat{p}_2})/\sigma_{\hat{p}_1-\hat{p}_2}$
        = (.233 - 0)/$\sqrt{(.377)(.623)/93 + (.377)(.623)/207}$
        = .233/.0605 = 3.86
P-value = P(z > 3.86) = 1 - P(z < 3.86) = 1 - .9999 = .0001
conclusion:
Reject H_o; there is sufficient evidence to conclude that p_1-p_2 > 0.
Yes; it does seem reasonable that drinking might be related to the type of crime. The kinds of problems and personalities associated with drinking may well be more likely to be associated with some crimes more than others.

17. Let the husband defendants be group 1.
original claim: p_1-p_2 > 0
    $\hat{p}_1$ = x_1/n_1 = 277/318 = .871
    $\hat{p}_2$ = x_2/n_2 = 155/222 = .698
    $\hat{p}_1$-$\hat{p}_2$ = .871 - .692 = .173
    $\bar{p}$ = $(x_1 + x_2)/(n_1 + n_2)$
       = (277 + 155)/(318 + 222)
       = 432/540 = .80

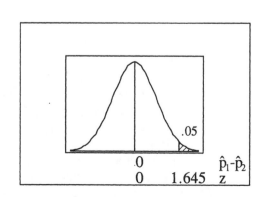

H_o: p_1-p_2 = 0
H_1: p_1-p_2 > 0
α = .05 [assumed]
C.R. z > $z_{.05}$ = 1.645

calculations:

$$z_{\hat{p}_1-\hat{p}_2} = (\hat{p}_1-\hat{p}_2 - \mu_{\hat{p}_1-\hat{p}_2})/\sigma_{\hat{p}_1-\hat{p}_2}$$
$$= (.173 - 0)/\sqrt{(.80)(.20)/318 + (.80)(.20)/222}$$
$$= .173/.0350 = 4.941$$

P-value $= P(z>4.94) = 1 - P(z<4.94) = 1 - .9999 = .0001$

conclusion:

Reject H_o; there is sufficient evidence to conclude that $p_1-p_2 > 0$.

In spouse murder cases the question is usually not about who committed the murder, but whether the murder was committed in self-defense. Since women are usually physically smaller and weaker than men, a self-defense plea would be more believable from a wife defendant.

18.   Let those receiving the Salk vaccine be group 1.

original claim: $p_1-p_2 < 0$

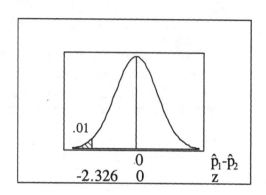

$\hat{p}_1 = x_1/n_1 = 33/200,000 = .000165$
$\hat{p}_2 = x_2/n_2 = 115/200,000 = .000575$
$\hat{p}_1-\hat{p}_2 = .000165 - .000575 = -.000410$
$\bar{p} = (x_1 + x_2)/(n_1 + n_2)$
$\quad = (33 + 115)/(200,000 + 200,000)$
$\quad = 148/400,000 = .00037$

H_o: $p_1-p_2 = 0$
H_1: $p_1-p_2 < 0$
$\alpha = .01$
C.R. $z < -z_{.01} = -2.326$

calculations:

$$z_{\hat{p}_1-\hat{p}_2} = (\hat{p}_1-\hat{p}_2 - \mu_{\hat{p}_1-\hat{p}_2})/\sigma_{\hat{p}_1-\hat{p}_2}$$
$$= (-.000410 - 0)/\sqrt{(.00037)(.99963)/200,000 + (.00037)(.99963)/200,000}$$
$$= -.000410/.0000608 = -6.7416 \text{ [from TI-83 Plus]}$$

P-value $= P(z < -6.74) = 7.88E-12 = .00000000000788$ [from TI-83 Plus]

conclusion:

Reject H_o; there is sufficient evidence to conclude that $p_1-p_2 < 0$.

Yes; assuming the group assignments were random, the vaccine appears to be effective.

19.   Let the Autozone stores be group 1.

original claim: $p_1-p_2 = 0$

$\hat{p}_1 = x_1/n_1 = 63/100 = .630$
$\hat{p}_2 = x_2/n_2 = 30/37 = .811$
$\hat{p}_1-\hat{p}_2 = .630 - .811 = -.181$
$\bar{p} = (x_1 + x_2)/(n_1 + n_2)$
$\quad = (63 + 30)/(100 + 37)$
$\quad = 93/137 = .679$

H_o: $p_1-p_2 = 0$
H_1: $p_1-p_2 \neq 0$
$\alpha = .05$
C.R. $z < -z_{.025} = -1.96$
$\quad\quad z > z_{.025} = 1.96$

calculations:

$$z_{\hat{p}_1-\hat{p}_2} = (\hat{p}_1-\hat{p}_2 - \mu_{\hat{p}_1-\hat{p}_2})/\sigma_{\hat{p}_1-\hat{p}_2}$$
$$= (-.181 - 0)/\sqrt{(.679)(.321)/100 + (.679)(.321)/37}$$
$$= -.181/.0898 = -2.01$$

P-value $= 2 \cdot P(z<-2.01) = 2 \cdot (.0222) = .0444$

conclusion:

Reject H_o; there is sufficient evidence to reject the claim that $p_1-p_2 = 0$ and conclude that $p_1-p_2 \neq 0$ (in fact, that $p_1-p_2 < 0$).

Yes; since Autozone has the lower failure rate, it appears to be the better choice.

20. Let Southwest be group 1.
a. original claim: $p_1-p_2 = 0$
$\hat{p}_1 = x_1/n_1 = 2181604/3131727 = .696613$
$\hat{p}_2 = x_2/n_2 = 1448255/2091859 = .692329$
$\hat{p}_1-\hat{p}_2 = .696613 - .692329 = .004285$
$\bar{p} = (x_1 + x_2)/(n_1 + n_2)$
     $= 3629859/5223586$
     $= .695$
H_o: $p_1-p_2 = 0$
H_1: $p_1-p_2 \neq 0$
$\alpha = .05$ [assumed]
C.R. $z < -z_{.025} = -1.96$
     $z > z_{.025} = 1.96$

calculations:
$z_{\hat{p}1-\hat{p}2} = (\hat{p}_1-\hat{p}_2 - \mu_{\hat{p}1-\hat{p}2})/\sigma_{\hat{p}1-\hat{p}2}$
     $= (.004285 - 0)/\sqrt{(.695)(.305)/3131727 + (.695)(.305)/2091859}$
     $= .004285/.0004112 = 10.42$
P-value $= 2 \cdot P(z > 10.42) = 2 \cdot [1 - P(z < 10.42) = 2 \cdot [1 - .9999] = 2 \cdot [.0001] = .0002$
conclusion:
Reject H_o; there is sufficient evidence to reject the claim that $p_1-p_2 = 0$ and conclude that $p_1-p_2 \neq 0$ (in fact, that $p_1-p_2 > 0$).

b. The very large sample sizes provide so much precision that it is possible to distinguish between the two values. In general, no two measurable values are <u>exactly</u> equal – i.e., given sufficiently large sample sizes and/or sufficiently precise measuring tools, the difference can always be detected. This illustrates the difference between statistical significance and practical significance. Some statisticians refer to this as "the insignificant significant difference."

c. "...can be statistically significant."

21. Let the single women be group 1. Since there is not enough information to determine the exact values of x_1 and x_2, the problem is limited to precision given below.
$\hat{p}_1 = x_1/n_1 = [49 \text{ or } 50]/205 = .24$ $\hat{p}_2 = x_2/n_2 = [70 \text{ or } 71]/260 = .27$
$\hat{p}_1-\hat{p}_2 = .24 - .27 = -.03$
$(\hat{p}_1-\hat{p}_2) \pm z_{.005}\sqrt{\hat{p}_1\hat{q}_1/n_1 + \hat{p}_2\hat{q}_2/n_2}$
$-.03 \pm 2.575 \cdot \sqrt{(.24)(.76)/205 + (.27)(.73)/260}$
$-.03 \pm .10$
$-.13 < p_1-p_2 < .07$
No; since the confidence interval includes 0, there does not appear to be a gender gap on this issue.

22. Refer to the data and calculations in exercise #22. Since the x's cannot be determined with certainty, one must accept the accuracy limitations imposed by the reported percents.
original claim: $p_1-p_2 \neq 0$
$\bar{p} = [n_1\hat{p}_1 - n_2\hat{p}_2]/(n_1 + n_2)$
     $= [205(.24) + 260(.27)]/(205 + 260)$
     $= 119.4/465 = .2568$
H_o: $p_1-p_2 = 0$
H_1: $p_1-p_2 \neq 0$
$\alpha = .01$
C.R. $z < -z_{.005} = -2.575$
     $z > z_{.005} = 2.575$

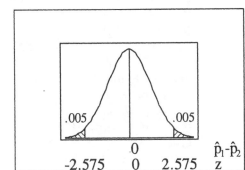

calculations:

$z_{\hat{p}_1-\hat{p}_2} = (\hat{p}_1-\hat{p}_2 - \mu_{\hat{p}_1-\hat{p}_2})/\sigma_{\hat{p}_1-\hat{p}_2}$

$= (-.03 - 0)/\sqrt{(.2568)(.7432)/205 + (.2568)(.7432)/260}$

$= -.03/.0408 = -.74$

P-value $= 2 \cdot P(z < -.74) = 2 \cdot (.2296) = .4592$

conclusion:

Do not reject H_o; there is not sufficient evidence to conclude that $p_1-p_2 \neq 0$.
No, there does not appear to be a difference in the proportions.

23.   Let those younger than 21 be group 1.

$\hat{p}_1 = x_1/n_1 = .0425$ $\hat{p}_2 = x_2/n_2 = .0455$

$\hat{p}_1-\hat{p}_2 = .0425 - .0455 = -.0029$

$(\hat{p}_1-\hat{p}_2) \pm z_{.025}\sqrt{\hat{p}_1\hat{q}_1/n_1 + \hat{p}_2\hat{q}_2/n_2}$

$-.0029 \pm 1.96 \cdot \sqrt{(.0425)(.9575)/2750 + (.0455)(.9545)/2200}$

$-.0029 \pm .0115$

$-.0144 < p_1-p_2 < .0086$

Yes; the interval contains zero, indicating no significant difference between the two rates of violent crimes.

24.   Let the vinyl gloves be group 1. Since the x's cannot be determined with certainty, one must accept the accuracy limitations imposed by the reported percents.

original claim: $p_1-p_2 > 0$

$\hat{p}_1 = x_1/n_1 = x_1/240 = .63$ [note: $x_1/240 = 63\%$ for $151 \leq x_1 \leq 152$]

$\hat{p}_2 = x_2/n_2 = x_2/240 = .07$ [note: $x_2/240 = 7\%$ for $16 \leq x_2 \leq 17$]

$\hat{p}_1-\hat{p}_2 = .63 - .07 = .56$

$\bar{p} = (x_1 + x_2)/(n_1 + n_2)$

$= (.63 \cdot 240 + .07 \cdot 240)/(240 + 240)$

$= 168/480 = .350$

H_o: $p_1-p_2 \leq 0$

H_1: $p_1-p_2 > 0$

$\alpha = .005$

C.R. $z > z_{.005} = 2.575$

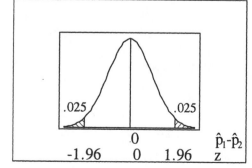

calculations:

$z_{\hat{p}_1-\hat{p}_2} = (\hat{p}_1-\hat{p}_2 - \mu_{\hat{p}_1-\hat{p}_2})/\sigma_{\hat{p}_1-\hat{p}_2}$

$= (.56 - 0)/\sqrt{(.350)(.650)/240 + (.350)(.650)/240}$

$= .56/.0435 = 12.86$

P-value $= P(z > 12.86) = 1 - P(z < 12.86) = 1 - .9999 = .0001$

conclusion:

Reject H_o; there is sufficient evidence to conclude that $p_1-p_2 > 0$.

25.   Let those given the written survey be group 1.

$\hat{p}_1 = x_1/n_1 = 67/850 = .079$ [note: $x_1 = (.079)(850) = 67$]

$\hat{p}_2 = x_2/n_2 = 105/850 = .124$ [note: $x_2 = (.124)(850) = 105$]

$\hat{p}_1-\hat{p}_2 = .079 - .124 = -.0447$

$\bar{p} = (x_1 + x_2)/(n_1 + n_2)$

$= (67 + 105)/(850 + 850)$

$= 172/1700 = .1012$

a. original claim: $p_1-p_2 = 0$

H_o: $p_1-p_2 = 0$

H_1: $p_1-p_2 \neq 0$

$\alpha = .05$ [assumed]

C.R. $z < -z_{.025} = -1.96$

$z > z_{.025} = 1.96$

calculations:

$z_{\hat{p}_1-\hat{p}_2} = (\hat{p}_1-\hat{p}_2 - \mu_{\hat{p}_1-\hat{p}_2})/\sigma_{\hat{p}_1-\hat{p}_2}$

$= (-.0447 - 0)/\sqrt{(.1012)(.8988)/850 + (.1012)(.8988)/850}$

$= -.0447/.0146 = -3.06$

P-value $= 2\cdot P(z < -3.06) = 2\cdot(.0011) = .0022$

conclusion:

Reject H_o; there is sufficient evidence to reject the claim that $p_1 - p_2 = 0$ and to conclude that $p_1-p_2 \neq 0$ (in fact, that $p_1 - p_2 < 0$ – i.e., that fewer students receiving the written test admit carrying a gun.)

Yes; based on this result the difference between 7.9% and 12.4% is significant.

b. $(\hat{p}_1-\hat{p}_2) \pm z_{.005}\sqrt{\hat{p}_1\hat{q}_1/n_1 + \hat{p}_2\hat{q}_2/n_2}$

$-.0447 \pm 2.575\cdot\sqrt{(.079)(.921)/850 + (.124)(.876)/850}$

$-.0447 \pm .0376$

$-.0823 < p_1-p_2 < -.0071$

The interval does not contain zero, indicating a significant difference between the two response rates. We are 99% confident the interval from -8.3% to -0.7% contains the true difference between the population percentages.

26. Let the Viagra users be group 1. Since the x's cannot be determined with certainty, one must accept the accuracy limitations imposed by the reported percents.

a. original claim: $p_1-p_2 > 0$

$\hat{p}_1 = x_1/n_1 = x_1/734 = .16$ [note: $x_1/734 = 16\%$ for $114 \leq x_1 \leq 121$]

$\hat{p}_2 = x_2/n_2 = x_2/725 = .04$ [note: $x_2/725 = 4\%$ for $26 \leq x_2 \leq 32$]

$\hat{p}_1-\hat{p}_2 = .16 - .04 = .12$

$\bar{p} = (x_1 + x_2)/(n_1 + n_2)$

$= (.16\cdot734 + .04\cdot725)/(734 + 725)$

$= 146.44/1459 = .1004$

H_o: $p_1-p_2 = 0$

H_1: $p_1-p_2 > 0$

$\alpha = .01$

C.R. $z > z_{.01} = 2.326$

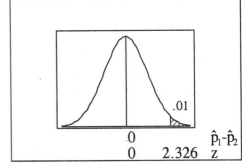

calculations:

$z_{\hat{p}_1-\hat{p}_2} = (\hat{p}_1-\hat{p}_2 - \mu_{\hat{p}_1-\hat{p}_2})/\sigma_{\hat{p}_1-\hat{p}_2}$

$= (.12 - 0)/\sqrt{(.1004)(.8996)/734 + (.1004)(.8996)/725}$

$= .12/.0157 = 7.63$

P-value $= P(z > 7.63) = 1 - P(z < 7.63) = 1 - .9999 = .0001$

conclusion:

Reject H_o; there is sufficient evidence to conclude that $p_1-p_2 > 0$.

Yes, men taking Viagra seem to experience more headaches.

b. $(\hat{p}_1-\hat{p}_2) \pm z_{.005}\sqrt{\hat{p}_1\hat{q}_1/n_1 + \hat{p}_2\hat{q}_2/n_2}$

$.12 \pm 2.575\cdot\sqrt{(.16)(.86)/734 + (.04)(.96)/725}$

$.12 \pm .04$

$.08 < p_1-p_2 < .16$

Since the interval does not contain zero, the headache rate was significantly larger for the Viagra group – i.e., headaches appear to be a side effect of Viagra.

27. Let the central city be group 1.

original claim: $p_1-p_2 = 0$

$\hat{p}_1 = x_1/n_1 = 85/294 = .289$ [note: $x_1 = (.289)(294) = 85$]

$\hat{p}_2 = x_2/n_2 = 174/1015 = .171$ [note: $x_2 = (.171)(1015) = 174$]

$\hat{p}_1-\hat{p}_2 = .289 - .171 = .118$

$\bar{p} = (x_1 + x_2)/(n_1 + n_2)$

$= (84 + 174)/(294 + 1015)$

$= 259/1309 = .198$

H_0: $p_1 - p_2 = 0$
H_1: $p_1 - p_2 \neq 0$
$\alpha = .01$
C.R. $z < -z_{.005} = -2.575$
$\quad\quad z > z_{.005} = 2.575$

calculations:

$z_{\hat{p}_1 - \hat{p}_2} = (\hat{p}_1 - \hat{p}_2 - \mu_{\hat{p}_1 - \hat{p}_2})/\sigma_{\hat{p}_1 - \hat{p}_2}$
$\quad\quad = (.118 - 0)/\sqrt{(.198)(.802)/294 + (.198)(.802)/1015}$
$\quad\quad = .118/.0264 = 4.47$

P-value $= 2 \cdot P(z > 4.47) = 2 \cdot [1 - P(z < 4.47)] = 2 \cdot [1 - .9999] = 2 \cdot [.0001] = .0002$

conclusion:

Reject H_0; there is sufficient evidence to reject the claim that $p_1 - p_2 = 0$ and to conclude that $p_1 - p_2 \neq 0$ (in fact, $p_1 - p_2 > 0$).

28. Let the basketball results be group 1.

$\hat{p}_1 = x_1/n_1 = 127/198 = .6414 \quad\quad\quad \hat{p}_2 = x_2/n_2 = 57/99 = .5758$
$\hat{p}_1 - \hat{p}_2 = .6414 - .5758 = .0657$

$(\hat{p}_1 - \hat{p}_2) \pm z_{.025}\sqrt{\hat{p}_1\hat{q}_1/n_1 + \hat{p}_2\hat{q}_2/n_2}$
$.0657 \pm 1.96 \cdot \sqrt{(.6414)(.3586)/198 + (.5758)(.4242)/99}$
$.0657 \pm .1181$
$-.052 < p_1 - p_2 < .184$

No; since the confidence interval includes zero, the home court advantage for basketball is not significantly different from the home field advantage in football. To decide whether there is a home advantage at all, one would have to see whether individual confidence intervals for p include the value .50.

29. Let the movies tested for alcohol use be group 1.

original claim: $p_1 - p_2 < 0$

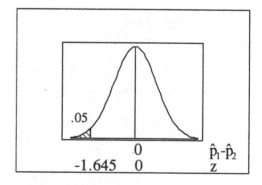

$\hat{p}_1 = x_1/n_1 = 25/50 = .50$
$\hat{p}_2 = x_2/n_2 = 28/50 = .56$
$\hat{p}_1 - \hat{p}_2 = .50 - .56 = -.06$
$\bar{p} = (x_1 + x_2)/(n_1 + n_2)$
$\quad = (25 + 28)/(50 + 50)$
$\quad = 53/100 = .53$

H_0: $p_1 - p_2 = 0$
H_1: $p_1 - p_2 < 0$
$\alpha = .05$ [assumed]
C.R. $z < -z_{.01} = -1.645$

calculations:

$z_{\hat{p}_1 - \hat{p}_2} = (\hat{p}_1 - \hat{p}_2 - \mu_{\hat{p}_1 - \hat{p}_2})/\sigma_{\hat{p}_1 - \hat{p}_2}$
$\quad\quad = (-.06 - 0)/\sqrt{(.53)(.47)/50 + (.53)(.47)/50}$
$\quad\quad = -.06/.0998 = -.60$

P-value $= P(z < -.60) = .2743$

conclusion:

Do not reject H_0; there is not sufficient evidence to conclude that $p_1 - p_2 < 0$.

No; even though the data match those in Data Set 7, the results do not apply. One requirement for this section is that the two samples be independent. The data in Data Set 7 are not from independent samples, but from the same sample – analogous to studying whether the proportion of people who declare bankruptcy is different from the proportion of people with more than $10,000 of credit card debt, and using the same 50 people.

30.   Let the men be group 1.
original claim: $p_1-p_2 = 0$
$\hat{p}_1 = x_1/n_1 = 23/40 = .575$
$\hat{p}_2 = x_2/n_2 = 22/40 = .550$
$\hat{p}_1-\hat{p}_2 = .575 - .550 = .025$
$\bar{p} = (x_1 + x_2)/(n_1 + n_2)$
        $= (23 + 22)/(40 + 40)$
        $= 45/80 = .5625$
H_o: $p_1-p_2 = 0$
H_1: $p_1-p_2 \neq 0$
$\alpha = .05$ [assumed]
C.R. $z < -z_{.025} = -1.96$
    $z > z_{.025} = 1.96$
calculations:
    $z_{\hat{p}_1-\hat{p}_2} = (\hat{p}_1-\hat{p}_2 - \mu_{\hat{p}_1-\hat{p}_2})/\sigma_{\hat{p}_1-\hat{p}_2}$
        $= (.025 - 0)/\sqrt{(.5625)(.4375)/40 + (.5625)(.4375)/40}$
        $= .025/.1109 = .23$
    P-value $= 2\cdot P(z > .23) = 2\cdot[1 - P(z < .23)] = 2\cdot[1 - .5910] = 2\cdot[.4090] = .8180$
conclusion:
    Do not reject H_o; there is not sufficient evidence to reject the claim that $p_1-p_2 = 0$.

31.   For all parts of this exercise.
$\hat{p}_1 = x_1/n_1 = 112/200 = .56$ $\hat{p}_2 = x_2/n_2 = 88/200 = .44$
$\hat{p}_1-\hat{p}_2 = .56 - .44 = .12$ $\bar{p} = (x_1+x_2)/(n_1+n_2) = 200/400 = .50$

a. $(\hat{p}_1-\hat{p}_2) \pm z_{.025}\sqrt{\hat{p}_1\hat{q}_1/n_1 + \hat{p}_2\hat{q}_2/n_2}$
    $.120 \pm 1.96\cdot\sqrt{(.56)(.44)/200 + (.44)(.56)/200}$
    $.120 \pm .097$
    $.023 < p_1-p_2 < .217$
Since the interval does not include zero, the implication is that p_1 and p_2 are different.
Since the interval lies entirely above, conclude that $p_1-p_2 > 0$.

b. for group 1   for group 2
    $\hat{p} \pm z_{.025}\sqrt{\hat{p}\hat{q}/n}$ $\hat{p} \pm z_{.025}\sqrt{\hat{p}\hat{q}/n}$
    $.560 \pm 1.96\sqrt{(.56)(.44)/200}$ $.440 \pm 1.96\sqrt{(.44)(.56)/200}$
    $.560 \pm .069$ $.440 \pm .069$
    $.491 < p < .629$ $.371 < p < .509$
Since the intervals overlap, the implication is that p_1 and p_2 could be the same.

c. original claim: $p_1-p_2 = 0$
    H_o: $p_1-p_2 = 0$
    H_1: $p_1-p_2 \neq 0$
    $\alpha = .05$
    C.R. $z < -z_{.025} = -1.96$
        $z > z_{.025} = 1.96$

    calculations:
        $z_{\hat{p}_1-\hat{p}_2} = (\hat{p}_1-\hat{p}_2 - \mu_{\hat{p}_1-\hat{p}_2})/\sigma_{\hat{p}_1-\hat{p}_2}$
            $= (.12 - 0)/\sqrt{(.5)(.5)/200 + (.5)(.5)/200}$
            $= .12/.05 = 2.40$

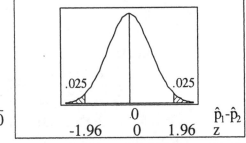

    P-value $= 2\cdot P(z > 2.40) = 2\cdot[1 - P(z < 2.40)] = 2\cdot[1 - .9918] = 2\cdot[.0082] = .0164$
    conclusion:
        Reject H_o; there is sufficient evidence to reject the claim that $p_1-p_2 = 0$ and conclude
        that $p_1-p_2 \neq 0$ (in fact, that $p_1-p_2 > 0$).

d. Based on parts (a)-(c), conclude that p_1 and p_2 are unequal, and that $p_1 > p_2$. The
    overlapping interval method of part (b) appears to be the least effective method for
    comparing two populations.

32. For all parts of this exercise.

$\hat{p}_1 = x_1/n_1 = 10/20 = .500$ $\hat{p}_2 = x_2/n_2 = 1404/2000 = .702$

$\hat{p}_1 - \hat{p}_2 = .500 - .702 = -.202$ $\bar{p} = (x_1 + x_2)/(n_1 + n_2) = 1414/2020 = .70$

The test of hypothesis is as follows.

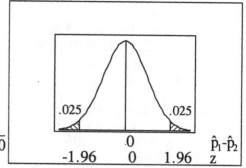

original claim: $p_1 - p_2 = 0$

H_o: $p_1 - p_2 = 0$

H_1: $p_1 - p_2 \neq 0$

$\alpha = .05$

C.R. $z < -z_{.025} = -1.96$
 $z > z_{.025} = 1.96$

calculations:

$z_{\hat{p}1-\hat{p}2} = (\hat{p}_1 - \hat{p}_2 - \mu_{\hat{p}1-\hat{p}2})/\sigma_{\hat{p}1-\hat{p}2}$

$= (-.202 - 0)/\sqrt{(.7)(.3)/20 + (.7)(.3)/2000}$

$= -.202/.10298 = -1.9615$

P-value $= 2 \cdot P(z < -1.96) = 2 \cdot (.0250) = .0500$ [actually, slightly less than .0500]

conclusion:

Reject H_o; there is sufficient evidence to reject the claim that $p_1 - p_2 = 0$ and conclude that $p_1 - p_2 \neq 0$ (in fact, that $p_1 - p_2 > 0$).

The confidence interval is as follows.

$(\hat{p}_1 - \hat{p}_2) \pm z_{.025}\sqrt{\hat{p}_1\hat{q}_1/n_1 + \hat{p}_2\hat{q}_2/n_2}$

$-.202 \pm 1.96 \cdot \sqrt{(.500)(.500)/20 + (.702)(.298)/2000}$

$-.202 \pm .220$

$-.422 < p_1 - p_2 < .018$

Since the interval include zero, the implication is that p_1 and p_2 could be the same that one should not reject the claim $p_1 - p_2 = 0$.

The test of hypothesis and the confidence interval lead to different conclusions. In this instance, they are not equivalent.

33. Let the black drivers be group 1.

The new test of hypothesis is as follows.

original claim: $p_1 - p_2 > 0$

$\hat{p}_1 = x_1/n_1 = 240/2000 = .120$

$\hat{p}_2 = x_2/n_2 = 1470/14,000 = .105$

$\hat{p}_1 - \hat{p}_2 = .120 - .105 = .015$

$\bar{p} = (x_1 + x_2)/(n_1 + n_2)$

$= (240 + 1470)/(2000 + 14000)$

$= 1710/16,000 = .107$

H_o: $p_1 - p_2 = 0$

H_1: $p_1 - p_2 > 0$

$\alpha = .05$

C.R. $z > z_{.05} = 1.645$

calculations:

$z_{\hat{p}1-\hat{p}2} = (\hat{p}_1 - \hat{p}_2 - \mu_{\hat{p}1-\hat{p}2})/\sigma_{\hat{p}1-\hat{p}2}$

$= (.015 - 0)/\sqrt{(.107)(.893)/2000 + (.107)(.893)/14000}$

$= .015/.007385 = 2.03$

P-value $= P(z > 2.03) = 1 - P(z < 2.03) = 1 - .9788 = .0212$

conclusion:

Reject H_o; there is sufficient evidence to conclude that $p_1 - p_2 > 0$.

The new confidence interval is as follows.

$(\hat{p}_1 - \hat{p}_2) \pm z_{.05}\sqrt{\hat{p}_1\hat{q}_1/n_1 + \hat{p}_2\hat{q}_2/n_2}$

$.015 \pm 1.645 \cdot \sqrt{(.120)(.880)/2000 + (.105)(.895)/14000}$

$.015 \pm .013$

$.002 < p_1 - p_2 < .028$

The test statistic increased from .64 to 2.03, now allowing one to conclude $p_1 - p_2 > 0$.

The confidence interval grew narrower to not include zero, now allowing one to conclude $p_1-p_2 > 0$. With the same point estimates, the increased sample size provides enough evidence to support the original claim.

34. Let the Viagra users be group 1. Since the x's cannot be determined with certainty, one must accept the accuracy limitations imposed by the reported percents.
original claim: $p_1-p_2 = .10$
$\hat{p}_1 = x_1/n_1 = x_1/734 = .16$ [note: $x_1/734 = 16\%$ for $114 \le x_1 \le 121$]
$\hat{p}_2 = x_2/n_2 = x_2/725 = .04$ [note: $x_2/725 = 4\%$ for $26 \le x_2 \le 32$]
$\hat{p}_1-\hat{p}_2 = .16 - .04 = .12$
H_o: $p_1-p_2 = .10$
H_1: $p_1-p_2 \ne .10$
$\alpha = .05$
C.R. $z < -z_{.025} = -1.96$
     $z > z_{.025} = 1.96$

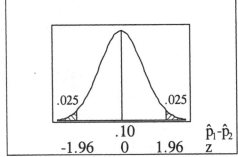

calculations:
$z_{\hat{p}1-\hat{p}2} = (\hat{p}_1-\hat{p}_2 - \mu_{\hat{p}1-\hat{p}2})/\sigma_{\hat{p}1-\hat{p}2}$
    $= (.12 - .10)/\sqrt{(.16)(.84)/734 + (.04)(.96)/725}$
    $= .02/.0154 = 1.30$
P-value $= 2 \cdot P(z > 1.30) = 2 \cdot [1 - P(z < 1.30)] = 2 \cdot [1 - .9032] = 2 \cdot [.0968] = .1936$
conclusion:
    Do not reject H_o; there is not sufficient evidence to reject the claim that $p_1-p_2 = .10$.

8-3 Inferences about Two Means: Independent Samples

NOTE: To be consistent with the previous notation, reinforcing the patterns and concepts presented in those sections, the manual uses the "usual" t formula written to apply to $\bar{x}_1-\bar{x}_2$'s
$$t_{\bar{x}1-\bar{x}2} = (\bar{x}_1-\bar{x}_2 - \mu_{\bar{x}1-\bar{x}2})/s_{\bar{x}1-\bar{x}2}$$
with $\mu_{\bar{x}1-\bar{x}2} = \mu_1 - \mu_2$ and $s_{\bar{x}1-\bar{x}2} = \sqrt{s_1^2/n_1 + s_2^2/n_2}$
And so the formula for the t statistic may also be written as
$$t_{\bar{x}1-\bar{x}2} = ((\bar{x}_1-\bar{x}_2) - (\mu_1-\mu_2))/\sqrt{s_1^2/n_1 + s_2^2/n_2}$$

1. Independent samples, since two groups are selected and evaluated separately.

2. Matched pairs, since each "before" measurement is paired with its "after" measurement.

3. Matched pairs, since each reported weight is paired with its measured weight.

4. Independent samples, since the two groups are selected and analyzed separately.

5. Let the light users be group 1.
original claim: $\mu_1-\mu_2 > 0$
    $\bar{x}_1-\bar{x}_2 = 53.3 - 51.3 = 2.0$
H_o: $\mu_1-\mu_2 = 0$
H_1: $\mu_1-\mu_2 > 0$
$\alpha = .01$
C.R. $t > t_{63,.01} = 2.385$
calculations:
$t_{\bar{x}1-\bar{x}2} = (\bar{x}_1-\bar{x}_2 - \mu_{\bar{x}1-\bar{x}2})/s_{\bar{x}1-\bar{x}2}$
    $= (2.0 - 0)/\sqrt{(3.6)^2/64 + (4.5)^2/65}$
    $= 2.0/.7170 = 2.790$
P-value $= P(t_{63} > 2.790) < .005$

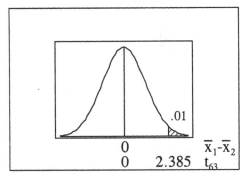

conclusion:

Reject H_o; there is sufficient evidence to conclude that $\mu_1 - \mu_2 > 0$.
Yes; based on these results, heavy marijuana use appears to impede performance.

6. Refer to the data and calculations of exercise #5.

$(\bar{x}_1 - \bar{x}_2) \pm t_{63,.01} \sqrt{s_1^2/n_1 + s_2^2/n_2}$

$2.0 \pm 2.385 \cdot \sqrt{(3.6)^2/64 + (4.5)^2/65}$

2.0 ± 1.7

$.3 < \mu_1 - \mu_2 < 3.7$

Since the confidence interval does not include zero, it suggests that the two population means are not equal – and that $\mu_1 > \mu_2$.

7. Let the placebo users be group 1.

$\bar{x}_1 - \bar{x}_2 = 21.57 - 20.38 = 1.19$

$(\bar{x}_1 - \bar{x}_2) \pm t_{32,.025} \sqrt{s_1^2/n_1 + s_2^2/n_2}$

$1.19 \pm 2.037 \cdot \sqrt{(3.87)^2/43 + (3.91)^2/33}$

1.19 ± 1.84

$-.65 < \mu_1 - \mu_2 < 3.03$

No; based on these results, we cannot be 95% certain that the two populations have different means. There is not enough evidence to make this the generally recommended treatment for bipolar depression.

8. Refer to the data and calculations of exercise #7.

original claim: $\mu_1 - \mu_2 = 0$

H_o: $\mu_1 - \mu_2 = 0$

H_1: $\mu_1 - \mu_2 \neq 0$

$\alpha = .05$

C.R. $t < -t_{32,.025} = -2.037$

$\qquad t > t_{32,.025} = 2.037$

calculations:

$t_{\bar{x}_1 - \bar{x}_2} = (\bar{x}_1 - \bar{x}_2 - \mu_{\bar{x}_1 - \bar{x}_2})/s_{\bar{x}_1 - \bar{x}_2}$

$\qquad = (1.19 - 0)/\sqrt{(3.87)^2/43 + (3.91)^2/33}$

$\qquad = 1.19/.9009 = 1.321$

$.10 < $ P-value $= 2 \cdot P(t_{32} > 1.321) < .20$

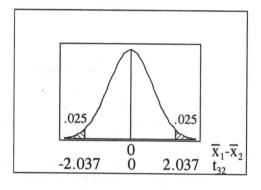

conclusion:

Do not reject H_o; there is not sufficient evidence to reject the claim that $\mu_1 - \mu_2 = 0$. This result indicates that there is not sufficient evidence to be 95% certain that the drug does any better than no drug at all.

9. Let those receiving the magnet treatment be group 1.

original claim: $\mu_1 - \mu_2 > 0$

$\bar{x}_1 - \bar{x}_2 = .49 - .44 = .05$

H_o: $\mu_1 - \mu_2 = 0$

H_1: $\mu_1 - \mu_2 > 0$

$\alpha = .05$

C.R. $t > t_{19,.05} = 1.729$

calculations:

$t_{\bar{x}_1 - \bar{x}_2} = (\bar{x}_1 - \bar{x}_2 - \mu_{\bar{x}_1 - \bar{x}_2})/s_{\bar{x}_1 - \bar{x}_2}$

$\qquad = (.05 - 0)/\sqrt{(.96)^2/20 + (1.4)^2/20}$

$\qquad = .05/.3796 = .132$

P-value $= P(t_{19} > .132) > .10$

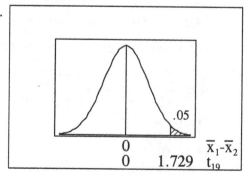

conclusion:

Do not reject H_o; there is not sufficient evidence to conclude that $\mu_1 - \mu_2 > 0$.
No, it does not appear that magnets are effective in treating back pain. If much larger

sample sizes achieved these same results, the calculated t could fall in the critical region and appear to provide evidence that the treatment is effective – but the observed difference would still be .05, and one would have to decide whether that statistically significant difference is of practical significance.

10. Refer to the data and calculations of exercise #9.
$(\bar{x}_1 - \bar{x}_2) \pm t_{19,.05}\sqrt{s_1^2/n_1 + s_2^2/n_2}$
$.05 \pm 1.729 \cdot \sqrt{(.96)^2/20 + (1.4)^2/20}$
$.05 \pm .66$
$-.61 < \mu_1 - \mu_2 < .71$
Since the interval includes zero, that the treatment has no effect is a reasonable possibility.

11. a. original claim: $\mu_1 - \mu_2 = 0$
$\bar{\bar{x}}_1 - \bar{x}_2 = .81682 - .78479 = .03203$
$H_o: \mu_1 - \mu_2 = 0$
$H_1: \mu_1 - \mu_2 \neq 0$
$\alpha = .01$
C.R. $t < -t_{35,.005} = -2.728$
$\quad\; t > t_{35,.005} = 2.728$
calculations:
$\quad t_{\bar{x}_1 - \bar{x}_2} = (\bar{x}_1 - \bar{x}_2 - \mu_{\bar{x}_1 - \bar{x}_2})/s_{\bar{x}_1 - \bar{x}_2}$

$\qquad = (.03203 - 0)/\sqrt{(.007507)^2/36 + (.004391)^2/36}$
$\qquad = .03203/.0014495 = 22.098$
P-value $= 2 \cdot P(t_{35} > 22.098) < .01$
conclusion:
Reject H_o; there is sufficient evidence to reject the claim that $\mu_1 - \mu_2 = 0$ and conclude that $\mu_1 - \mu_2 \neq 0$ (in fact, that $\mu_1 - \mu_2 > 0$).
Diet Coke probably weighs less because it uses an artificial sweetener that weighs less than real sugar – or perhaps because it simply uses less sweetener, and sweeteners in general are more dense than the rest of the product.

b. $(\bar{x}_1 - \bar{x}_2) \pm t_{35,.005}\sqrt{s_1^2/n_1 + s_2^2/n_2}$
$.03203 \pm 2.728 \cdot \sqrt{(.007507)^2/36 + (.004391)^2/36}$
$.03203 \pm .00395$
$.02808 < \mu_1 - \mu_2 < .03598$

12. a. original claim: $\mu_1 - \mu_2 < 0$
$\bar{x}_1 - \bar{x}_2 = .94 - 1.65 = -.71$
$H_o: \mu_1 - \mu_2 = 0$
$H_1: \mu_1 - \mu_2 < 0$
$\alpha = .05$
C.R. $t < -t_{7,.05} = -1.895$
calculations:
$\quad t_{\bar{x}_1 - \bar{x}_2} = (\bar{x}_1 - \bar{x}_2 - \mu_{\bar{x}_1 - \bar{x}_2})/s_{\bar{x}_1 - \bar{x}_2}$
$\qquad = (-.71 - 0)/\sqrt{(.31)^2/21 + (.16)^2/8}$
$\qquad = -.71/.08818 = -8.051$
P-value $= P(t_7 < -8.051) < .005$

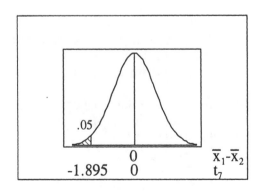

conclusion:
Reject H_o; there is sufficient evidence to conclude that $\mu_1 - \mu_2 < 0$.

b. $(\bar{x}_1 - \bar{x}_2) \pm t_{7,.05}\sqrt{s_1^2/n_1 + s_2^2/n_2}$
$-.71 \pm 1.895 \cdot \sqrt{(.31)^2/21 + (.16)^2/8}$
$-.71 \pm .17$
$-.88 < \mu_1 - \mu_2 < -.54$

c. Yes, cigarette filters appear to be effective in reducing the amount of nicotine transferred from the cigarette to the user. There is, of course, a fool-proof way to eliminate completely the amount of such nicotine taken into the body.

13.   Let the control subjects be group 1.
$$\overline{x}_1 - \overline{x}_2 = .45 - .34 = .11$$
$$(\overline{x}_1 - \overline{x}_2) \pm t_{9,.005} \sqrt{s_1^2/n_1 + s_2^2/n_2}$$
$$.11 \pm 3.250 \cdot \sqrt{(.08)^2/10 + (.08)^2/10}$$
$$.11 \pm .12$$
$$-.01 < \mu_1 - \mu_2 < .23$$
The confidence intervals suggests that the two samples could come from populations with the same mean. Based on this result, one cannot be 99% certain that there is such a biological basis for the disorders.

14.   Refer to the data and calculations of exercise #13.
original claim: $\mu_1 - \mu_2 = 0$
H_o: $\mu_1 - \mu_2 = 0$
H_1: $\mu_1 - \mu_2 \neq 0$
$\alpha = .01$
C.R. $t < -t_{9,.005} = -3.250$
        $t > t_{9,.005} = 3.250$
calculations:

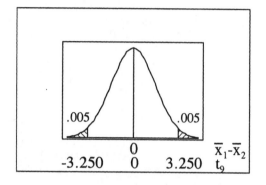

$$t_{\overline{x}_1 - \overline{x}_2} = (\overline{x}_1 - \overline{x}_2 - \mu_{\overline{x}_1 - \overline{x}_2})/s_{\overline{x}_1 - \overline{x}_2}$$
$$= (.11 - 0)/\sqrt{(.08)^2/10 + (.08)^2/10}$$
$$= .11/.0358 = 3.075$$
$$.01 < \text{P-value} = 2 \cdot P(t_9 > 3.075) < .02$$
conclusion:
    Do not reject H_o; there is not sufficient evidence to reject the claim that $\mu_1 - \mu_2 = 0$. The test of hypothesis suggests that the two samples could come from populations with the same mean. Based on this result, one cannot be 99% certain that there is such a biological basis for the disorders.

15.   Let the treatment subjects be group 1.
$$\overline{x}_1 - \overline{x}_2 = 4.20 - 1.71 = 2.49$$
$$(\overline{x}_1 - \overline{x}_2) \pm t_{21,.025} \sqrt{s_1^2/n_1 + s_2^2/n_2}$$
$$2.49 \pm 2.080 \cdot \sqrt{(2.20)^2/22 + (.72)^2/22}$$
$$2.49 \pm 1.03$$
$$1.46 < \mu_1 - \mu_2 < 3.52$$
Yes, since high scores indicate the presence of more errors and the confidence interval falls entirely above zero, the results support the common belief that drinking alcohol is hazardous for operators of passenger vehicles – and for their passengers.

16.   Refer to the data and calculations of exercise #15.
original claim: $\mu_1 - \mu_2 = 0$
H_o: $\mu_1 - \mu_2 = 0$
H_1: $\mu_1 - \mu_2 \neq 0$
$\alpha = .05$
C.R. $t < -t_{21,.025} = -2.080$
        $t > t_{21,.025} = 2.080$
calculations:

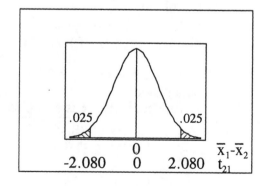

$$t_{\overline{x}_1 - \overline{x}_2} = (\overline{x}_1 - \overline{x}_2 - \mu_{\overline{x}_1 - \overline{x}_2})/s_{\overline{x}_1 - \overline{x}_2}$$
$$= (2.49 - 0)/\sqrt{(2.20)^2/22 + (.72)^2/22}$$
$$= 2.49/.4935 = 5.045$$
$$\text{P-value} = 2 \cdot P(t_{21} > 5.045) < .01$$
conclusion:
    Reject H_o; there is sufficient evidence to reject the claim that $\mu_1 - \mu_2 = 0$ and conclude

that $\mu_1-\mu_2 \neq 0$ (in fact, that $\mu_1-\mu_2 > 0$).
Yes; if there was no difference other than the treatment between the two groups, we can be 95% certain that the treatment was responsible for the decrease in visual and motor skills.

17. original claim: $\mu_1-\mu_2 > 0$
$\overline{x}_1-\overline{x}_2 = 53.3 - 45.3 = 8.0$
H_o: $\mu_1-\mu_2 = 0$
H_1: $\mu_1-\mu_2 > 0$
$\alpha = .01$
C.R. $t > t_{39,.01} = 2.429$
calculations:
$t_{\overline{x}_1-\overline{x}_2} = (\overline{x}_1-\overline{x}_2 - \mu_{\overline{x}_1-\overline{x}_2})/s_{\overline{x}_1-\overline{x}_2}$
     $= (8.0 - 0)/\sqrt{(11.6)^2/40 + (13.2)^2/40}$
     $= 8.0/2.778 = 2.879$
P-value $= P(t_{39} > 2.879) < .005$
conclusion:
Reject H_o; there is sufficient evidence to conclude that $\mu_1-\mu_2 > 0$.

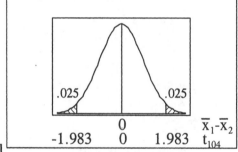

18. Refer to the data and calculations of exercise #17.
$(\overline{x}_1-\overline{x}_2) \pm t_{39,.01} \sqrt{s_1^2/n_1 + s_2^2/n_2}$
$8.0 \pm 2.429 \cdot \sqrt{(11.6)^2/40 + (13.2)^2/40}$
8.0 ± 6.7
$1.3 < \mu_1-\mu_2 < 14.7$
Yes, since high scores indicate more recall and the confidence interval falls entirely above zero, the results support the claim that stress decreased the amount recalled.

19. Let the westbound stowaways be group 1.
original claim: $\mu_1-\mu_2 = 0$
$\overline{x}_1-\overline{x}_2 = 26.71 - 24.84 = 1.87$
H_o: $\mu_1-\mu_2 = 0$
H_1: $\mu_1-\mu_2 \neq 0$
$\alpha = .05$
C.R. $t < -t_{104,.025} = -1.983$ [from Excel]
     $t > t_{104,.025} = 1.983$
calculations:
$t_{\overline{x}_1-\overline{x}_2} = (\overline{x}_1-\overline{x}_2 - \mu_{\overline{x}_1-\overline{x}_2})/s_{\overline{x}_1-\overline{x}_2}$
     $= (1.87 - 0)/\sqrt{(103.30)/56 + (67.81)/75}$
     $= 1.130$ [from Excel]
P-value $= 2 \cdot P(t_{104} > 1.130) = .2609$ [from Excel]
conclusion:
Do not reject H_o; there is not sufficient evidence to reject the claim that $\mu_1-\mu_2 = 0$.
No, there appears to be no significant difference between the ages.

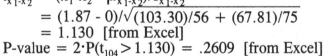

20. Let the Clancy pages be group 1.
original claim: $\mu_1-\mu_2 = 0$
$\overline{x}_1-\overline{x}_2 = 70.73 - 80.75 = -10.02$
H_o: $\mu_1-\mu_2 = 0$
H_1: $\mu_1-\mu_2 \neq 0$
$\alpha = .05$ [assumed]
C.R. $t < -t_{14.65,.025} =$ [unstated by TI-83 Plus]
     $t > t_{14.65,.025} =$ [unstated by TI-83 Plus]
calculations:
$t_{\overline{x}_1-\overline{x}_2} = (\overline{x}_1-\overline{x}_2 - \mu_{\overline{x}_1-\overline{x}_2})/s_{\overline{x}_1-\overline{x}_2}$
     $= (-10.02 - 0)/\sqrt{(s_1)^2/12 + (s_2)^2/12}$
     $= -2.831$ [from TI-83 Plus]

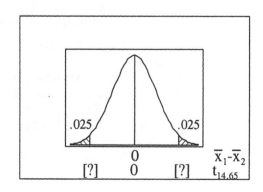

P-value = $2 \cdot P(t_{14.65} < -2.831) = .0127$ [from TI-83 Plus]
conclusion:

Reject H_o; there is sufficient evidence to reject the claim that $\mu_1 - \mu_2 = 0$ and conclude $\mu_1 - \mu_2 \neq 0$ (in fact, $\mu_1 - \mu_2 < 0$).

Yes, there is sufficient reason to believe the reading ease scores are different. Since a higher score represents greater reading ease, conclude that the Rowling material is easier reading that the Clancy material.

21. Let the filtered cigarettes be group 1

group 1: filtered (n = 21)   group 2: unfiltered (n = 8)

$\Sigma x = 279$ $\Sigma x = 192$

$\Sigma x^2 = 3987$ $\Sigma x^2 = 4628$

$\overline{x} = 13.286$ $\overline{x} = 24.000$

$s = 3.744$ $s = 1.690$

original claim: $\mu_1 - \mu_2 < 0$

$\overline{x}_1 - \overline{x}_2 = 13.286 - 24.000 = -10.714$

H_o: $\mu_1 - \mu_2 = 0$

H_1: $\mu_1 - \mu_2 < 0$

$\alpha = .05$

C.R. $t < -t_{7,.05} = -1.895$

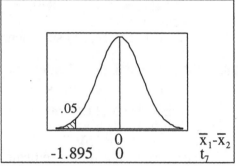

calculations:

$$t_{\overline{x}_1 - \overline{x}_2} = (\overline{x}_1 - \overline{x}_2 - \mu_{\overline{x}_1 - \overline{x}_2})/s_{\overline{x}_1 - \overline{x}_2}$$
$$= (-10.714 - 0)/\sqrt{(3.744)^2/21 + (1.690)^2/8}$$
$$= -.10.714/1.0122 = -10.585$$

P-value = $P(t_7 < -10.585) < .005$

conclusion:

Reject H_o; there is sufficient evidence to conclude that $\mu_1 - \mu_2 < 0$.

22. Let the easy to difficult items be group 1

group 1: E to D (n = 25)   group 2: D to E (n = 16)

$\Sigma x = 677.88$ $\Sigma x = 507.65$

$\Sigma x^2 = 19,509.3278$ $\Sigma x^2 = 16,379.0161$

$\overline{x} = 27.115$ $\overline{x} = 31.728$

$s^2 = 47.0198$ $s^2 = 18.1489$

original claim: $\mu_1 - \mu_2 = 0$

$\overline{x}_1 - \overline{x}_2 = 27.115 - 31.728 = -4.613$

H_o: $\mu_1 - \mu_2 = 0$

H_1: $\mu_1 - \mu_2 \neq 0$

$\alpha = .05$ [assumed]

C.R. $t < -t_{15,.025} = -2.131$

      $t > t_{15,.025} = 2.131$

calculations:

$$t_{\overline{x}_1 - \overline{x}_2} = (\overline{x}_1 - \overline{x}_2 - \mu_{\overline{x}_1 - \overline{x}_2})/s_{\overline{x}_1 - \overline{x}_2}$$
$$= (-4.613 - 0)/\sqrt{47.0198/25 + 18.1489/16}$$
$$= -4.613/1.736 = -2.657$$

$.01 < $ P-value $= 2 \cdot P(t_{15} < -2.657) < .02$

conclusion:

Reject H_o; there is sufficient evidence to reject the claim that $\mu_1 - \mu_2 = 0$ and conclude $\mu_1 - \mu_2 \neq 0$ (in fact, $\mu_1 - \mu_2 < 0$).

Yes; since high scores correspond to high anxiety, it appears that the easy to difficult arrangement is associated with less anxiety.

23. Let the men be group 1
<u>group 1: men</u> (n = 40)   <u>group 2: women</u> (n = 40)
$\sum x = 1039.9$ $\sum x = 1029.6$
$\sum x^2 = 27{,}493.83$ $\sum x^2 = 27{,}984.46$
$\bar{x} = 25.9975$ $\bar{x} = 25.7400$
$s = 3.43$ $s = 6.17$
original claim: $\mu_1 - \mu_2 = 0$
$\bar{x}_1 - \bar{x}_2 = 25.9975 - 25.7400 = .2575$
H_o: $\mu_1 - \mu_2 = 0$
H_1: $\mu_1 - \mu_2 \neq 0$
$\alpha = .05$ [assumed]
C.R. $t < -t_{39,.025} = -2.024$
      $t > t_{39,.025} = 2.024$
calculations:

$t_{\bar{x}_1-\bar{x}_2} = (\bar{x}_1 - \bar{x}_2 - \mu_{\bar{x}_1-\bar{x}_2})/s_{\bar{x}_1-\bar{x}_2}$
      $= (.2575 - 0)/\sqrt{(3.43)^2/40 + (6.17)^2/40}$
      $= .2575/1.1156 = .231$

P-value $= 2 \cdot P(t_{39} > .231) > .20$
conclusion:
Do not reject H_o; there is not sufficient evidence to reject the claim that $\mu_1 - \mu_2 = 0$.

24. Let the males be group 1
<u>group 1: males</u> (n = 111)   <u>group 2: females</u> (n=39)
$\sum x = 4397$ $\sum x = 1433$
$\sum x^2 = 184{,}083$ $\sum x^2 = 57{,}841$
$\bar{x} = 39.613$ $\bar{x} = 36.744$
$s = 9.49$ $s = 11.68$
original claim: $\mu_1 - \mu_2 = 0$
$\bar{x}_1 - \bar{x}_2 = 39.613 - 36.744 = 2.869$
H_o: $\mu_1 - \mu_2 = 0$
H_1: $\mu_1 - \mu_2 \neq 0$
$\alpha = .05$ [assumed]
C.R. $t < -t_{38,.025} = -2.024$
      $t > t_{38,.025} = 2.024$
calculations:

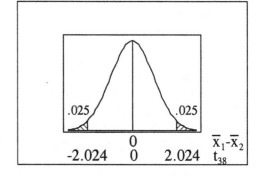

$t_{\bar{x}_1-\bar{x}_2} = (\bar{x}_1 - \bar{x}_2 - \mu_{\bar{x}_1-\bar{x}_2})/s_{\bar{x}_1-\bar{x}_2}$
      $= (2.869 - 0)/\sqrt{(9.49)^2/111 + (11.68)^2/39}$
      $= 2.869/2.076 = 1.382$

$.10 < \text{P-value} = 2 \cdot P(t_{38} > 1.382) < .20$
conclusion:
Do not reject H_o; there is not sufficient evidence to reject the claim that $\mu_1 - \mu_2 = 0$.

25. Let the placebo users be group 1.
$\bar{x}_1 - \bar{x}_2 = 21.57 - 20.38 = 1.19$
$s_p^2 = [(n_1-1) \cdot s_1^2 + (n_2-1) \cdot s_2^2]/(n_1 + n_2 - 2)$ $df = df_1 + df_2$
     $= [42(3.87)^2 + 32(3.91)^2]/74$ $= 42 + 32$
     $= 15.111$ $= 74$
$(\bar{x}_1 - \bar{x}_2) \pm t_{74,.025} \sqrt{s_p^2/n_1 + s_p^2/n_2}$
$1.19 \pm 1.992 \cdot \sqrt{15.111/43 + 15.111/33}$
1.19 ± 1.79
$-.60 < \mu_1 - \mu_2 < 2.98$
No; based on these results, we cannot be 95% certain that the two populations have different means. There is not enough evidence to make this the generally recommended treatment for bipolar depression.

▸The conclusion is the same, but the willingness to accept another assumption allows the confidence interval to be slightly narrower.

26. Refer to the data and calculations of exercise #25.
original claim: $\mu_1 - \mu_2 = 0$
H_o: $\mu_1 - \mu_2 = 0$
H_1: $\mu_1 - \mu_2 \neq 0$
$\alpha = .05$
C.R. $t < -t_{74,.025} = -1.992$
$\quad\quad t > t_{74,.025} = 1.992$
calculations:

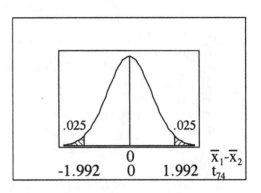

$$t_{\bar{x}_1 \cdot \bar{x}_2} = (\bar{x}_1 - \bar{x}_2 - \mu_{\bar{x}_1 \cdot \bar{x}_2})/s_{\bar{x}_1 \cdot \bar{x}_2}$$
$$= (1.19 - 0)/\sqrt{15.111/43 + 15.111/33}$$
$$= 1.19/.8996 = 1.323$$
$.10 < $ P-value $= 2 \cdot P(t_{74} > 1.323) < .20$
conclusion:
 Do not reject H_o; there is not sufficient evidence to reject the claim that $\mu_1 - \mu_2 = 0$. This result indicates that there is not sufficient evidence to be 95% certain that the drug does any better than no drug at all.
▸The conclusion is the same, but the willingness to accept another assumption makes rejection slightly more likely – the absolute value of the critical value is slightly smaller and the absolute value of the calculated test statistic is slightly larger.

27. Let those receiving the magnet treatment be group 1.
original claim: $\mu_1 - \mu_2 > 0$
$\bar{x}_1 - \bar{x}_2 = .49 - .44 = .05$
$s_p^2 = [(n_1 - 1) \cdot s_1^2 + (n_2 - 1) \cdot s_2^2]/(n_1 + n_2 - 2)$
$\quad = [19(.96)^2 + 19(1.41)^2]/38 = 1.4408$
H_o: $\mu_1 - \mu_2 = 0$
H_1: $\mu_1 - \mu_2 > 0$
$\alpha = .05$
C.R. $t > t_{38,.05} = 1.686$
calculations:

df $= df_1 + df_2$
$\quad = 19 + 19 = 38$

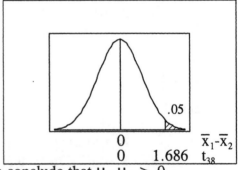

$$t_{\bar{x}_1 \cdot \bar{x}_2} = (\bar{x}_1 - \bar{x}_2 - \mu_{\bar{x}_1 \cdot \bar{x}_2})/s_{\bar{x}_1 \cdot \bar{x}_2}$$
$$= (.05 - 0)/\sqrt{1.4408/20 + 1.4408/20}$$
$$= .05/.3796 = .132$$
P-value $= P(t_{38} > .132) > .10$
conclusion:
 Do not reject H_o; there is not sufficient evidence to conclude that $\mu_1 - \mu_2 > 0$. No, it does not appear that magnets are effective in treating back pain. If much larger sample sizes achieved these same results, the calculated t could fall in the critical region and appear to provide evidence that the treatment is effective – but the observed difference would still be .05, and one would have to decide whether that statistically significant difference is of practical significance.
▸The conclusion is the same, but the willingness to accept another assumption makes rejection slightly more likely – the absolute value of the critical value is slightly smaller and the absolute value of the calculated test statistic is (since $n_1 = n_2$) the same.

28. Refer to the data and calculations of exercise #27.
$(\bar{x}_1 - \bar{x}_2) \pm t_{38,.05}\sqrt{s_p^2/n_1 + s_p^2/n_2}$
$.05 \pm 1.686 \cdot \sqrt{1.4408/20 + 1.4408/20}$
$.05 \pm .64$
$-.59 < \mu_1 - \mu_2 < .69$
Since the interval includes zero, that the treatment has no effect is a reasonable possibility.
▸The conclusion is the same, but the willingness to accept another assumption allows

the confidence interval to be slightly narrower.

29.   NOTE: Exercise #19 used df=104 as determined by Excel, to produce CV = ±1.983. Even though changing the sample size and the variance of one of the groups will change these values, this manual re-uses them unchanged – both to avoid a discussion of Excel's algorithm for determining df, and to better compare the new result to the original one.

a. Let the westbound stowaways be group 1.
   new group 1 values based on n = 57
   $\Sigma x = 1496+90 = 1586$
   $\Sigma x^2 = 45646+8100 = 53746$
   $\overline{x} = 27.825$ $s^2 = 171.72$
   original claim: $\mu_1-\mu_2 = 0$
   $\overline{x}_1-\overline{x}_2 = 27.825 - 24.840 = 2.985$
   H_o: $\mu_1-\mu_2 = 0$
   H_1: $\mu_1-\mu_2 \neq 0$
   $\alpha = .05$
   C.R. t < $-t_{104,.025} = -1.983$ [from Excel]
        t > $t_{104,.025} = 1.983$
   calculations:

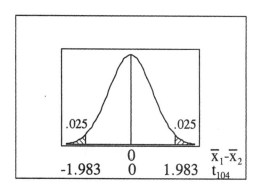

   $t_{\overline{x}_1-\overline{x}_2} = (\overline{x}_1-\overline{x}_2 - \mu_{\overline{x}_1-\overline{x}_2})/s_{\overline{x}_1-\overline{x}_2}$
        $= (2.985 - 0)/\sqrt{(171.72)/57 + (67.81)/75}$
        $= 2.985/1.979 = 1.508$
   $.10 < \text{P-value} = 2\cdot P(t_{104}>1.508) < .20$
   conclusion:
   Do not reject H_o; there is not sufficient evidence to reject the claim that $\mu_1-\mu_2 = 0$. No, there appears to be no significant difference between the ages.
   ▸The conclusion is the same, but the P-value is smaller because the calculated t increased from 1.130 to 1.508.

b. Let the westbound stowaways be group 1.
   new group 1 values based on n = 57
   $\Sigma x = 1496+5000 = 6496$
   $\Sigma x^2 = 45,646+25,000,000 = 25,045,646$
   $\overline{x} = 27.825$ $s^2 = 434023$
   original claim: $\mu_1-\mu_2 = 0$
   $\overline{x}_1-\overline{x}_2 = 113.965 - 24.840 = 89.125$
   H_o: $\mu_1-\mu_2 = 0$
   H_1: $\mu_1-\mu_2 \neq 0$
   $\alpha = .05$
   C.R. t < $-t_{104,.025} = -1.983$ [from Excel]
        t > $t_{104,.025} = 1.983$
   calculations:

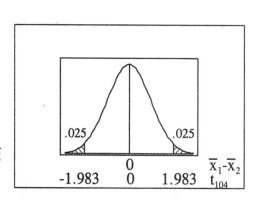

   $t_{\overline{x}_1-\overline{x}_2} = (\overline{x}_1-\overline{x}_2 - \mu_{\overline{x}_1-\overline{x}_2})/s_{\overline{x}_1-\overline{x}_2}$
        $= (89.125 - 0)/\sqrt{434023/57 + 67.81/75}$
        $= 89.125/87.266 = 1.021$
   $\text{P-value} = 2\cdot P(t_{104}>1.021) > .20$
   conclusion:
   Do not reject H_o; there is not sufficient evidence to reject the claim that $\mu_1-\mu_2 = 0$. No, there appears to be no significant difference between the ages.
   ▸The conclusion is the same, but the calculated t statistic actually decreased from 1.130 to 1.021. Even though the difference between the sample means increased, the variability in the problem (which in a sense is a measure of uncertainty) increased even more.

30. $A = s_1^2/n_1 = .0064/10 = .00064$ $df = (A + B)^2/(A^2/df_1 + B^2/df_2)$
          $B = s_2^2/n_2 = .0064/10 = .00064$ $= (.00064 + .00064)^2/(.00064^2/9 + .00064^2/9)$
          $\qquad\qquad\qquad\qquad\qquad\qquad = .000001638/.000000091$
          $\qquad\qquad\qquad\qquad\qquad\qquad = 18$

When $s_1^2=s_2^2$ and $n_1=n_2$, formula 8-1 yields $df = df_1 {}_+ df_2$.
In this exercise the tabled t value changes from $t_{9,.005} = 3.250$ to $t_{18,.005} = 2.878$.
In general, the larger df signifies a "tighter" t distribution that is closer to the z
distribution. In the test of hypothesis, the sampling distribution will be "tighter" and the
critical t value will be smaller – since the calculated t is not affected, the P-value will be
smaller. In the confidence interval, the tabled t value will be smaller – since the other
values are not affected, the interval will be narrower. Using $df = $ (smaller of df_1 or df_2) is
more conservative in that will not reject H_o as often and will lead to wider confidence
intervals – i.e., it will allows for a wider range of possible values for the parameter.

8-4 Inferences from Matched Pairs

NOTE: To be consistent with the notation of the previous sections, and thereby reinforcing the
patterns and concepts presented in those sections, the manual uses the "usual" t formula written
to apply to $\overline{d}$'s
$\qquad t_{\overline{d}} = (\overline{d} - \mu_{\overline{d}})/s_{\overline{d}}$, with $\mu_{\overline{d}} = \mu_d$ and $s_{\overline{d}} = s_d/\sqrt{n}$
And so the formula for the t statistic may also be written as
$\qquad t_{\overline{d}} = (\overline{d} - \mu_d)/(s_d/\sqrt{n})$

1. $d = x - y$: 1 -1 -2 -3 4
    summary: $n = 5$, $\Sigma d = -1$, $\Sigma d^2 = 31$
    a. $\overline{d} = (\Sigma d)/n = -1/5 = -.2$
    b. $s_d^2 = [n \cdot \Sigma d^2 - (\Sigma d)^2]/[n(n-1)]$
        $= [5 \cdot 31 - (-1)^2]/[5(4)] = 154/20 = 7.7$
        $s_d = 2.8$
    c. $t_{\overline{d}} = (\overline{d} - \mu_{\overline{d}})/s_{\overline{d}}$
        $= (-.2 - 0)/(2.774/\sqrt{5})$
        $= -.2/1.241 = -.161$
    d. $\pm t_{4,.025} = \pm 2.776$

2. $d = x - y$: 0 2 5 3 -4 1
    summary: $n = 6$, $\Sigma d = 7$, $\Sigma d^2 = 55$
    a. $\overline{d} = (\Sigma d)/n = 7/6 = 1.2$
    b. $s_d^2 = [n \cdot \Sigma d^2 - (\Sigma d)^2]/[n(n-1)]$
        $= [6 \cdot 55 - (7)^2]/[6(5)] = 281/30 = 9.367$
        $s_d = 3.1$
    c. $t_{\overline{d}} = (\overline{d} - \mu_{\overline{d}})/s_{\overline{d}}$
        $= (1.167 - 0)/(3.061/\sqrt{6})$
        $= 1.167/1.249 = .934$
    d. $\pm t_{5,.025} = \pm 2.571$

3. $\overline{d} \pm t_{4,.025} \cdot s_d/\sqrt{n}$
    $-.2 \pm 2.776 \cdot 2.775/\sqrt{5}$
    $-.2 \pm 3.4$
    $-3.6 < \mu_d < 3.2$

4. $\overline{d} \pm t_{5,.005} \cdot s_d/\sqrt{n}$
    $1.167 \pm 4.032 \cdot 3.061/\sqrt{6}$
    1.167 ± 5.037
    $-3.9 < \mu_d < 6.2$

5. $d = x - y$: -5.1 1.3 -0.1 1.2 0.8 -1.4 0.4 -0.5 -2.8 0.1 1.9 -1.5
    $n = 12$
    $\Sigma d = -5.7$ $\overline{d} = -.475$
    $\Sigma d^2 = 45.87$ $s_d = 1.981$
    a. original claim: $\mu_d = 0$
        $H_o: \mu_d = 0$
        $H_1: \mu_d \neq 0$
        $\alpha = .05$
        C.R. $t < -t_{11,.025} = -2.201$
        $\quad\;\; t > t_{11,.025} = 2.201$
        calculations:
        $t_{\overline{d}} = (\overline{d} - \mu_{\overline{d}})/s_{\overline{d}}$
        $= (-.475 - 0)/(1.981/\sqrt{12})$
        $= -.475/.5718 = -.831$

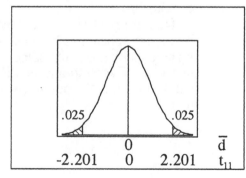

P-value $= 2 \cdot P(t_{11} < -.831) > .20$
conclusion:
    Do not reject H_o; there is not sufficient evidence to reject the claim that $\mu_d = 0$.

b. $\overline{d} \pm t_{11,.025} \cdot s_d/\sqrt{n}$
  $-.475 \pm 2.201 \cdot 1.981/\sqrt{12}$
  $-.475 \pm 1.259$
  $-1.73 < \mu_d < .78$

Since the confidence interval contains 0, there is no significant difference between the reported and measured heights.

6. $d = x - y$: 0.1 1.1 -1.9 1.7 0.7 -0.6 0.5 -3.0 -1.6 -11.2 1.0 1.2
    $n = 12$
    $\Sigma d = -12.0$ $\overline{d} = -1.0$
    $\Sigma d^2 = 148.26$ $s_d = 3.520$

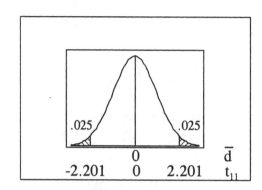

    a. original claim: $\mu_d = 0$
      H_o: $\mu_d = 0$
      H_1: $\mu_d \neq 0$
      $\alpha = .05$
      C.R. $t < -t_{11,.025} = -2.201$
           $t > t_{11,.025} = 2.201$
      calculations:
        $t_{\overline{d}} = (\overline{d} - \mu_{\overline{d}})/s_{\overline{d}}$
           $= (-1.0 - 0)/(3.520/\sqrt{12})$
           $= -1.0/1.016 = -.984$
      P-value $= 2 \cdot P(t_{11} < -.984) > .20$

    conclusion:
      Do not reject H_o; there is not sufficient evidence to reject the claim that $\mu_d = 0$.

    b. $\overline{d} \pm t_{11,.025} \cdot s_d/\sqrt{n}$
      $-1.0 \pm 2.201 \cdot 3.520/\sqrt{12}$
      -1.0 ± 2.2
      $-3.2 < \mu_d < 1.2$

    Since the confidence interval contains 0, there is no significant difference between the reported and measured heights.

NOTE: The one person who understated his height by 11.2 inches (63 vs. 74.2) deserves special consideration. This almost certainly represents someone who meant to report 6'3" – and either mis-converted and entered 63", or entered 6'3" and it was mis-read as 63". The practicing statistician encounters data like this frequently and has 4 options: (1) go back to the original source and/or data sheet for clarification, (2) change the entry to 75", (3) throw out that pair of data, (4) accept the entry as is.

7. $d = x - y$: -20 0 10 -40 -30 -10 30 -20 -20 -10
    $n = 10$
    $\Sigma d = -110$ $\overline{d} = -11.0$
    $\Sigma d^2 = 4900$ $s_d = 20.248$

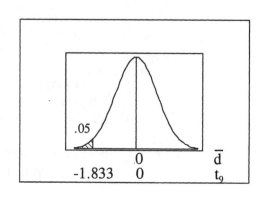

    a. original claim: $\mu_d < 0$
      H_o: $\mu_d = 0$
      H_1: $\mu_d < 0$
      $\alpha = .05$
      C.R. $t < -t_{9,.05} = -1.833$
      calculations:
        $t_{\overline{d}} = (\overline{d} - \mu_{\overline{d}})/s_{\overline{d}}$
           $= (-11.0 - 0)/(20.248/\sqrt{10})$
           $= -11.0/6.40$
           $= -1.718$
      $.05 < $ P-value $= P(t_9 < -1.718) < .10$

conclusion:

Do not reject H_o; there is not sufficient evidence to conclude that $\mu_d < 0$.

b. $\bar{d} \pm t_{9,.025} \cdot s_d/\sqrt{n}$

$-11.0 \pm 2.262 \cdot 20.248/\sqrt{10}$

-11.0 ± 14.5

$-25.5 < \mu_d < 3.5$

We have 95% confidence that the interval from -25.5 to 3.5 contains the true mean population difference. Since this interval includes 0, the mean before and after scores are not significantly different, and there is not enough evidence to say that the course has any effect.

8. $d = x_B - x_A$: 9 4 21 3 20 31 17 26 26 10 23 33

$n = 12$

$\Sigma d = 223$ $\bar{d} = 18.58$

$\Sigma d^2 = 5267$ $s_d = 10.104$

a. $\bar{d} \pm t_{11,.005} \cdot s_d/\sqrt{n}$

$18.58 \pm 3.106 \cdot 10.104/\sqrt{12}$

18.58 ± 9.06

$9.5 < \mu_d < 27.6$

b. original claim: $\mu_d > 0$

H_o: $\mu_d \le 0$

H_1: $\mu_d > 0$

$\alpha = .05$ [assumed]

C.R. $t > t_{11,.05} = 1.796$

calculations:

$t_{\bar{d}} = (\bar{d} - \mu_{\bar{d}})/s_{\bar{d}}$

$= (18.58 - 0)/(10.104/\sqrt{12})$

$= 6.371$

P-value = $P(t_{11} > 6.371) < .005$

conclusion:

Reject H_o; there is sufficient evidence to conclude that $\mu_d > 0$.

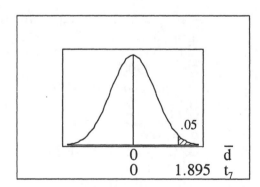

9. $d = x_B - x_A$: -.2 4.1 1.6 1.8 3.2 2.0 2.9 9.6

$n = 8$

$\Sigma d = 25.0$ $\bar{d} = 3.125$

$\Sigma d^2 = 137.46$ $s_d = 2.9114$

a. $\bar{d} \pm t_{7,.025} \cdot s_d/\sqrt{n}$

$3.125 \pm 2.365 \cdot 2.9114/\sqrt{8}$

3.125 ± 2.434

$.69 < \mu_d < 5.56$

b. original claim: $\mu_d > 0$

H_o: $\mu_d = 0$

H_1: $\mu_d > 0$

$\alpha = .05$

C.R. $t > t_{7,.05} = 1.895$

calculations:

$t_{\bar{d}} = (\bar{d} - \mu_{\bar{d}})/s_{\bar{d}}$

$= (3.125 - 0)/(2.9114/\sqrt{8})$

$= 3.125/1.029 = 3.036$

$.005 < $ P-value $= P(t_7 > 3.036) < .01$

conclusion:

Reject H_o; there is sufficient evidence to conclude that $\mu_d > 0$.

c. Yes; hypnotism appears to be effective in reducing pain.

10. $d = x_1 - x_2$: 0 13 5 15 15 126 28 -2 -5 31 3 51 3 14 37
   $n = 15$
   $\Sigma d = 334$ $\bar{d} = 22.27$
   $\Sigma d^2 = 22478$ $s_d = 32.777$

   a. original claim: $\mu_d = 0$
      H_o: $\mu_d = 0$
      H_1: $\mu_d \neq 0$
      $\alpha = .01$
      C.R. $t < -t_{14,.005} = -2.977$
         $t > t_{14,.005} = 2.977$
      calculations:
         $t_{\bar{d}} = (\bar{d} - \mu_{\bar{d}})/s_{\bar{d}}$
            $= (22.27 - 0)/(32.777/\sqrt{15})$
            $= 22.27/8.463 = 2.631$
         $.01 < $ P-value $= 2 \cdot P(t_{14} > 2.631) < .02$

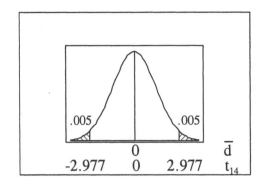

   conclusion:
      Do not reject H_o; there is not sufficient evidence to reject the claim that $\mu_d = 0$.

   b. $\bar{d} \pm t_{14,.005} \cdot s_d/\sqrt{n}$
      $22.27 \pm 2.977 \cdot 32.777/\sqrt{15}$
      22.27 ± 25.19
      $-2.9 < \mu_d < 47.5$
      Yes; the confidence interval limits contain 0, thus indicating we cannot be 99% certain
      there is a difference between the first and second trials.

11. $d = x - y$: -106 20 -101 33 -72 36 -62 -38 70 -127 -24
   $n = 11$
   $\Sigma d = -371$ $\bar{d} = -33.73$
   $\Sigma d^2 = 56299$ $s_d = 66.171$

   a. original claim: $\mu_d = 0$
      H_o: $\mu_d = 0$
      H_1: $\mu_d \neq 0$
      $\alpha = .05$
      C.R. $t < -t_{10,.025} = -2.228$
         $t > t_{10,.025} = 2.228$
      calculations:
         $t_{\bar{d}} = (\bar{d} - \mu_{\bar{d}})/s_{\bar{d}}$
            $= (-33.73 - 0)/(66.171/\sqrt{11})$
            $= -33.73/19.951 = -1.690$
         $.10 < $ P-value $= 2 \cdot P(t_{10} < -1.690) < .20$

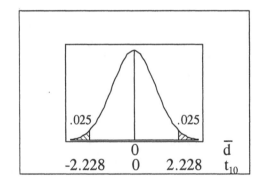

      conclusion:
      Do not reject H_o; there is not sufficient evidence to reject the claim that $\mu_d = 0$.

   b. $\bar{d} \pm t_{10,.025} \cdot s_d/\sqrt{n}$
      $-33.73 \pm 2.228 \cdot 66.171/\sqrt{11}$
      -33.73 ± 44.45
      $-78.2 < \mu_d < 10.7$

   c. We cannot be 95% certain that either type of seed is better. If there are no differences
      in cost, or any other considerations, choose the kiln dried – even though we can't be
      sure that it's generally better, it did have the higher yield in this particular trial.

12. $d = x - y$: -4 -11 2 -3 -4 -4 -8 -10 2 -4 -3 -4 -10 3 -10 -1 -8 -1 -6 -4
   $n = 20$
   $\Sigma d = -88$ $\bar{d} = -4.4$
   $\Sigma d^2 = 718$ $s_d = 4.173$

a. original claim: $\mu_d < 0$
   H_o: $\mu_d = 0$
   H_1: $\mu_d < 0$
   $\alpha = .01$
   C.R. $t < -t_{19,.01} = -2.539$
   calculations:
   $t_{\bar{d}} = (\bar{d} - \mu_{\bar{d}})/s_{\bar{d}}$
   $= (-4.4 - 0)/(4.173/\sqrt{20})$
   $= -4.4/.933 = -4.716$
   P-value $= P(t_{19} < -4.716) < .005$
   conclusion:
   Reject H_o; there is sufficient evidence to conclude that $\mu_d < 0$.

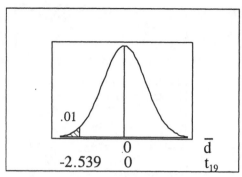

b. $\bar{d} \pm t_{19,.01} \cdot s_d/\sqrt{n}$
   $-4.4 \pm 2.539 \cdot 4.173/\sqrt{20}$
   -4.4 ± 2.4
   $-6.8 < \mu_d < -2.0$

13. a. original claim: $\mu_d \neq 0$
    H_o: $\mu_d = 0$
    H_1: $\mu_d \neq 0$
    $\alpha = .05$
    C.R. $t < -t_{9,.025} = -2.262$
    $ t > t_{9,.025} = 2.262$
    calculations:
    $t_{\bar{d}} = (\bar{d} - \mu_{\bar{d}})/s_{\bar{d}}$
    $= (-7.5 - 0)/(57.7/\sqrt{10})$
    $= -7.5/18.2 = -.41$ [from Minitab]
    P-value $= 2 \cdot P(t_9 < -.41) = .691$ [from Minitab]
    conclusion:
    Do not reject H_o; there is not sufficient evidence to conclude that $\mu_d \neq 0$.
    No; based on this result, do not spend the money for the drug.

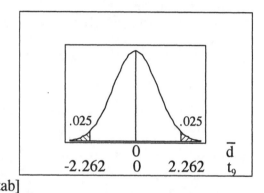

b. original claim: $\mu_d < 0$
   H_o: $\mu_d = 0$
   H_1: $\mu_d < 0$
   $\alpha = .05$
   C.R. $t < -t_{9,.05} = -1.833$
   calculations:
   $t_{\bar{d}} = (\bar{d} - \mu_{\bar{d}})/s_{\bar{d}}$
   $= (-7.5 - 0)/(57.7/\sqrt{10})$
   $= -7.5/18.2 = -.41$ [from Minitab]
   P-value $= P(t_9 < -.41) = \frac{1}{2}(.691) = .3455$
   conclusion:
   Do not reject H_o; there is not sufficient evidence to conclude that $\mu_d < 0$.
   All the calculations remain the same. The alternative hypothesis and critical region change to reflect the one-tailed test. The P-value is ½ the .691 given by Minitab for the two-tailed test.

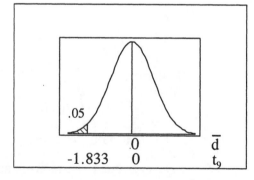

14. a. original claim: $\mu_d > 0$
    H_o: $\mu_d = 0$
    H_1: $\mu_d > 0$
    $\alpha = .05$
    C.R. $t > t_{6,.05} = 1.943$
    calculations:
    $t_{\bar{d}} = (\bar{d} - \mu_{\bar{d}})/s_{\bar{d}}$
    $= (5.142 - 0)/(2.116/\sqrt{7})$
    $= 6.431$ [from TI-83 Plus]

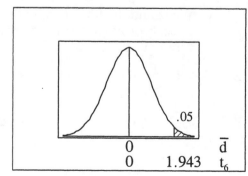

P-value $= P(t_6 > 6.431) = 3.34 \times 10^{-4} = .000334$
conclusion:
   Reject H_o; there is sufficient evidence to conclude that $\mu_d > 0$.
Yes; only $.0334\%$ of the time would such a weight loss occur by chance if the diet had no effect.

b. $\overline{d} = 5.142$ lbs.
   Yes; the weight loss is large enough to make the diet practical

c. $\overline{d} \pm t_{6,.025} \cdot s_d / \sqrt{n}$
   $5.14 \pm 2.447 \cdot 2.116 / \sqrt{7}$
   5.14 ± 1.96
   $3.2 < \mu_d < 7.1$

15. original claim: $\mu_d \neq 0$
     H_o: $\mu_d = 0$
     H_1: $\mu_d \neq 0$
     $\alpha = .05$ [assumed]
     C.R. $t < -t_{11,.025} = -2.201$
          $t > t_{11,.025} = 2.201$
     calculations:
        $t_{\overline{d}} = (\overline{d} - \mu_{\overline{d}})/s_{\overline{d}}$
              $= -.501$ [from Excel]
        P-value $= 2 \cdot P(t_{11} < -.51) = .626$ [from Excel]
     conclusion:
        Do not reject H_o; there is not sufficient evidence to conclude $\mu_d \neq 0$.

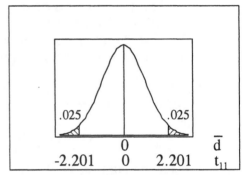

16. original claim: $\mu_d > 0$
     H_o: $\mu_d = 0$
     H_1: $\mu_d > 0$
     $\alpha = .05$
     C.R. $t > t_{10,.05} = 1.812$
     calculations:
        $t_{\overline{d}} = (\overline{d} - \mu_{\overline{d}})/s_{\overline{d}}$
              $= (.6727 - 0)/(.8259/\sqrt{11})$
              $= .6727/.2490 = 2.701$ [from Statdisk]
        P-value $= P(t_{10} > 2.701) = .011$ [from Statdisk]
     conclusion:
        Reject H_o; there is sufficient evidence to conclude that $\mu_d > 0$.
     Yes, these is enough evidence to support the claim that male statistics students exaggerate their heights.

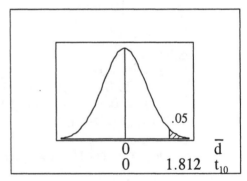

17. $d = x_8 - x_{12}$: given at the right
     $n = 11$
     $\Sigma d = -8.6$ $\overline{d} = -.782$
     $\Sigma d^2 = 15.06$ $s_d = .913$

     a. $\overline{d} \pm t_{10,.025} \cdot s_d / \sqrt{n}$
        $-.782 \pm 2.228 \cdot .913 / \sqrt{11}$
        $-.782 \pm .613$
        $-1.40 < \mu_d < -.17$

sbj#	8am	12am	diff
19	97.0	97.7	-0.7
20	98.0	98.8	-0.8
22	96.4	98.0	-1.6
26	98.2	98.7	-0.5
71	98.8	98.0	0.8
78	98.6	98.5	0.1
80	97.8	98.3	-0.5
81	98.7	98.7	0.0
83	97.8	99.1	-1.3
98	96.4	98.2	-1.8
99	96.9	99.2	-2.3

b. original claim: $\mu_d = 0$
   H_o: $\mu_d = 0$
   H_1: $\mu_d \neq 0$
   $\alpha = .05$
   C.R. $t < -t_{10,.025} = -2.228$
       $t > t_{10,.025} = 2.228$
   calculations:
      $t_{\bar{d}} = (\bar{d} - \mu_{\bar{d}})/s_{\bar{d}}$
         $= (-.782 - 0)/(.913/\sqrt{11})$
         $= -.782/.275 = -2.840$
      $.01 < $ P-value $= 2 \cdot P(t_{10} < -2.840) < .02$
   conclusion:

    Reject H_o; there is sufficient evidence to reject the claim that $\mu_d = 0$ and conclude that $\mu_d \neq 0$ (in fact, that $\mu_d < 0$.

No; based on this result. morning and night body temperatures do not appear to be about the same. The 8 am (morning) temperatures are significantly lower.

18. The Minitab output is given below.
   MTB > let c6 = c4-c5
   MTB > ttest c6   TEST OF MU = 0.0 VS MU N.E. 0.0
              N   MEAN   STDEV SE MEAN   T   P VALUE
     C6   50   25.0   109.2   15.4 1.62   0.11
   a. original claim: $\mu_d = 0$
     H_o: $\mu_d = 0$
     H_1: $\mu_d \neq 0$
     $\alpha = .05$ [assumed]
     C.R. $t < -t_{49,.025} = -2.009$
        $t > t_{49,.025} = 2.009$
     calculations:
       $t_{\bar{d}} = (\bar{d} - \mu_{\bar{d}})/s_{\bar{d}}$
          $= (25.0 - 0)/(109.2/\sqrt{50})$
          $= 25.0/15.44 = 1.62$ [Minitab]
     P-value $= 2 \cdot P(t_{49} > 1.62) = .11$ [Minitab]
   conclusion:
       Do not reject H_o; there is not sufficient evidence to reject the claim that $\mu_d = 0$.
   b. $\bar{d} \pm t_{49,.005} \cdot s_d/\sqrt{n}$
     $25.0 \pm 2.678 \cdot 109.2/\sqrt{50}$
     25.0 ± 41.4
     $-16.4 < \mu_d < 66.4$
   No; since the interval includes zero, there does not appear to be a significant difference in the times.

19. The Minitab output is given below.
   MTB > let c11=c3-c9
   MTB > ttest c11   TEST OF MU = 0.00 VS MU N.E. 0.00
              N   MEAN STDEV SE MEAN   T P VALUE
     C11   31   -6.00   11.26   2.02 -2.97   0.0059

a. original claim: $\mu_d = 0$
   H_o: $\mu_d = 0$
   H_1: $\mu_d \neq 0$
   $\alpha = .05$
   C.R. $t < -t_{30,.025} = -2.042$
       $t > t_{30,.025} = 2.042$
   calculations:
       $t_{\bar{d}} = (\bar{d} - \mu_{\bar{d}})/s_{\bar{d}}$
           $= (-6.0 - 0)/(11.26/\sqrt{31})$
           $= -6.0/2.022 = -2.97$ [Minitab]
       P-value $= 2 \cdot P(t_{30} < -2.97) = .0059$ [Minitab]
   conclusion:
       Reject H_o; there is sufficient evidence to reject the claim that $\mu_d = 0$ and conlcude
       that $\mu_d \neq 0$ (in fact, that $\mu_d < 0$).

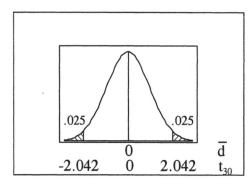

b. $\bar{d} \pm t_{30,.025} \cdot s_d/\sqrt{n}$
   $-6.0 \pm 2.042 \cdot 11.26/\sqrt{31}$
   -6.0 ± 4.1
   $-10.1 < \mu_d < -1.9$

c. Even though the conclusions are different for the example in the chapter (using the first 5 values) and this exercise (using all the data), the results are not contradictory. With n=5, there was almost (but not quite) enough evidence to declare a difference; with n=31 (even though the mean difference is smaller), there is enough evidence to declare a difference. It appears that the five-day low forecasts tend to be higher than the low temperatures actually reached.

20. The Minitab output is given below.
   MTB > let c11 = c3-c5
   MTB > ttest c11   TEST OF MU = 0.00 VS MU N.E. 0.00

	N	MEAN	STDEV	SE MEAN	T	P VALUE
C11	31	-3.52	11.81	2.12	-1.66	0.11

a. original claim: $\mu_d = 0$
   H_o: $\mu_d = 0$
   H_1: $\mu_d \neq 0$
   $\alpha = .05$
   C.R. $t < -t_{30,.025} = -2.042$
       $t > t_{30,.025} = 2.042$
   calculations:
       $t_{\bar{d}} = (\bar{d} - \mu_{\bar{d}})/s_{\bar{d}}$
           $= (-3.52 - 0)/(11.81/\sqrt{31})$
           $= -3.52/2.121 = -1.66$ [Minitab]
       P-value $= 2 \cdot P(t_{30} < -1.66) = .11$ [Minitab]
   conclusion:
       Do not reject H_o; there is not sufficient evidence to reject the claim that $\mu_d = 0$.

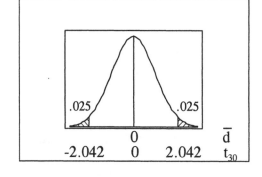

b. $\bar{d} \pm t_{30,.025} \cdot s_d/\sqrt{n}$
   $-3.52 \pm 2.042 \cdot 11.81/\sqrt{31}$
   -3.52 ± 4.331
   $-7.9 < \mu_d < 0.8$

c. In exercise #19 there was a significant difference between the five-day forecasts and the actual temperatures. In this exercise there is not a significant difference between the one-day forecasts and the actual temperatures. Yes, the one-day forecasts appear more accurate than the five-day forecasts.

21. a. Yes, an outlier can have a drastic effect on the test of hypothesis and/or the confidence interval. Depending on the data an outlier could increase the mean difference to create a significant difference where none exists, or an outlier could increase the variability to

hide a significant different that does exist.
b. Since the test statistic is unit free, it will be same no matter what units are used. The confidence interval will be stated in the new units, but it will include precisely the same climactic conditions no matter how those conditions are described in the various units.

22.   If the lower limit of the 95% confidence interval is 0, then
$$\overline{d} - t_{df,.025} \cdot s_d/\sqrt{n} = 0$$
$$\overline{d} = t_{df,.025} \cdot s_d/\sqrt{n}$$
$$\overline{d} - 0 = t_{df,.025} \cdot s_d/\sqrt{n}$$
$$(\overline{d} - 0)/(s_d/\sqrt{n}) = t_{df,.025}$$
Now consider the following test of hypothesis.
$H_o: \mu_d = 0$
$H_1: \mu_d > 0$
$\alpha =$
C.R. $t > t_{df,\alpha}$
calculations
$$t_{\overline{d}} = (\overline{d} - \mu_{\overline{d}})/s_{\overline{d}}$$
$$= (\overline{d} - 0)/(s_d/\sqrt{n})$$
$$= t_{df,.025} \text{ [from the algebraic rearrangement above]}$$
This means that the calculated t will fall right on the boundary of the critical region when testing at the $\alpha = .025$ level of significance. For $\alpha > .025$, $t_{df,\alpha}$ will be smaller and H_o is rejected. For $\alpha < .025$, $t_{df,\alpha}$ will be larger and H_o is not rejected. The smallest possible level of significance at which $H_1: \mu_d > 0$ will be supported is .025.

23.   The following table of summary statistics applies to all parts of this exercise.

	values										n	Σv	Σv^2	$\overline{v}$	s_v
x:	1	3	2	2	1	2	3	3	2	1	10	20	46	2.0	.816
y:	1	2	1	2	1	2	1	2	1	2	10	15	25	1.5	.527
d=x-y:	0	1	1	0	0	0	2	1	1	-1	10	5	9	.5	.850

a. original claim: $\mu_d > 0$
$H_o: \mu_d = 0$
$H_1: \mu_d > 0$
$\alpha = .05$
C.R. $t > t_{9,.05} = 1.833$
calculations:
$$t_{\overline{d}} = (\overline{d} - \mu_{\overline{d}})/s_{\overline{d}}$$
$$= (.5 - 0)/(.850/\sqrt{10})$$
$$= .5/.2687 = 1.861$$
$.025 <$ P-value $= P(t_9 > 1.861) < .05$
conclusion:
    Reject H_o; there is sufficient evidence to conclude that $\mu_d > 0$.

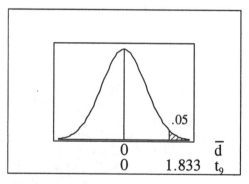

b. original claim: $\mu_1 - \mu_2 > 0$
$\overline{x}_1 - \overline{x}_2 = 2.0 - 1.5 = .5$
$H_o: \mu_1 - \mu_2 = 0$
$H_1: \mu_1 - \mu_2 > 0$
$\alpha = .01$
C.R. $t > t_{9,.05} = 1.833$
calculations:
$$t_{\overline{x}_1 - \overline{x}_2} = (\overline{x}_1 - \overline{x}_2 - \mu_{\overline{x}_1 - \overline{x}_2})/s_{\overline{x}_1 - \overline{x}_2}$$
$$= (.5 - 0)/\sqrt{(.816)^2/10 + (.527)^2/10}$$
$$= .5/.3073 = 1.627$$
$.05 <$ P-value $= P(t_9 > 1.627) < .10$
conclusion:
    Do not reject H_o; there is not sufficient evidence to conclude that $\mu_1 - \mu_2 > 0$.

c. Yes; since different methods can give different results, it is important that the correct method is used.

Review Exercises

1. Let those that were warmed be group 1.
    a. original claim: $p_1 - p_2 < 0$
    $\hat{p}_1 = x_1/n_1 = 6/104 = .0577$
    $\hat{p}_2 = x_2/n_2 = 18/96 = .1875$
    $\hat{p}_1 - \hat{p}_2 = .0577 - .1875 = -.1298$
    $\bar{p} = (x_1 + x_2)/(n_1 + n_2)$
      $= (6 + 18)/(104 + 96)$
      $= 24/200 = .12$
    H_o: $p_1 - p_2 = 0$
    H_1: $p_1 - p_2 < 0$
    $\alpha = .05$
    C.R. $z < -z_{.05} = -1.645$
    calculations:

    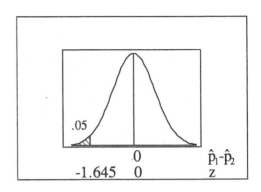

    $z_{\hat{p}1-\hat{p}2} = (\hat{p}_1 - \hat{p}_2 - \mu_{\hat{p}1-\hat{p}2})/\sigma_{\hat{p}1-\hat{p}2}$
      $= (-.1298 - 0)/\sqrt{(.12)(.88)/104 + (.12)(.88)/96}$
      $= -.1298/.0460 = -2.82$
    P-value $= P(z < -2.82) = .0024$
    conclusion:
       Reject H_o; there is sufficient evidence to conclude that $p_1 - p_2 < 0$.
    Yes; if these results are verified, surgical patients should be routinely warmed.
    b. The test in part (a) places 5% in the lower tail. To correspond with this test, use a 90% two-sided confidence interval [or a 95% one-sided confidence interval].
    c. $(\hat{p}_1 - \hat{p}_2) \pm z_{.05}\sqrt{\hat{p}_1\hat{q}_1/n_1 + \hat{p}_2\hat{q}_2/n_2}$
    $-.1298 \pm 1.645 \cdot \sqrt{(.0577)(.9423)/104 + (.1875)(.8125)/96}$
    $-.1298 \pm .0756$
    $-.205 < p_1 - p_2 < -.054$
    d. Since the test of hypothesis and the confidence interval use different estimates for $\sigma_{\hat{p}1-\hat{p}2}$, they are not mathematically equivalent and it is possible that they may might lead to different conclusions.

2. $d = x - y$: -5.75 -1.25 -1.00 -5.00 0.00 0.25 2.25 -0.50 0.75 -1.50 -0.25
    $n = 11$
    $\Sigma d = -12.00$ $\bar{d} = -1.091$
    $\Sigma d^2 = 68.8750$ $s_d = 2.3619$
    a. original claim: $\mu_d = 0$
       H_o: $\mu_d = 0$
       H_1: $\mu_d \neq 0$
       $\alpha = .05$
       C.R. $t < -t_{10,.025} = -2.228$
          $t > t_{10,.025} = 2.228$
       calculations:

    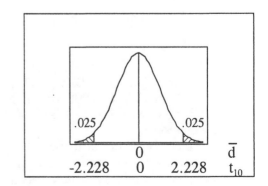

       $t_{\bar{d}} = (\bar{d} - \mu_{\bar{d}})/s_{\bar{d}}$
          $= (-1.091 - 0)/(2.3619/\sqrt{11})$
          $= -1.091/.7121 = -1.532$
       $.10 < $ P-value $ = 2 \cdot P(t_{11} < -1.532) < .20$
    conclusion:
       Do not reject H_o; there is not sufficient evidence to reject the claim that $\mu_d = 0$.

b. $\bar{d} \pm t_{10,.025} \cdot s_d/\sqrt{n}$
-1.091 $\pm$ 2.228·2.3619/$\sqrt{11}$
-1.091 $\pm$ 1.587
-2.67 $< \mu_d <$ .50

c. We cannot be 95% certain that either type of seed is better. If there are no differences in cost, or any other considerations, choose the kiln dried – even though we can't be sure that it's generally better, it did have the higher yield in this particular trial.

3.   Let the obsessive-compulsive patients be group 1.

   $\bar{x}_1 - \bar{x}_2 = 1390.03 - 1268.41 = 121.62$

a. $(\bar{x}_1 - \bar{x}_2) \pm t_{9,.025} \sqrt{s_1^2/n_1 + s_2^2/n_2}$
   121.62 $\pm$ 2.262·$\sqrt{(156.84)^2/10 + (137.97)^2/10}$
   121.62 $\pm$ 149.42
   -27.80 $< \mu_1 - \mu_2 <$ 271.04

b. original claim: $\mu_1 - \mu_2 = 0$
   H_o: $\mu_1 - \mu_2 = 0$
   H_1: $\mu_1 - \mu_2 \neq 0$
   $\alpha = .05$
   C.R. t $<$ -$t_{9,.025}$ = -2.262
        t $>$ $t_{9,.025}$ = 2.262
   calculations:

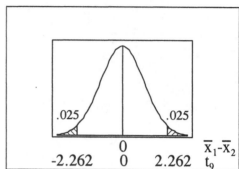

   $t_{\bar{x}_1 - \bar{x}_2} = (\bar{x}_1 - \bar{x}_2 - \mu_{\bar{x}_1 - \bar{x}_2})/s_{\bar{x}_1 - \bar{x}_2}$
   $= (121.62 - 0)/\sqrt{(156.84)^2/10 + (137.97)^2/10}$
   $= 121.62/66.056 = 1.841$
   .05 $<$ P-value = 2·P($t_9 >$ 1.841) $<$ .10
   conclusion:
       Do not reject H_o; there is not sufficient evidence to reject the claim that $\mu_1 - \mu_2 = 0$.

c. No, it does not appear that the total brain volume can be used as a reliable indicator.

4.   Let the filtered cigarettes be group 1
   group 1: filtered (n = 21)   group 2: unfiltered (n = 8)
       Σx = 270 Σx = 125
       Σx^2 = 3660 Σx^2 = 1963
       $\bar{x}$ = 12.857 $\bar{x}$ = 15.625
       s = 3.071   s = 1.188
   original claim: $\mu_1 - \mu_2 = 0$
       $\bar{x}_1 - \bar{x}_2 = 12.857 - 15.625 = -2.768$
   H_o: $\mu_1 - \mu_2 = 0$
   H_1: $\mu_1 - \mu_2 \neq 0$
   $\alpha = .05$
   C.R. t $<$ -$t_{7,.025}$ = -2.365
        t $>$ $t_{7,.025}$ = 2.365
   calculations:

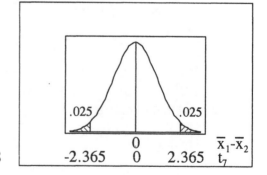

       $t_{\bar{x}_1 - \bar{x}_2} = (\bar{x}_1 - \bar{x}_2 - \mu_{\bar{x}_1 - \bar{x}_2})/s_{\bar{x}_1 - \bar{x}_2}$
       $= (-2.768 - 0)/\sqrt{(3.071)^2/21 + (1.188)^2/8}$
       $= -2.768/.7908 = -3.500$
   P-value = 2·P($t_7 <$ -3.500) $\approx$ .01
conclusion:
   Reject H_o; there is sufficient evidence to reject the claim that $\mu_1 - \mu_2 = 0$ and conclude that $\mu_1 - \mu_2 \neq 0$ (in fact, that $\mu_1 - \mu_2 < 0$).
Yes; based on this result, cigarette filters are effective in reducing the amount of carbon monoxide.

5. Let those receiving the zinc supplement be group 1.
    original claim: $\mu_1 - \mu_2 > 0$
    $\bar{x}_1 - \bar{x}_2 = 3214 - 3088 = 126$
    H_o: $\mu_1 - \mu_2 = 0$
    H_1: $\mu_1 - \mu_2 > 0$
    $\alpha = .05$
    C.R. $t > t_{285, .05} = 1.650$
    calculations:
    $t_{\bar{x}_1 - \bar{x}_2} = (\bar{x}_1 - \bar{x}_2 - \mu_{\bar{x}_1 - \bar{x}_2})/s_{\bar{x}_1 - \bar{x}_2}$
    $= (126 - 0)/\sqrt{(669)^2/294 + (728)^2/286}$
    $= 126/58.098 = 2.169$
    $.01 < $ P-value $= P(t_{285} > 2.169) < .025$
    conclusion:
    Reject H_o; there is sufficient evidence to conclude that $\mu_1 - \mu_2 > 0$.
    Yes, there is sufficient evidence to support the claim that the zinc supplement results in increased birth weights.

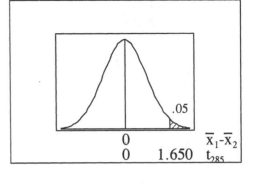

6. Let those who saw the first woman be group 1.
    original claim: $p_1 - p_2 > 0$
    $\hat{p}_1 = x_1/n_1 = 58/2000 = .0290$
    $\hat{p}_2 = x_2/n_2 = 35/2000 = .0175$
    $\hat{p}_1 - \hat{p}_2 = .0290 - .0175 = .0115$
    $\bar{p} = (x_1 + x_2)/(n_1 + n_2)$
    $= (58 + 35)/(2000 + 2000)$
    $= 93/4000 = .02325$
    H_o: $p_1 - p_2 = 0$
    H_1: $p_1 - p_2 > 0$
    $\alpha = .05$
    C.R. $z > z_{.05} = 1.645$
    calculations:
    $z_{\hat{p}_1 - \hat{p}_2} = (\hat{p}_1 - \hat{p}_2 - \mu_{\hat{p}_1 - \hat{p}_2})/\sigma_{\hat{p}_1 - \hat{p}_2}$
    $= (.0115 - 0)/\sqrt{(.02325)(.97675)/2000 + (.02325)(.97576)/2000}$
    $= .0115/.004765 = 2.41$
    P-value $= P(z > 2.41) = 1 - P(z < 2.41) = 1 - .9920 = .0080$
    conclusion:
    Reject H_o; there is sufficient evidence to conclude that $p_1 - p_2 > 0$.

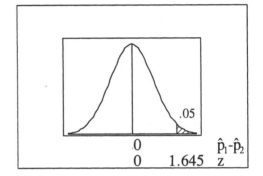

7. The summary statistics are as follows.
    $d = x_1 - x_2$: 5 0 0 0 8 1 1 4 0 1
    $n = 10$
    $\Sigma d = 20$ $\bar{d} = 2.00$
    $\Sigma d^2 = 108$ $s_d = 2.749$
    a. original claim: $\mu_d = 0$
    H_o: $\mu_d = 0$
    H_1: $\mu_d \neq 0$
    $\alpha = .05$ [assumed]
    C.R. $t < -t_{9, .025} = -2.262$
          $t > t_{9, .025} = 2.262$
    calculations:
    $t_{\bar{d}} = (\bar{d} - \mu_{\bar{d}})/s_{\bar{d}}$
    $= (2.00 - 0)/(2.749/\sqrt{10})$
    $= 2.00/.869 = 2.301$
    $.02 < $ P-value $< .05$

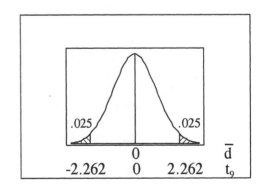

conclusion:

Reject H_o; there is sufficient evidence to reject the claim that $\mu_d = 0$ and to conclude that $\mu_d \neq 0$ (in fact, that $\mu_d > 0$ – i.e., that training reduces the weights).

b. $\bar{d} \pm t_{9,.025} \cdot s_d / \sqrt{n}$

$2.00 \pm 2.262 \cdot 2.749 / \sqrt{10}$

2.00 ± 1.97

$0.0 < \mu_d < 4.0$

Cumulative Review Exercises

1. Refer to the summary table at the right.

a. $P(Y) = 53/750 = .071$

b. $P(M \text{ or } Y) = P(M) + P(Y) - P(M \text{ and } Y)$
$= 250/750 + 53/750 - 26/750$
$= 277/750 = .369$

c. $P(Y | M) = 26/250 = .104$

d. $P(Y | F) = 27/500 = .054$

e. Let the males be group 1.

original claim: $p_1 - p_2 > 0$

$\hat{p}_1 = x_1/n_1 = 26/250 = .104$

$\hat{p}_2 = x_2/n_2 = 27/500 = .054$

$\hat{p}_1 - \hat{p}_2 = .104 - .054 = .050$

$\bar{p} = (x_1 + x_2)/(n_1 + n_2)$
$= (26 + 27)/(250 + 500)$
$= 53/750 = .0707$

H_o: $p_1 - p_2 = 0$

H_1: $p_1 - p_2 > 0$

$\alpha = .05$

C.R. $z > z_{.05} = 1.645$

calculations:

$z_{\hat{p}_1 - \hat{p}_2} = (\hat{p}_1 - \hat{p}_2 - \mu_{\hat{p}_1 - \hat{p}_2})/\sigma_{\hat{p}_1 - \hat{p}_2}$
$= (.050 - 0)/\sqrt{(.0707)(.9293)/250 + (.0707)(.9293)/500}$
$= .050/.0199 = 2.52$

P-value $= P(z > 2.52) = 1 - P(z < 2.52) = 1 - .9941 = .0059$

conclusion:

Reject H_o; there is sufficient evidence to conclude that $p_1 - p_2 > 0$.

No; while we can conclude that men receive more speeding tickets than women, we cannot conclude that men speed more often. That conclusion would be valid only if there were a perfect correspondence between speeding and receiving a ticket. It could be that women speed just as often as men but get fewer tickets because they (a) tend to exceed the posted limit by smaller amounts than men do or (b) are more likely to be let off with only a warning than men are. It could also be that men drive more, and so they would be expected to get more tickets even if they did not speed more – consider a population that is ½ male and ½ female in which all people speed equally: if the men do 80% of the driving, for example, then they would receive 80% of the tickets.

2. There is a problem with the reported results, and no statistical analysis would be appropriate. Since there were 100 drivers in each group, and the number in each group owning a cell phone must be a whole number between 0 and 100 inclusive, the sample proportion for each group must be a whole percent. The reported values of 13.7% and 10.6% are not mathematical possibilities for the sample success rates of groups of 100.

3. Let the Viagra users be group 1. The following summary statistics apply to all parts [and, as usual, the unrounded values are used in all subsequent calculations.]

$\hat{p}_1 = x_1/n_1 = 29/734 = .040$

$\hat{p}_2 = x_2/n_2 = 15/725 = .021$

$\hat{p}_1 - \hat{p}_2 = .040 - .021 = .019$

a. $\hat{p}_1 \pm z_{.025}\sqrt{\hat{p}_1\hat{q}_1/n_1}$

$.040 \pm 1.96 \sqrt{(.040)(.960)/734}$

$.040 \pm .014$

$.025 < p_1 < .054$

b. $\hat{p}_2 \pm z_{.025}\sqrt{\hat{p}_2\hat{q}_2/n_2}$

$.021 \pm 1.96 \sqrt{(.021)(.979)/725}$

$.021 \pm .010$

$.010 < p_1 < .031$

c. $(\hat{p}_1 - \hat{p}_2) \pm z_{.025}\sqrt{\hat{p}_1\hat{q}_1/n_1 + \hat{p}_2\hat{q}_2/n_2}$

$.019 \pm 1.96 \sqrt{(.040)(.960)/734 + (.021)(.979)/725}$

$.019 \pm .018$

$.001 < p_1 - p_2 < .036$

d. The method in part (iii) is best. It uses all the information at once and asks whether the data is consistent with the claim that $p_1 = p_2$. Method (ii) constructs an interval with no specific claim in mind. Method (i) does not use all the information at once – in general, methods that incorporate all the information into a single statistical procedure are superior to ones that use smaller sample sizes to give partial answers that need to be combined and/or compared afterward.

4. a. Let p = the proportion of runners who finished the race that were females.

original claim: $p < .50$

$\hat{p} = x/n = 39/150 = .26$

H_0: $p = .50$

H_1: $p < .50$

$\alpha = .05$ [assumed]

C.R. $z < -z_{.05} = -1.645$

calculations:

$z_{\hat{p}} = (\hat{p} - \mu_{\hat{p}})/\sigma_{\hat{p}}$

$= (.26 - .50)/\sqrt{(.50)(.50)/150}$

$= -.24/.0408$

$= -5.88$

P-value = $P(z < -5.88) = .0001$

conclusion:

Reject H_0; there is sufficient evidence to conclude that $p < .50$.

b. The ordered 39 times are as follows.

12047	12289	13593	13704	13854	14216	14235	14721	15036	15077
15326	15357	15402	16013	16297	16352	16401	16758	16771	16792
16871	16991	17211	17260	17286	17636	17726	17799	18469	18580
18647	10177	20084	20675	20891	21911	21983	25399	25858	

The summary statistics are as follows.

$n = 39$ $\Sigma x = 670735$ $\Sigma x^2 = 11,902,396,416$

$\bar{x} = (\Sigma x)/n = 670735/39 = 17198.3$

$\tilde{x} = x_{20} = 17792$

$s^2 = [n(\Sigma x^2) - (\Sigma x)^2]/[n(n-1)] = [39(11902396416) - (670735)^2]/[39(38)]$

$= 9654534.25$

$s = 3107.2$

The following frequency distribution indicates that the times appear to be approximately normally distributed.

time (seconds)	frequency
11000 – 12999	2
13000 – 14999	6
15000 – 16999	14
17000 – 18999	9
19000 – 20999	4
21000 – 22999	2
23000 – 24999	0
25000 – 26999	2
	39

There is no absolute definition of an outlier. The section on boxplots suggests that any score more than $(1.5)(IQR)$ from the median is an outlier.

$IQR = Q_3 - Q_1 = x_{30} - x_{10} = 18580 - 15077 = 3503$
$16792 \pm 2(3503)$
16792 ± 7006
9786 to 23798

By this definition, the 25399 and 25989 may be considered outliers.

c. original claim: $\mu < 5$ hours $= 18000$ seconds
H_o: $\mu = 18000$
H_1: $\mu < 18000$
$\alpha = .05$
C.R. $t < -t_{38,.05} = -1.686$
calculations:

$t_{\bar{x}} = (\bar{x} - \mu)/s_{\bar{x}}$
$= (17198.3 - 18000)/(3107.2/\sqrt{39})$
$= -801.7/497.6$
$= -1.611$
$.05 < $ P-value $< .10$
conclusion:
Do not reject H_o; there is not sufficient evidence to conclude that $\mu < 5$ hours.

d. Let the females be group 1.
original claim: $\mu_1 - \mu_2 \neq 0$
$\bar{x}_1 - \bar{x}_2 = 17198.3 - 15415.2 = 1783.1$
H_o: $\mu_1 - \mu_2 = 0$
H_1: $\mu_1 - \mu_2 \neq 0$
$\alpha = .05$
C.R. $t < -t_{38,.025} = -2.024$
    $t > t_{38,.025} = 2.024$
calculations:

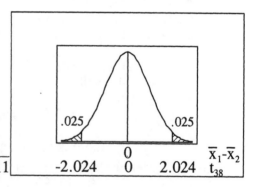

$t_{\bar{x}_1 - \bar{x}_2} = (\bar{x}_1 - \bar{x}_2 - \mu_{\bar{x}_1 - \bar{x}_2})/s_{\bar{x}_1 - \bar{x}_2}$
$= (1783.1 - 0)/\sqrt{(3107)^2/39 + (3037)^2/111}$
$= 1783.1/572.0 = 3.101$
P-value $= 2 \cdot P(t_{38} > 3.101) < .01$
conclusion:
Reject H_o; there is sufficient evidence to conclude that $\mu_1 - \mu_2 \neq 0$ (in fact, that $\mu_1 - \mu_2 < 0$).

e. Let the females be group 1.
$\hat{p}_1 = x_1/n_1 = 39/150 = .26$
$\hat{p}_2 = x_2/n_2 = 111/150 = .74$
The methods of this chapter cannot be used to make inferences about $p_1 - p_2$ because the data is not from two independent samples. The "n_2" above is really the same 150 that was n_1. Whatever the value of $\hat{p}_1$ is, the value of $\hat{p}_2$ will have to be $1 - \hat{p}_1$. To test whether p_1 and p_2 are equal (which means each must be .5), use only the data for one of the genders – for example, test H_o: $p_1 = .50$.

Chapter 9

Correlation and Regression

9-2 Correlation

1. a. From Table A-6, CV = ±.707; therefore r = .993 indicates a significant (positive) linear correlation.
    b. The proportion of the variation in weight that can be explained in terms of the variation in chest size is $r^2 = (.993)^2 = .986$, or 98.6%.

2. a. From Table A-6, CV = ±.707; therefore r = .885 indicates a significant (positive) linear correlation.
    b. The proportion of the variation in the murder rate that can be explained in terms of the variation in registered automatic weapons is $r^2 = (.885)^2 = .783$, or 78.3%.

3. a. From Table A-6, CV = ±.444; therefore r = -.133 does not indicate a significant linear correlation.
    b. The proportion of the variation in Super Bowl points that can be explained in terms of the variation in the DJIA high values is $r^2 = (-.133)^2 = .017$, or 1.7%.

4. a. From Table A-6, CV = ±.444; therefore r = -.284 does not indicate a significant linear correlation.
    b. The proportion of the variation in US car sales that can be explained in terms of the variation in sunspot number is $r^2 = (-.284)^2 = .081$, or 8.1%.

NOTE: In addition to the value of n, calculation of r requires five sums: Σx, Σy, Σx^2, Σy^2 and Σxy. The next problem shows the chart prepared to find these sums. As the sums can usually be found conveniently using a calculator and without constructing the chart, subsequent problems typically give only the values of the sums and do not show a chart.

Also, calculation of r also involves three subcalculations.

(1) $n(\Sigma xy) - (\Sigma x)(\Sigma y)$ determines the sign of r. If large values of x are associated with large values of y, it will be positive. If large values of x are associated with small values of y, it will be negative. If not, a mistake has been made.

(2) $n(\Sigma x^2) - (\Sigma x)^2$ cannot be negative. If it is, a mistake has been made.

(3) $n(\Sigma y^2) - (\Sigma y)^2$ cannot be negative. If it is, a mistake has been made.

Finally, r must be between -1 and 1 inclusive. If not, a mistake has been made. If this or any of the previous mistakes occurs, stop immediately and find the error; continuing will be a fruitless waste of effort.

5.

x	y	xy	x^2	y^2
0	4	0	0	16
1	1	1	1	1
2	0	0	4	0
3	1	3	9	1
4	4	16	16	16
10	10	20	30	34

$n(\Sigma xy) - (\Sigma x)(\Sigma y) = 5(20) - (10)(10) = 0$
$n(\Sigma x^2) - (\Sigma x)^2 = 5(30) - (10)^2 = 50$
$n(\Sigma y^2) - (\Sigma y)^2 = 5(34) - (10)^2 = 70$

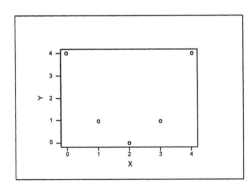

a. According to the scatter diagram, there appears to be a significant "U-shaped" pattern, but no <u>linear</u> relationship between x and y. Expect a value for r close to 0.

b. $r = [n(\Sigma xy) - (\Sigma x)(\Sigma y)]/[\sqrt{n(\Sigma x^2) - (\Sigma x)^2} \cdot \sqrt{n(\Sigma y^2) - (\Sigma y)^2}]$
   $= 0/[\sqrt{50} \cdot \sqrt{70}] = 0$

From Table A-6, assuming $\alpha = .05$, CV $= \pm .878$; therefore r = 0 does not indicate a significant linear correlation. This agrees with the interpretation of the scatter diagram in part (a).

6.

x	y	xy	x^2	y^2
1	2	2	1	4
2	5	10	4	25
2	4	8	4	16
5	15	75	25	225
6	15	90	36	225
16	41	185	70	495

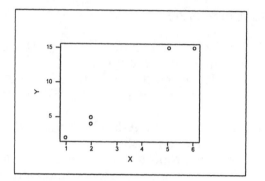

$n(\Sigma xy) - (\Sigma x)(\Sigma y) = 5(185) - (16)(41) = 269$
$n(\Sigma x^2) - (\Sigma x)^2 = 5(70) - (16)^2 = 94$
$n(\Sigma y^2) - (\Sigma y)^2 = 5(495) - (41)^2 = 794$

a. According to the scatter diagram, there appears to be a significant linear relationship between x and y. Expect a positive value for r fairly near 1.00.

b. $r = [n(\Sigma xy) - (\Sigma x)(\Sigma y)]/[\sqrt{n(\Sigma x^2) - (\Sigma x)^2} \cdot \sqrt{n(\Sigma y^2) - (\Sigma y)^2}]$
   $= 269/[\sqrt{94} \cdot \sqrt{794}] = .985$

From Table A-6, assuming $\alpha = .05$, CV $= \pm .878$; therefore r = .976 indicates a significant (positive) linear correlation. This agrees with the interpretation of the scatter diagram in part (a).

7.   The following table and summary statistics apply to all parts of this exercise.
   x: 1 1 1 2 2 2 3 3 3 10
   y: 1 2 3 1 2 3 1 2 3 10
   using all the points: n=10 $\Sigma x=28$ $\Sigma y=28$ $\Sigma xy=136$ $\Sigma x^2=142$ $\Sigma y^2=142$
   without the outlier: n=9 $\Sigma x=18$ $\Sigma y=18$ $\Sigma xy=36$ $\Sigma x^2=42$ $\Sigma y^2=42$

a. There appears to be a strong positive linear correlation, with r close to 1.

b. $n(\Sigma xy) - (\Sigma x)(\Sigma y) = 10(136) - (28)(28) = 576$
   $n(\Sigma x^2) - (\Sigma x)^2 = 10(142) - (28)^2 = 636$
   $n(\Sigma y^2) - (\Sigma y)^2 = 10(142) - (28)^2 = 636$
   $r = [n(\Sigma xy) - (\Sigma x)(\Sigma y)]/[\sqrt{n(\Sigma x^2) - (\Sigma x)^2} \cdot \sqrt{n(\Sigma y^2) - (\Sigma y)^2}]$
   $= 576/[\sqrt{636} \cdot \sqrt{636}] = .906$

From Table A-6, assuming $\alpha = .05$, CV $= \pm .632$; therefore r = .906 indicates a significant (positive) linear correlation. This agrees with the interpretation of the scatter diagram in part (a).

c. There appears to be no linear correlation, with r close to 0.
   $n(\Sigma xy) - (\Sigma x)(\Sigma y) = 9(36) - (18)(18) = 0$
   $n(\Sigma x^2) - (\Sigma x)^2 = 9(42) - (18)^2 = 54$
   $n(\Sigma y^2) - (\Sigma y)^2 = 9(42) - (18)^2 = 54$
   $r = [n(\Sigma xy) - (\Sigma x)(\Sigma y)]/[\sqrt{n(\Sigma x^2) - (\Sigma x)^2} \cdot \sqrt{n(\Sigma y^2) - (\Sigma y)^2}]$
   $= 0/[\sqrt{54} \cdot \sqrt{54}] = 0$

From Table A-6, assuming $\alpha = .05$, CV $= \pm .666$; therefore r = 0 does not indicate a significant linear correlation. This agrees with the interpretation of the scatter diagram.

d. The effect of a single pair of values can be dramatic, changing the conclusion entirely.

NOTE: In each of exercises 8-14, the first variable listed is designated x, and the second variable listed is designated y. In correlation problems, the designation of x and y is arbitrary – so long as a person remains consistent after making the designation. For use in the next section, the following summary statistics should be saved for each exercise: n, Σx, Σy, Σx^2, Σy^2, Σxy.

8. a. n = 11
Σx = 677
Σy = 33.4
Σx^2 = 43105
Σy^2 = 126.04
Σxy = 2153.0

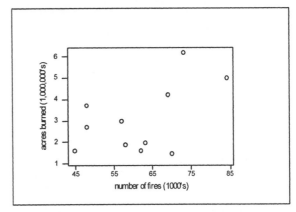

b. $n(\Sigma xy) - (\Sigma x)(\Sigma y) = 11(2153.0) - (677)(33.4) = 1071.2$
$n(\Sigma x^2) - (\Sigma x)^2 = 11(43105) - (677)^2 = 15826$
$n(\Sigma y^2) - (\Sigma y)^2 = 11(126.04) - (33.4)^2 = 270.88$
$r = [n(\Sigma xy) - (\Sigma x)(\Sigma y)]/[\sqrt{n(\Sigma x^2) - (\Sigma x)^2} \cdot \sqrt{n(\Sigma y^2) - (\Sigma y)^2}]$
$= 1071.2/[\sqrt{15826} \cdot \sqrt{270.88}] = .517$

c. H_o: $\rho = 0$
H_1: $\rho \neq 0$
$\alpha = .05$
C.R. r < -.602   OR C.R. t < $-t_{9,.025}$ = -2.262
      r > .602   t > $t_{9,.025}$ = 2.262

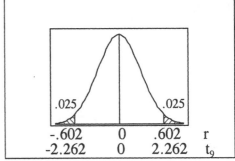

calculations: calculations:
   r = .517 $t_r = (r - \mu_r)/s_r$
                          $= (.517 - 0)/\sqrt{(1-(.517)^2)/9}$
                          $= .517/.2853 = 1.814$
conclusion:
    Do not reject H_o; there is not sufficient evidence to reject the claim that $\rho = 0$.
No; there is no significant correlation between the number of fires and the number of acres burned.
No; the results do not support any conclusion about the removal of trees affecting the risk of fires, because none of the variables addresses the removal/density of trees.

9. a. n = 8
Σx = 188.2
Σy = 52.0
Σx^2 = 11850.04
Σy^2 = 402.90
Σxy = 1141.22

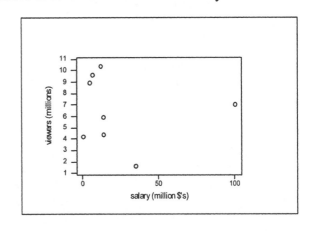

b. $n(\Sigma xy) - (\Sigma x)(\Sigma y) = 8(1141.22) - (188.2)(52.0) = -656.64$
$n(\Sigma x^2) - (\Sigma x)^2 = 8(11850.04) - (188.2)^2 = 59381.08$
$n(\Sigma y^2) - (\Sigma y)^2 = 8(402.90) - (52.0)^2 = 519.20$
$r = [n(\Sigma xy) - (\Sigma x)(\Sigma y)]/[\sqrt{n(\Sigma x^2) - (\Sigma x)^2} \cdot \sqrt{n(\Sigma y^2) - (\Sigma y)^2}]$
$= -656.64/[\sqrt{59381.08} \cdot \sqrt{519.20}] = -.118$

c. $H_o: \rho = 0$
$H_1: \rho \neq 0$
$\alpha = .05$
C.R. $r < -.707$ OR   C.R. $t < -t_{6,.025} = -2.447$
    $r > .707$ $t > t_{6,.025} = 2.447$

calculations: calculations:
   $r = -.118$ $t_r = (r - \mu_r)/s_r$
                                $= (-.118 - 0)/\sqrt{(1-(-.118)^2)/6}$
conclusion: $= -.118/.4054 = -.292$

   Do not reject H_o; there is not sufficient evidence to reject the claim that $\rho = 0$.
No; there is no significant correlation between salary and number of viewers.
Susan Lucci (1/4.2 = $0.24 per viewer) has the lowest cost per viewer, and Kelsey
Grammar (35.2/1.6 = $22.00 per viewer) has the highest cost per viewer.

10.   a. $n = 9$
$\Sigma x = 632.0$
$\Sigma y = 1089$
$\Sigma x^2 = 44399.50$
$\Sigma y^2 = 132223$
$\Sigma xy = 76546.0$

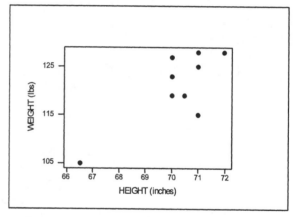

b. $n(\Sigma xy) - (\Sigma x)(\Sigma y) = 9(76546) - (632)(1089) = 666$
$n(\Sigma x^2) - (\Sigma x)^2 = 9(44399.5) - (632)^2 = 171.5$
$n(\Sigma y^2) - (\Sigma y)^2 = 9(132223) - (1089)^2 = 4086$
$r = [n(\Sigma xy) - (\Sigma x)(\Sigma y)]/[\sqrt{n(\Sigma x^2) - (\Sigma x)^2} \cdot \sqrt{n(\Sigma y^2) - (\Sigma y)^2}]$
$= 666/[\sqrt{171.5} \cdot \sqrt{4086}] = .796$

c. $H_o: \rho = 0$
$H_1: \rho \neq 0$
$\alpha = .05$
C.R. $r < -.666$ OR   C.R. $t < -t_{7,.025} = -2.365$
    $r > .666$ $t > t_{7,.025} = 2.365$

calculations: calculations:
   $r = .796$ $t_r = (r - \mu_r)/s_r$
                                $= (.796 - 0)/\sqrt{(1-(.796)^2)/7}$
conclusion: $= .796/.229 = 3.475$

   Reject H_o; there is sufficient evidence to reject the claim that $\rho = 0$ and to conclude
that $\rho \neq 0$ (in fact, that $\rho > 0$).

Yes; there is a correlation between height and weight for the supermodels.
No; since the supermodels are not representative of all adult women, these results cannot be used to make any conclusions about that population.

11. a. n = 14
     Σx = 1875
     Σy = 1241
     Σx^2 = 252179
     Σy^2 = 111459
     Σxy = 167023

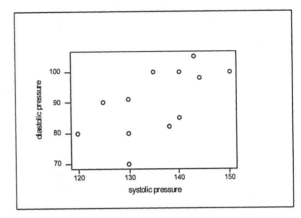

   b. $n(\Sigma xy) - (\Sigma x)(\Sigma y) = 14(167023) - (1875)(1241) = 11447$
      $n(\Sigma x^2) - (\Sigma x)^2 = 14(252179) - (1875)^2 = 14881$
      $n(\Sigma y^2) - (\Sigma y)^2 = 14(111459) - (1241)^2 = 20345$
      $r = [n(\Sigma xy) - (\Sigma x)(\Sigma y)]/[\sqrt{n(\Sigma x^2) - (\Sigma x)^2} \cdot \sqrt{n(\Sigma y^2) - (\Sigma y)^2}]$
      $= 11447/[\sqrt{14881} \cdot \sqrt{20345}] = .658$

   c. $H_o: \rho = 0$
      $H_1: \rho \neq 0$
      $\alpha = .05$
      C.R. r < -.532   OR   C.R. $t < -t_{12,.025} = -2.179$
          r > .532 $t > t_{12,.025} = 2.179$

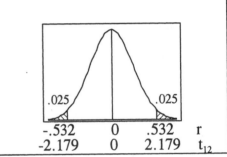

      calculations: calculations:
        r = .658 $t_r = (r - \mu_r)/s_r$
                                 $= (.658 - 0)/\sqrt{(1-(.658)^2)/12}$
                                 $= .658/.2174 = 3.026$
      conclusion:
        Reject H_o; there is sufficient evidence to reject the claim that $\rho = 0$ and to conclude that $\rho \neq 0$ (in fact, $\rho > 0$).
      Yes; there is a correlation between systolic and diastolic pressure.
      Yes; since the measurements were on the same patient, one could study the variability in a person's blood pressure – or in the variability of medical student readings?

12. a. n = 8
     Σx = 478
     Σy = 1176.617
     Σx^2 = 29070
     Σy^2 = 173068.664832
     Σxy = 70318.992

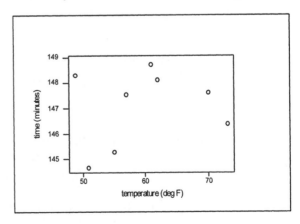

b. $n(\Sigma xy) - (\Sigma x)(\Sigma y) = 8(70318.992) -= (478)(1176.617) = 129.010$
$n(\Sigma x^2) - (\Sigma x)^2 = 8(29070) - (478)^2 = 4076$
$n(\Sigma y^2) - (\Sigma y)^2 = 8(173068.664832) - (1176.617)^2 = 121.75371$
$r = [n(\Sigma xy) - (\Sigma x)(\Sigma y)]/[\sqrt{n(\Sigma x^2) - (\Sigma x)^2} \cdot \sqrt{n(\Sigma y^2) - (\Sigma y)^2}]$
$= 129.010/[\sqrt{4076} \cdot \sqrt{121.75371}] = .183$

c. $H_o: \rho = 0$
$H_1: \rho \neq 0$
$\alpha = .05$
C.R. $r < -.707$ OR   C.R. $t < -t_{6,.025} = -2.447$
$r > .707$ $t > t_{6,.025} = 2.447$

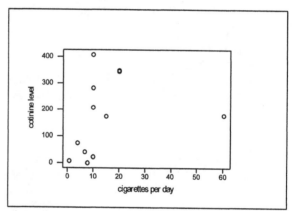

calculations: calculations:
$r = .183$ $t_r = (r - \mu_r)/s_r$
                                $= (.183 - 0)/\sqrt{(1-(.183)^2)/6}$
conclusion: $= .183/.4013 = .456$

Do not reject H_o; there is not sufficient evidence to reject the claim that $\rho = 0$.
No; there is no correlation between temperature and winning time.
No; winning times do not appear to be affected by temperature.

13.   a. $n = 12$
$\Sigma x = 175$
$\Sigma y = 2102.46$
$\Sigma x^2 = 5155$
$\Sigma y^2 = 601709.8240$
$\Sigma xy = 37111.51$

b. $n(\Sigma xy) - (\Sigma x)(\Sigma y) = 12(37111.51) - (175)(2102.46) = 77407.62$
$n(\Sigma x^2) - (\Sigma x)^2 = 12(5155) - (175)^2 = 31235$
$n(\Sigma y^2) - (\Sigma y)^2 = 12(601709.8240 - (2102.46)^2 = 2800179.836$
$r = [n(\Sigma xy) - (\Sigma x)(\Sigma y)]/[\sqrt{n(\Sigma x^2) - (\Sigma x)^2} \cdot \sqrt{n(\Sigma y^2) - (\Sigma y)^2}]$
$= 77407.62/[\sqrt{31235} \cdot \sqrt{2800179.836}] = .262$

c. $H_o: \rho = 0$
$H_1: \rho \neq 0$
$\alpha = .05$
C.R. $r < -.576$ OR   C.R. $t < -t_{10,.025} = -2.228$
$r > .576$ $t > t_{10,.025} = 2.228$

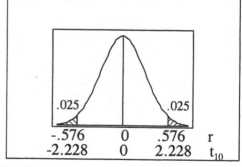

calculations: calculations:
$r = .262$ $t_r = (r - \mu_r)/s_r$
                                $= (.262 - 0)/\sqrt{(1-(.262)^2)/10}$
conclusion: $= .262/.3052 = .858$

Do not reject H_o; there is not sufficient evidence to reject the claim that $\rho = 0$.
No; based on these results, there is not a correlation between number of cigarettes
smoked and the amount of cotinine in the body. Possible explanations for not

identifying the expected correlation are (1) the subjects may not have accurately self-reported their number of cigarettes smoked, (2) the survey did not consider whether or not the cigarettes smoked had filters (which would affect the amounts nicotine reaching the body), and (3) the results could be affected by exposure to second-hand smoke.

14.   a. n = 14
$\Sigma x = 66.4$
$\Sigma y = 669.1$
$\Sigma x^2 = 444.54$
$\Sigma y^2 = 37365.71$
$\Sigma xy = 3865.67$

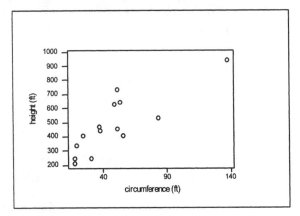

b. $n(\Sigma xy) - (\Sigma x)(\Sigma y) = 14(3865.67) - (66.4)(669.1) = 9691.14$
$n(\Sigma x^2) - (\Sigma x)^2 = 14(444.54) - (66.4)^2 = 1814.60$
$n(\Sigma y^2) - (\Sigma y)^2 = 14(37365.71) - (669.1)^2 = 75425.13$
$r = [n(\Sigma xy) - (\Sigma x)(\Sigma y)]/[\sqrt{n(\Sigma x^2) - (\Sigma x)^2} \cdot \sqrt{n(\Sigma y^2) - (\Sigma y)^2}]$
$= 9691.14/[\sqrt{1814.60} \cdot \sqrt{75425.13}] = .828$

c. $H_o: \rho = 0$
$H_1: \rho \neq 0$
$\alpha = .05$
C.R. r < -.532   OR   C.R. $t < -t_{12,.025} = -2.179$
r > .532 $t > t_{12,.025} = 2.179$

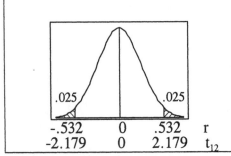

calculations: calculations:
r = .828 $t_r = (r - \mu_r)/s_r$
$= (.828 - 0)/\sqrt{(1-(.828)^2)/12}$
conclusion: $= .828/.1617 = 5.123$
   Reject H_o; there is sufficient evidence to reject the claim that $\rho = 0$ and to conclude that $\rho \neq 0$ (in fact, $\rho > 0$).
Yes; there is a correlation between trunk circumference and height.
There should be such a correlation because both circumference and height increase with age.

15.   a. n = 16
$\Sigma x = .35$
$\Sigma y = 60.2$
$\Sigma x^2 = .0143$
$\Sigma y^2 = 227.24$
$\Sigma xy = 1.342$

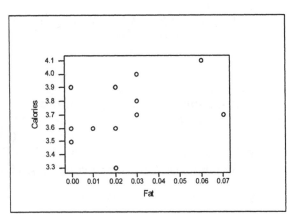

b. $n(\Sigma xy) - (\Sigma x)(\Sigma y) = 16(1.342) - (.35)(60.2) = .402$
$n(\Sigma x^2) - (\Sigma x)^2 = 16(.0143) - (.35)^2 = .1063$
$n(\Sigma y^2) - (\Sigma y)^2 = 16(227.24) - (60.2)^2 = 11.80$
$r = [n(\Sigma xy) - (\Sigma x)(\Sigma y)]/[\sqrt{n(\Sigma x^2) - (\Sigma x)^2} \cdot \sqrt{n(\Sigma y^2) - (\Sigma y)^2}]$
$= .402/[\sqrt{.1063} \cdot \sqrt{11.80}] = .359$

c. H_o: $\rho = 0$
H_1: $\rho \neq 0$
$\alpha = .05$
C.R. r < -.497   OR   C.R. t < $-t_{14,.025}$ = -2.145
     r > .497   t > $t_{14,.025}$ = 2.145

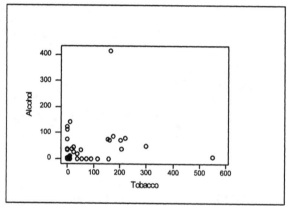

calculations: calculations:
   r = .359 $t_r = (r - \mu_r)/s_r$
                              $= (.359 - 0)/\sqrt{(1-(.359)^2)/14}$
                              $= .359/.2495 = 1.439$
conclusion:
   Do not reject H_o; there is not sufficient evidence to reject the claim that $\rho = 0$.

16. a. n = 50
     Σx = 2872
     Σy = 1623
     Σx^2 = 694918
     Σy^2 = 268331
     Σxy = 173771

b. $n(\Sigma xy) - (\Sigma x)(\Sigma y) = 50(173771) - (2872)(1623) = 4027294$
$n(\Sigma x^2) - (\Sigma x)^2 = 50(694918) - (2872)^2 = 26497516$
$n(\Sigma y^2) - (\Sigma y)^2 = 50(268331) - (1623)^2 = 10782421$
$r = [n(\Sigma xy) - (\Sigma x)(\Sigma y)]/[\sqrt{n(\Sigma x^2) - (\Sigma x)^2} \cdot \sqrt{n(\Sigma y^2) - (\Sigma y)^2}]$
$= 4027294/[\sqrt{26497516} \cdot \sqrt{10782421}] = .238$

c. H_o: $\rho = 0$
H_1: $\rho \neq 0$
$\alpha = .05$
C.R. r < -.279   OR   C.R. t < $-t_{48,.025}$ = -2.009
     r > .279   t > $t_{48,.025}$ = 2.009

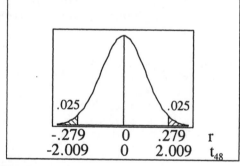

calculations: calculations:
   r = .238 $t_r = (r - \mu_r)/s_r$
                              $= (.238 - 0)/\sqrt{(1-(.238)^2)/48}$
conclusion: $= .238/.1402 = 1.700$
   Do not reject H_o; there is not sufficient evidence to reject the claim that $\rho = 0$.

17.   a. n = 40
$\Sigma x = 9635$
$\Sigma y = 1029.6$
$\Sigma x^2 = 3669819$
$\Sigma y^2 = 27984.46$
$\Sigma xy = 269551.6$

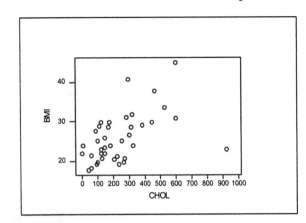

b. $n(\Sigma xy) - (\Sigma x)(\Sigma y) = 40(269551.6) - (9635)(1029.6) = 861868.0$
$n(\Sigma x^2) - (\Sigma x)^2 = 40(3669819) - (9635)^2 = 53959535$
$n(\Sigma y^2) - (\Sigma y)^2 = 40(27984.46) - (1029.6)^2 = 59302.24$
$r = [n(\Sigma xy) - (\Sigma x)(\Sigma y)]/[\sqrt{n(\Sigma x^2) - (\Sigma x)^2} \cdot \sqrt{n(\Sigma y^2) - (\Sigma y)^2}]$
$= 861868.0/[\sqrt{53959535} \cdot \sqrt{59302.24}] = .482$

c. $H_o: \rho = 0$
$H_1: \rho \neq 0$
$\alpha = .05$
C.R. r < -.312   OR   C.R. $t < -t_{38,.025} = -2.024$
   r > .312 $t > t_{38,.025} = 2.024$

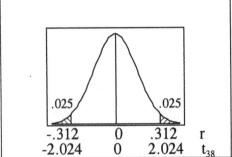

.025   .025
-.312   0   .312   r
-2.024   0   2.024 t_{38}

calculations: calculations:
   r = .482 $t_r = (r - \mu_r)/s_r$
                       $= (.482 - 0)/\sqrt{(1-(.482)^2)/38}$
conclusion: $= .482/.1422 = 3.389$

   Reject H_o; there is sufficient evidence to reject the claim that $\rho = 0$ and to conclude
   that $\rho \neq 0$ (in fact, $\rho > 0$).

18.   a. n = 12
$\Sigma x = 848.8$
$\Sigma y = 78.0$
$\Sigma x^2 = 61449.54$
$\Sigma y^2 = 572.94$
$\Sigma xy = 5238.66$

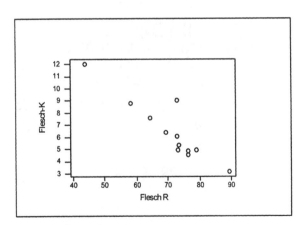

b. $n(\Sigma xy) - (\Sigma x)(\Sigma y) = 12(5238.66) - (848.8)(78.0) = -3342.48$
$n(\Sigma x^2) - (\Sigma x)^2 = 12(61449.54) - (848.8)^2 = 16933.04$
$n(\Sigma y^2) - (\Sigma y)^2 = 12(572.94) - (78.0)^2 = 791.28$
$r = [n(\Sigma xy) - (\Sigma x)(\Sigma y)]/[\sqrt{n(\Sigma x^2) - (\Sigma x)^2} \cdot \sqrt{n(\Sigma y^2) - (\Sigma y)^2}]$
$= -3342.48/[\sqrt{16933.04} \cdot \sqrt{791.28}] = -.913$

c. H_o: $\rho = 0$
   H_1: $\rho \neq 0$
   $\alpha = .05$
   C.R. r < -.576 <u>OR</u> C.R. t < $-t_{10,.025}$ = -2.228
       r > .576   t > $t_{10,.025}$ = 2.228

calculations: calculations:
   r = -.913 $t_r = (r - \mu_r)/s_r$
                          $= (-.913 - 0)/\sqrt{(1-(-.913)^2)/10}$
                          $= -.913/.1289 = -7.084$

conclusion:
   Reject H_o; there is sufficient evidence to reject the claim that $\rho = 0$ and to conclude
   that $\rho \neq 0$ (in fact, $\rho < 0$).

There is a negative correlation because the Reading Ease scale assigns high values to the
easier material while the Grade Level scale assigns high values to the more difficult
material.

19.   A. Selling price-list price relationship?
   a. n = 50
      Σx = 8917
      Σy = 8517.0
      Σx^2 = 1899037
      Σy^2 = 1710311.50
      Σxy = 1801273.0

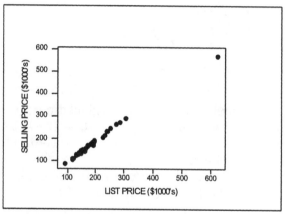

   b. $n(\Sigma xy) - (\Sigma x)(\Sigma y) = 50(1801273.0) - (8917)(8517.0) = 14117561$
      $n(\Sigma x^2) - (\Sigma x)^2 = 50(1899037) - (8917)^2 = 15438961$
      $n(\Sigma y^2) - (\Sigma y)^2 = 50(1710311.50) - (8517.0)^2 = 12976286$
      $r = [n(\Sigma xy) - (\Sigma x)(\Sigma y)]/[\sqrt{n(\Sigma x^2) - (\Sigma x)^2} \cdot \sqrt{n(\Sigma y^2) - (\Sigma y)^2}\,]$
        $= 14117561/[\sqrt{15438961} \cdot \sqrt{12976286}\,] = .9974$

   c. H_o: $\rho = 0$
      H_1: $\rho \neq 0$
      $\alpha = .05$
      C.R. r < -.279 <u>OR</u> C.R. t < $-t_{48,.025}$ = -1.960
          r > .279   t > $t_{48,.025}$ = 1.960

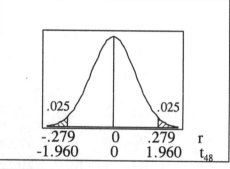

calculations: calculations:
   r = .9974 $t_r = (r - \mu_r)/s_r$
                          $= (.9974 - 0)/\sqrt{(1-(.9974)^2)/48}$
                          $= .9974/.0101 = 96.149$

conclusion:
   Reject H_o; there is sufficient evidence to reject the claim that $\rho = 0$ and to conclude
   that $\rho \neq 0$ (in fact, that $\rho > 0$). The data support the given expectation.

B. Selling price-taxes relationship?

a. n = 50
   Σx = 185305
   Σy = 8517.0
   Σx^2 = 809069344
   Σy^2 = 1710311.50
   Σxy = 36631916.5

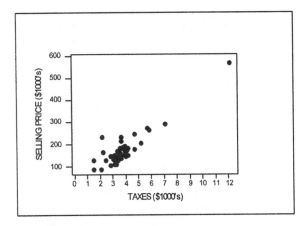

b. $n(\Sigma xy) - (\Sigma x)(\Sigma y) = 50(36631916.5) - (185305)(8517.0) = 253353140$
   $n(\Sigma x^2) - (\Sigma x)^2 = 50(809069344) - (185305)^2 = 6115524175$
   $n(\Sigma y^2) - (\Sigma y)^2 = 50(1710311.50) - (8517.0)^2 = 12976286$
   $r = [n(\Sigma xy) - (\Sigma x)(\Sigma y)]/[\sqrt{n(\Sigma x^2) - (\Sigma x)^2} \cdot \sqrt{n(\Sigma y^2) - (\Sigma y)^2}\,]$
   $= 253353140/[\sqrt{6115524175} \cdot \sqrt{12976286}\,] = .8994$

c. H_o: $\rho = 0$
   H_1: $\rho \neq 0$
   $\alpha = .05$
   C.R. r < -.279 <u>OR</u> C.R. t < $-t_{48,.025}$ = -1.960
        r > .279   t > $t_{48,.025}$ = 1.960

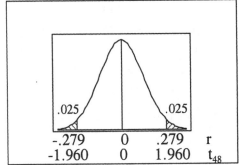

calculations: calculations:
   r = .8994 $t_r = (r - \mu_r)/s_r$
                        $= (.8994 - 0)/\sqrt{(1-(.8994)^2)/48}$
                        $= .8994/.0631 = 14.252$
conclusion:
   Reject H_o; there is sufficient evidence to reject the claim that $\rho = 0$ and to conclude that $\rho \neq 0$ (in fact, that $\rho > 0$).
   Yes; the tax bill appears to be based on the value of the house – since the selling price is assumed to represent the true value of the house, and there is a strong correlation between selling price and the amount of the taxes. The tax assessments appear to be valid.

20. A. Nicotine-tar relationship?

a. n = 29
   Σx = 351
   Σy = 27.3
   Σx^2 = 4849
   Σy^2 = 28.45
   Σxy = 369.5

b. $n(\Sigma xy) - (\Sigma x)(\Sigma y) = 29(369.5) - (351)(27.3) = 1133.2$
   $n(\Sigma x^2) - (\Sigma x)^2 = 29(4849) - (351)^2 = 17420$
   $n(\Sigma y^2) - (\Sigma y)^2 = 29(28.45) - (27.3)^2 = 79.76$

$$r = [n(\Sigma xy) - (\Sigma x)(\Sigma y)]/[\sqrt{n(\Sigma x^2) - (\Sigma x)^2} \cdot \sqrt{n(\Sigma y^2) - (\Sigma y)^2}]$$
$$= 1133.2/[\sqrt{17420} \cdot \sqrt{79.76}] = .961$$

c. H_o: $\rho = 0$
H_1: $\rho \neq 0$
$\alpha = .05$
C.R. $r < -.361$ <u>OR</u> C.R. $t < -t_{27,.025} = -2.052$
$r > .361$ $t > t_{27,.025} = 2.052$

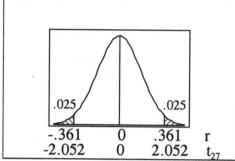

calculations: calculations:
$r = .961$ $t_r = (r - \mu_r)/s_r$
$$= (.961 - 0)/\sqrt{(1-(.961)^2)/27}$$
$$= .961/.0530 = 18.148$$

conclusion:
Reject H_o; there is sufficient evidence to reject the claim that $\rho = 0$ and to conclude that $\rho \neq 0$ (in fact, that $\rho > 0$).

Yes; based on this result there is a significant positive linear correlation, suggesting that researchers might be able to reduce their laboratory expenses by measuring only one of these two variables.

B. Nicotine-CO relationship?

a. $n = 29$
$\Sigma x = 359$
$\Sigma y = 27.3$
$\Sigma x^2 = 5003$
$\Sigma y^2 = 28.45$
$\Sigma xy = 371.8$

note: some dots represent multiple occurrences

b. $n(\Sigma xy) - (\Sigma x)(\Sigma y) = 29(371.8) - (359)(27.3) = 981.5$
$n(\Sigma x^2) - (\Sigma x)^2 = 29(5003) - (359)^2 = 16206$
$n(\Sigma y^2) - (\Sigma y)^2 = 29(28.45) - (27.3)^2 = 79.76$
$$r = [n(\Sigma xy) - (\Sigma x)(\Sigma y)]/[\sqrt{n(\Sigma x^2) - (\Sigma x)^2} \cdot \sqrt{n(\Sigma y^2) - (\Sigma y)^2}]$$
$$= 981.5/[\sqrt{16206} \cdot \sqrt{79.76}] = .863$$

c. H_o: $\rho = 0$
H_1: $\rho \neq 0$
$\alpha = .05$
C.R. $r < -.361$ <u>OR</u> C.R. $t < -t_{27,.025} = -2.052$
$r > .361$ $t > t_{27,.025} = 2.052$

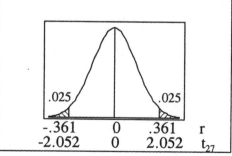

calculations: calculations:
$r = .863$ $t_r = (r - \mu_r)/s_r$
$$= (.863 - 0)/\sqrt{(1-(.863)^2)/27}$$
$$= .863/.0971 = 8.888$$

conclusion:
Reject H_o; there is sufficient evidence to reject the claim that $\rho = 0$ and to conclude that $\rho \neq 0$ (in fact, that $\rho > 0$).

Yes; based on this result there is a significant positive linear correlation, suggesting that researchers might be able to reduce their laboratory expenses by measuring only one of these two variables.

C. Tar is the better choice, since it is more highly correlated with nicotine.

21.   A. Actual-fiveday relationship?

a. n = 31
   Σx = 1069
   Σy = 1082
   Σx^2 = 37381
   Σy^2 = 38352
   Σxy = 37628

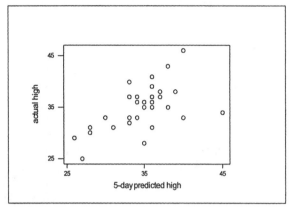

b. $n(\Sigma xy) - (\Sigma x)(\Sigma y) = 31(37628) - (1069)(1082) = 9810$
   $n(\Sigma x^2) - (\Sigma x)^2 = 31(37381) - (1069)^2 = 16050$
   $n(\Sigma y^2) - (\Sigma y)^2 = 31(38352) - (1082)^2 = 18188$
   $r = [n(\Sigma xy) - (\Sigma x)(\Sigma y)]/[\sqrt{n(\Sigma x^2) - (\Sigma x)^2} \cdot \sqrt{n(\Sigma y^2) - (\Sigma y)^2}]$
   $= 9810/[\sqrt{16050} \cdot \sqrt{18188}] = .574$

c. H_o: $\rho = 0$
   H_1: $\rho \neq 0$
   α = .05
   C.R. r < -.361   OR   C.R. t < $-t_{29,.025}$ = -2.045
        r > .361   t > $t_{29,.025}$ = 2.045

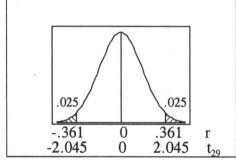

calculations: calculations:
   r = .574 $t_r = (r - \mu_r)/s_r$
                             $= (.574 - 0)/\sqrt{(1-(.574)^2)/29}$
conclusion: $= .574/.1520 = 3.777$

   Reject H_o; there is sufficient evidence to reject the claim that $\rho = 0$ and to conclude that $\rho \neq 0$ (in fact, that $\rho > 0$).

Yes; there is a linear correlation between the 5-day forecast and the actual temperature. No; a correlation means only that there is a relationship between the values, not that they agree with each other. If the 5-day forecasts were always exactly 20 degrees too cold, for example, there would be a perfected correlation but not agreement.

   B. Actual-oneday relationship?

a. n = 31
   Σx = 1033
   Σy = 1082
   Σx^2 = 35107
   Σy^2 = 38352
   Σxy = 36489

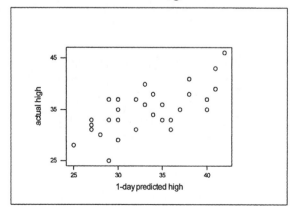

b. $n(\Sigma xy) - (\Sigma x)(\Sigma y) = 31(36489) - (1033)(1082) = 13453$
$n(\Sigma x^2) - (\Sigma x)^2 = 31(35107) - (1033)^2 = 21228$
$n(\Sigma y^2) - (\Sigma y)^2 = 31(38352) - (1082)^2 = 18188$
$r = [n(\Sigma xy) - (\Sigma x)(\Sigma y)]/[\sqrt{n(\Sigma x^2) - (\Sigma x)^2} \cdot \sqrt{n(\Sigma y^2) - (\Sigma y)^2}\,]$
$\quad = 13453/[\sqrt{21228} \cdot \sqrt{18188}\,] = .685$

c. $H_o: \rho = 0$
$H_1: \rho \neq 0$
$\alpha = .05$
C.R. $r < -.361$ $\underline{\text{OR}}$ C.R. $t < -t_{29,.025} = -2.045$
$\quad\;\; r > .361$ $\qquad\qquad t > t_{29,.025} = 2.045$

calculations:
$\quad r = .685$

calculations:
$\quad t_r = (r - \mu_r)/s_r$
$\quad\quad = (.685 - 0)/\sqrt{(1-(.685)^2)/29}$
$\quad\quad = .685/.1353 = 5.059$

conclusion:
Reject H_o; there is sufficient evidence to reject the claim that $\rho = 0$ and to conclude that $\rho \neq 0$ (in fact, that $\rho > 0$).

Yes; there is a linear correlation between the 1-day forecast and the actual temperature. No; a correlation means only that there is a relationship between the values, not that they agree with each other. If the 1-day forecasts were always exactly 20 degrees too cold, for example, there would be a perfected correlation but not agreement.

C. One would expect the 1-day forecasts to have a higher correlation with the actual temperatures than the 5-day forecasts would, and the results support this expectation. But even a very high correlation means only that there is a relationship between the predicted and the actual temperatures, not that they agree with each other. If the predictions were always exactly 20 degrees too cold, for example, there would be a perfected correlation but not agreement.

22. A. Conductivity-temperature relationship?
a. $n = 61$
$\Sigma x = 1853.0$
$\Sigma y = 2874.5$
$\Sigma x^2 = 56457.63$
$\Sigma y^2 = 139786.58$
$\Sigma xy = 87422.02$

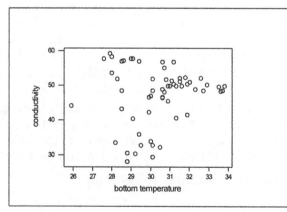

b. $n(\Sigma xy) - (\Sigma x)(\Sigma y) = 61(87422.02) - (1853.0)(2874.5) = 6294.72$
$n(\Sigma x^2) - (\Sigma x)^2 = 61(56457.63) - (1853.0)^2 = 10306.43$
$n(\Sigma y^2) - (\Sigma y)^2 = 61(139786.58) - (2874.5)^2 = 264231.13$
$r = [n(\Sigma xy) - (\Sigma x)(\Sigma y)]/[\sqrt{n(\Sigma x^2) - (\Sigma x)^2} \cdot \sqrt{n(\Sigma y^2) - (\Sigma y)^2}\,]$
$\quad = 6294.72/[\sqrt{10306.43} \cdot \sqrt{264231.13}\,] = .121$

c. H_o: $\rho = 0$
  H_1: $\rho \neq 0$
  $\alpha = .05$
  C.R. r < -.254   OR   C.R. t < -$t_{59,.025}$ = -2.000
        r > .254   t > $t_{59,.025}$ = 2.000

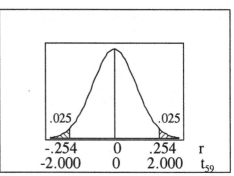

calculations: calculations:
  r = .121 $t_r = (r - \mu_r)/s_r$
                          $= (.121 - 0)/\sqrt{(1-(.121)^2)/59}$
                          $= .121/.1292 = .933$
conclusion:
  Do not reject H_o; there is not sufficient evidence to reject the claim that $\rho = 0$.

B. Conductivity-rainfall relationship?

a. n = 61
  Σx = 16.51
  Σy = 2874.5
  Σx^2 = 22.6397
  Σy^2 = 139786.58
  Σxy = 744.641

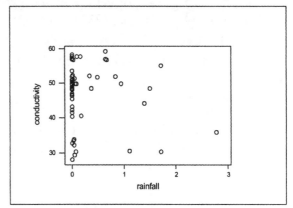

b. $n(\Sigma xy) - (\Sigma x)(\Sigma y) = 61(744.641) - (16.51)(2874.5) = -2034.894$
  $n(\Sigma x^2) - (\Sigma x)^2 = 61(22.6397) - (16.51)^2 = 1108.4416$
  $n(\Sigma y^2) - (\Sigma y)^2 = 61(139786.58) - (2874.5)^2 = 264231.13$
  $r = [n(\Sigma xy) - (\Sigma x)(\Sigma y)]/[\sqrt{n(\Sigma x^2) - (\Sigma x)^2} \cdot \sqrt{n(\Sigma y^2) - (\Sigma y)^2}\,]$
    $= -2034.894/[\sqrt{1108.4416} \cdot \sqrt{264231.13}\,] = -.119$

c. H_o: $\rho = 0$
  H_1: $\rho \neq 0$
  $\alpha = .05$
  C.R. r < -.254   OR   C.R. t < -$t_{59,.025}$ = -2.000
        r > .254   t > $t_{59,.025}$ = 2.000

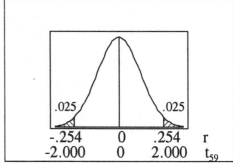

calculations: calculations:
  r = -.119 $t_r = (r - \mu_r)/s_r$
                          $= (-.119 - 0)/\sqrt{(1-(-.119)^2)/59}$
                          $= -.119/.1293 = -.920$
conclusion:
  Do not reject H_o; there is not sufficient evidence to reject the claim that $\rho = 0$.

C. Since the correlation between conductivity and salinity is nearly 1.00, the above
  conclusions regarding conductivity apply to salinity – i.e., neither bottom temperature
  nor rainfall amount has a significant linear correlation with salinity. Notice that the
  negative sign for the calculated sample correlation in part (b) agrees with the notion that
  high rainfall means low salinity – which, if there is close to a perfect positive
  correlation between salinity and conductivity, means low conductivity.

23.   A. Interval-duration relationship?

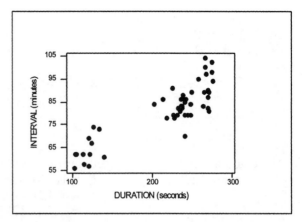

a. $n = 50$
   $\Sigma x = 10832$
   $\Sigma y = 4033$
   $\Sigma x^2 = 2513280$
   $\Sigma y^2 = 332331$
   $\Sigma xy = 903488$

b. $n(\Sigma xy) - (\Sigma x)(\Sigma y) = 50(903488) - (10832)(4033) = 1488944$
   $n(\Sigma x^2) - (\Sigma x)^2 = 50(2513280) - (10832)^2 = 8331776$
   $n(\Sigma y^2) - (\Sigma y)^2 = 50(332331) - (4033)^2 = 351461$
   $r = [n(\Sigma xy) - (\Sigma x)(\Sigma y)]/[\sqrt{n(\Sigma x^2) - (\Sigma x)^2} \cdot \sqrt{n(\Sigma y^2) - (\Sigma y)^2}\,]$
   $= 1488944/[\sqrt{8331776} \cdot \sqrt{351461}\,] = .870$

c. $H_0: \rho = 0$
   $H_1: \rho \neq 0$
   $\alpha = .05$
   C.R. $r < -.279$ OR   C.R. $t < -t_{48,.025} = -1.960$
   $r > .279$ $t > t_{48,.025} = 1.960$

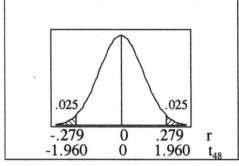

calculations: calculations:
$r = .870$ $t_r = (r - \mu_r)/s_r$
$= (.870 - 0)/\sqrt{(1-(.870)^2)/48}$

conclusion: $= .870/.0711 = 12.231$

   Reject H_0; there is sufficient evidence to reject the claim that $\rho = 0$ and to conclude
   that $\rho \neq 0$ (in fact, that $\rho > 0$).
   Yes; there is a significant positive linear correlation, suggesting that the interval after an
   eruption is related to the duration of the eruption. NOTE: The longer the duration of an
   eruption, the more pressure has been released and the longer it will take the geyser to
   build back up for another eruption. In fact, the park rangers use the duration of one
   eruption to predict the time of the next eruption.

B. Interval-height relationship?

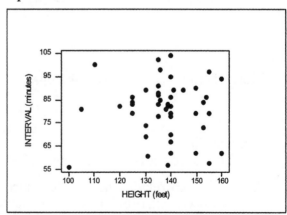

a. $n = 50$
   $\Sigma x = 6904$
   $\Sigma y = 4033$
   $\Sigma x^2 = 961150$
   $\Sigma y^2 = 332331$
   $\Sigma xy = 556804$

b. $n(\Sigma xy) - (\Sigma x)(\Sigma y) = 50(556804) - (6904)(4033) = -3632$
   $n(\Sigma x^2) - (\Sigma x)^2 = 50(961150) - (6904)^2 = 392284$
   $n(\Sigma y^2) - (\Sigma y)^2 = 50(332331) - (4033)^2 = 351461$

$r = [n(\Sigma xy) - (\Sigma x)(\Sigma y)]/[\sqrt{n(\Sigma x^2) - (\Sigma x)^2} \cdot \sqrt{n(\Sigma y^2) - (\Sigma y)^2}]$
$= -3632/[\sqrt{392284} \cdot \sqrt{351461}] = -.00978$

c. $H_o: \rho = 0$
$H_1: \rho \neq 0$
$\alpha = .05$
C.R. $r < -.279$ **OR**   C.R. $t < -t_{48,.025} = -1.960$
      $r > .279$ $t > t_{48,.025} = 1.960$

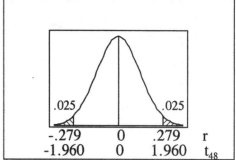

calculations: calculations:
  $r = -.00978$ $t_r = (r - \mu_r)/s_r$
                          $= (-.00978 - 0)/\sqrt{(1-(-.00978)^2)/48}$
                          $= -.00978/.144 = -.068$

conclusion:
Do not reject H_o; there is not sufficient evidence to reject the claim that $\rho = 0$.
No; there is not a significant linear correlation, suggesting that the interval after an eruption is not so related to the height of the eruption.

C. Duration is the more relevant predictor of the interval until the next eruption -- because it has a significant correlation with interval, while height does not.

24. A. Price-weight relationship? [NOTE: For convenience, we measure the price y in $1000's.]

a. $n = 30$
$\Sigma x = 50.65$
$\Sigma y = 433.23$
$\Sigma x^2 = 109.74$
$\Sigma y^2 = 12378.86$
$\Sigma xy = 1027.03$

b. $n(\Sigma xy) - (\Sigma x)(\Sigma y) = 30(1027.03) - (50.65)(433.23) = 8867.80$
$n(\Sigma x^2) - (\Sigma x)^2 = 30(109.74) - (50.65)^2 = 726.78$
$n(\Sigma y^2) - (\Sigma y)^2 = 30(12378.86) - (433.23)^2 = 183677.57$
$r = [n(\Sigma xy) - (\Sigma x)(\Sigma y)]/[\sqrt{n(\Sigma x^2) - (\Sigma x)^2} \cdot \sqrt{n(\Sigma y^2) - (\Sigma y)^2}]$
$= 8867.80/[\sqrt{726.78} \cdot \sqrt{183677.57}] = .767$

c. $H_o: \rho = 0$
$H_1: \rho \neq 0$
$\alpha = .05$
C.R. $r < -.361$ **OR**   C.R. $t < -t_{28,.025} = -2.048$
      $r > .361$ $t > t_{28,.025} = 2.048$

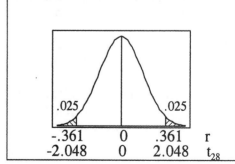

calculations: calculations:
  $r = .767$ $t_r = (r - \mu_r)/s_r$
                          $= (.767 - 0)/\sqrt{(1-(.767)^2)/28}$
conclusion: $= .767/.121 = 6.325$
Reject H_o; there is sufficient evidence to reject the claim that $\rho = 0$ and to conclude that $\rho \neq 0$ (in fact, that $\rho > 0$).

Yes; based on this result there is a significant positive linear correlation between the price of a diamond and its weight in carats.

B. Price-color relationship? [NOTE: For convenience, we measure the price y in $1000's.]

a. $n = 30$
$\Sigma x = 140$
$\Sigma y = 433.23$
$\Sigma x^2 = 782$
$\Sigma y^2 = 12378.86$
$\Sigma xy = 1630.03$

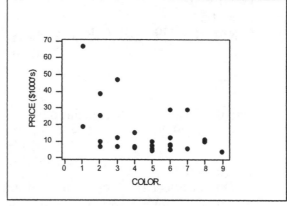

b. $n(\Sigma xy) - (\Sigma x)(\Sigma y) = 30(1630.03) - (140)(433.23) = -11751.30$
$n(\Sigma x^2) - (\Sigma x)^2 = 30(782) - (140)^2 = 3860$
$n(\Sigma y^2) - (\Sigma y)^2 = 30(12378.86) - (433.23)^2 = 183677.57$
$r = [n(\Sigma xy) - (\Sigma x)(\Sigma y)]/[\sqrt{n(\Sigma x^2) - (\Sigma x)^2} \cdot \sqrt{n(\Sigma y^2) - (\Sigma y)^2}]$
$= -11751.30/[\sqrt{3860} \cdot \sqrt{183677.57}] = -.441$

c. $H_0: \rho = 0$
$H_1: \rho \neq 0$
$\alpha = .05$
C.R. $r < -.361$ __OR__ C.R. $t < -t_{28,.025} = -2.048$
$r > .361$ $t > t_{28,.025} = 2.048$

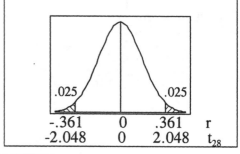

calculations: calculations:
$r = -.441$ $t_r = (r - \mu_r)/s_r$
$= (-.441 - 0)/\sqrt{(1-(-.441)^2)/28}$
conclusion: $= -.441/.170 = -2.600$

Reject H_0; there is sufficient evidence to reject the claim that $\rho = 0$ and to conclude that $\rho \neq 0$ (in fact, that $\rho < 0$).

Yes; based on this result there is a significant negative linear correlation between price and color – i.e., the lower the color number, the higher the price.

C. When determining the value of a diamond, weight is more important than color. The weight of a diamond is more highly correlated (i.e., has an r value farther from 0) with the selling price than is the color.

25. A linear correlation coefficient very close to zero indicates <u>no</u> significant linear correlation and no tendencies can be inferred.

26. A significant linear correlation indicates that the factors are associated, not that there is a cause and effect relationship. Even if there is a cause and effect relationship, correlation analysis cannot identify which factor is the cause and which factor is the effect.

27. A linear correlation coefficient very close to zero indicates no significant <u>linear</u> correlation, but there may some other type of relationship between the variables.

28. A significant linear correlation between group averages indicates nothing about the relationship between the individual scores -- which may be uncorrelated, correlated in the opposite direction, or have different correlations within each of the groups.

29. There are n=13 data points.
     From the scatterplot, it appears that the correlation is about +.75.
     H_o: $\rho = 0$
     H_1: $\rho \neq 0$
     $\alpha = .05$
     C.R. r < -.553   OR   C.R. t < $-t_{11,.025}$ = -2.201
          r > .553   t > $t_{11,.025}$ = 2.201

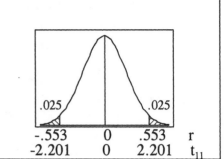

     calculations: calculations:
        r = .75 $t_r = (r - \mu_r)/s_r$
                                    $= (.75 - 0)/\sqrt{(1-(.75)^2)/11}$
                                    $= .75/.199 = 3.761$
     conclusion:
        Reject H_o; there is sufficient evidence to reject the claim that $\rho = 0$ and to conclude
        that $\rho \neq 0$ (in fact, that $\rho > 0$).
     Yes; based on this result there is a significant positive linear correlation between the
     mortality rate and the rate of infections acquired in intensive care units.

30. The following table gives the values for y, x, x^2, log x, $\sqrt{x}$ and 1/x. The rows at the
     bottom of the table give the sum of the values (i.e., Σv), the sum of squares of the values
     (i.e., Σv^2), the sum of each value times the corresponding y value (i.e., Σvy), and the
     quantity $n\Sigma v^2 - (\Sigma v)^2$ needed in subsequent calculations.

	y	x	x^2	log x	$\sqrt{x}$	1/x
	.11	1.3	1.69	.1139	1.1402	.7692
	.38	2.4	5.76	.3802	1.5492	.4167
	.41	2.6	6.76	.4150	1.6125	.3846
	.45	2.8	7.84	.4472	1.6733	.3571
	.39	2.4	5.76	.3802	1.5492	.4167
	.48	3.0	9.00	.4771	1.7321	.3333
	.61	4.1	16.81	.6128	2.0248	.2439
Σv	2.83	18.6	53.62	2.8264	11.2814	2.9216
Σv^2	1.2817	53.62	539.95	1.2774	18.6000	1.3850
Σvy		8.258	25.495	1.2795	4.7989	1.0326
$n\Sigma v^2-(\Sigma v)^2$	.9630	29.38	904.55	.9533	2.9300	1.1593

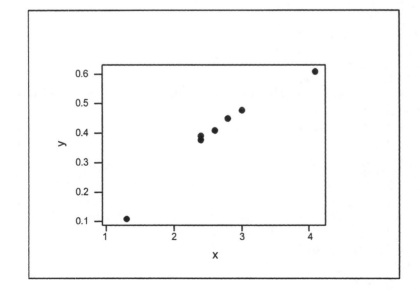

In general, $r = [n(\Sigma vy) - (\Sigma v)(\Sigma y)]/[\sqrt{n(\Sigma v^2) - (\Sigma v)^2} \cdot \sqrt{n(\Sigma y^2) - (\Sigma y)^2}\,]$

  a. For $v = x$,
    $r = [7(8.258) - (18.6)(2.83)]/[\sqrt{29.38} \cdot \sqrt{.9630}\,] = .9716$

  b. For $v = x^2$,
    $r = [7(25.495) - (53.62)(2.83)]/[\sqrt{904.55} \cdot \sqrt{.9630}\,] = .9053$

  c. For $v = \log x$,
    $r = [7(1.2795) - (2.8264)(2.83)]/[\sqrt{.9533} \cdot \sqrt{.9630}\,] = .9996$

  d. For $v = \sqrt{x}$,
    $r = [7(4.7989) - (11.2814)(2.83)]/[\sqrt{2.9300} \cdot \sqrt{.9630}\,] = .9918$

  e. For $v = 1/x$,
    $r = [7(1.0326) - (2.9216)(2.83)]/[\sqrt{29.38} \cdot \sqrt{1.1593}\,] = -.9842$

In each case, the critical values from Table A-6 for testing significance at the .05 level are $\pm.754$. While all the correlations are significant, the largest value for r occurs in part (c).

31. a. For $\pm t_{48,.025} = \pm 1.960$,
    the critical values are $r = \pm 1.960/\sqrt{(\pm 1.960)^2 + 48} = \pm.272$.

  b. For $\pm t_{73,.05} = \pm 1.645$,
    the critical values are $r = \pm 1.645/\sqrt{(\pm 1.645)^2 + 73} = \pm.189$.

  c. For $-t_{18,.05} = -1.734$,
    the critical value is $r = -1.734/\sqrt{(-1.734)^2 + 18} = -.378$.

  d. For $t_{8,.05} = 1.860$,
    the critical value is $r = 1.860/\sqrt{(1.860)^2 + 8} = .549$.

  e. For $t_{10,.01} = 2.764$,
    the critical value is $r = 2.764/\sqrt{(2.764)^2 + 10} = .658$.

32. The following summary statistics apply to all parts of the exercise.

both genders	females only	males only
n = 16	n = 8	n = 8
$\Sigma x = 2408$	$\Sigma x = 1042$	$\Sigma x = 1366$
$\Sigma y = 195$	$\Sigma y = 34$	$\Sigma y = 161$
$\Sigma x^2 = 369474$	$\Sigma x^2 = 135958$	$\Sigma x^2 = 233516$
$\Sigma y^2 = 3463$	$\Sigma y^2 = 164$	$\Sigma y^2 = 3299$
$\Sigma xy = 31884$	$\Sigma xy = 4414$	$\Sigma xy = 27470$

  a. There appears to be a strong positive linear correlation between weight and remote use.

  b. $n(\Sigma xy) - (\Sigma x)(\Sigma y) = 16(31884) - (2408)(195) = 40584$
    $n(\Sigma x^2) - (\Sigma x)^2 = 16(369474) - (2408)^2 = 113120$
    $n(\Sigma y^2) - (\Sigma y)^2 = 16(3463) - (195)^2 = 17383$

    $r = [n(\Sigma xy) - (\Sigma x)(\Sigma y)]/[\sqrt{n(\Sigma x^2) - (\Sigma x)^2} \cdot \sqrt{n(\Sigma y^2) - (\Sigma y)^2}\,]$
    $= 40584/[\sqrt{113120} \cdot \sqrt{17383}\,] = .915$

    Since CV $= \pm.497$ at the .05 level of significance, conclude that there is a positive correlation between weight and remote use.

  c. $n(\Sigma xy) - (\Sigma x)(\Sigma y) = 8(4414) - (1042)(34) = -116$
    $n(\Sigma x^2) - (\Sigma x)^2 = 8(135958) - (1042)^2 = 1900$
    $n(\Sigma y^2) - (\Sigma y)^2 = 8(164) - (34)^2 = 156$

    $r = [n(\Sigma xy) - (\Sigma x)(\Sigma y)]/[\sqrt{n(\Sigma x^2) - (\Sigma x)^2} \cdot \sqrt{n(\Sigma y^2) - (\Sigma y)^2}\,]$
    $= -116/[\sqrt{1900} \cdot \sqrt{156}\,] = -.213$

    Since CV $= \pm.707$ at the .05 level of significance, there is not evidence of a linear correlation between weight and remote use for the females.

  d. $n(\Sigma xy) - (\Sigma x)(\Sigma y) = 8(27470) - (1366)(161) = -166$
    $n(\Sigma x^2) - (\Sigma x)^2 = 8(233516) - (1366)^2 = 2172$
    $n(\Sigma y^2) - (\Sigma y)^2 = 8(3299) - (161)^2 = 471$

    $r = [n(\Sigma xy) - (\Sigma x)(\Sigma y)]/[\sqrt{n(\Sigma x^2) - (\Sigma x)^2} \cdot \sqrt{n(\Sigma y^2) - (\Sigma y)^2}\,]$
    $= -166/[\sqrt{2172} \cdot \sqrt{471}\,] = -.164$

Since CV $= \pm.707$ at the .05 level of significance, there is not evidence of a linear correlation between weight and remote use for the males.

e. Combining different groups can give a misleading impression of the true correlation within the separate groups.

33. For r $= .600$, $(1+r)/(1-r) = (1.6)/(.4) = 4$. Following the procedure outlined in the text,

Step a. $z_{.025} = 1.960$

Step b. $w_L = \frac{1}{2} \cdot \ln(4) - 1.960/\sqrt{47} = .407$
$w_R = \frac{1}{2} \cdot \ln(4) + 1.960/\sqrt{47} = .979$

Step c. $(e^{.814} - 1)/(e^{.814} + 1) < \rho < (e^{1.958} - 1)/(e^{1.958} + 1)$
$(1.258)/(3.258) < \rho < (6.086)/(8.086)$
$.386 < \rho < .753$

NOTE: While the distribution of r is not normal, $\tanh^{-1}(r)$ [i.e., the inverse hyperbolic tangent of r] follows a normal distribution with $\mu_r = \tanh^{-1}(\rho)$ and $\sigma_r = 1/\sqrt{n-3}$. The steps above are equivalent to finding $\tanh^{-1}(r)$, constructing a confidence interval for $\tanh^{-1}(\rho)$, and then applying the hyperbolic tangent function to the endpoints to produce a confidence interval for ρ.

9-3 Regression

1. a. For n=20, CV$=\pm.444$; since r$=.987>.444$, use the regression line for predictions.
    $\hat{y} = 6.00 + 4.00x$
    $\hat{y}_{3.00} = 6.00 + 4.00(3.00) = 18.00$
    b. For n=20, CV$=\pm.444$; since r$=.052<.444$, use the mean for predictions.
    $\hat{y} = \bar{y}$
    $\hat{y}_{3.00} = \bar{y} = 5.00$

2. a. For n=30, CV$=\pm.361$; since r$=-.123>-.361$, use the mean for predictions.
    $\hat{y} = \bar{y}$
    $\hat{y}_{2.00} = \bar{y} = 8.00$
    b. For n=30, CV$=\pm.361$; since r$=-.567<-.361$, use the regression line for predictions.
    $\hat{y} = 7.00 - 2.00x$
    $\hat{y}_{2.00} = 7.00 - 2.00(2.00) = 3.00$

3. For n=8, CV$=\pm.707$; since r$=.993>.707$, use the regression line for predictions.
    $\hat{y} = -187 + 11.3x$
    $\hat{y}_{52} = -187 + 11.3(52) = 401$

4. For n=21, CV$=\pm.444$; since r$=-.133>-.444$, use the mean for predictions.
    $\hat{y} = \bar{y}$
    $\hat{y}_{1200} = \bar{y} = 51.4$

NOTE: For exercises 5-24, the exact summary statistics (i.e., without any rounding) are given on the right. While the intermediate calculations on the left are presented rounded to various degrees of accuracy, the entire unrounded values were preserved in the calculator until the end.

5. $\bar{x} = 2.00$
   $\bar{y} = 2.00$
   $b_1 = [n(\Sigma xy) - (\Sigma x)(\Sigma y)]/[n(\Sigma x^2) - (\Sigma x)^2]$
   $= [5(20) - (10)(10)]/[5(30) - (10)^2]$
   $= 0/50$
   $= 0.00$

   $n = 5$
   $\Sigma x = 10$
   $\Sigma y = 10$
   $\Sigma x^2 = 30$
   $\Sigma y^2 = 344$
   $\Sigma xy = 20$

$b_o = \bar{y} - b_1\bar{x}$
$= 2.00 - (0.00)(2.00) = 2.00$
$\hat{y} = b_o + b_1x = 2.00 + 0.00x$

6. $\bar{x} = 3.20$
$\bar{y} = 8.20$
$b_1 = [n(\Sigma xy) - (\Sigma x)(\Sigma y)]/[n(\Sigma x^2) - (\Sigma x)^2]$
$= [5(185) - (16)(41)]/[5(70) - (16)^2]$
$= 269/94$
$= 2.862$
$b_o = \bar{y} - b_1\bar{x}$
$= 8.20 - (2.862)(3.20) = -.597$
$\hat{y} = b_o + b_1x = -.597 + 2.862x$

$n = 5$
$\Sigma x = 16$
$\Sigma y = 41$
$\Sigma x^2 = 70$
$\Sigma y^2 = 495$
$\Sigma xy = 185$

7. a. $\bar{x} = 2.80$
$\bar{y} = 2.80$
$b_1 = [n(\Sigma xy) - (\Sigma x)(\Sigma y)]/[n(\Sigma x^2) - (\Sigma x)^2]$
$= 576/636$
$= .906$
$b_o = \bar{y} - b_1\bar{x}$
$= 2.80 - .906(2.80) = .264$
$\hat{y} = b_o + b_1x = .264 + .906x$

$n = 10$
$\Sigma x = 28$
$\Sigma y = 28$
$\Sigma x^2 = 142$
$\Sigma y^2 = 142$
$\Sigma xy = 136$

b. $\bar{x} = 2.00$
$\bar{y} = 2.00$
$b_1 = [n(\Sigma xy) - (\Sigma x)(\Sigma y)]/[n(\Sigma x^2) - (\Sigma x)^2]$
$= 0/54$
$= .000$
$b_o = \bar{y} - b_1\bar{x}$
$= 2.00 - .000(2.00) = 2.00$
$\hat{y} = b_o + b_1x = 2.00 + 0.00x$

$n = 9$
$\Sigma x = 18$
$\Sigma y = 18$
$\Sigma x^2 = 42$
$\Sigma y^2 = 42$
$\Sigma xy = 136$

c. The two regression lines are very different, illustrating that one point can affect the regression dramatically.

NOTE: In the exercises that follow, this manual uses the full accuracy of b_o and b_1 when calculating $\hat{y}$. Using only the rounded values as stated in the equation produces slightly different answers. More detail for calculating the numerator and denominator of b_1 is given in the corresponding exercise in the previous section.

8. $\bar{x} = 61.55$
$\bar{y} = 3.04$
$b_1 = [n(\Sigma xy) - (\Sigma x)(\Sigma y)]/[n(\Sigma x^2) - (\Sigma x)^2]$
$= 1071.2/15826 = .0677$
$b_o = \bar{y} - b_1\bar{x}$
$= 3.04 - (.0677)(61.55) = -1.13$
$\hat{y} = b_o + b_1x = -1.13 + .0677x$
$\hat{y}_{80} = \bar{y} = 3.04$ [no significant correlation]

$n = 11$
$\Sigma x = 677$
$\Sigma y = 33.4$
$\Sigma x^2 = 43105$
$\Sigma y^2 = 126.04$
$\Sigma xy = 2153.0$

9. $\bar{x} = 23.525$
$\bar{y} = 6.500$
$b_1 = [n(\Sigma xy) - (\Sigma x)(\Sigma y)]/[n(\Sigma x^2) - (\Sigma x)^2]$
$= -656.64/59381.08 = -.0111$
$b_o = \bar{y} - b_1\bar{x}$
$= 6.5000 - (-.0111)(23.525) = 6.76$
$\hat{y} = b_o + b_1x = 6.76 - .0111x$
$\hat{y}_{16} = \bar{y} = 6.5$ [no significant correlation]
In this instance, the predicted value is far from actual value.

$n = 8$
$\Sigma x = 188.2$
$\Sigma y = 52.0$
$\Sigma x^2 = 11850.04$
$\Sigma y^2 = 402.90$
$\Sigma xy = 1141.22$

10. $\bar{x} = 70.22$ $n = 9$

$\bar{y} = 121.00$ $\Sigma x = 632.0$

$b_1 = [n(\Sigma xy) - (\Sigma x)(\Sigma y)]/[n(\Sigma x^2) - (\Sigma x)^2]$ $\Sigma y = 1089$

$\quad = 666/171.5 = 3.88$ $\Sigma x^2 = 44399.50$

$b_0 = \bar{y} - b_1\bar{x}$ $\Sigma y^2 = 132223$

$\quad = 121.00 - (3.88)(70.22) = -151.7$ $\Sigma xy = 76546.0$

$\hat{y} = b_0 + b_1x = -151.7 + 3.88x$

$\hat{y}_{69} = -151.7 + 3.88(69) = 116$

11. $\bar{x} = 133.93$ $n = 14$

$\bar{y} = 88.64$ $\Sigma x = 1875$

$b_1 = [n(\Sigma xy) - (\Sigma x)(\Sigma y)]/[n(\Sigma x^2) - (\Sigma x)^2]$ $\Sigma y = 1241$

$\quad = 11447/14881 = .769$ $\Sigma x^2 = 252179$

$b_0 = \bar{y} - b_1\bar{x}$ $\Sigma y^2 = 111459$

$\quad = 88.64 - (.769)(133.93) = -14.4$ $\Sigma xy = 167023$

$\hat{y} = b_0 + b_1x = -14.4 + .769x$

$\hat{y}_{122} = -14.4 + .769(112) = 79$

12. $\bar{x} = 59.750$ $n = 8$

$\bar{y} = 147.077$ $\Sigma x = 478$

$b_1 = [n(\Sigma xy) - (\Sigma x)(\Sigma y)]/[n(\Sigma x^2) - (\Sigma x)^2]$ $\Sigma y = 1176.617$

$\quad = 129.010/4076 = .0317$ $\Sigma x^2 = 29070$

$b_0 = \bar{y} - b_1\bar{x}$ $\Sigma y^2 = 173068.664832$

$\quad = 147.077 - (.0317)(59.750) = 145.2$ $\Sigma xy = 70318.992$

$\hat{y} = b_0 + b_1x = 145.2 + .0317x$

$\hat{y}_{73} = \bar{y} = 147.077$ [no significant correlation]

The predicted value is over 3 minutes off; considering the variability in times, this seems like a large error.

13. $\bar{x} = 14.583$ $n = 12$

$\bar{y} = 175.205$ $\Sigma x = 175$

$b_1 = [n(\Sigma xy) - (\Sigma x)(\Sigma y)]/[n(\Sigma x^2) - (\Sigma x)^2]$ $\Sigma y = 2102.46$

$\quad = 77407.62/31235 = 2.478$ $\Sigma x^2 = 5155$

$b_0 = \bar{y} - b_1\bar{x}$ $\Sigma y^2 = 601709.8240$

$\quad = 175.205 - (2.478)(14.583) = 139.1$ $\Sigma xy = 37111.51$

$\hat{y} = b_0 + b_1x = 139.1 + 2.478x$

$\hat{y}_{40} = \bar{y} = 175.2$ [no significant correlation]

14. $\bar{x} = 4.743$ $n = 14$

$\bar{y} = 47.793$ $\Sigma x = 66.4$

$b_1 = [n(\Sigma xy) - (\Sigma x)(\Sigma y)]/[n(\Sigma x^2) - (\Sigma x)^2]$ $\Sigma y = 669.1$

$\quad = 9691.14/1814.60 = 5.34$ $\Sigma x^2 = 444.54$

$b_0 = \bar{y} - b_1\bar{x}$ $\Sigma y^2 = 37365.71$

$\quad = 47.793 - (5.34)(4.743) = 22.5$ $\Sigma xy = 3865.67$

$\hat{y} = b_0 + b_1x = 22.5 + 5.34x$

$\hat{y}_{4.0} = 22.5 + 5.34(4.0) = 43.8$

Circumferences are more easily and more accurately measured than heights.

15. $\bar{x} = .0219$ $n = 16$

$\bar{y} = 3.7625$ $\Sigma x = .35$

$b_1 = [n(\Sigma xy) - (\Sigma x)(\Sigma y)]/[n(\Sigma x^2) - (\Sigma x)^2]$ $\Sigma y = 60.2$

$\quad = .402/.1063 = 3.78$ $\Sigma x^2 = .0143$

$b_0 = \bar{y} - b_1\bar{x}$ $\Sigma y^2 = 227.24$

$\quad = 3.7625 - (3.78)(.0219) = 3.68$ $\Sigma xy = 1.342$

$\hat{y} = b_0 + b_1x = 3.68 + 3.78x$

$\hat{y}_{.05} = \bar{y} = 3.76$ [no significant correlation]

16. $\bar{x} = 57.44$ $n = 50$
$\bar{y} = 32.46$ $\Sigma x = 2872$
$b_1 = [n(\Sigma xy) - (\Sigma x)(\Sigma y)]/[n(\Sigma x^2) - (\Sigma x)^2]$ $\Sigma y = 1623$
    $= 4027294/26497516 = .152$ $\Sigma x^2 = 694918$
$b_0 = \bar{y} - b_1\bar{x}$ $\Sigma y^2 = 268331$
    $= 32.46 - (.152)(57.44) = 23.7$ $\Sigma xy = 173771$
$\hat{y} = b_0 + b_1x = 23.7 + .152x$
$\hat{y}_0 = \bar{y} = 32$ [no significant correlation]

17. $\bar{x} = 240.875$ $n = 40$
$\bar{y} = 25.740$ $\Sigma x = 9635$
$b_1 = [n(\Sigma xy) - (\Sigma x)(\Sigma y)]/[n(\Sigma x^2) - (\Sigma x)^2]$ $\Sigma y = 1029.6$
    $= 861868.8/53959535 = .0160$ $\Sigma x^2 = 3669819$
$b_0 = \bar{y} - b_1\bar{x}$ $\Sigma y^2 = 27984.46$
    $= 25.740 - (.0160)(240.875) = 21.9$ $\Sigma xy = 269551.6$
$\hat{y} = b_0 + b_1x = 21.9 + .0160x$
$\hat{y}_{500} = 21.9 + .0160(500) = 29.9$

18. $\bar{x} = 70.73$ $n = 12$
$\bar{y} = 6.50$ $\Sigma x = 848.8$
$b_1 = [n(\Sigma xy) - (\Sigma x)(\Sigma y)]/[n(\Sigma x^2) - (\Sigma x)^2]$ $\Sigma y = 78.0$
    $= -3342.48/16933.04 = -.197$ $\Sigma x^2 = 61449.54$
$b_0 = \bar{y} - b_1\bar{x}$ $\Sigma y^2 = 572.94$
    $= 6.50 - (-.197)(70.73) = 20.5$ $\Sigma xy = 5238.66$
$\hat{y} = b_0 + b_1x = 20.5 - .197x$
$\hat{y}_{50} = 20.5 - .197(50) = 10.6$

19. a. selling price/asking price relationship
    $\bar{x} = 178.34$ $n = 50$
    $\bar{y} = 170.34$ $\Sigma x = 8917$
    $b_1 = [n(\Sigma xy) - (\Sigma x)(\Sigma y)]/[n(\Sigma x^2) - (\Sigma x)^2]$ $\Sigma y = 8517.0$
       $= 14117561/15438961 = .914$ $\Sigma x^2 = 1899037$
    $b_0 = \bar{y} - b_1\bar{x}$ $\Sigma y^2 = 1710311.50$
       $= 170.34 - (.914)(178.34) = 7.26$ $\Sigma xy = 1801273$
    $\hat{y} = b_0 + b_1x = 7.26 + .914x$
    $\hat{y}_{200} = 7.26 + .914(200) = 190.1$ [$190,100]

b. NOTE: These x-y values are reversed from what they were in the corresponding exercise in section 9.2.
    selling price/taxes relationship
    $\bar{x} = 3706.10$ $n = 50$
    $\bar{y} = 170.34$ $\Sigma x = 8517.0$
    $b_1 = [n(\Sigma xy) - (\Sigma x)(\Sigma y)]/[n(\Sigma x^2) - (\Sigma x)^2]$ $\Sigma y = 185305$
       $= 253353140/12976286 = 19.5$ $\Sigma x^2 = 1710311.50$
    $b_0 = \bar{y} - b_1\bar{x}$ $\Sigma y^2 = 809069344$
       $= 3706.10 - (19.5)(170.34) = 380.3$ $\Sigma xy = 36631916.5$
    $\hat{y} = b_0 + b_1x = 380.3 + 19.5x$
    $\hat{y}_{400} = 380.3 + 19.5(400) = 8190$

20. a. nicotine/tar relationship
    $\bar{x} = 12.1$ $n = 29$
    $\bar{y} = .941$ $\Sigma x = 351$
    $b_1 = [n(\Sigma xy) - (\Sigma x)(\Sigma y)]/[n(\Sigma x^2) - (\Sigma x)^2]$ $\Sigma y = 27.3$
       $= 1133.2/17420 = .0651$ $\Sigma x^2 = 4849$
    $b_0 = \bar{y} - b_1\bar{x}$ $\Sigma y^2 = 28.45$
       $= .941 - (.0651)(12.1) = .154$ $\Sigma xy = 369.5$
    $\hat{y} = b_0 + b_1x = .154 + .0651x$

$\hat{y}_{15} = .154 + .0651(15) = 1.1$

b. nicotine/CO relationship

$\bar{x} = 12.4$ $n = 29$

$\bar{y} = .941$ $\Sigma x = 359$

$b_1 = [n(\Sigma xy) - (\Sigma x)(\Sigma y)]/[n(\Sigma x^2) - (\Sigma x)^2]$ $\Sigma y = 27.3$

   $= 981.5/16206 = .0606$ $\Sigma x^2 = 5003$

$b_0 = \bar{y} - b_1\bar{x}$ $\Sigma y^2 = 28.45$

   $= .941 - (.0606)(12.4) = .192$ $\Sigma xy = 371.8$

$\hat{y} = b_0 + b_1x = .192 + .0606x$

$\hat{y}_{15} = .192 + .0606(15) = 1.1$

21. a. actual/five-day relationship

$\bar{x} = 34.48$ $n = 31$

$\bar{y} = 34.90$ $\Sigma x = 1069$

$b_1 = [n(\Sigma xy) - (\Sigma x)(\Sigma y)]/[n(\Sigma x^2) - (\Sigma x)^2]$ $\Sigma y = 1082$

   $= 9810/16050 = .611$ $\Sigma x^2 = 37381$

$b_0 = \bar{y} - b_1\bar{x}$ $\Sigma y^2 = 38352$

   $= 34.90 - (.611)(34.48) = 13.8$ $\Sigma xy = 37628$

$\hat{y} = b_0 + b_1x = 13.8 + .611x$

$\hat{y}_{28} = 13.8 + .611(28) = 31$

b. actual/one-day relationship

$\bar{x} = 33.32$ $n = 31$

$\bar{y} = 34.90$ $\Sigma x = 1033$

$b_1 = [n(\Sigma xy) - (\Sigma x)(\Sigma y)]/[n(\Sigma x^2) - (\Sigma x)^2]$ $\Sigma y = 1082$

   $= 13453/21228 = .634$ $\Sigma x^2 = 35107$

$b_0 = \bar{y} - b_1\bar{x}$ $\Sigma y^2 = 38352$

   $= 34.90 - (.634)(33.32) = 13.8$ $\Sigma xy = 36489$

$\hat{y} = b_0 + b_1x = 13.8 + .634x$

$\hat{y}_{28} = 13.8 + .634(28) = 32$

c. The predicted value in part (b) is better, because the correlation was higher.

22. a. conductivity/temperature relationship

$\bar{x} = 30.38$ $n = 61$

$\bar{y} = 47.12$ $\Sigma x = 1853.0$

$b_1 = [n(\Sigma xy) - (\Sigma x)(\Sigma y)]/[n(\Sigma x^2) - (\Sigma x)^2]$ $\Sigma y = 2874.5$

   $= 6294.72/10306.43 = .611$ $\Sigma x^2 = 56457.63$

$b_0 = \bar{y} - b_1\bar{x}$ $\Sigma y^2 = 139786.58$

   $= 47.12 - (.611)(30.38) = 28.6$ $\Sigma xy = 87422.02$

$\hat{y} = b_0 + b_1x = 28.6 + .611x$

$\hat{y}_{30} = \bar{y} = 47.12$ [no significant correlation]

b. conductivity/rainfall relationship

$\bar{x} = .271$ $n = 61$

$\bar{y} = 47.12$ $\Sigma x = 16.51$

$b_1 = [n(\Sigma xy) - (\Sigma x)(\Sigma y)]/[n(\Sigma x^2) - (\Sigma x)^2]$ $\Sigma y = 2874.5$

   $= -2034.894/1108.4416 = -1.84$ $\Sigma x^2 = 22.6397$

$b_0 = \bar{y} - b_1\bar{x}$ $\Sigma y^2 = 139786.58$

   $= 47.12 - (-1.84)(.271) = 47.6$ $\Sigma xy = 744.641$

$\hat{y} = b_0 + b_1x = 47.6 - 1.84x$

$\hat{y}_0 = \bar{y} = 47.12$ [no significant correlation]

c. No; since neither relationship involves a significant correlation, the predicted values are not likely to be very accurate.

23. a. interval/duration relationship

$\bar{x} = 216.64$ $n = 50$
$\bar{y} = 80.66$ $\Sigma x = 10832$
$b_1 = [n(\Sigma xy) - (\Sigma x)(\Sigma y)]/[n(\Sigma x^2) - (\Sigma x)^2]$ $\Sigma y = 4033$
$\quad = 1488944/8331776 = .179$ $\Sigma x^2 = 2513280$
$b_0 = \bar{y} - b_1\bar{x}$ $\Sigma y^2 = 332331$
$\quad = 80.66 - (.179)(216.64) = 41.9$ $\Sigma xy = 903488$
$\hat{y} = b_0 + b_1x = 41.9 + .179x$
$\hat{y}_{210} = 41.9 + .179(210) = 79.5$ minutes

b. interval/height relationship

$\bar{x} = 138.08$ $n = 50$
$\bar{y} = 80.66$ $\Sigma x = 6904$
$b_1 = [n(\Sigma xy) - (\Sigma x)(\Sigma y)]/[n(\Sigma x^2) - (\Sigma x)^2]$ $\Sigma y = 4033$
$\quad = -3632/392284 = -.00926$ $\Sigma x^2 = 961150$
$b_0 = \bar{y} - b_1\bar{x}$ $\Sigma y^2 = 332331$
$\quad = 80.66 - (-.00926)(138.08) = 81.9$ $\Sigma xy = 556804$
$\hat{y} = b_0 + b_1x = 81.9 - .00926x$
$\hat{y}_{275} = \bar{y} = 80.7$ minutes [no significant correlation]

c. The predicted time in part (a) is better, since interval and duration are significantly correlated. Since interval and height are not significantly correlated, the predicted time in part (b) did not even use the height data.

24. a. price/weight relationship [NOTE: For convenience, we measure the price y in $1000's.]

$\bar{x} = 1.688$ $n = 30$
$\bar{y} = 14.441$ $\Sigma x = 50.65$
$b_1 = [n(\Sigma xy) - (\Sigma x)(\Sigma y)]/[n(\Sigma x^2) - (\Sigma x)^2]$ $\Sigma y = 433.23$
$\quad = 8867.80/726.78 = 12.202$ $\Sigma x^2 = 109.74$
$b_0 = \bar{y} - b_1\bar{x}$ $\Sigma y^2 = 12378.86$
$\quad = 14.441 - (12.202)(1.688) = -6.159$ $\Sigma xy = 1027.03$
$\hat{y} = b_0 + b_1x = -6.159 + 12.202x$
$\hat{y}_{1.5} = -6.159 + 12.202(1.5) = 12.143$ [$12,143]

b. price/color relationship [NOTE: For convenience, we measure the price y in $1000's.]

$\bar{x} = 4.667$ $n = 50$
$\bar{y} = 14.441$ $\Sigma x = 140$
$b_1 = [n(\Sigma xy) - (\Sigma x)(\Sigma y)]/[n(\Sigma x^2) - (\Sigma x)^2]$ $\Sigma y = 433.23$
$\quad = -11751.3/3860 = -3.044$ $\Sigma x^2 = 782$
$b_0 = \bar{y} - b_1\bar{x}$ $\Sigma y^2 = 12378.86$
$\quad = 14.441 - (-3.044)(4.667) = 28.648$ $\Sigma xy = 1630.03$
$\hat{y} = b_0 + b_1x = 28.648 + (-3.044)x$
$\hat{y}_3 = 28.648 - 3.044(3) = 19.515$ [$19,515]

c. The predicted time in part (a) is better, since there is a stronger correlation between price and weight than between price and color.

25. Yes; the point is an outlier, since it is far from the other data points – 120 is far from the other boat values, and 160 is far from the other manatee death values.
No; the point is not an influential one, since it will not change the regression line by very much – the original regression line predicts $\hat{y} = -113 + 2.27(120) = 159.4$, and so the new point is consistent with the others.

26. Yes; the point is an outlier, since it is far from the other data points – 120 is far from the other boat values, and 10 is far from the other manatee death values.
Yes; the point is an influential one, since it will dramatically alter the regression line – the original regression line predicts $\hat{y} = -113 + 2.27(120) = 159.4$, and so the new regression line will have to change considerably to come close to (120,10).

27. <u>original data</u>
     n=5
     $\Sigma x = 4,234,178$
     $\Sigma y = 576$
     $\Sigma x^2 = 3,595,324,583,102$
     $\Sigma y^2 = 67552$
     $\Sigma xy = 491,173,342$

<u>original data divided by 1000</u>
     $n = 5$
     $\Sigma x = 4,234.178$
     $\Sigma y = 576$
     $\Sigma x^2 = 3,595,324.583102$
     $\Sigma y^2 = 67552$
     $\Sigma xy = 491,173.342$

<u>original data</u>
     $\bar{x} = 846835.6$
     $\bar{y} = 115.2$
     $n\Sigma xy - (\Sigma x)(\Sigma y) = 16,980,182$
     $n\Sigma x^2 - (\Sigma x)^2 = 48,459,579,826$
     $b_1 = 16,980,182/48,459,579,826$
       $= .0003504$
     $b_0 = \bar{y} - b_1\bar{x}$
       $= 115.2 - .0003504(846835.6)$
       $= -181.53$
     $\hat{y} = b_0 + b_1 x$
       $= -181.53 + .0003504x$

<u>original data divided by 1000</u>
     $\bar{x} = 846.8356$
     $\bar{y} = 115.2$
     $n\Sigma xy - (\Sigma x)(\Sigma y) = 16,980.182$
     $n\Sigma x^2 - (\Sigma x)^2 = 48,459.579826$
     $b_1 = 16,980.182/48,459.579826$
       $= .3504$
     $b_0 = \bar{y} - b_1\bar{x}$
       $= 115.2 - .3504(846.8356)$
       $= -181.53$
     $\hat{y} = b_0 + b_1 x$
       $= -181.53 + .3504x$

Dividing each x by 1000 multiplies b_1, the coefficient of x in the regression equation, by 1000; multiplying the x coefficient by 1000 and dividing x by 1000 will "cancel out" and all predictions remain the same.

Dividing each y by 1000 divides both b_1 and b_0 by 1000; consistent with the new "units" for y, all predictions will also turn out divided by 1000.

28. Using $\hat{y} = 8 + 3x$ produces the table at the right. As expected $\Sigma(y-\hat{y})^2$ is less [364 < 374] using the proper regression equation $\hat{y} = 5 + 4x$ as given in the text.

x	y	$\hat{y}$	$y-\hat{y}$	$(y-\hat{y})^2$
1	4	11	-7	49
2	24	14	10	100
4	8	20	-12	144
5	32	23	9	81
12	68	68	0	374

29. •original data

x	y
2.0	12.0
2.5	18.7
4.2	53.0
10.0	225.0

     $n = 4$
     $\Sigma x = 18.7$
     $\Sigma y = 308.7$
     $\Sigma x^2 = 127.89$
     $\Sigma y^2 = 53927.69$
     $\Sigma xy = 2543.35$

$b_1 = [n(\Sigma xy) - (\Sigma x)(\Sigma y)]/[n(\Sigma x^2) - (\Sigma x)^2] = 4400.71/161.87 = 27.2$
$b_0 = \bar{y} - b_1\bar{x} = (308.7/4) - (27.2)(18.7/4) = -49.9$
$\hat{y} = b_0 + b_1 x = -49.9 + 27.2x$
$r = [n(\Sigma xy) - (\Sigma x)(\Sigma y)]/[\sqrt{n(\Sigma x^2) - (\Sigma x)^2} \cdot \sqrt{n(\Sigma y^2) - (\Sigma y)^2}]$
   $= 4400.71/[\sqrt{161.87} \cdot \sqrt{120415.07}] = .9968$

•using ln(x) for x

x	y
.693	12.0
.916	18.7
1.435	53.0
2.303	225.0

     $n = 4$
     $\Sigma x = 5.347$
     $\Sigma y = 308.7$
     $\Sigma x^2 = 8.681$
     $\Sigma y^2 = 53927.69$
     $\Sigma xy = 619.594$

$b_1 = [n(\Sigma xy) - (\Sigma x)(\Sigma y)]/[n(\Sigma x^2) - (\Sigma x)^2] = 827.7220/6.134071 = 134.9$
$b_0 = \bar{y} - b_1\bar{x} = (308.7/4) - (134.9)(5.347/4) = 103.2$
$\hat{y} = b_0 + b_1 \cdot \ln(x) = -103.2 + 134.9 \cdot \ln(x)$ [since the "x" is really ln(x)]

$$r = [n(\Sigma xy) - (\Sigma x)(\Sigma y)]/[\sqrt{n(\Sigma x^2) - (\Sigma x)^2} \cdot \sqrt{n(\Sigma y^2) - (\Sigma y)^2}]$$
$$= 827.7220/[\sqrt{6.134071} \cdot \sqrt{120415.07}] = .9631$$

Based on the value of the associated correlations (.9968 > .9631), the equation using the original data seems to fit the data better than the equation using ln(x) instead of x.

NOTE: Both x and y (perhaps, especially y) seem to grow exponentially. A wiser choice for a transformation might be to use both ln(x) for x and ln(y) for y [or, perhaps, only ln(y) for y].

30. If $H_o: \rho = 0$ is true, there is no linear correlation between x and y and $\hat{y} = \bar{y}$ is the appropriate prediction for y for any x.

If $H_o: \beta_1 = 0$ is true then the true regression line is $y = \beta_o + 0x = \beta_o$ and the best estimate for β_o is $b_o = \bar{y} - 0\bar{x} = \bar{y}$, producing the line $\hat{y} = \bar{y}$.

Since both null hypotheses imply precisely the same result, they are equivalent.

31. Refer to the table below at the left, where $\hat{y} = -112.71 + 2.2741x$ and the residual is $y - \hat{y}$. The residual plot is given below at the right, with x on the horizontal axis and the residuals on the vertical axis.

year	x	y	$\hat{y}$	residual
1991	68	53	41.9	11.1
1992	68	38	41.9	-3.9
1993	67	35	39.7	-4.7
1994	70	49	46.5	2.5
1995	71	42	48.8	-6.8
1996	73	60	53.3	6.7
1997	76	54	60.1	-6.1
1998	81	67	71.5	-4.5
1999	83	82	76.0	6.0
2000	84	78	78.3	-0.3
	741	558	558.0	0.0

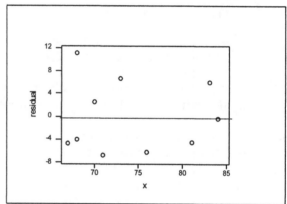

9-4 Variation and Prediction Intervals

1. The coefficient of determination is $r^2 = (.8)^2 = .64$.
The portion of the total variation explained by the regression line is $r^2 = .64 = 64\%$

2. The coefficient of determination is $r^2 = (-.6)^2 = .36$
The portion of the total variation explained by the regression line is $r^2 = .36 = 36\%$.

3. The coefficient of determination is $r^2 = (-.503)^2 = .253$.
The portion of the total variation explained by the regression line is $r^2 = .253 = 25.3\%$.

4. The coefficient of determination is $r^2 = (.636)^2 = .404$
The portion of the total variation explained by the regression line is $r^2 = .404 = 40.4\%$.

5. Since $r^2 = .924$, $r = +.961$ (positive because $b_1 = 12.5$ is positive).
From Table A-6, the critical values necessary for significance are $\pm.361$.
Since .961 > .361, we conclude there is a significant positive linear correlation between the tar and nicotine contents of cigarettes.

6. $R^2 = 92.4\%$

7. Use 1.2599, from the "fit" value on the Minitab display. This also agrees with the regression equation: $\hat{y} = .154 + .0651x$

$$\hat{y}_{17} = .154 + .0651(17) = 1.26$$

8. $1.07 < y_{17} < 1.45$

We are 95% confident that the interval from 1.07 mg to 1.45 mg contains the true amount of nicotine for an individual cigarette with a tar level of 17 mg.

NOTE: The following summary statistics apply to exercises 9-12 and 13-16. They may be used in the chapter formulas to calculate any values needed in the process of working the problems.

exercise 9	exercise 10	exercise 11	exercise 12
$n = 9$	$n = 14$	$n = 14$	$n = 12$
$\Sigma x = 632.0$	$\Sigma x = 1875$	$\Sigma x = 66.4$	$\Sigma x = 51.4$
$\Sigma y = 1089$	$\Sigma y = 1241$	$\Sigma y = 669.1$	$\Sigma y = 969.0$
$\Sigma x^2 = 44399.50$	$\Sigma x^2 = 252179$	$\Sigma x^2 = 444.54$	$\Sigma x^2 = 220.42$
$\Sigma y^2 = 132223$	$\Sigma y^2 = 111459$	$\Sigma y^2 = 37365.71$	$\Sigma y^2 = 78487.82$
$\Sigma xy = 76546.0$	$\Sigma xy = 167023$	$\Sigma xy = 3865.67$	$\Sigma xy = 4144.61$
see also 9.2-3, #10	see also 9.2-3,#11	see also 9.2-3,#14	not used previously

9. The predicted values were calculated using the regression line $\hat{y} = -151.6977 + 3.883382x$.

x	y	$\hat{y}$	$\overline{y}$	$\hat{y}-\overline{y}$	$(\hat{y}-\overline{y})^2$	$y-\hat{y}$	$(y-\hat{y})^2$	$y-\overline{y}$	$(y-\overline{y})^2$
71.0	125	124.02	121	3.0204	9.123	0.97958	0.960	4	16
70.5	119	122.08	121	1.0787	1.164	-3.07874	9.479	-2	4
71.0	128	124.02	121	3.0204	9.123	3.97958	15.837	7	49
72.0	128	127.90	121	6.9038	47.663	0.09619	0.009	7	49
70.0	119	120.14	121	-0.8630	0.745	-1.13702	1.293	-2	4
70.0	127	120.14	121	-0.8630	0.745	6.86298	47.100	6	36
66.5	105	106.55	121	-14.4548	208.941	-1.54520	2.388	-16	256
70.0	123	120.14	121	-0.8630	0.745	2.86298	8.197	2	4
71.0	115	124.02	121	3.0204	9.123	-9.02042	81.368	-6	36
632.0	1089	1089.00	1089	0.0001	287.371	-0.00006	166.630	0	454

a. The explained variation is $\Sigma(\hat{y}-\overline{y})^2 = 287.37$
b. The unexplained variation is $\Sigma(y-\hat{y})^2 = 166.63$
c. The total variation is $\Sigma(y-\overline{y})^2 = 454$
d. $r^2 = \Sigma(\hat{y}-\overline{y})^2/\Sigma(y-\overline{y})^2 = 287.37/454 = .6330$
e. $s_e^2 = \Sigma(y-\hat{y})^2/(n-2) = 166.63/7 = 23.8043$
   $s_e = 4.8790$

NOTE: A table such as the one in the preceding problem organizes the work and provides all the values needed to discuss variation. In such a table, the following must always be true (except for minor discrepancies due to rounding) and can be used as a check before proceeding.
* $\Sigma y = \Sigma\hat{y} = \Sigma\overline{y}$ * $\Sigma(\hat{y}-\overline{y}) = \Sigma(y-\hat{y}) = \Sigma(y-\overline{y}) = 0$ * $\Sigma(y-\overline{y})^2 + \Sigma(y-\hat{y})^2 = \Sigma(y-\overline{y})^2$

10. The predicted values were calculated using the regression line $\hat{y} = -14.37981 + .7692359x$.

x	y	$\hat{y}$	$\overline{y}$	$\hat{y}-\overline{y}$	$(\hat{y}-\overline{y})^2$	$y-\hat{y}$	$(y-\hat{y})^2$	$y-\overline{y}$	$(y-\overline{y})^2$
138	82	91.77	88.64	3.1319	9.808	-9.7747	95.546	-6.64	44.13
130	91	85.62	88.64	-3.0220	9.133	5.3791	28.935	2.36	5.56
135	100	89.47	88.64	0.8241	0.679	10.5330	110.943	11.36	128.98
140	100	93.31	88.64	4.6703	21.812	6.6868	44.713	11.36	128.98
120	80	77.93	88.64	-10.7144	114.798	2.0715	4.291	-8.64	74.70
125	90	81.77	88.64	-6.8682	47.173	8.2253	67.656	1.36	1.84
120	80	77.93	88.64	-10.7144	114.798	2.0715	4.291	-8.64	74.70
130	80	85.62	88.64	-3.0220	9.133	-5.6209	31.594	-8.64	74.70
130	80	85.62	88.64	-3.0220	9.133	-5.6209	31.594	-8.64	74.70
144	98	96.39	88.64	7.7473	60.020	1.6098	2.592	9.36	87.56
143	105	95.62	88.64	6.9780	48.693	9.3791	87.967	16.36	267.55
140	85	93.31	88.64	4.6703	21.812	-8.3132	69.110	-3.64	13.27
130	70	85.62	88.64	-3.0220	9.133	-15.6209	244.011	-18.64	347.56
150	100	101.01	88.64	12.3627	152.836	-1.0056	1.011	11.36	128.98
1875	1241	1241.00	1240.96	-0.0006	628.960	-0.0000	824.254	0.04	1453.21

a. The explained variation is $\Sigma(\hat{y}-\bar{y})^2 = 628.96$

b. The unexplained variation is $\Sigma(y-\hat{y})^2 = 824.25$

c. The total variation is $\Sigma(y-\bar{y})^2 = 1453.21$

d. $r^2 = \Sigma(\hat{y}-\bar{y})^2/\Sigma(y-\bar{y})^2 = 628.96/1453.21 = .4328$

e. $s_e^2 = \Sigma(y-\hat{y})^2/(n-2) = 824.254/12 = 68.6878$
   $s_e = 8.2878$

11. The predicted values were calculated using the regression line $\hat{y} = 22.46293 + 5.340648x$.

x	y	$\hat{y}$	$\bar{y}$	$\hat{y}-\bar{y}$	$(\hat{y}-\bar{y})^2$	$y-\hat{y}$	$(y-\hat{y})^2$	$y-\bar{y}$	$(y-\bar{y})^2$
1.8	21.0	32.076	47.793	-15.7169	247.02	-11.0761	122.68	-26.793	717.86
1.9	33.5	32.610	47.793	-15.1828	230.52	0.8898	0.79	-14.293	204.29
1.8	24.6	32.076	47.793	-15.7169	247.02	-7.4761	55.89	-23.193	537.92
2.4	40.7	35.280	47.793	-12.5125	156.56	5.4195	29.37	-7.093	50.31
5.1	73.2	49.700	47.793	1.9072	3.64	23.4998	552.24	25.407	645.52
3.1	24.9	39.019	47.793	-8.7741	76.98	-14.1189	199.34	-22.893	524.09
5.5	40.4	51.836	47.793	4.0435	16.35	-11.4365	130.79	-7.393	54.66
5.1	45.3	49.700	47.793	1.9072	3.64	-4.4002	19.36	-2.493	6.22
8.3	53.5	66.790	47.793	18.9973	360.90	-13.2903	176.63	5.707	32.57
13.7	93.8	95.630	47.793	47.8368	2288.36	-1.8298	3.35	46.007	2116.64
5.3	64.0	50.768	47.793	2.9754	8.85	13.2316	175.08	16.207	262.67
4.9	62.7	48.632	47.793	0.8391	0.70	14.0679	197.91	14.907	222.22
3.7	47.2	42.223	47.793	-5.5697	31.02	4.9767	24.77	-0.593	0.35
3.8	44.3	42.757	47.793	-5.0356	25.36	1.5426	2.38	-3.493	12.20
66.4	669.1	669.100	669.102	-0.0019	3696.93	-0.0001	1690.58	-0.002	5387.51

a. The explained variation is $\Sigma(\hat{y}-\bar{y})^2 = 3696.93$

b. The unexplained variation is $\Sigma(y-\hat{y})^2 = 1690.58$

c. The total variation is $\Sigma(y-\bar{y})^2 = 5387.51$

d. $r^2 = \Sigma(\hat{y}-\bar{y})^2/\Sigma(y-\bar{y})^2 = 3696.93/5387.51 = .6862$

e. $s_e^2 = \Sigma(y-\hat{y})^2/(n-2) = 1690.58/12 = 140.8817$
   $s_e = 11.8694$

12. The predicted values were calculated using the regression line $\hat{y} = 179.88 - 23.143x$.

x	y	$\hat{y}$	$\bar{y}$	$\hat{y}-\bar{y}$	$(\hat{y}-\bar{y})^2$	$y-\hat{y}$	$(y-\hat{y})^2$	$y-\bar{y}$	$(y-\bar{y})^2$
4.1	85.3	84.994	80.75	4.2437	18.009	0.30630	0.094	4.55	20.703
4.2	84.3	82.679	80.75	1.9294	3.723	1.62059	2.626	3.55	12.603
4.2	79.5	82.679	80.75	1.9294	3.723	-3.17941	10.109	-1.25	1.563
4.4	82.5	78.051	80.75	-2.6992	7.286	4.44920	19.795	1.75	3.063
4.3	80.2	80.365	80.75	-0.3849	0.148	-0.16511	0.027	-0.55	0.303
4.2	84.6	82.679	80.75	1.9294	3.723	1.92059	3.689	3.85	14.822
4.5	79.2	75.737	80.75	-5.0135	25.135	3.46349	11.996	-1.55	2.403
4.5	70.9	75.737	80.75	-5.0135	25.135	-4.83650	23.392	-9.85	97.022
4.3	78.6	80.365	80.75	-0.3849	0.148	-1.76511	3.116	-2.15	4.623
4.0	86.2	87.308	80.75	6.5580	43.007	-1.10801	1.228	5.45	29.702
4.4	74.0	78.051	80.75	-2.6992	7.286	-4.05080	16.409	-6.75	45.563
4.3	83.7	80.365	80.75	-0.3849	0.148	3.33489	11.122	2.95	8.702
51.4	969.0	969.010	969.00	0.0098	137.470	-0.00989	103.601	0.00	241.070

a. The explained variation is $\Sigma(\hat{y}-\bar{y})^2 = 137.47$

b. The unexplained variation is $\Sigma(y-\hat{y})^2 = 103.60$

c. The total variation is $\Sigma(y-\bar{y})^2 = 241.07$

d. $r^2 = \Sigma(\hat{y}-\bar{y})^2/\Sigma(y-\bar{y})^2 = 137.47/241.07 = .5702$

e. $s_e^2 = \Sigma(y-\hat{y})^2/(n-2) = 103.601/10 = 10.3601$
   $s_e = 3.2187$

13. a. $\hat{y} = -151.6977 + 3.883382x$.
   $\hat{y}_{69} = -151.6977 + 3.883382(69) = 116.29$

b. preliminary calculations

n = 9

$\sum x = 632.0$ $\bar{x} = (\sum x)/n = 632.0/9 = 70.222$

$\sum x^2 = 44399.50$ $n\sum x^2 - (\sum x)^2 = 9(44399.50) - (632.0)^2 = 171.50$

$\hat{y} \pm t_{n-2,\alpha/2} s_e \sqrt{1 + 1/n + n(x_o - \bar{x})^2/[n\sum x^2 - (\sum x)^2]}$

$\hat{y}_{69} \pm t_{7,.025}(4.8790)\sqrt{1 + 1/9 + 9(69-70.222)^2/[171.50]}$

$116.29 \pm (2.365)(4.8790)\sqrt{1.18948}$

116.29 ± 12.58

$103.7 < y_{69} < 128.9$

14. a. $\hat{y} = -14.37981 + .7692359x$

$\hat{y}_{120} = -14.37981 + .7692359(120) = 77.92$

b. preliminary calculations

n = 14

$\sum x = 1875$ $\bar{x} = (\sum x)/n = 1875/14 = 133.929$

$\sum x^2 = 252179$ $n\sum x^2 - (\sum x)^2 = 14(252179) - (1875)^2 = 14881$

$\hat{y} \pm t_{n-2,\alpha/2} s_e \sqrt{1 + 1/n + n(x_o - \bar{x})^2/[n\sum x^2 - (\sum x)^2]}$

$\hat{y}_{120} \pm t_{12,.025}(8.2878)\sqrt{1 + 1/14 + 14(120-133.929)^2/[14881]}$

$77.92 \pm (2.179)(8.2878)\sqrt{1.25395}$

77.92 ± 20.22

$57.7 < y_{120} < 98.2$

15. a. $\hat{y} = 22.46293 + 5.340648x$

$\hat{y}_{4.0} = 22.46293 + 5.340648 (4.0) = 43.83$

b. preliminary calculations

n = 14

$\sum x = 66.4$ $\bar{x} = 66.4/14 = 4.743$

$\sum x^2 = 444.54$ $n\sum x^2 - (\sum x)^2 = 14(444.54) - (66.4)^2 = 1814.60$

$\hat{y} \pm t_{n-2,\alpha/2} s_e \sqrt{1 + 1/n + n(x_o - \bar{x})^2/[n\sum x^2 - (\sum x)^2]}$

$\hat{y}_{4.0} \pm t_{12,.005}(11.8694)\sqrt{1 + 1/14 + 14(4.0-4.743)^2/[1814.60]}$

$43.83 \pm (3.055)(11.8694)\sqrt{1.07569}$

43.83 ± 37.61

$6.2 < y_{4.0} < 81.4$

16. a. $\hat{y} = 179.88 - 23.143x$

$\hat{y}_{4.0} = 179.88 - 23.143(4.0) = 87.31$

b. preliminary calculations

n = 12

$\sum x = 51.4$ $\bar{x} = (\sum x)/n = 51.4/12 = 4.283$

$\sum x^2 = 220.42$ $n\sum x^2 - (\sum x)^2 = 12(220.42) - (51.4)^2 = 3.08$

$\hat{y} \pm t_{n-2,\alpha/2} s_e \sqrt{1 + 1/n + n(x_o - \bar{x})^2/[n\sum x^2 - (\sum x)^2]}$

$\hat{y}_{4.0} \pm t_{10,.005}(3.2187)\sqrt{1 + 1/12 + 12(4.0-4.283)^2/[3.08]}$

$87.31 \pm (3.169)(3.2187)\sqrt{1.39610}$

87.31 ± 12.05

$75.3 < y_{4.0} < 99.4$

Exercises 17-20 refer to the chapter problem of Table 9-1. They use the following, which are calculated and/or discussed at various places in the text,

n = 10

$\sum x = 741$ $\hat{y} = -112.7098976 + 2.274087687x$

$\sum x^2 = 55289$ $s_e = 6.6123487$

and the values obtained below.

$\bar{x} = (\Sigma x)/n = 741/10 = 74.1$
$n\Sigma x^2 - (\Sigma x)^2 = 10(55289) - (741)^2 = 3809$

17. $\hat{y}_{85} = -112.7098976 + 2.274087687(85) = 80.58$
$\hat{y} \pm t_{n-2,\alpha/2}s_e\sqrt{1 + 1/n + n(x_o-\bar{x})^2/[n\Sigma x^2-(\Sigma x)^2]}$
$\hat{y}_{85} \pm t_{8,.005}(6.6123487)\sqrt{1 + 1/10 + 10(85-74.1)^2/[3809]}$
$80.58 \pm (3.355)(6.6123487)\sqrt{1.41192}$
80.58 ± 26.36
$54.2 < y_{85} < 106.9$

18. $\hat{y}_{85} = -112.7098976 + 2.274087687(85) = 80.58$
$\hat{y} \pm t_{n-2,\alpha/2}s_e\sqrt{1 + 1/n + n(x_o-\bar{x})^2/[n\Sigma x^2-(\Sigma x)^2]}$
$\hat{y}_{85} \pm t_{8,.05}(6.6123487)\sqrt{1 + 1/10 + 10(85-74.1)^2/[3809]}$
$80.58 \pm (1.860)(6.6123487)\sqrt{1.41192}$
80.58 ± 14.61
$66.0 < y_{85} < 95.2$

19. $\hat{y}_{90} = -112.7098976 + 2.274087687(90) = 91.96$
$\hat{y} \pm t_{n-2,\alpha/2}s_e\sqrt{1 + 1/n + n(x_o-\bar{x})^2/[n\Sigma x^2-(\Sigma x)^2]}$
$\hat{y}_{90} \pm t_{8,.025}(6.6123487)\sqrt{1 + 1/10 + 10(90-74.1)^2/[3809]}$
$91.96 \pm (2.306)(6.6123487)\sqrt{1.76372}$
91.96 ± 20.25
$71.7 < y_{90} < 112.2$

20. $\hat{y}_{90} = -112.7098976 + 2.274087687(90) = 91.96$
$\hat{y} \pm t_{n-2,\alpha/2}s_e\sqrt{1 + 1/n + n(x_o-\bar{x})^2/[n\Sigma x^2-(\Sigma x)^2]}$
$\hat{y}_{90} \pm t_{8,.005}(6.6123487)\sqrt{1 + 1/10 + 10(90-74.1)^2/[3809]}$
$91.96 \pm (3.355)(6.6123487)\sqrt{1.76372}$
91.96 ± 29.46
$62.5 < y_{90} < 121.4$

21. This exercise uses the following values from the chapter problem of Table 9-1, which are calculated and/or discussed at various places in the text,

$n = 10$ $\Sigma x = 741$ $b_o = -112.7098976$ $s_e = 6.6123487$
$\Sigma x^2 = 55289$ $b_1 = 2.274087687$

and the values obtained below.
$\bar{x} = (\Sigma x)/n = 741/10 = 74.1$
$\Sigma x^2 - (\Sigma x)^2/n = 55289 - (741)^2/10 = 380.9$

a. $b_o \pm t_{n-2,\alpha/2}s_e\sqrt{1/n + \bar{x}^2/[\Sigma x^2-(\Sigma x)^2/n]}$
$-112.7098976 \pm t_{8,.025}(6.6123487)\sqrt{1/10 + (74.1)^2/[380.9]}$
$-112.7098976 \pm (2.306)(6.6123487)\sqrt{14.5153}$
$-112.7098976 \pm 58.093686$
$-170.8 < \beta_o < 54.6$

b. $b_1 \pm t_{n-2,\alpha/2}s_e/\sqrt{\Sigma x^2-(\Sigma x)^2/n}$
$2.274087687 \pm t_{8,.025}(6.6123487)/\sqrt{380.9}$
$2.274087687 \pm (2.306)(6.6123487)/\sqrt{380.9}$
$2.274087687 \pm .781285$
$1.5 < \beta_1 < 3.1$

22. a. If $s_e = 0$, then $\Sigma(y-\hat{y})^2 = 0$ – which means that all the observed data lie on the regression line and $r = 1.00$ or $r = -1.00$.

b. If $\Sigma(\hat{y}-\bar{y})^2=0$, then $\hat{y}=\bar{y}$ for all x – which means the regression line is parallel to the x axis and has slope 0.

23. a. Since $s_e^2 = \Sigma(y-\hat{y})^2/(n-2)$, $(n-2){\cdot}s_e^2 = \Sigma(y-\hat{y})^2$.
And so (explained variation) = $(n-2){\cdot}s_e^2$.

b. Let EXPV = explained variation = $\Sigma(\hat{y}-\bar{y})^2$.
Let UNXV = unexplained variation = $\Sigma(y-\hat{y})^2$.
Let TOTV = total variation = $\Sigma(y-\bar{y})^2$.
$$r^2 = (EXPV)/(TOTV)$$
$$(TOTV){\cdot}r^2 = (EXPV)$$
$$(EXPV + UNXV){\cdot}r^2 = (EXPV)$$
$$(EXPV){\cdot}r^2 + (UNXV){\cdot}r^2 = (EXPV)$$
$$(UNXV){\cdot}r^2 = (EXPV) - (EXPV){\cdot}r^2$$
$$(UNXV){\cdot}r^2 = (EXPV){\cdot}(1-r^2)$$
$$(UNXV){\cdot}r^2/(1-r^2) = (EXPV)$$
And so (explained variation) = $[r^2/(1-r^2)]{\cdot}$(unexplained variation)

c. If $r^2=.900$, than $r=\pm.949$.
Since the regression line has a negative slope (i.e., $b_1=-2$), choose the negative root.
And so the linear correlation coefficient is -.949.

24. $\hat{y}_{85} = -112.7098976 + 2.274087687(85) = 80.58$
$\hat{y} \pm t_{n-2,\alpha/2}s_e\sqrt{1/n + n(x_o-\bar{x})^2/[n\Sigma x^2-(\Sigma x)^2]}$
$\hat{y}_{85} \pm t_{8,.025}(6.6123487)\sqrt{1/10 + 10(85-74.1)^2/[3809]}$
$80.58 \pm (2.306)(6.6123487)\sqrt{0.41192}$
80.58 ± 9.79
$70.8 < \mu_{y|x=85} < 90.4$

9-5 Rank Correlation

NOTE: This manual calculates $d = R_x - R_y$, thus preserving the sign of d. This convention means Σd must equal 0 and provides a check for the assigning and differencing of the ranks. In addition, it must always be true that $\Sigma R_x = \Sigma R_y = n(n+1)/2$.

1. In each case the n=5 pairs are pairs of ranks, called R_x and R_y below to stress that fact.

a.

R_x	R_y	d	d^2
1	1	0	0
3	3	0	0
5	5	0	0
4	4	0	0
2	2	0	0
15	15	0	0

```
r_s = 1 - [6(Σd²)]/[n(n²-1)]
    = 1 - [6(0)]/[5(24)]
    = 1 - 0
    = 1
```

Yes; there appears to be a perfect positive correlation between R_x and R_y.

b.

R_x	R_y	d	d^2
1	5	-4	16
2	4	-2	4
3	3	0	0
4	2	2	4
5	1	-4	16
15	15	0	40

```
r_s = 1 - [6(Σd²)]/[n(n²-1)]
    = 1 - [6(40)]/[5(24)]
    = 1 - 2
    = -1
```

Yes; there appears to be a perfect negative correlation between R_x and R_y.

c.

	R_x	R_y	d	d^2
	1	2	-1	1
	2	5	-3	9
	3	3	0	0
	4	1	3	9
	5	4	1	1
	15	15	0	20

$r_s = 1 - [6(\Sigma d^2)]/[n(n^2-1)]$
$= 1 - [6(20)]/[5(24)]$
$= 1 - 1$
$= 0$

No; there does not appear to be any correlation between R_x and R_y.

2. a. Since $n \leq 30$, use Table A-9.
     CV: $r_s = \pm.450$
    b. Since $n > 30$, use Formula 12-1.
     CV: $r_s = \pm1.960/\sqrt{49} = \pm.280$
    c. Since $n > 30$, use Formula 12-1.
     CV: $r_s = \pm2.327/\sqrt{39} = \pm.373$
    d. Since $n \leq 30$, use Table A-9.
     CV: $r_s = \pm.689$
    e. Since $n > 30$, use Formula 12.1.
     CV: $r_s = \pm2.05/\sqrt{81} = \pm.228$

3. The following table summarizes the calculations.

R_x	R_y	d	d^2
2	2	0	0
6	7	-1	1
3	7	-3	9
5	4	1	1
7	5	2	4
10	8	2	4
9	9	0	0
8	10	-2	4
4	3	1	1
1	1	0	0
55	55	0	24

$r_s = 1 - [6(\Sigma d^2)]/[n(n^2-1)]$
$= 1 - [6(24)]/[10(99)]$
$= 1 - .145$
$= .855$

H_0: $\rho_s = 0$
H_1: $\rho_s \neq 0$
$\alpha = .05$
C.R. $r_s < -.648$
 $r_s > .648$
calculations:
 $r_s = .855$
conclusion:

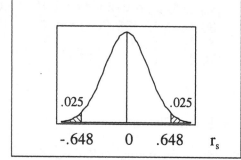

Reject H_0; there is sufficient evidence to reject the claim that $\rho_s = 0$ and to conclude that $\rho_s \neq 0$ (in fact, that $\rho > 0$).

Yes; it does appear that salary increases as stress increases.

IMPORTANT NOTE: The rank correlation is correctly calculated using the ranks in the Pearson product moment correlation formula 9-1 of chapter 9 to produce
$$r_s = [\Sigma R_x R_y - (\Sigma R_x)(\Sigma R_y)]/[\sqrt{\Sigma R_x^2 - (\Sigma R_x)^2} \cdot \sqrt{\Sigma R_y^2 - (\Sigma R_y)^2}]$$
Since $\Sigma R_x = \Sigma R_y = 1+2+...+n = n(n+1)/2$ [always]
 and $\Sigma R_x^2 = \Sigma R_y^2 = 1^2+2^2+...+n^2 = n(n+1)(2n+1)/6$ [when there are ties in the ranks],
it can be shown by algebra that the above formula can be shortened to
 $r_s = 1 - [6(\Sigma d^2)]/[n(n^2-1)]$ when there are no ties in the ranks.
As ties typically make no difference in the first 3 decimals of r_s, this manual uses the shortened formula exclusively and notes when use of the longer formula gives a slightly different result.

4. The following table summarizes the calculations.

R_x	R_y	d	d^2
2	5	-3	9
6	2	4	16
3	3	0	0
5	8	-3	9
7	10	-3	9
10	9	1	1
9	1	8	64
8	7	1	1
4	6	-2	4
1	4	-3	9
55	55	0	122

$$r_s = 1 - [6(\Sigma d^2)]/[n(n^2-1)]$$
$$= 1 - [6(122)]/[10(99)]$$
$$= 1 - .739$$
$$= .261$$

H_o: $\rho_s = 0$
H_1: $\rho_s \neq 0$
$\alpha = .05$
C.R. $r_s < -.648$
      $r_s > .648$
calculations:
    $r_s = .261$
conclusion:

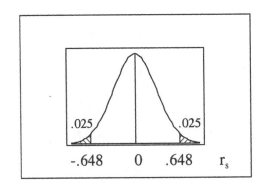

Do not reject H_o; there is not sufficient evidence to reject the claim that $\rho_s = 0$.
No; there does not appear to be a relationship between salary and physical demands.

5. The following table summarizes the calculations.

R_x	R_y	d	d^2
1	3	-2	4
2	5	-3	9
4	4	0	0
5	1	4	16
3	10	-7	49
6	7	-1	1
8	6	2	4
7	8	-1	1
10	2	8	64
9	9	0	0
55	55	0	148

$$r_s = 1 - [6(\Sigma d^2)]/[n(n^2-1)]$$
$$= 1 - [6(148)]/[10(99)]$$
$$= 1 - .897$$
$$= .103$$

H_o: $\rho_s = 0$
H_1: $\rho_s \neq 0$
$\alpha = .05$
C.R. $r_s < -.648$
      $r_s > .648$
calculations:
    $r_s = .261$
conclusion:

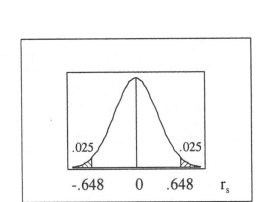

Do not reject H_o; there is not sufficient evidence to reject the claim that $\rho_s = 0$.
No; there does not appear to be a relationship between the two rankings.

6. The following table summarizes the calculations.

x	R_x	y	R_y	d	d^2
33.46	1	5.50	2	-1	1
50.68	2	5.00	2	1	1
87.92	4	8.08	3	1	1
98.84	5	17.00	6	-1	1
63.60	3	12.00	4	-1	1
107.34	6	16.00	5	1	1
	21		21	0	6

$$r_s = 1 - [6(\Sigma d^2)]/[n(n^2-1)]$$
$$= 1 - [6(6)]/[6(35)]$$
$$= 1 - .171$$
$$= .829$$

H_o: $\rho_s = 0$
H_1: $\rho_s \neq 0$
$\alpha = .05$
C.R. $r_s < -.886$
        $r_s > .886$
calculations:
    $r_s = .829$
conclusion:
    Do not reject H_o; there is not sufficient evidence
    to conclude that $\rho_s \neq 0$.

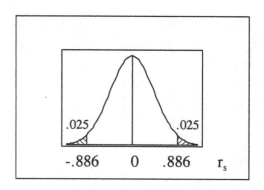

7. The following table summarizes the calculations.

x	R_x	y	R_y	d	d^2
71	7.0	125	6	1	1
70.5	5	119	3.5	1.5	2.25
71	7.0	128	8.5	-1.5	2.25
72	9	128	8.5	.5	.25
70	3.0	119	3.5	-.5	.25
70	3.0	127	7	-4	16
66.5	1	105	1	0	0
70	3.0	123	5	-2	4
71.0	7	115	2	5	25
	45.0		45.0	0.0	51.00

$r_s = 1 - [6(\Sigma d^2)]/[n(n^2-1)]$
$= 1 - [6(51.00)]/[9(80)]$
$= 1 - .425$
$= .575$

H_o: $\rho_s = 0$

H_1: $\rho_s \neq 0$
$\alpha = .05$
C.R. $r_s < -.683$
        $r_s > .683$
calculations:
    $r_s = .575$
conclusion:

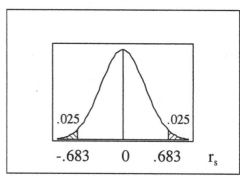

Do not reject H_o; there is not sufficient evidence to conclude that there is a correlation
between heights and weights of supermodels.

NOTE: Using formula 9-1 (since there are ties) yields $r_s = .557$. Compare this to the
parametric hypothesis test using Pearson's correlation in section 9-2 exercise #10.

8. The following table summarizes the calculations.

x	R_x	y	R_y	d	d^2
100	8	7	5	3	9
14	5.5	4.4	3	2.5	6.25
14	5.5	5.9	4	1.5	2.25
35.2	7	1.6	1	6	36
12	4	10.4	8	-4	16
7	3	9.6	7	-4	16
5	2	8.9	6	-4	16
1	1	4.2	2	-1	1
	36.0		36.0	0.0	102.50

$r_s = 1 - [6(\Sigma d^2)]/[n(n^2-1)]$
$= 1 - [6(102.5)]/[8(63)]$
$= 1 - 1.220$
$= -.220$

H_o: $\rho_s = 0$
H_1: $\rho_s \neq 0$
$\alpha = .05$
C.R. $r_s < -.738$
        $r_s > .738$
calculations:
    $r_s = -.220$
conclusion:

Do not reject Ho; there is not enough evidence to conclude that there is any correlation
between salary and number of viewers.

NOTE: Using formula 9-1 in the preceding problem (since there are ties) yields $r_s = -.228$. Compare this to the parametric hypothesis test using Pearson's correlation in section 9-2 exercise #9.

9. The following table summarizes the calculations, where grams of fat is denoted x.

x	R_x	y	R_y
.07	16	3.7	7.5
.02	8.0	3.6	4.5
.01	6	3.6	4.5
.03	12.0	4.0	14.0
.03	12.0	4.0	14.0
.00	3.0	3.6	4.5
.03	12.0	3.8	9
.03	12.0	3.7	7.5
.06	15	4.1	16
.00	3.0	3.9	11.0
.02	8.0	3.9	11.0
.02	8.0	3.3	1
.00	3.0	3.5	2
.00	3.0	3.6	4.5
.00	3.0	3.9	11.0
.03	12.0	4.0	14.0
	136.0		136.0

Since there are so many ties, use formula 9-1 on the ranks.

$n = 16$
$\Sigma R_x = 136$
$\Sigma R_x^2 = 1474$
$\Sigma R_y = 136$
$\Sigma R_y^2 = 1486.5$
$\Sigma R_x R_y = 1320$

$n(\Sigma R_x^2) - (\Sigma R_x)^2 = 16(1474) - (136)^2$
$= 5088$
$n(\Sigma R_y^2) - (\Sigma R_y)^2 = 16(1486.5) - (136)^2$
$= 5288$
$n(\Sigma R_x R_y) - (\Sigma R_x)(\Sigma R_y) = 16(1320) - (136)(136)$
$= 2624$
$r_s = 2624/[\sqrt{5088}\sqrt{5288}]$
$= .5058$

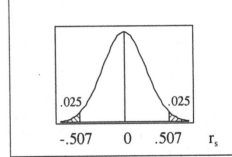

$H_0: \rho_s = 0$
$H_1: \rho_s \neq 0$
$\alpha = .05$
C.R. $r_s < -.507$
$\quad\quad r_s > .507$
calculations:
$\quad r_s = .506$
conclusion:

Do not reject H_0; there is not sufficient evidence to conclude that there is a correlation between grams of fat and calorie count.

NOTE: Compare this to the parametric hypothesis test using Pearson's correlation in section 9-2 exercise #15.

10. Refer to the data page for exercises #10, #11 and #12.
Since there are many ties, use formula 9-1 applied to the ranks.
The critical values are $\pm z/\sqrt{n-1} = \pm 1.96/\sqrt{39} = \pm.314$.
$\quad n(\Sigma R_c^2) - (\Sigma R_c)^2 = 40(22138.50) - (820)^2 = 213140$
$\quad n(\Sigma R_B^2) - (\Sigma R_B)^2 = 40(22138.00) - (820)^2 = 213120$
$\quad n(\Sigma R_c R_B) - (\Sigma R_c)(\Sigma R_B) = 40(19581.50) - (820)(820) = 110860$

$H_0: \rho_s = 0$
$H_1: \rho_s \neq 0$
$\alpha = .05$
C.R. $r_s < -.314$
$\quad\quad r_s > .314$
calculations:
$\quad r_s = 110860/[\sqrt{213140}\sqrt{213120}]$
$\quad\quad = .5202$

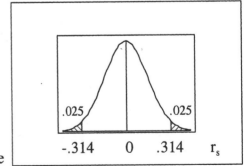

conclusion:
Reject H_0; there is sufficient evidence to conclude that $\rho_s \neq 0$ (in fact, that $\rho_s > 0$).
Yes, there is a significant positive correlation between cholesterol level and body mass.
NOTE: Compare this to the parametric hypothesis test using Pearson's correlation in section 9-2 exercise #17.

Below are the relevant values for exercises #10, #11 and #12.

#	cho	R_i	BMI	R_d
01	264	25	19.6	5.5
12	181	20	23.8	19.5
03	267	26	19.6	5.5
04	384	34	29.1	30
05	98	8.5	35.2	23
06	62	4.5	21.4	12
07	126	13	22.0	15
08	89	6	27.5	26
09	531	37	33.5	37
10	130	14	20.6	9
11	175	19	29.9	33
12	44	3	17.7	1
13	8	2	24.0	21
14	112	10	28.9	29
15	462	36	37.7	38
16	62	4.5	18.3	2
17	98	8.5	19.8	7
18	447	35	29.8	32
19	125	12	29.7	31
20	318	32	31.7	36
21	325	33	23.8	19.5
22	600	39	44.9	40
23	237	23	19.2	3
24	173	18	28.7	28
25	309	31	28.5	27
26	94	7	19.3	4
27	280	28	31.0	35
28	254	24	25.1	22
29	123	11	22.8	16.5
30	596	38	30.9	34
31	301	30	26.5	25
32	223	22	21.2	11
33	293	29	40.6	39
34	146	15	21.9	13.5
35	149	16.5	26.0	24
36	149	16.5	23.5	18
37	920	40	22.8	16.5
38	271	27	20.7	10
39	207	21	20.5	8
40	2	1	21.9	13.5
		820.0		820.0

exercise #11

nic	R_n	tar	R_t	car	R_c
1.2	24.0	16	23.5	15	19.0
1.2	24.0	16	23.5	15	19.0
1.0	15.0	16	23.5	17	26.0
0.8	8.5	9	8.0	6	3
0.1	1	1	1	1	1
0.8	8.5	8	5.5	8	6
0.8	8.5	10	10	10	8.0
1.0	15.0	16	23.5	17	26.0
1.0	15.0	14	16.5	13	14.0
1.0	15.0	13	14.0	13	14.0
1.1	20.0	13	14.0	13	14.0
1.2	24.0	15	19.0	15	19.0
1.2	24.0	16	23.5	15	19.0
0.7	5.5	9	8.0	11	10.5
0.9	11	11	11	15	19.0
0.2	2	2	2	3	2
1.4	28.5	18	28.5	18	28.5
1.2	24.0	15	19.0	15	19.0
1.1	20.0	13	14.0	12	12
1.0	15.0	15	19.0	16	23.5
1.3	27	17	27	16	23.5
0.8	8.5	9	8.0	10	8.0
1.0	15.0	12	12	10	8.0
1.0	15.0	14	16.5	17	26.0
0.5	3	5	3	7	4.5
0.6	4	6	4	7	4.5
0.7	5.5	8	5.5	11	10.5
1.4	28.5	18	28.5	15	19.0
1.1	20.0	16	23.5	18	28.5
	435.0		435.0		435.0

exercise #12

act	R_a	1dp	R_1	5dp	R_5
30	4.0	28	5.0	28	3.5
25	1	29	7.0	27	2
31	6.0	32	13.5	28	3.5
33	11.0	29	7.0	30	5.5
29	3	30	10.5	26	1
36	19.0	35	20	35	16.0
39	19.0	35	20.0	34	13.0
37	22.5	32	13.5	34	13.0
32	8	27	3.0	33	9.5
28	2	25	1	35	16.0
43	30	41	29.5	38	26.5
37	22.5	30	10.5	37	24.5
36	19.0	33	15.5	36	20.5
37	22.5	40	27.5	36	20.5
34	14	34	17.5	45	31
41	29	38	25.5	36	20.5
40	28	33	15.5	33	9.5
33	11.0	35	20.0	34	13.0
35	16.0	40	27.5	36	20.5
33	11.0	27	3.0	33	9.5
31	6.0	27	3.0	31	7
33	11.0	30	10.5	30	5.5
35	16.0	37	24	38	26.5
38	25.5	38	25.5	39	28
37	22.5	29	7.0	33	9.5
31	6.0	36	22.5	36	20.5
38	25.5	34	17.5	37	24.5
35	16.0	30	10.5	35	16.0
33	11.0	36	22.5	40	20.5
39	27	41	29.5	36	20.5
46	31	42	31	40	29.5
	496.0		496.0		496.0

exercise #10

$\Sigma R_c^2 = 22138.50$

$\Sigma R_B^2 = 22138.00$

$\Sigma R_c R_B = 19581.50$

exercise #11

$\Sigma R_n^2 = 8509.00$

$\Sigma R_t^2 = 8530.00$

$\Sigma R_c^2 = 8519.00$

$\Sigma R_n R_t = 8355.50$

$\Sigma R_n R_c = 7994.25$

exercise #12

$\Sigma R_a^2 = 10394.50$

$\Sigma R_1^2 = 10401.50$

$\Sigma R_5^2 = 10887.00$

$\Sigma R_a R_1 = 9531.75$

$\Sigma R_a R_5 = 9369.50$

11.   Refer to the data page for exercises #10, #11 and #12.
       Since there are many ties, use formula 9-1 applied to the ranks.
       The critical values are $\pm z/\sqrt{n-1} = \pm 1.96/\sqrt{28}$ $\pm.370$.
       $n(\sum R_n^2) - (\sum R_n)^2 = 29(8509) - (435)^2 = 57536$
       $n(\sum R_t^2) - (\sum R_t)^2 = 29(8530) - (435)^2 = 58145$
       $n(\sum R_c^2) - (\sum R_c)^2 = 29(8519) - (435)^2 = 57826$
       $n(\sum R_n R_t) - (\sum R_n)(\sum R_t) = 29(8355.50) - (435)(435) = 53084.50$
       $n(\sum R_n R_c) - (\sum R_n)(\sum R_c) = 29(7994.25) - (435)(435) = 42608.25$

   a. Use the nicotine (n) & tar (t) values.
      $H_0: \rho_s = 0$
      $H_1: \rho_s \neq 0$
      $\alpha = .05$
      C.R. $r_s < -.370$
           $r_s > .370$
      calculations:
           $r_s = 53084.50/[\sqrt{57536}\sqrt{58145}]$
              $= .9177$

      conclusion:
          Reject H_0; there is sufficient evidence to conclude that the nicotine content is
          (positively) correlated with the amount of tar.

   b. Use the nicotine (n) & carbon monoxide (c) values.
      $H_0: \rho_s = 0$
      $H_1: \rho_s \neq 0$
      $\alpha = .05$
      C.R. $r_s < -.370$
           $r_s > .370$
      calculations:
           $r_s = 42608.25/[\sqrt{57536}\sqrt{57826}]$
              $= .7387$

      conclusion:
          Reject H_0; there is sufficient evidence to conclude that the nicotine content is
          (positively) correlated with the amount of carbon monoxide.

   c. Tar is a better predictor than carbon monoxide, because it has a higher correlation with
      nicotine.
   NOTE: Compare this to the parametric hypothesis test using Pearson's correlation in
   section 9-2 exercise #20.

12.   Refer to the data page for exercises #10, #11 and #12.
       Since there are many ties, use formula 9-1 applied to the ranks.
       The critical values are $\pm z/\sqrt{n-1} = \pm 1.96/\sqrt{30} = \pm.358$.
       $n(\sum R_a^2) - (\sum R_a)^2 = 31(10394.50) - (496)^2 = 76213.5$
       $n(\sum R_1^2) - (\sum R_1)^2 = 31(10401.50) - (496)^2 = 76430.5$
       $n(\sum R_5^2) - (\sum R_5)^2 = 31(10887.00) - (496)^2 = 75981.0$
       $n(\sum R_a R_1) - (\sum R_a)(\sum R_1) = 31(9531.75) - (496)(496) = 49468.25$
       $n(\sum R_a R_5) - (\sum R_a)(\sum R_5) = 31(9369.50) - (496)(496) = 44438.50$

a. Use the actual (a) & five-day predicted (5) values.
   H_o: $\rho_s = 0$
   H_1: $\rho_s \neq 0$
   $\alpha = .05$
   C.R. $r_s < -.358$
   $\quad\quad r_s > .358$
   calculations:
   $\quad r_s = 44438.50/[\sqrt{76213.5}\sqrt{75981.0}]$
   $\quad\quad = .5840$

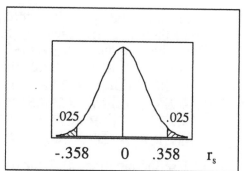

conclusion:
   Reject H_o; there is sufficient evidence to conclude that $\rho_s \neq 0$ (in fact, that $\rho_s > 0$). Yes, there is a correlation between the actual and the 5-day predicted temperatures. No, correlation does not imply agreement.

b. Use the actual (a) & one-day predicted (1) values.
   H_o: $\rho_s = 0$
   H_1: $\rho_s \neq 0$
   $\alpha = .05$
   C.R. $r_s < -.358$
   $\quad\quad r_s > .358$
   calculations:
   $\quad r_s = 49468.25/[\sqrt{76213.5}\sqrt{76430.5}]$
   $\quad\quad = .6482$

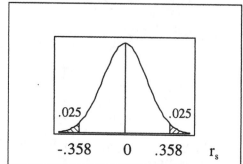

conclusion:
   Reject H_o; there is sufficient evidence to conclude that $\rho_s \neq 0$ (in fact, that $\rho_s > 0$). Yes, there is a correlation between the actual and the 1-day predicted temperatures. No, correlation does not imply agreement.

c. One expects the 1-day prediction to be more highly correlated with the actual temperature, and the results in parts (a) and (b) support that expectation. A high correlation implies only that the temperatures are related, not that they are the same – if the predictions were always exactly 30 degrees too high, the correlation would be perfect despite the lack of agreement. In many correlation problems the two variables cannot agree (no matter how high the correlation) because they don't even have the same units (e.g., height and weight).

NOTE: Compare this to the parametric hypothesis test using Pearson's correlation in section 9-2 exercise #21.

13. a. $t_{6,.025} = 2.365$; $r_s^2 = (2.447)^2/[(2.447)^2 + 6] = .499$, $r_s = \pm.707$
   b. $t_{13,.025} = 2.160$; $r_s^2 = (2.160)^2/[(2.160)^2 + 13] = .264$, $r_s = \pm.514$
   c. $t_{28,.025} = 2.048$; $r_s^2 = (2.048)^2/[(2.048)^2 + 28] = .130$, $r_s = \pm.361$
   d. $t_{28,.005} = 2.763$; $r_s^2 = (2.763)^2/[(2.763)^2 + 28] = .214$, $r_s = \pm.463$
   e. $t_{6,.005} = 3.707$; $r_s^2 = (3.707)^2/[(3.707)^2 + 6] = .696$, $r_s = \pm.834$

14. Let x = the tobacco times
   $\quad\quad$ y = the alcohol times
   Ranking the scores produces the following summary statistics.
   $\quad \Sigma R_x = 1275 \quad\quad\quad\quad \Sigma R_y = 1275 \quad\quad\quad$ for d = R_x-R_y, $\Sigma d = 0$
   $\quad \Sigma R_x^2 = 42038.00 \quad\quad \Sigma R_y^2 = 41624.50 \quad\quad\quad\quad\quad\quad \Sigma d^2 = 10700.00$
   $\quad \Sigma R_x R_y = 36481.25$
   Using the first formula,
   $\quad r_s = 1 - [6(\Sigma d^2)]/[n(n^2-1)]$
   $\quad\quad = 1 - [6(10700.00)]/[50(2499)] = 1 - 64200/124950 \ 1 - .514 = .486$

Using the second formula,
$n(\Sigma R_x^2) - (\Sigma R_x)^2 = 50(42038.00) - (1275)^2 = 476275$
$n(\Sigma R_y^2) - (\Sigma R_y)^2 = 50(41624.50) - (1275)^2 = 455600$
$n(\Sigma R_x R_y) - (\Sigma R_x)(\Sigma R_y) = 50(36481.25) - (1275)(1275) = 198437.5$
$r_s = 198437.5/[\sqrt{476275}\ \sqrt{455600}\ ] = .426$

The difference appears to be non-trivial. Since the first formula is exact only when there are no ties and the second formula is always exact, the result from the second formula is better. For n=50, both results are well into the critical region and would lead to the rejection of the hypothesis of no correlation – but in other cases, the use of the different formulas could result in different conclusions.

Review Exercises

1. $n = 8$
$\Sigma x = 276.6$
$\Sigma y = 1.66$
$\Sigma x^2 = 10680.48$
$\Sigma y^2 = .35220$
$\Sigma xy = 57.191$

$n(\Sigma xy) - (\Sigma x)(\Sigma y) = 8(57.191) - (276.6)(1.66) = -1.628$
$n(\Sigma x^2) - (\Sigma x)^2 = 8(10680.48) - (276.6)^2 = 8936.28$
$n(\Sigma y^2) - (\Sigma y)^2 = 8(.3522) - (1.66)^2 = .0620$
$r = [n(\Sigma xy) - (\Sigma x)(\Sigma y)]/[\sqrt{n(\Sigma x^2) - (\Sigma x)^2}\ \cdot\sqrt{n(\Sigma y^2) - (\Sigma y)^2}\ ]$
$= -1.628/[\sqrt{8936.28}\ \cdot\sqrt{.0620}\ ] = -.069$

$H_o: \rho = 0$
$H_1: \rho \neq 0$
$\alpha = .05$
C.R. $r < -.707$ __OR__   C.R. $t < -t_{6,.025} = -2.447$
    $r > .707$ $t > t_{6,.025} = 2.447$

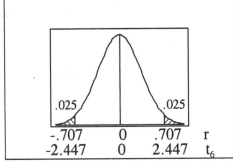

calculations: calculations:
    $r = -.069$ $t_r = (r - \mu_r)/s_r$
                         $= (-.069 - 0)/\sqrt{(1-(-.069)^2)/6}$
conclusion: $= -.069/.4073 = -.170$

Do not reject H_o; there is not sufficient evidence to reject the claim that $\rho = 0$.
No; there is no significant linear correlation between age and BAC.

2. a. $n = 6$
$\Sigma x = 441.84$
$\Sigma y = 63.58$
$\Sigma x^2 = 36754.1408$
$\Sigma y^2 = 809.5364$
$\Sigma xy = 5308.7436$

$n(\Sigma xy) - (\Sigma x)(\Sigma y) = 6(5308.7436)-(441.84)(63.58) = 3760.2744$
$n(\Sigma x^2) - (\Sigma x)^2 = 6(36754.1408) - (441.84)^2 = 25302.2592$
$n(\Sigma y^2) - (\Sigma y)^2 = 6(809.5364) - (63.58)^2 = 414.8020$
$r = [n(\Sigma xy) - (\Sigma x)(\Sigma y)]/[\sqrt{n(\Sigma x^2) - (\Sigma x)^2}\ \cdot\sqrt{n(\Sigma y^2) - (\Sigma y)^2}\ ]$
$= 3760.2744/[\sqrt{25302.2592}\cdot\sqrt{414.8020}\ ] = .828$

$H_o: \rho = 0$
$H_1: \rho \neq 0$
$\alpha = .05$
C.R. $r < -.811$ __OR__ C.R. $t < -t_{4,.025} = -2.776$
    $r > .811$ $t > t_{4,.025} = 2.776$

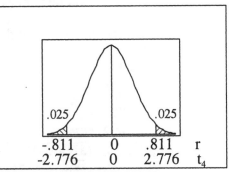

calculations: calculations:
    $r = .828$ $t_r = (r - \mu_r)/s_r$
                         $= (.828 - 0)/\sqrt{(1-(.828)^2)/4} = .828/.2802 = 2.955$

conclusion:
   Reject H_o; there is sufficient evidence to reject the claim that $\rho = 0$ and conclude that $\rho \neq 0$ (in fact, that $\rho > 0$).

b. $\bar{x} = 441.84/6 = 73.64$
   $\bar{y} = 63.58/6 = 10.597$
   $b_1 = [n(\Sigma xy) - (\Sigma x)(\Sigma y)]/[n(\Sigma x^2) - (\Sigma x)^2]$
      $= 3760.2744/25302.2592 = .1486$
   $b_o = \bar{y} - b_1\bar{x}$
      $= 10.597 - (.1486)(73.64) = -.3473$
   $\hat{y} = b_o + b_1x = -.347 + .149x$
   The tips left are slightly less than 15% of the bill – to follow the established pattern, leave 35¢ less than 14.9% of the bill.

3. Let x be the price and y be the consumption.
   $n = 10$ $n(\Sigma xy) - (\Sigma x)(\Sigma y) = 10(4.74330) - (13.66)(3.468)$
   $\Sigma x = 13.66$ $= .06012$
   $\Sigma y = 3.468$ $n(\Sigma x^2) - (\Sigma x)^2 = 10(18.6694) - (13.66)^2$
   $\Sigma x^2 = 18.6694$ $= .0984$
   $\Sigma y^2 = 1.234888$ $n(\Sigma y^2) - (\Sigma y)^2 = 10(1.234888) - (3.468)^2$
   $\Sigma xy = 4.74330$ $= .321856$

   $r = [n(\Sigma xy) - (\Sigma x)(\Sigma y)]/[\sqrt{n(\Sigma x^2) - (\Sigma x)^2} \cdot \sqrt{n(\Sigma y^2) - (\Sigma y)^2}]$
      $= [.06012]/[\sqrt{.0984} \cdot \sqrt{.321856}] = .338$

   a. $H_o: \rho = 0$
      $H_1: \rho \neq 0$
      $\alpha = .05$
      C.R. $r < -.632$ OR   C.R. $t < -t_{8,.025} = -2.306$
         $r > .632$ $t > t_{8,.025} = 2.306$

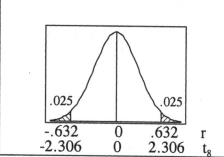

.025   .025

-.632   0   .632   r
-2.306   0   2.306 t_8

   calculations: calculations:
      $r = .338$ $t_r = (r - \mu_r)/s_r$
                             $= (.338 - 0)/\sqrt{(1-(.338)^2)/8}$
                             $= .338/.333 = 1.015$
   conclusion:
      Do not reject H_o; there is not sufficient evidence to reject the claim that $\rho = 0$.
   b. $r^2 = (.338)^2 = .114 = 11.4\%$
   c. $b_1 = [n(\Sigma xy) - (\Sigma x)(\Sigma y)]/[n(\Sigma x^2) - (\Sigma x)^2] = .06012/.0984 = .611$
      $b_o = \bar{y} - b_1\bar{x} = (3.468/10) - (.611)(13.66/10) = -.488$
      $\hat{y} = b_o + b_1x$
         $= -.488 + .611x$
   d. $\hat{y} = -.488 + .611x$
      $\hat{y}_{1.38} = \bar{y} = .3468$ pints per capita per week [no significant correlation]

4. Let x be the income and y be the consumption.
   $n = 10$ $n(\Sigma xy) - (\Sigma x)(\Sigma y) = 10(1230.996) - (3548)(3.468)$
   $\Sigma x = 3548$ $= 5.496$
   $\Sigma y = 3.468$ $n(\Sigma x^2) - (\Sigma x)^2 = 10(1259524) - (3548)^2$
   $\Sigma x^2 = 1259524$ $= 6936$
   $\Sigma y^2 = 1.234888$ $n(\Sigma y^2) - (\Sigma y)^2 = 10(1.234888) - (3.468)^2$
   $\Sigma xy = 1230.996$ $= .321856$
   $r = [n(\Sigma xy) - (\Sigma x)(\Sigma y)]/[\sqrt{n(\Sigma x^2) - (\Sigma x)^2} \cdot \sqrt{n(\Sigma y^2) - (\Sigma y)^2}]$
      $= [5.496]/[\sqrt{6936} \cdot \sqrt{.321856}] = .116$

a. H_o: $\rho = 0$
   H_1: $\rho \neq 0$
   $\alpha = .05$
   C.R. $r < -.632$ __OR__ C.R. $t < -t_{8,.025} = -2.306$
   $r > .632$ $t > t_{8,.025} = 2.306$

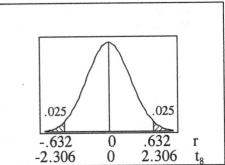

calculations: calculations:
 r = .116 $t_r = (r - \mu_r)/s_r$
 $= (.116 - 0)/\sqrt{(1-(.116)^2)/8}$
 $= .116/.351 = .331$

conclusion:
 Do not reject H_o; there is not sufficient evidence to reject the claim that $\rho = 0$.

b. $r^2 = (.116)^2 = .013 = 1.3\%$

c. $b_1 = [n(\Sigma xy) - (\Sigma x)(\Sigma y)]/[n(\Sigma x^2) - (\Sigma x)^2] = 5.496/6936 = .000792$
 $b_o = \bar{y} - b_1\bar{x} = (3.468/10) - (.000792)(3548/10) = .0657$
 $\hat{y} = b_o + b_1x$
 $= .0657 + .000792x$

d. $\hat{y} = .0657 + .000792x$
 $\hat{y}_{365} = \bar{y} = .3468$ pints per capita per week [no significant correlation]

5. Let x be the temperature and y be the consumption.
 n = 10 $n(\Sigma xy) - (\Sigma x)(\Sigma y) = 10(189.038) - (526)(3.468)$
 $\Sigma x = 526$ $= 66.212$
 $\Sigma y = 3.468$ $n(\Sigma x^2) - (\Sigma x)^2 = 10(29926) - (526)^2$
 $\Sigma x^2 = 29926$ $= 22584$
 $\Sigma y^2 = 1.234888$ $n(\Sigma y^2) - (\Sigma y)^2 = 10(1.234888) - (3.468)^2$
 $\Sigma xy = 189.038$ $= .321856$
 $r = [n(\Sigma xy) - (\Sigma x)(\Sigma y)]/[\sqrt{n(\Sigma x^2) - (\Sigma x)^2} \cdot \sqrt{n(\Sigma y^2) - (\Sigma y)^2}]$
 $= [66.212]/[\sqrt{22584} \cdot \sqrt{.321856}] = .777$

a. H_o: $\rho = 0$
   H_1: $\rho \neq 0$
   $\alpha = .05$
   C.R. $r < -.632$ __OR__ C.R. $t < -t_{8,.025} = -2.306$
   $r > .632$ $t > t_{8,.025} = 2.306$

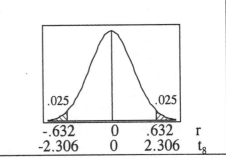

calculations: calculations:
 r = .777 $t_r = (r - \mu_r)/s_r$
 $= (.777 - 0)/\sqrt{(1-(.777)^2)/8}$
 $= .777/.223 = 3.486$

conclusion:
 Reject H_o; there is sufficient evidence to reject the claim that $\rho = 0$ and to conclude
 that $\rho \neq 0$ (in fact, that $\rho > 0$).

b. $r^2 = (.777)^2 = .604 = 60.4\%$

c. $b_1 = [n(\Sigma xy) - (\Sigma x)(\Sigma y)]/[n(\Sigma x^2) - (\Sigma x)^2] = 66.212/22584 = .00293$
 $b_o = \bar{y} - b_1\bar{x} = (3.468/10) - (.00293)(526/10) = .193$
 $\hat{y} = b_o + b_1x$
 $= .193 + .00293x$

d. $\hat{y} = .193 + .00293x$
 $\hat{y}_{32} = .193 + .00293(32) = .2864$ pints per capita per week

6. Let x be the consumption and y be the temperature. The following table summarizes the calculations.

x	R_x	y	R_y	d	d^2
.386	7	41	3	4	16
.374	6	56	5	1	1
.393	8	63	7	1	1
.425	10	68	9	1	1
.406	9	69	10	−1	1
.344	5	65	8	−3	9
.327	4	61	6	−2	4
.288	3	47	4	−1	1
.269	2	32	2	0	0
.256	1	24	1	0	0
	55		55	0	34

$$r_s = 1 - [6(\Sigma d^2)]/[n(n^2-1)]$$
$$= 1 - [6(34)]/[10(99)]$$
$$= 1 - .206$$
$$= .794$$

$H_o: \rho_s = 0$

$H_1: \rho_s \neq 0$

$\alpha = .05$

C.R. $r_s < -.648$
     $r_s > .648$

calculations:
     $r_s = .794$

conclusion:

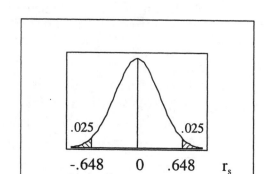

Reject H_o; there is sufficient evidence to reject the claim that $\rho_s=0$ conclude that $\rho_s \neq 0$ (in fact, that $\rho_s>0$).

Yes; based on these results there appears to be a significant positive correlation between consumption and temperature.

NOTE: In this instance, the point estimate and conclusion agree with those in the parametric analysis in #5 above.

Cumulative Review Exercises

1. Let x be the F-K Grade Level score and y be the Flesch Reading Ease score.

n = 12
$\Sigma x = 101.2$
$\Sigma y = 793.8$
$\Sigma x^2 = 897.82$
$\Sigma y^2 = 53189.10$
$\Sigma xy = 6540.86$

$n(\Sigma xy) - (\Sigma x)(\Sigma y) = 12(6540.86) - (101.2)(793.8)$
$= -1842.24$
$n(\Sigma x^2) - (\Sigma x)^2 = 12(897.82) - (101.2)^2$
$= 532.40$
$n(\Sigma y^2) - (\Sigma y)^2 = 12(53189.10) - (793.8)^2$
$= 8150.76$

$r = [n(\Sigma xy) - (\Sigma x)(\Sigma y)]/[\sqrt{n(\Sigma x^2) - (\Sigma x)^2} \cdot \sqrt{n(\Sigma y^2) - (\Sigma y)^2}]$
$= [-1842.24]/[\sqrt{532.40} \cdot \sqrt{8150.76}] = -.884$

a. $H_o: \rho = 0$
   $H_1: \rho \neq 0$
   $\alpha = .05$
   C.R. $r < -.576$ OR   C.R. $t < -t_{10,.025} = -2.228$
        $r > .576$ $t > t_{10,.025} = 2.228$

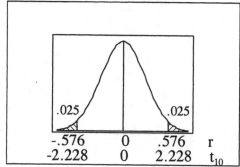

calculations: calculations:
     $r = -.884$ $t_r = (r - \mu_r)/s_r$
                                   $= (-.884 - 0)/\sqrt{(1-(-.884)^2)/10}$
conclusion: $= -.884/.1476 = -5.991$

Reject H_o; there is sufficient evidence to reject the claim that $\rho = 0$ and to conclude that $\rho \neq 0$ (in fact, that $\rho < 0$).

b. $b_1 = [n(\Sigma xy) - (\Sigma x)(\Sigma y)]/[n(\Sigma x^2) - (\Sigma x)^2] = -1842.24/532.40 = -3.460$
   $b_0 = \bar{y} - b_1\bar{x} = (793.80/12) - (-3.460)(101.20/12) = 95.33$
   $\hat{y} = b_0 + b_1 x$
   $\quad = 95.33 - 3.460x$

c. Yes; in general it's always possible to test wether two parameter values are equal.
   No; since the two measures do not use the same approach or the same units to the
   problem, it would not make sense to test wether the values are numerically equal.

d. First find the mean and standard deviation of y, the Flesch Reading Ease scores.
   $\bar{y} = (\Sigma y)/n = 793.8/12 = 66.15$
   $s^2 = [n(\Sigma y^2) - (\Sigma y)^2]/[n(n-1)] = [12(53189.10) - (793.8)^2]/[12(11)]$
   $\quad = (8150.76)/132 = 61.748$
   $s = 7.858$
   $\bar{x} \pm t_{11,.025} \cdot s/\sqrt{n}$
   $66.15 \pm 2.201 \cdot (7.858)/\sqrt{12}$
   66.15 ± 4.99
   $61.16 < \mu < 71.14$

2. Let x and y be as given.
   $\quad n = 12$ $\qquad\qquad\qquad\qquad\qquad n(\Sigma xy) - (\Sigma x)(\Sigma y) = 12(122836) - (1189)(1234)$
   $\quad \Sigma x = 1189$ $\qquad\qquad\qquad\qquad\qquad\qquad\qquad = 6806$
   $\quad \Sigma y = 1234$ $\qquad\qquad\qquad n(\Sigma x^2) - (\Sigma x)^2 = 12(118599) - (1189)^2$
   $\quad \Sigma x^2 = 118599$ $\qquad\qquad\qquad\qquad\qquad\qquad = 9467$
   $\quad \Sigma y^2 = 127724$ $\qquad\qquad\qquad n(\Sigma y^2) - (\Sigma y)^2 = 12(127724) - (1234)^2$
   $\quad \Sigma xy = 122836$ $\qquad\qquad\qquad\qquad\qquad\qquad = 9932$
   $r = [n(\Sigma xy) - (\Sigma x)(\Sigma y)]/[\sqrt{n(\Sigma x^2) - (\Sigma x)^2} \cdot \sqrt{n(\Sigma y^2) - (\Sigma y)^2}]$
   $\quad = [6806]/[\sqrt{9467}\,\sqrt{9932}\,] = .702$

a. $\bar{x} = 1189/12 = 99.1$ $\qquad\qquad s_x = \sqrt{9467/(12 \cdot 11)} = 8.47$

b. $\bar{y} = 1234/12 = 102.8$ $\qquad\qquad s_y = \sqrt{9932/(12 \cdot 11)} = 8.67$

c. No; there does not appear to be a difference between the means of the two populations.
   In exploring the relationship between the IQ's of twins, such a two sample approach is
   not appropriate because it completely ignores the pairings of the scores.

d. Combing the scores produces the following summary statistics.
   summary statistics: $n = 24$, $\Sigma x = 2423$, $\Sigma x^2 = 246,323$, $\bar{x} = 100.958$, $s = 8.5997$
   original claim: $\mu \neq 100$
   $H_0: \mu = 100$
   $H_1: \mu \neq 100$
   $\alpha = .05$
   C.R. $t < -t_{23,.025} = -2.069$
   $\qquad t > t_{23,.025} = 2.069$
   calculations:
   $\quad t_{\bar{x}} = (\bar{x} - \mu)/s_{\bar{x}}$
   $\qquad = (100.958 - 100)/(8.5997/\sqrt{24})$
   $\qquad = .958/1.755 = .546$
   $\quad$ P-value $= 2 \cdot P(t_{23} > .546) > .20$
   conclusion:
   $\qquad$ Do not reject H_0; there is not sufficient evidence to conclude that $\mu \neq 120$.

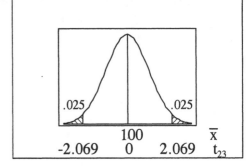

e. Correlation would be appropriate for answering the question "is there a (linear) relationship?"

H_o: $\rho = 0$

H_1: $\rho \neq 0$

$\alpha = .05$ [assumed]

C.R. r < -.576 <u>OR</u>   C.R. t < $-t_{10,.025}$ = -2.228

     r > .576   t > $t_{10,.025}$ = 2.228

calculations: calculations:

   r = .702 $t_r = (r - \mu_r)/s_r$

                       $= (.702 - 0)/\sqrt{(1-(.702)^2)/10}$

conclusion: $= .702/.225 = 3.116$

Reject H_o; there is sufficient evidence to reject the claim that $\rho = 0$ and to conclude that $\rho \neq 0$ (in fact, $\rho > 0$).

Ordinarily, the conclusion would be that about $R^2 = (.702)^2 = .493 = 49.3\%$ of the variation in x can be explained in terms of y (and vice-versa). In this context that means that about 49.3% of the variation among the IQ's in one group can be explained in terms of the IQ's of their twins (i.e, in terms of heredity). In simplest terms, it seems intelligence is about ½ due to heredity and ½ due to environment.

NOTE: Exercise #2 contains at least two interesting subtleties. (1) Correlation addresses only whether there is a relationship between the IQ's, and not whether the IQ's are close to each other. If each older twin had an IQ 20 points higher than the corresponding younger twin, there would be a perfect correlation – but the twins would not be similar in IQ at all. Beware of the misconception that correlation implies similarity. (2) Within each pair, the older twin was designated x. That was an arbitrary decision to produce an objective rule. The x-y designation within pairs could just as properly have been made alphabetically, randomly, or by another rule. But the rule affects the results. If it happens to designate all the twins with the higher IQ as x, the correlation rises to r = .810. If it happens to designate the twins with the higher IQ as x in the first six pairs and as y in the last six, the correlation falls to r = .633.

One technique which addresses both of the above issues (i.e., it tests for similarity and does not depend upon an x-y designation at all) involves comparing the variation within pairs to the overall variation in IQ's. If there is significantly less variability between the twins than there is variability in the general population (or between non-identical twins raised apart), then there is a significant relationship (i.e., in the sense of similarity) between the IQ's of identical twins.

Chapter 10

Chi-Square and Analysis of Variance

10-2 Multinomial Experiments: Goodness-of-Fit

1. a. H_o: $p_1 = p_2 = p_3 = p_4 = .25$

   b. Since $\Sigma O = (5+6+8+13) = 32$, the hypothesis of equally likely categories indicates $E_i = .25(32) = 8$ for $i=1,2,3,4$.

   c. $\chi^2 = \Sigma[(O-E)^2/E] = (5-8)^2/8 + (6-8)^2/8 + (8-8)^2/8 + (13-8)^2/8$
   $$= 9/8 + 4/8 + 0/8 + 25/8$$
   $$= 38/8 = 4.750$$

   d. $\chi^2_{3,.05} = 7.815$

   e. There is not enough evidence to reject the claim that the four categories are equally likely.

2. a. H_o: $p_1 = p_2 = p_3 = .20$, $p_4 = .30$, $p_5 = .10$

   b. Since $\Sigma O = (9+8+13+14+6) = 50$, the hypothesis indicates
   $E_i = .20(50) = 10$ for $i=1,2,3$
   $E_4 = .30(50) = 15$
   $E_5 = .10(50) = 5$

   c. $\chi^2 = \Sigma[(O-E)^2/E] = (9-10)^2/10 + (8-10)^2/10 + (13-10)^2/10 + (14-15)^2/15 + (6-5)^2/5$
   $$= 1/10 + 4/10 + 9/10 + 1/15 + 1/5$$
   $$= .100 + .400 + .900 + .067 + .200 = 1.667$$

   d. $\chi^2_{4,.05} = 9.488$

   e. There is not enough evidence to reject the claim that the five categories occur as specified.

3. a. $\chi^2_{37,.10} = 51.085$

   b. Since $\chi^2_{37,.10} = 51.085 > 38.232 > 29.051 = \chi^2_{37,.90}$, $.10 <$ P-value $< .90$.

   c. There is not enough evidence to reject the claim that the 38 results are equally likely.

4. a. $\chi^2_{9,.05} = 16.919$

   b. Since $\chi^2_{9,.10} = 14.684 > 8.815 > 4.168 = \chi^2_{9,.90}$, $.10 <$ P-value $< .90$.

   c. There is not enough evidence to reject the claim that the observed outcomes agree with the expected frequencies. Yes, the machine appears to be working correctly.

NOTES FOR THE REMAINING EXERCISES:
(1) In multinomial problems, always verify that $\Sigma E = \Sigma O$ before proceeding. If these sums are not equal, then an error has been made and further calculations have no meaning.
(2) As in the previous uses of the chi-squared distribution, the accompanying illustrations follow the "usual" shape – even though that shape is not correct for df=1 or df=2.

5. $H_o: p_1 = p_2 = p_3 = \ldots = p_6 = 1/6$
$H_1:$ at least one of the proportions is different from 1/6
$\alpha = .05$
C.R. $\chi^2 > \chi^2_{5,.05} = 11.071$
calculations:

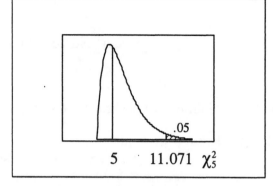

outcome	O	E	$(O-E)^2/E$
1	27	33.33	1.2033
2	31	33.33	.1633
3	42	33.33	2.2533
4	40	33.33	1.3333
5	28	33.33	.8533
6	32	33.33	.0533
	200	200.00	5.8600

$\chi^2 = \Sigma[(O-E)^2/E] = 5.860$

conclusion:
Do not reject H_o; there is not sufficient evidence to conclude that at least one of the proportions is different from 1/6.
No, this particular loaded die did not behave noticeably differently from a fair die.

6. $H_o: p_{LF} = p_{RF} = p_{LR} = p_{RR} = .25$
$H_1:$ at least one of the proportions is different from .25
$\alpha = .05$
C.R. $\chi^2 > \chi^2_{3,.05} = 7.815$
calculations:

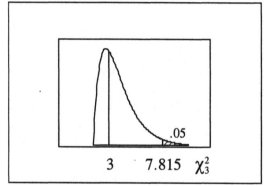

tire	O	E	$(O-E)^2/E$
LF	11	10	.100
RF	15	10	2.500
LR	8	10	.400
RR	6	10	1.600
	40	40	4.600

$\chi^2 = \Sigma[(O-E)^2/E] = 4.600$

conclusion:
Do not reject H_o; there is not sufficient evidence to conclude that at least one of the proportions is different from .25.
While we cannot be 95% certain that there is a tendency to pick one tire more than any other, it might be worthwhile to take a larger sample to see if the trend toward picking front tires becomes significant.

7. $H_o: p_{Sun} = p_{Mon} = p_{Tue} = \ldots = p_{Sat} = 1/7$
$H_1:$ at least one of the proportions is different from 1/7
$\alpha = .05$
C.R. $\chi^2 > \chi^2_{6,.05} = 12.592$
calculations:

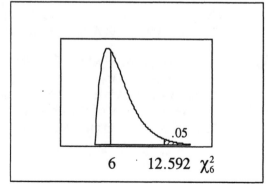

day	O	E	$(O-E)^2/E$
Sun	31	25.714	1.0865
Mon	20	25.714	1.2698
Tue	20	25.714	1.2698
Wed	22	25.714	.5365
Thu	22	25.714	.5365
Fri	29	25.714	.4198
Sat	36	25.714	4.1143
	180	180.000	9.2332

$\chi^2 = \Sigma[(O-E)^2/E] = 9.233$

conclusion:
Do not reject H_o; there is not sufficient evidence to conclude that at least one of the proportions is different from 1/7.

8. H_o: $p_{Sun} = p_{Mon} = p_{Tue} = \ldots = p_{Sat} = 1/7$
H_1: at least one of the proportions is different from 1/7
$\alpha = .05$
C.R. $\chi^2 > \chi^2_{6,.05} = 12.592$
calculations:

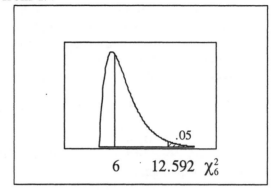

day	O	E	$(O-E)^2/E$
Sun	40	30.857	2.709
Mon	24	30.857	1.524
Tue	25	30.857	1.112
Wed	28	30.857	.265
Thu	29	30.857	.112
Fri	32	30.857	.042
Sat	38	30.857	1.653
	216	216.000	7.417

$\chi^2 = \Sigma[(O-E)^2/E] = 7.417$

conclusion:
Do not reject H_o; there is not sufficient evidence to conclude that at least one of the proportions is different from 1/7.
There is not enough evidence to reject with 95% confidence the theory that fatal DWI car crashes are caused by those who drink daily.

9. H_o: $p_{Mon} = p_{Tue} = p_{Wed} = p_{Thu} = p_{Fri} = 1/5$
H_1: at least one of the proportions is different from 1/5
$\alpha = .05$ [assumed]
C.R. $\chi^2 > \chi^2_{4,.05} = 9.488$
calculations:

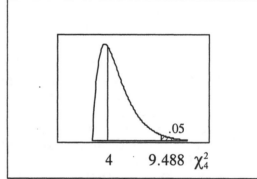

day	O	E	$(O-E)^2/E$
Mon	31	29.4	.087
Tue	42	29.4	5.400
Wed	18	29.4	4.420
Thu	25	29.4	.659
Fri	31	29.4	.087
	147	147.0	10.653

$\chi^2 = \Sigma[(O-E)^2/E] = 10.653$

conclusion:
Reject H_o; there is sufficient evidence to conclude that at least one of the proportions is different from 1/5.
The accidents seem to occur less frequently on Wednesday, and with increasing frequency toward the start and end of the week. This could be due to Monday workers still thinking about the past weekend and Friday workers thinking about the coming weekend. The only exception to this pattern is Tuesday.

10. H_o: $p_F = p_M = p_B = 1/3$
H_1: at least one of the proportions is different from 1/3
$\alpha = .05$ [assumed]
C.R. $\chi^2 > \chi^2_{2,.05} = 5.991$
calculations:

place	O	E	$(O-E)^2/E$
Front	17	10.33	4.301
Middle	9	10.33	.172
Back	5	10.33	2.753
	31	31.00	7.226

$\chi^2 = \Sigma[(O-E)^2/E] = 7.226$

conclusion:
Reject H_o; there is sufficient evidence to support the claim that A students are not evenly distributed throughout the class room.

Not necessarily; since it is probably the type of student that determines the seat position and not vice versa. Reasons supporting the possibility that seat position determines the type of student, however, include the following. (1) Sitting in the front and in the midst of good students makes it more likely that a student will pay attention and learn more. (2) Sitting in the front with good students builds relationships and makes it more likely that a student will study with those same people outside class. (3) Sitting in the front with good students could affect the professor's perception and (especially in classes where grading is more subjective) and make it more likely that a student will get a better grade – or at least the benefit of the doubt in borderline cases.

11. H_o: $p_1 = p_2 = p_3 = ... = p_8 = 1/8$
H_1: at least one of the proportions is different from 1/8
$\alpha = .05$ [assumed]
C.R. $\chi^2 > \chi^2_{7,.05} = 14.067$
calculations:

start	O	E	$(O-E)^2/E$
1	29	18	6.722
2	19	18	.056
3	18	18	.000
4	25	18	2.722
5	17	18	.056
6	10	18	3.556
7	15	18	.500
8	11	18	2.722
	144	144	16.333

$\chi^2 = \Sigma[(O-E)^2/E] = 16.333$

conclusion:
  Reject H_o; there is sufficient evidence to conclude that at least one of the proportions is different from 1/8 – i.e., that the probabilities of winning in the different starting positions are not all the same.

12. H_o: $p_0 = p_1 = p_2 = ... = p_9 = 1/10$
H_1: at least one of the proportions is different from 1/10
$\alpha = .05$ [assumed]
C.R. $\chi^2 > \chi^2_{9,.05} = 16.919$
calculations:

digit	O	E	$(O-E)^2/E$
0	16	8	8.000
1	0	8	8.000
2	14	8	4.500
3	0	8	8.000
4	17	8	10.125
5	0	8	8.000
6	16	8	8.000
7	0	8	8.000
8	17	8	10.125
9	0	8	8.000
	80	80	80.750

$\chi^2 = \Sigma[(O-E)^2/E] = 80.750$

conclusion:
  Reject H_o; there is sufficient evidence to conclude that at least one of the proportions is different from 1/10 – i.e., that last digits are not uniformly distributed.
All of the observed last digits are even numbers. Further inspection reveals that all 80 of the pulse rates per minute are multiples of 4 – because the standard technique for taking pulses manually is to count the beats for 15 seconds and then multiply by 4. One can infer that these pulse rates were obtained manually (i.e., not by a machine) by the standard technique.

13. H_o: $p_0 = p_1 = p_2 = ... = p_9 = 1/10$
     H_1: at least one of the proportions is different from 1/10
     $\alpha = .05$
     C.R. $\chi^2 > \chi^2_{9,.05} = 16.919$
     calculations:

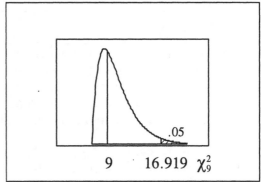

digit	O	E	$(O-E)^2/E$
0	18	16	0.2500
1	12	16	1.0000
2	14	16	0.2500
3	9	16	3.0625
4	17	16	0.0625
5	20	16	1.0000
6	21	16	1.5625
7	26	16	6.2500
8	7	16	5.0625
9	16	16	0.0000
	160	160	18.5000

$$\chi^2 = \Sigma[(O-E)^2/E] = 18.500$$

conclusion:
Reject H_o; there is sufficient evidence to conclude that at least one of the proportions is different from 1/10 – i.e., that the digits are not equally likely.
If the .01 level of significance is used, the critical region is $\chi^2 > \chi^2_{9,.01} = 21.666$ and the decision changes. While we can be 95% confident that the digits are not being equally selected, we cannot be 99% confident that such is the case. If the digits are not being equally selected, (1) something is wrong with the device/method used to make the selections and (2) a person could use that knowledge to increase his chances of winning.

14. **NOTE:** The goodness of fit tests works with actual frequencies, and not with percents or proportions. In this case, there is not enough accuracy in the reported observed proportions to determine the exact observed frequencies – e.g., any $108958 \leq x \leq 110382$ yields the $x/1424287 = 7.7\%$ reported for January. Furthermore, the reported observed percents sum to 100.1% – guaranteeing that the calculations will be flawed due to rounding in the given numbers. One approach is as follows.
     For sample size n, $O_i = n\hat{p}_i$ and $E_i = np_i$ mean that the calculated test statistic can be rewritten as
$$\chi^2 = \Sigma[(O-E)^2/E] = \Sigma[(n\hat{p}-np)^2/np] = \Sigma[n^2(\hat{p}-p)^2/np] = \Sigma n[(\hat{p}-p)^2/p] = n\Sigma[(\hat{p}-p)^2/p]$$
     In this particular problem, calculate $\Sigma[(\hat{p}-p)^2/p]$ and use $\chi^2 = n\Sigma[(\hat{p}-p)^2/p]$. This allows one to work with more convenient numbers. Furthermore, since $\Sigma\hat{p} = 1.001$ use $p = 1.001/12 = .0834167$ to test the claim that the reported occurrences are equally spread among the 12 categories.
     H_o: $p_{Jan} = p_{Feb} = p_{Mar} = ... = p_{Dec} = 1/12$
     H_1: at least one of the proportions is different from 1/12
     $\alpha = .01$
     C.R. $\chi^2 > \chi^2_{11,.05} = 24.725$
     calculations:

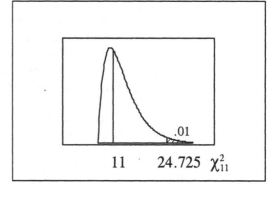

month	$\hat{p}$	p	$(\hat{p}-p)^2/p$
Jan	.077	.0834	.00049360
Feb	.074	.0834	.00106303
Mar	.084	.0834	.00000408
Apr	.083	.0834	.00000208
May	.092	.0834	.00088319
Jun	.086	.0834	.00008000
Jul	.090	.0834	.00051956
Aug	.089	.0834	.00037370
Sep	.086	.0834	.00008000
Oct	.087	.0834	.00015393
Nov	.076	.0834	.00065943
Dec	.077	.0834	.00049360
	1.001	1.0010	.00480620

$$\chi^2 = n\Sigma[(\hat{p}-p)^2/p] = (1424287)(.00480620) = 6845.408$$

conclusion:

> Reject H_o; there is sufficient evidence to conclude that at least one of the proportions is different from 1/12 – i.e., that the crimes are not equally distributed among the 12 months.

The evidence so overwhelmingly calls for rejection, even though the listed percentages do not differ all that dramatically, because the sample size is so large. The 12 months are certainly not <u>exactly</u> equal, and a large enough sample will detect even the smallest differences – even though they may be of no practical importance. In this case there do appear to be some practical differences, as it appears that there may be less violent crime from November to February – i.e., during the winter months.

15. H_o: $p_{Bro}=.3$, $p_{Yel}=.2$, $p_{Red}=.2$, $p_{Ora}=.1$, $p_{Gre}=.1$, $p_{Blu}=.1$
H_1: at least one of the proportions is not as claimed
$\alpha = .05$
C.R. $\chi^2 > \chi^2_{5,.05} = 11.071$
calculations:

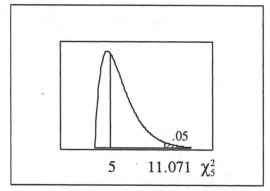

color	O	E	$(O-E)^2/E$
Bro	33	30	.300
Yel	26	20	1.800
Red	21	20	.050
Ora	8	10	.400
Gre	7	10	.900
Blu	5	10	2.500
	100	100	5.950

$\chi^2 = \Sigma[(O-E)^2/E] = 5.950$

conclusion:

> Do not reject H_o; there is not sufficient evidence to conclude that at least one of the proportions is not as claimed.

16. H_o: $p_1=.16$, $p_2=.44$, $p_3=.27$, $p_4=.13$
H_1: at least one of the proportions is different from the license proportions
$\alpha = .05$
C.R. $\chi^2 > \chi^2_{3,.05} = 7.815$
calculations:

group	O	E	$(O-E)^2/E$
1: <25	36	14.08	34.125
2: 25-44	21	38.72	8.109
3: 45-64	12	23.76	5.821
4: >64	19	11.44	4.996
	88	88.00	53.051

$\chi^2 = \Sigma[(O-E)^2/E] = 53.051$

conclusion:

> Reject H_o; there is sufficient evidence to conclude that at least one of the proportions is different from the license proportions.

Yes; the "under 25" group appears to have a disproportionately large number of crashes – but it would be fairer, although much more difficult, to base the E values on the proportion of miles driven and not on the proportion of licenses possessed.

17. H_o: $p_0 = p_1 = p_2 = \ldots = p_9 = 1/10$
H_1: at least one of the proportions is different from 1/10
$\alpha = .05$
C.R. $\chi^2 > \chi^2_{9,.05} = 16.919$

calculations:

digit	O	E	$(O-E)^2/E$
0	8	10	.400
1	8	10	.400
2	12	10	.400
3	11	10	.100
4	10	10	.000
5	8	10	.400
6	9	10	.100
7	8	10	.400
8	12	10	.400
9	14	10	1.600
	100	100	4.200

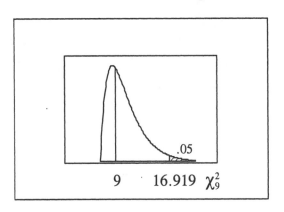

$$\chi^2 = \Sigma[(O-E)^2/E] = 4.200$$

conclusion:

Do not reject H_0; there is not sufficient evidence to conclude that at least one of the proportions is different from 1/10.

18. $H_0: p_0 = p_1 = p_2 = \ldots = p_9 = 1/10$
 H_1: at least one of the proportions is different from 1/10
 $\alpha = .05$
 C.R. $\chi^2 > \chi^2_{9,.05} = 16.919$
 calculations:

digit	O	E	$(O-E)^2/E$
0	0	10	10.000
1	17	10	4.900
2	17	10	4.900
3	1	10	8.100
4	17	10	4.900
5	16	10	3.600
6	0	10	10.000
7	16	10	3.600
8	16	10	3.600
9	0	10	10.000
	100	100	63.600

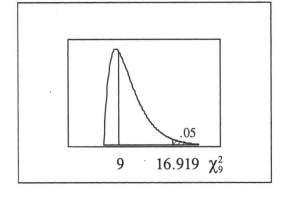

$$\chi^2 = \Sigma[(O-E)^2/E] = 63.600$$

conclusion:

Reject H_0; there is sufficient evidence to conclude that at least one of the proportions is different from 1/10 – i.e., that the digits do not appear with equal frequencies.
The result differs dramatically from that of exercise #17. Since 22/7 is a repeating decimal, once the repetitions begin only those digits will appear and other digits will not appear at all.

19. H_0: the leading digit proportions conform to Benford's law.
 H_1: at least one of the proportions is different from those specified by Benford's law.
 $\alpha = .05$
 C.R. $\chi^2 > \chi^2_{8,.05} = 15.507$
 calculations:

digit	O	p	E	$(O-E)^2/E$
1	72	.301	60.2	2.3130
2	23	.176	35.2	4.2284
3	26	.125	25.0	.0400
4	20	.097	19.4	.0186
5	21	.079	15.8	1.7114
6	18	.067	13.4	1.5791
7	8	.058	11.6	1.1172
8	8	.051	10.2	.4745
9	4	.046	9.2	2.9391
	200	1.000	200.0	14.4213

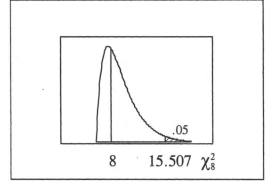

$$\chi^2 = \Sigma[(O-E)^2/E] = 14.421$$

conclusion:
    Do not reject H_o; there is not sufficient evidence to conclude that at least one of the proportions is different those specified by Benford's law.

20. H_o: the proportions conform to those specified by the Poisson distribution
H_1: at least one of the proportions is different from those specified by the Poisson
$\alpha = .05$
C.R. $\chi^2 > \chi^2_{4,.05} = 9.488$
calculations:

hits	O	E	$(O-E)^2/E$
0	229	227.5	.00989
1	211	211.4	.00076
2	93	97.9	.24525
3	35	30.5	.66393
4+	8	8.7	.05632
	576	576.0	.97615

$\chi^2 = \Sigma[(O-E)^2/E] = .976$

conclusion:
    Do not reject H_o; there is not sufficient evidence to conclude that at least one of the proportions is different from those specified by the Poisson distribution.

21. H_o: $p_{LF} = p_{RF} = p_{LR} = p_{RR} = .25$
H_1: at least one of the proportions is different from .25
$\alpha = .05$
C.R. $\chi^2 > \chi^2_{3,.05} = 7.815$
calculations:

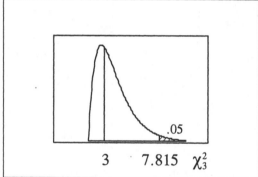

tire	O	E	$(O-E)^2/E$
LF	11	23.5	6.649
RF	15	23.5	3.074
LR	8	23.5	10.223
RR	60	23.5	56.691
	94	94.0	76.638

$\chi^2 = \Sigma[(O-E)^2/E] = 76.638$

conclusion:
    Reject H_o; there is sufficient evidence to conclude that at least one of the proportions is different from .25.
In general, an "outlier" is a point that is different from the normal pattern. Since that (i.e., "difference from the normal pattern") is essentially what the goodness-of-fit test is designed to detect, an outlier will tend to increase the probability of rejecting H_o.

22. Use the lower tail of the χ^2 distribution to determine the critical region. If the null hypothesis is true and only random fluctuation exists, the expected value of $\chi^2 = \Sigma[(O-E)^2/E]$ is the degrees of freedom df. If $\Sigma[(O-E)^2/E]$ is significantly greater than df, then there is more variation than can be expected by chance and the data do not fit the null hypothesis. If $\Sigma[(O-E)^2/E]$ is significantly less than df, then there is less variation than can be expected by chance and the data fit the null hypothesis too well.

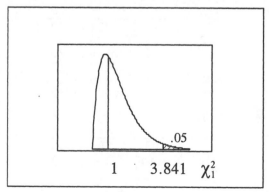

23. NOTE: Both outcomes having the same expected frequency is equivalent to $p_1 = p_2 = .5$.
    a. H_o: $p_1 = p_2 = .5$
      H_1: at least one of the p_i is different from .5
      $\alpha = .05$
      C.R. $\chi^2 > \chi^2_{1,.05} = 3.841$

calculations

type	O	E	O-E	$(O-E)^2$	$(O-E)^2/E$
A	f_1	$(f_1+f_2)/2$	$(f_1-f_2)/2$	$(f_1-f_2)^2/4$	$[(f_1-f_2)^2/4]/[(f_1+f_2)/2]$
B	f_2	$(f_1+f_2)/2$	$(f_2-f_1)/2$	*$(f_1-f_2)^2/4$	$[(f_1-f_2)^2/4]/[(f_1+f_2)/2]$
f_1+f_2	f_1+f_2				$[(f_1-f_2)^2/2]/[(f_1+f_2)/2]$

*NOTE: $(f_2-f_1)^2 = (f_1-f_2)^2$

$$\chi^2 = \Sigma[(O-E)^2/E] = [(f_1-f_2)^2/2]/[(f_1+f_2)/2] = (f_1-f_2)^2/(f_1+f_2)$$

b. H_0: p = .5
   H_1: p ≠ .5
   α = .05
   C.R. z < $-z_{.025}$ = -1.960
       z > $z_{.025}$ = 1.960
   calculations:

   $z_{\hat{p}} = (\hat{p} - \mu_{\hat{p}})/\sigma_{\hat{p}}$

   $= [f_1/(f_1+f_2) - .5]/\sqrt{(.5)(.5)/(f_1+f_2)}$

   $= [.5(f_1-f_2)/(f_1+f_2)]/\sqrt{(.5)(.5)/(f_1+f_2)}$

   $= [(f_1-f_2)/(f_1+f_2)]/\sqrt{1/(f_1+f_2)}$

   $= (f_1-f_2)/\sqrt{f_1+f_2}$

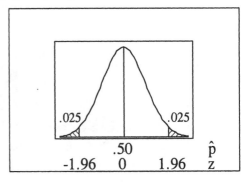

Since $[(f_1-f_2)/\sqrt{f_1+f_2}]^2 = (f_1-f_2)^2/(f_1+f_2)$ and $(\pm1.960)^2 = 3.841$, $z^2 = \chi^2$.

24. a. Use the binomial formula $P(x) = [n!/x!(n-x)!]\cdot p^x\cdot(1-p)^{n-x}$ with n=3 and p=1/3.
    $P(x=0) = 1(1/3)^0(2/3)^3 = 8/27 = .296$
    $P(x=1) = 3(1/3)^1(2/3)^2 = 12/27 = .444$
    $P(x=2) = 3(1/3)^2(2/3)^1 = 6/27 = .222$
    $P(x=3) = 1(1/3)^3(2/3)^0 = 1/27 = .037$

    b.
x	O	E	$(O-E)^2/E$
0	89	88.89	.000
1	133	133.33	.001
2	52	66.67	3.227
3	26	11.11	19.951
	300	300.00	23.179

    c. H_0: there is goodness of fit to the binomial
           distribution with n=3 and p=1/3
       H_1: there is not goodness of fit
       α = .05
       C.R. $\chi^2 > \chi^2_{3,.05}$ = 7.815
       calculations:
       $\chi^2 = \Sigma[(O-E)^2/E]$
           $= 23.179$

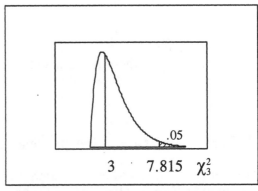

    conclusion:
       Reject H_0; there is sufficient evidence to conclude that the observed frequencies do
       not fit a binomial distribution with n=3 and p=1/3.
    NOTE: While the phrase "goodness of fit" is the accepted statistical terminology in this
    context, the test could also be expressed as
       H_0: $p_0 = 8/27$, $p_1 = 12/27$, $p_2 = 6/27$, $p_3 = 1/27$
       H_1: at least p_i is not as claimed

25.   a. Refer to the illustration below.
$P(x<79.5) = P(z<-1.37) = .0853$
$P(79.5<x<95.5) = P(z<-.30) - P(z<-1.37) = .3821 - .0853 = .2968$
$P(95.5<x<110.5) = P(z<.70) - P(z<-.30) = .7580 - .3821 = .3759$
$P(110.5<x<120.5) = P(z<1.37) - P(z<.70) = .9147 - .7850 = .1567$
$P(x>120.5) = 1 - P(z<1.37) = 1 - .9147 = .0853$

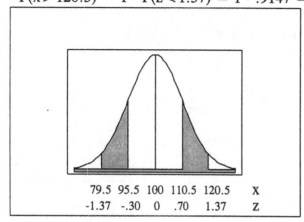

X	79.5	95.5	100	110.5	120.5
Z	-1.37	-.30	0	.70	1.37

b.

score	O	E	$(O-E)^2/E$
< 80	20	17.06	.507
80- 95	20	59.36	26.099
96-110	80	75.18	.309
111-120	40	31.34	2.393
>120	40	17.06	30.847
	200	200.00	60.154

c. H_0: there is goodness of fit to the normal
    distribution with $\mu=100$ and $\sigma=15$
H_1: there is not goodness of fit
$\alpha = .01$
C.R. $\chi^2 > \chi^2_{4,.01} = 13.277$
calculations:
$\chi^2 = \Sigma[(O-E)^2/E]$
    $= 60.154$

conclusion:
    Reject H_0; there is sufficient evidence to conclude that the observed frequencies do
    not fit a normal distribution with $\mu=100$ and $\sigma=15$.

10-3 Contingency Tables: Independence and Homogeneity

NOTE: For each row and each column it must be true that $\Sigma O = \Sigma E$. After the marginal row
and column totals are calculated, both the row totals and the column totals must sum to produce
the same grand total. If either of the preceding is not true, then an error has been made and
further calculations have no meaning. In addition, the following are true for all χ^2 contingency
table analyses in this manual.
* The E values for each cell are given in parentheses below the O values.
* The addends used to calculate the χ^2 test statistic follow the physical arrangement of the cells
    in the original contingency table. This practice makes it easier to monitor the large
    number of intermediate steps involved and helps to prevent errors caused by missing or
    double-counting cells.
* The accompanying chi-square illustrations follow the "usual" shape, even though that shape is
    not correct for df=1 or df=2.

1. H_o: ethnicity and being stopped are independent*
    H_1: ethnicity and being stopped are related*
    $\alpha = .05$
    C.R. $\chi^2 > \chi^2_{1,.05} = 3.841$
    calculations:

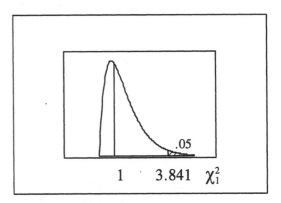

ETHNICITY

		B	W	
STOPPED?	Y	24 (21.375)	147 (149.625)	171
	N	176 (178.625)	1253 (1250.375)	1429
		200	1400	1600

$\chi^2 = \Sigma[(O-E)^2/E]$
$= .3224 + .0461$
$\quad .0386 + .0055 = .413$

conclusion:
    Do not reject H_o; there is not sufficient evidence to reject the claim that ethnicity and being stopped are independent.
    NOTE: The P-value from Minitab can also be used to make the decision. Since .521 > .05, do not reject H_o.
No, we cannot conclude that racial profiling is being used.
*NOTE: While the table claims to summarize "results for randomly selected drivers stopped by police," it appears that fixed numbers (200 black, 1400 white) of the ethnic groups were asked whether or not they had been stopped by the police. If so, the test should use "H_o: the proportion of drivers stopped is the same for both ethnic groups" to test homogeneity and not independence.

2. H_o: wearing a helmet and receiving facial injuries are independent
    H_1: wearing a helmet and receiving facial injuries are related
    $\alpha = .05$
    C.R. $\chi^2 > \chi^2_{1,.05} = 3.841$
    calculations:

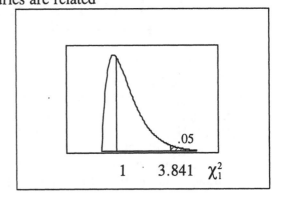

HELMET

		Y	N	
INJURY	Y	30 (45.11)	182 (166.89)	212
	N	83 (67.89)	236 (251.11)	319
		113	418	531

$\chi^2 = \Sigma[(O-E)^2/E]$
$= 5.0640 + 1.3690$
$\quad 3.3654 + .9098 = 10.708$

conclusion:
    Reject H_o; there is sufficient evidence to conclude that wearing a helmet and receiving facial injuries are related.
    NOTE: The P-value from TI-83 Plus can also be used to make the decision.   Since .00107 < .05, reject H_o.
NOTE: There is a statistical relationship, but not necessarily a cause-and-effect relationship. This test does not really address the question "Does a helmet seem to be effective in helping to prevent facial injuries in a crash?" The fact that people who wear helmets receive statistically fewer facial injuries could be due to other factors than the helmet preventing the injury – e.g., people who wear helmets might be safer people who go slower and whose accidents are less serious.

3. H_o: response is independent of company status
   H_1: response is related to company status
   $\alpha = .05$
   C.R. $\chi^2 > \chi^2_{1,.05} = 3.841$
   calculations:

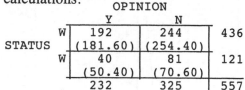

OPINION

		Y	N	
STATUS	W	192 (181.60)	244 (254.40)	436
	W	40 (50.40)	81 (70.60)	121
		232	325	557

$\chi^2 = \Sigma[(O-E)^2/E]$
   $= .5954 + .4250$
   $2.1454 + 1.5316 = 4.697$

conclusion:
   Reject H_o; there is sufficient evidence to reject the claim that response is independent of company status and to conclude that the two variables are related.
   Yes, the decision changes if the .01 level is used – since $4.697 > \chi^2_{1,.01} = 6.635$.
   No, workers and bosses no not appear to agree on this issue.

4. H_o: subject's truthfulness and polygraph reading are independent
   H_1: subject's truthfulness and polygraph reading are related
   $\alpha = .05$
   C.R. $\chi^2 > \chi^2_{1,.05} = 3.841$
   calculations:

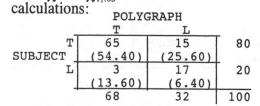

POLYGRAPH

		T	L	
SUBJECT	T	65 (54.40)	15 (25.60)	80
	L	3 (13.60)	17 (6.40)	20
		68	32	100

$\chi^2 = \Sigma[(O-E)^2/E]$
   $= 2.0654 + 4.3891$
   $8.2618 + 17.5562 = 32.273$

conclusion:
   Reject H_o; there is sufficient evidence to reject the claim that a subject's truthfulness and the polygraph reading are independent and to conclude that those variables are related.
   The results suggest that the two variables are related – i.e., that one can be predicted from the other. The results do not suggest how accurate that prediction might be.

5. H_o: there is homogeneity of proportions across gender of interviewer
   H_1: there is not homogeneity of proportions across gender of interviewer
   $\alpha = .01$
   C.R. $\chi^2 > \chi^2_{1,.01} = 6.635$
   calculations:

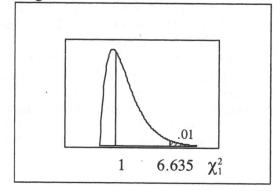

INTERVIEWER

		M	F	
RESPONSE	A	512 (565.3)	336 (282.7)	848
	D	288 (234.7)	64 (117.3)	352
		800	400	1200

$\chi^2 = \Sigma[(O-E)^2/E]$
   $= 5.031 + 10.063$
   $12.121 + 24.242 = 51.458$

conclusion:
  Reject H_o; there is sufficient evidence to reject the claim that the proportion of agree/disagree responses are homogeneous across the gender of the interviewer.

6. H_o: the proportion who pass is homogeneous across the groups
  H_1: the proportion who pass is not homogeneous across the groups
  $\alpha = .05$
  C.R. $\chi^2 > \chi^2_{1,.05} = 3.841$
  calculations:

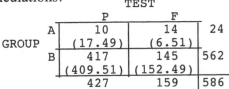

		TEST		
		P	F	
GROUP	A	10 (17.49)	14 (6.51)	24
	B	417 (409.51)	145 (152.49)	562
		427	159	586

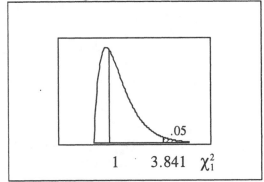

$\chi^2 = \Sigma[(O-E)^2/E]$
  $= 3.2062 + 8.6105$
  $0.1369 + 0.3677 = 12.321$

conclusion:
  Reject H_o; there is sufficient evidence to reject the claim that the proportion who pass is homogeneous across the groups.
Yes, the test appears to "discriminate" in the sense that it distinguished between the two groups. This does bot necessarily indicate anything unfair (e.g., that the test is culturally biased) or illegal (e.g., that the minority group's tests were graded unfairly).

7. The lack of precision in the reported results prevents this exercise from having a well-defined unique solution. Any $482 \leq x \leq 491$, for example, produces the $x/1014 = 48\%$ males as stated. The exercise is worked using the closest integers that yield the stated percents, and the possible extreme solutions are given in a NOTE at the end.
  H_o: gender and fear are flying are independent
  H_1: gender and fear of flying are related
  $\alpha = .05$
  C.R. $\chi^2 > \chi^2_{1,.05} = 3.841$
  calculations:

		GENDER		
		M	F	
FEAR?	Y	58 (111.42)	174 (120.58)	232
	N	429 (375.58)	353 (406.42)	782
		487	527	1014

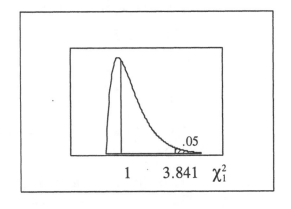

$\chi^2 = \Sigma[(O-E)^2/E]$
  $= 25.615 + 23.671$
  $7.599 + 7.023 = 63.908$

conclusion:
  Reject H_o; there is sufficient evidence to reject the claim that gender and fear of flying are independent and to conclude that the two variables are related.
NOTE: The following spread over more than 10 in the calculated χ^2 is possible from the following frequencies which also meet all the criteria in the statement of the exercise.

		GENDER		
		M	F	
FEAR?	Y	60 (110.76)	173 (122.24)	233
	N	422 (371.24)	359 (409.76)	781
		482	532	1014

$\chi^2 = \Sigma[(O-E)^2/E] = 57.559$

		GENDER		
		M	F	
FEAR?	Y	57 (112.34)	175 (119.66)	232
	N	434 (378.66)	348 (403.34)	782
		491	523	1014

$\chi^2 = \Sigma[(O-E)^2/E] = 68.533$

8. H_o: success in stopping to smoke is independent of the method used
H_1: success in stopping to smoke is related to the method used
$\alpha = .05$
C.R. $\chi^2 > \chi^2_{1,.05} = 3.841$
calculations:

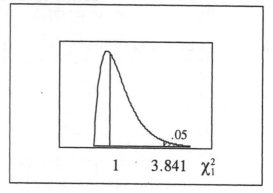

		METHOD		
		GUM	PATCH	
	N	191	263	454
SUCCESS?		(199.12)	(254.88)	
	Y	59	57	116
		(50.88)	(65.12)	
		250	320	570

$\chi^2 = \Sigma[(O-E)^2/E]$
$= 0.331 + 0.259$
$\quad 1.297 + 1.013 = 2.900$

conclusion:

Do not reject H_o; there is not sufficient evidence to reject the claim that success in stopping to smoke is independent of the method used.

If someone wants to stop smoking, it appears that the method used does not make a difference – and that a person's motivation is probably the most important factor.
NOTE: While the text asked for a test of independence, it appears from the data that the sample sizes of 250 and 320 may have been fixed and selected from the populations of gum and patch users. If that were the case, this should be a test of homogeneity of proportions – and not of independence of variables.

9. H_o: success in stopping to smoke is independent of the method used
H_1: success in stopping to smoke is related to the method used.
$\alpha = .05$
C.R. $\chi^2 > \chi^2_{2,.05} = 5.991$
calculations:

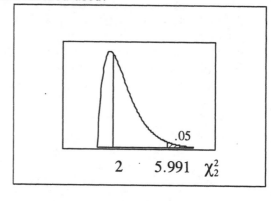

		METHOD			
		GUM	PATCH	INHALER	
	N	191	263	95	549
STOP?		(198.34)	(253.87)	(96.79)	
	Y	59	57	27	143
		(51.66)	(66.13)	(25.21)	
		250	320	122	692

$\chi^2 = \Sigma[(O-E)^2/E]$
$= 0.271 + 0.328 + 0.033$
$\quad 1.042 + 1.260 + 0.127 = 3.062$

conclusion:

Do not reject H_o; there is not sufficient evidence to reject the claim that success in stopping to smoke is independent of the method used.

10. H_o: smoking and level of education are independent
H_1: smoking and level of education are related
$\alpha = .05$
C.R. $\chi^2 > \chi^2_{2,.05} = 5.991$
calculations:

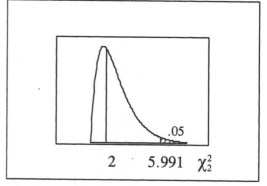

		EDUCATION			
		PRIM	MIDD	COLL	
	Y	606	1234	100	1940
SMOKE		(564.53)	(1210.5)	(164.97)	
	N	205	505	137	847
		(246.47)	(528.5)	(72.03)	
		811	1739	237	2787

$\chi^2 = \Sigma[(O-E)^2/E]$
$= 3.047 + 0.456 + 25.589$
$\quad 6.978 + 1.045 + 58.610 = 95.725$

conclusion:
Reject H_o; there is sufficient evidence to reject the claim that smoking and level of education are independent and to conclude that the two variables are related.
It appears (in China) that those with more education are more likely to have never smoked – as most dramatically illustrated by those who have a college level education.

11. H_o: death by homicide and occupation are independent
H_1: death by homicide and occupation are related
$\alpha = .05$ [assumed]
C.R. $\chi^2 > \chi^2_{3,.05} = 7.815$
calculations:

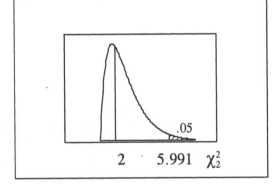

	OCCUPATION				
	POL	CAS	TAX	GUA	
Y	82	107	70	59	318
H	(112.92)	(75.28)	(64.25)	(65.55)	
N	92	9	29	42	172
	(61.08)	(40.72)	(34.75)	(35.45)	
	174	116	99	101	490

$$\chi^2 = \Sigma[(O-E)^2/E]$$
$$= 8.468 + 13.364 + 0.515 + 0.654$$
$$15.655 + 24.708 + 0.952 + 1.209 = 65.524$$

conclusion:
Reject H_o; there is sufficient evidence to reject the claim that death by homicide and occupation are independent.
Yes, the occupation cashier appears to be significantly more prone to death by homicide.

12. H_o: scanner accuracy and type of price are independent
H_1: scanner accuracy and type of price are related
$\alpha = .05$ [assumed]
C.R. $\chi^2 > \chi^2_{2,.05} = 5.991$
calculations:

		PRICE		
		regular	special	
	under	20	7	27
SCANNER		(13.81)	(13.19)	
	over	15	29	44
ACCURACY		(22.51)	(21.49)	
	exact	384	364	748
		(382.68)	(365.32)	
		419	400	819

$$\chi^2 = \Sigma[(O-E)^2/E]$$
$$= 2.7710 + 2.9016$$
$$2.5058 + 2.2648$$
$$0.0046 + 0.0048 = 10.814$$

conclusion:
Reject H_o; there is sufficient evidence conclude that scanner accuracy is related to the type of price being scanned.
Since it appears that disproportionately more overcharges occur with advertised special prices, consumers should be especially diligent to monitor the price flashed when items on special are being scanned.

13. Refer to the following table.

		AGE						
		18-21	22-29	30-39	40-49	50-59	60+	
	Y	73	255	245	136	138	202	1049
CO-OP		(73.13)	(239.4)	(242.0)	(132.3)	(143.6)	(218.5)	
	N	11	20	33	16	27	49	156
		(10.87)	(35.6)	(36.0)	(19.7)	(21.4)	(33.5)	
		84	275	278	152	165	251	1205

H_o: age and cooperation are independent
H_1: age and cooperation are related
$\alpha = .01$
C.R. $\chi^2 > \chi^2_{5,.01} = 15.086$

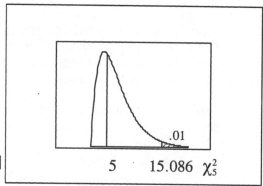

calculations:

[refer to the table at the start of the problem]
$\chi^2 = \Sigma[(O-E)^2/E]$
$\quad = .0002 + 1.0168 + .0369 + .1022 + .2214 + 1.2468$
$\quad\quad .0014 + 6.8371 + .2484 + .6875 + 1.4886 + 8.3838 = 20.271$

conclusion:

Reject H_o; there is sufficient evidence to conclude that a person's age and level of cooperation are related.

Yes, those aged 60+ appear to be particularly more uncooperative than the others.

14. H_o: gun storage method and firearm training are independent
H_1: gun storage method and firearm training are related
$\alpha = .05$
C.R. $\chi^2 > \chi^2_{1,.05} = 3.841$

calculations:

UNSAFE STORAGE?

		Y	N	
TRAINING	Y	122 (95.52)	329 (354.48)	451
	N	49 (74.48)	299 (273.52)	348
		171	628	799

$\chi^2 = \Sigma[(O-E)^2/E]$
$\quad = 6.7252 + 1.8312$
$\quad\quad 8.7158 + 2.3732 = 19.645$

conclusion:

Reject H_o; there is sufficient evidence to conclude that gun storage method is related to whether the owner had formal firearm training.

No, the relationship appears to be in the negative direction – i.e., there was more unsafe storage than expected by chance alone among those who had formal firearm training. Since the test identifies only relationship and not cause and effect, it is not necessarily true that the training course had a negative effect. One possible likely explanation is that those who consider guns important and use them regularly are more likely to (a) keep their firearms handy [i.e., loaded and unlocked] and (b) support courses in firearm training.

15. H_o: type of crime and criminal/victim connection are independent
H_1: type of crime and criminal/victim connection are related
$\alpha = .05$
C.R. $\chi^2 > \chi^2_{2,.05} = 5.991$

calculations:

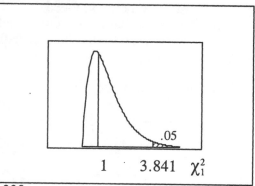

CRIME

		H	R	A	
C/V	S	12 (29.93)	379 (284.64)	727 (803.43)	1118
	A	39 (21.07)	106 (200.36)	642 (565.57)	787
		51	485	1369	1905

$\chi^2 = \Sigma[(O-E)^2/E]$
$\quad = 10.7418 + 31.2847 + 7.2715$
$\quad\quad 15.2600 + 44.4425 + 10.3298 = 119.330$

conclusion:
Reject H_o; there is sufficient evidence to reject the claim that the type of crime and the criminal/victim connection are related and to conclude that the two variables are related.

16. H_o: amount of smoking and seat belt use are independent
H_1: amount of smoking and seat belt use are related
$\alpha = .05$ [assumed]
C.R. $\chi^2 > \chi^2_{3,.05} = 7.815$
calculations:

NUMBER OF CIGARETTES

		0	1-14	15-34	35+	
U	Y	175	20	42	6	243
S		(171.5)	(19.59)	(43.94)	(7.941)	
E	N	149	17	41	9	216
		(152.5)	(17.41)	(39.06)	(7.059)	
		324	37	83	15	459

$$\chi^2 = \Sigma[(O-E)^2/E]$$
$$= .0702 + .0087 + .0858 + .4745$$
$$.0790 + .0097 + .0965 + .5338 = 1.358$$

conclusion:
Do not reject H_o; there is not sufficient evidence to conclude that amount of smoking and seat belt use are related.
No; while the direction of the data agrees with that theory, we cannot be 95% certain that the patterns in these data are anything other than chance occurrences.

17. H_o: sentence and plea are independent
H_1: sentence and plea are related
$\alpha = .05$
C.R. $\chi^2 > \chi^2_{1,.05} = 3.841$
calculations:

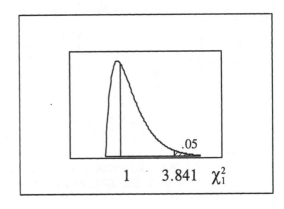

PLEA

		G	NG	
	P	392	58	450
SENTENCE		(418.48)	(31.52)	
	NP	564	14	578
		(537.52)	(40.48)	
		956	72	1028

$$\chi^2 = \Sigma[(O-E)^2/E]$$
$$= 1.6759 + 22.2518$$
$$1.3047 + 17.3241 = 42.557$$

conclusion:
Reject H_o; there is sufficient evidence to reject the claim that sentence and plea are independent and to conclude that a person's sentence and his original plea are related.
Yes; assuming that those who are really guilty will indeed be convicted with a trial, these results suggest that a guilty plea should be encouraged. But the study reported only those who plead not guilty and were convicted in trials. Suppose there were also guilty 50 persons who plead not guilty and were acquitted. Including them in the no prison category changes the conclusion entirely and yields the following.

PLEA

		G	NG	
	P	392	58	450
SENTENCE		(399.07)	(50.93)	
	NP	564	64	628
		(556.93)	(71.07)	
		956	112	1078

$$\chi^2 = \Sigma[(O-E)^2/E]$$
$$= .125 + .982$$
$$.090 + .704 = 1.901$$

18. H_o: size of home advantage and sport are independent
H_1: size of home advantage and sport are related
$\alpha = .10$
C.R. $\chi^2 > \chi^2_{3,.10} = 6.251$
calculations:

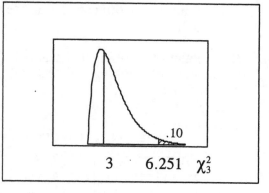

W		SPORT				
I	H	bask	base	hock	foot	
		127	53	50	57	287
N		(115.97)	(58.57)	(54.47)	(57.99)	
N	V	71	47	43	42	203
E		(82.03)	(41.43)	(38.53)	(41.01)	
R		198	100	93	99	490

$$\chi^2 = \Sigma[(O-E)^2/E]$$
$$= 1.049 + .530 + .367 + .017$$
$$1.483 + .749 + .519 + .024 = 4.737$$

conclusion:
Do not reject H_o; there is not sufficient evidence to conclude that size of home advantage and the sport are related.

19. H_o: getting a headache and the amount pf drug used are independent
H_1: getting a headache and the amount of drug used are related
$\alpha = .05$
C.R. $\chi^2 > \chi^2_{3,.05} = 7.815$
calculations:

A		DOSE (mg)				
C	Y	0	10	20/40	80	
H		19	47	8	6	80
E		(16.10)	(51.45)	(6.86)	(5.60)	
?	N	251	816	107	88	203
		(253.90)	(811.55)	(108.14)	(88.40)	
		270	863	115	94	1342

$$\chi^2 = \Sigma[(O-E)^2/E]$$
$$= .524 + .384 + .191 + .028$$
$$.033 + .024 + .012 + .002 = 1.199$$

conclusion:
Do not reject H_o; there is not sufficient evidence to conclude that size of home advantage and the sport are related.

20.   Refer to the following table and calculations.

		EXERCISE LEVEL				
		<200	200-599	600-1499	≥1500	
	0	4997	5205	5784	4155	20141
		(5584.18)	(5197.50)	(5481.33)	(3877.99)	
SMOKING	<15	604	484	447	359	1894
LEVEL		(525.12)	(488.76)	(515.45)	(364.67)	
	≥15	1403	830	644	350	3227
		(894.70)	(832.75)	(878.22)	(621.33)	
		7004	6519	6875	4864	25262

$$\chi^2 = \Sigma[(O-E)^2/E]$$
$$=\ 61.742 + 0.011 + 16.713 +\ 19.787$$
$$11.849 + 0.046 +\ 9.089 +\ \ 0.088$$
$$288.777 + 0.009 + 62.467 + 118.490$$
$$= 589.069$$

H_o: smoking and exercise levels are independent
H_1: smoking and exercise levels are related
$\alpha = .05$
C.R. $\chi^2 > \chi^2_{6,.05} = 12.592$
calculations:

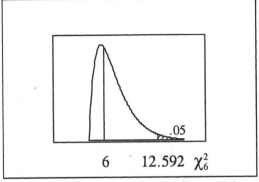

   [refer to the table and calculations
   at the start of the problem]

   $\chi^2 = \Sigma[(O-E)^2/E]$
   $= 589.069$

conclusion:
   Reject H_o; there is sufficient evidence to reject the claim that level of smoking and level
   of exercise are independent and to conclude that the two variables are related.

21. H_o: ethnicity and being stopped are independent
     H_1: ethnicity and being stopped are related
     $\alpha = .05$
     C.R. $\chi^2 > \chi^2_{1,.05} = 3.841$
     calculations:

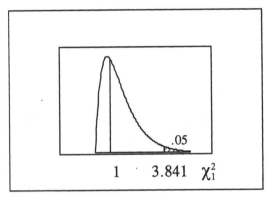

ETHNICITY

		B	W	
STOPPED?	Y	24 (21.375)	147 (149.625)	171
	N	176 (178.625)	1253 (1250.375)	1429
		200	1400	1600

   $\chi^2 = \Sigma[(|O-E|-.5)^2/E]$
   $= .2113 + .0302$
   $ .0253 + .0036 = .270$

conclusion:
   Do not reject H_o; there is not sufficient evidence to reject the claim that ethnicity and
   being stopped are independent.
   No, we cannot conclude that racial profiling is being used.
   Without the correction for continuity [see the solution for exercise #1 for the details] the
   calculated test statistic is .413. Since $(|O-E|-.5)^2 < (O-E)^2$ whenever $|O-E| > .25$,
   Yates' correction generally lowers the calculated test statistic.

22. a. In the format of this section, the 2x2 contingency table is

a	b	R1
c	d	R2
C1	C2	N

   where R1 = a+b, R2 = c+d
       C1 = a+c, C2 = b+d
       N = C1+C2 = R1+R2 = a+b+c+d

   Since the $\Sigma O = \Sigma E$ for each row and column, the (O-E) "misses" must add out to zero
   in each row and column. Let $a - E_a = M$, then $b - E_b = -M$
   $$c - E_c = -M$$
   $$d - E_d = M$$

   NOTE: This is a complex exercise. We proceed by presenting fact 1 and fact 2, then
   verifying the given equation.

   fact 1: $N^2 = N \cdot N$
   $ = (C1+C2) \cdot (R1+R2)$
   $ = C1 \cdot R1 + C1 \cdot R2 + C2 \cdot R1 + C2 \cdot R2$

   fact 2: $M = a - E_a$
   $ = a - (a+c)(a+b)/(a+b+c+d)$
   $ = [a(a+b+c+d) - (a+c)(a+b)]/(a+b+c+d)$
   $ = [a^2 + ab + ac + ad - a^2 - ab - ac - bc]/N$
   $ = (ad - bc)/N$

Together, these facts yield

$M^2 = (ad - bc)^2/N^2$

$\quad = (ad - bc)^2/(C1{\cdot}R1 + C1{\cdot}R2 + C2{\cdot}R1 + C2{\cdot}R2)$ from fact 1

$\chi^2 = \Sigma[(O-E)^2/E]$

$\quad = M^2/(C1{\cdot}R1/N) + M^2/(C2{\cdot}R1/N) + M^2/(C1{\cdot}R2/N) + M^2/(C2{\cdot}R2/N)$

$\quad = (N{\cdot}M^2)/(C1{\cdot}R1) + (N{\cdot}M^2)/(C2{\cdot}R1) + (N{\cdot}M^2)/(C1{\cdot}R2) + (N{\cdot}M^2)/(C2{\cdot}R2)$

$\quad = (N{\cdot}M^2{\cdot}C2{\cdot}R2)/(C1{\cdot}R1{\cdot}C2{\cdot}R2) + (N{\cdot}M^2{\cdot}C1{\cdot}R2)/(C1{\cdot}R1{\cdot}C2{\cdot}R2) +$

$\qquad\qquad (N{\cdot}M^2{\cdot}C2{\cdot}R1)/(C1{\cdot}R1{\cdot}C2{\cdot}R2) + (N{\cdot}M^2{\cdot}C1{\cdot}R1)/(C1{\cdot}R1{\cdot}C2{\cdot}R2)$

$\quad = N{\cdot}M^2{\cdot}(C2{\cdot}R2 + C1{\cdot}R2 + C2{\cdot}R1 + C1{\cdot}R1)/(C1{\cdot}R1{\cdot}C2{\cdot}R2)$

$\quad = N{\cdot}(ad - bc)^2/(C1{\cdot}R1{\cdot}C2{\cdot}R2)$ from fact 2

$\quad = N{\cdot}(ad - bc)^2/(R1{\cdot}R2{\cdot}C2{\cdot}C1)$

$\quad = (a+b+c+d){\cdot}(ad - bc)^2/[(a+b)(c+d)(b+d)(a+c)]$

b. In the format of a two-population proportion problem, the 2x2 contingency table is

GROUP

SUCCESS
$\begin{array}{c|c|c|c}
 & \text{a} & \text{b} & x \\
\hline
 & \text{c} & \text{d} & n-x \\
\hline
 & n_1 & n_2 & n
\end{array}$
Y
N

where $x = a+b$, $n-x = c+d$

$\qquad n_1 = a+c$, $n_2 = b+d$

$\qquad n = n_1 + n_2 = n + (n-x) = a+b+c+d$

$\qquad \overline{p} = x/n = (a+b)/(a+b+c+d)$

When testing $H_o{:}p_1{-}p_2 = 0$, $z_{\hat{p}_1-\hat{p}_2} = ((\hat{p}_1-\hat{p}_2) - 0)/\sqrt{\overline{p}\,\overline{q}/n_1 + \overline{p}\,\overline{q}/n_2}$.
We consider the numerator NUM and the denominator DEN separately.

$NUM = \hat{p}_1 - \hat{p}_2$

$\quad = a/n_1 - b/n_2$

$\quad = [an_2 - bn_1]/n_1 n_2$

$\quad = [a(b+d) - b(a+c)]/n_1 n_2$

$\quad = [ad - ac]/n_1 n_2$

$(NUM)^2 = (ad - bc)^2/n_1 n_2 n_1 n_2$

$(DEN)^2 = \overline{p}\,\overline{q}/n_1 + \overline{p}\,\overline{q}/n_2$

$\quad = \overline{p}\,\overline{q}[1/n_1 + 1/n_2]$

$\quad = \overline{p}\,\overline{q}[(n_2 + n_1)/n_1 n_2]$

$\quad = \overline{p}\,\overline{q}[n/n_1 n_2]$

$\quad = [x/n]{\cdot}[(n-x)/n]{\cdot}[n/n_1 n_2]$

$\quad = [x(n-x)]/[nn_1 n_2]$

$z^2 = (NUM)^2{\cdot}[1/(DEN)^2]$

$\quad = [(ad - bc)^2/n_1 n_2 n_1 n_2]{\cdot}[nn_1 n_2]/[x(n-x)]$

$\quad = n{\cdot}(ad - bc)^2/[x(n-x)n_2 n_1]$

$\quad = (a+b+c+d){\cdot}(ad - bc)^2/[(a+b)(c+d)(b+d)(a+c)]$

$\quad = \chi^2$ as calculated in part (a) above

10-4 Analysis of Variance

1. a. H_o: $\mu_1 = \mu_2 = \mu_3$
    b. H_1: at least one mean is different

    c. $F^2_{33} = 8.98$
    d. $F^2_{33,.05} = 3.3158$ [closest entry in Table A-5]
    e. P-value = .001

    f. Since $8.98 > 3.3158$, reject H_o and conclude the three mean F-K Grade Level scores are not all the same.

2. a. H_o: $\mu_1 = \mu_2 = \mu_3 = \mu_4 = \mu_5$
    b. H_1: at least one mean is different

    c. $F^4_{43} = 2.9493$
    d. $F^4_{43,.05} = 2.5888$ [from Excel]
    e. P-value = .0307

    f. Yes; since $2.9493 > 2.5888$, there is sufficient evidence at the .05 level to support the claim that the means for the five different laboratories are not all the same.

3. a. H_o: $\mu_1 = \mu_2 = \mu_3$
    b. H_1: at least one mean is different

    c. $F^2_{108} = .1887$
    d. $F^2_{108,.05} = 3.0804$ [from Excel]
    e. P-value = .8283

f. No; since $.1887 < 3.0804,$ there is not sufficient evidence to support the claim that the means for three different age groups are not all the same.

4. a. $H_o: \mu_1 = \mu_2 = \mu_3$ c. $F_{37}^2 = 1.65$
   b. $H_1:$ at least one mean is different   d. P-value $= .205$
   e. No; since $.205 > .05,$ there is not sufficient evidence to support the claim that the means for the three different age groups are not all the same.

NOTE: This section is calculation-oriented. Do not get so involved with the formulas that you miss concepts. This manual arranges the calculations to promote both computational efficiency and understanding of the underlying principles. The following notation is used in this section.

k = the number of groups
n_i = the number of scores in group i (where i = 1,2,...,k)
$\overline{x}_i$ = the mean of group i
s_i^2 = the variance of group i
$\overline{\overline{x}}$ = the overall mean of all the scores in all the groups
   $= \Sigma n_i \overline{x}_i / \Sigma n_i$ = the (weighted) mean of the group means
   $= \Sigma \overline{x}_i / k$ = simplified form when each group has equal size n
s_B^2 = the variance between the groups
   $= \Sigma n_i (\overline{x}_i - \overline{\overline{x}})^2 / (k-1)$
   $= n \Sigma (\overline{x}_i - \overline{\overline{x}})^2 / (k-1) = n s_{\overline{x}}^2$ = simplified form when each group has equal size n
s_p^2 = the variance within the groups
   $= \Sigma df_i s_i^2 / \Sigma df_i$ = the (weighted) mean of the group variances
      $=$ the two-sample formula for s_p^2 generalized to k samples
   $= \Sigma s_i^2 / k$ = simplified form when each group has equal size n
numerator df $= k-1$
denominator df $= \Sigma df_i$
         $= k(n-1)$ = simplified form when each group has equal size n
$F = s_B^2 / s_p^2$ = (variance between groups)/(variance within groups)

5. Since each group has equal size n, the simplified forms can be used.
   The following preliminary values are identified and/or calculated.

	subcompact	compact	midsize	full size
n	5	5	5	5
Σx	3344	2779	2434	2689
Σx^2	2470638	1577659	1297312	1541765
$\overline{x}$	668.8	555.8	486.8	537.8
s^2	58542.7	8272.8	28110.2	23905.2

   $k = 4$ $\overline{\overline{x}} = \Sigma \overline{x}_i / k$
   $n = 5$ $= 562.3$
   $s_{\overline{x}}^2 = \Sigma (\overline{x}_i - \overline{\overline{x}})^2 / (k-1)$ $s_p^2 = \Sigma s_i^2 / k$
      $= 5895$ $= 29707.725$

$H_o: \mu_1 = \mu_2 = \mu_3 = \mu_4$
$H_1:$ at least one mean is different
$\alpha = .05$
C.R. $F > F_{16,.05}^3 = 3.2389$
calculations:
   $F = n s_{\overline{x}}^2 / s_p^2$
      $= 5(5895)/29797.725 = .9922$
conclusion:

   Do not reject H_o; there is not sufficient evidence to conclude that at least one mean is different.
No, these data do not suggest that larger cars are safer.

6. Since each group has equal size n, the simplified forms can be used. The following preliminary values are identified and/or calculated.

	subcompact	compact	midsize	full size
n	5	5	5	5
Σx	252	265	244	230
Σx^2	12880	14131	11952	10782
$\bar{x}$	50.4	53.0	48.8	46.0
s^2	44.8	21.5	11.2	50.5

$k = 4$ $\quad\quad\quad \bar{\bar{x}} = \Sigma\bar{x}_i/k$
$n = 5$ $\quad\quad\quad\quad = 49.55$
$s_{\bar{x}}^2 = \Sigma(\bar{x}_i - \bar{\bar{x}})^2/(k-1)$ $\quad s_p^2 = \Sigma s_i^2/k$
$\quad\quad = 8.597$ $\quad\quad\quad\quad\quad = 32.000$

$H_o: \mu_1 = \mu_2 = \mu_3 = \mu_4$
$H_1:$ at least one mean is different
$\alpha = .05$
C.R. $F > F_{16,.05}^3 = 3.2389$
calculations:
$\quad F = ns_{\bar{x}}^2/s_p^2$
$\quad\quad = 5(8.597)/32.000 = 1.3432$
conclusion:

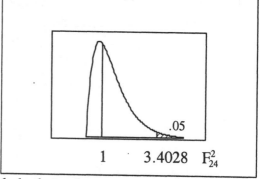

Do not reject H_o; there is not sufficient evidence to conclude that at least one mean is different.

No, these data do not suggest that larger cars are safer.

7. Since each group has equal size n, the simplified forms can be used. The following preliminary values are identified and/or calculated.

	4000 BC	1850 BC	150 AD
n	9	9	9
Σx	1194	1210	1243
Σx^2	158544	162768	171853
$\bar{x}$	132.67	134.44	138.11
s^2	17.500	11.278	22.611

$k = 3$ $\quad\quad\quad \bar{\bar{x}} = \Sigma\bar{x}_i/k$
$n = 9$ $\quad\quad\quad\quad = 135.07$
$s_{\bar{x}}^2 = \Sigma(\bar{x}_i - \bar{\bar{x}})^2/(k-1)$ $\quad s_p^2 = \Sigma s_i^2/k$
$\quad\quad = 15.416/2$ $\quad\quad\quad\quad = 51.389/3$
$\quad\quad = 7.708$ $\quad\quad\quad\quad\quad = 17.130$

$H_o: \mu_1 = \mu_2 = \mu_3$
$H_1:$ at least one mean is different
$\alpha = .05$
C.R. $F > F_{24,.05}^2 = 3.4028$
calculations:
$\quad F = ns_{\bar{x}}^2/s_p^2$
$\quad\quad = 9(7.708)/17.130 = 4.0498$
conclusion:

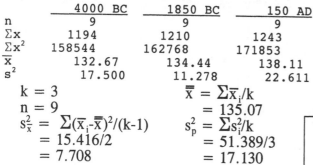

Reject H_o; there is sufficient evidence to conclude that at least one mean is different.

8. Since each group has equal size n, the simplified forms can be used. The following preliminary values are identified and/or calculated.

	sunny	cloudy	rainy
n	6	6	6
Σx	81.4	76.5	72.3
Σx^2	1105.14	975.59	871.55
$\bar{x}$	13.567	12.750	12.050
s^2	.1627	.0430	.0670

$k = 3$ $\quad\quad\quad\quad\quad\quad\quad\quad \bar{\bar{x}} = \Sigma\bar{x}_i/k$
$n = 6$ $\quad\quad\quad\quad\quad\quad\quad\quad\quad = 49.55$
$s_{\bar{x}}^2 = \Sigma(\bar{x}_i - \bar{\bar{x}})^2/(k-1) = .5762$ $\quad s_p^2 = \Sigma s_i^2/k = .0909$

H_0: $\mu_1 = \mu_2 = \mu_3$
H_1: at least one mean is different
$\alpha = .05$
C.R. $F > F^2_{15,.05} = 3.6823$
calculations:
$$F = ns^2_{\bar{x}}/s^2_p$$
$$= 6(.5762)/.0909 = 38.0379$$

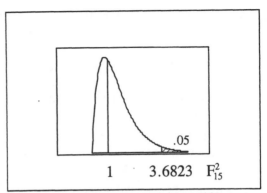

conclusion:
   Reject H_0; there is sufficient evidence to conclude that at least one mean is different. While it appears that sunny days provide more solar energy that either cloudy or rainy days, all that can be concluded from this test is that there is at least one difference. Determining exactly what that difference is requires more advanced techniques. It could be, for example, that the difference between sunny and rainy days is significant but the difference between sunny and cloudy days is not.

9.   The following preliminary values are identified and/or calculated.

	R	O	Y	Br	Bl	G	total
n	21	8	26	33	5	7	100
Σx	19.104	7.401	23.849	30.123	4.507	6.846	91.470
Σx^2	17.934278	6.862429	21.904543	27.546793	4.075729	6.018734	83.802506
$\bar{x}$	.90971	.92513	.91272	.91282	.90140	.92657	.91470
s^2	.000755	.002226	.001144	.001562	.003280	.001499	

$\bar{\bar{x}} = \Sigma n_i \bar{x}_i / \Sigma n_i$
   $= [21(.90971) + 8(.92513) + 26(.91272) + 33(.91282) + 5(.90140) + 7(.92657)]/100$
   $= 91.470/100$
   $= .91470$ [NOTE: $\bar{\bar{x}}$ must always agree with the $\bar{x}$ in the "total" column.]
$\Sigma n_i(\bar{x}_i - \bar{\bar{x}})^2 = 21(.90971-.91470)^2 + 8(.92513-.91470)^2 + 26(.91272-.91470)^2 +$
      $33(.91282-.91470)^2 + 5(.90140-.91470)^2 + 7(.92657-.91470)^2$
      $= .00355$
$\Sigma df_i s^2_i = 20(.000755) + 7(.002226) + 25(.001144) +$
      $32(.001562) + 4(.003280) + 6(.001499)$
      $= .13135$
$s^2_B = \Sigma n_i(\bar{x}_i - \bar{\bar{x}})^2/(k-1)$
   $= .00355/5 = .00071$
$s^2_p = \Sigma df_i s^2_i / \Sigma df_i$
   $= .13135/94 = .001398$

H_0: $\mu_R = \mu_O = \mu_Y = \mu_{Br} = \mu_{Bl} = \mu_G$
H_1: at least one mean is different
$\alpha = .05$
C.R. $F > F^5_{94,.05} = 2.2899$
calculations:
$$F = s^2_B/s^5_p$$
$$= .00071/.001398 = .5081$$
conclusion:
   Do not reject H_0; there is not sufficient evidence to conclude that at least one mean is different.

No. If the intent is to make the different colors have the same mean, there is no evidence that this is not being accomplished. Corrective action is not required.

NOTE: An ANOVA table may be completed for problem #9 as follows:

$F = MS_{Trt}/MS_{Err}$
$= .00071/.00140$
$= .51$

source	SS	df	MS	F
Trt	.00355	5	.00071	.51
Error	.13135	94	.00140	
Total	.13490	99		

(1) Enter $SS_{Trt} = \Sigma n_i(\bar{x}_i-\bar{\bar{x}})^2$ and $SS_{Err} = \Sigma df_i s_i^2$ values from the preliminary calculations.

(2) Enter $df_{Trt} = k-1$ and $df_{Err} = \Sigma df_i = \Sigma(n_i-1) = \Sigma n_i - k$.

(3) Add the SS and df columns to find SS_{Tot} and df_{Tot}. [The df_{Tot} must equal $\Sigma n_i - 1$.]

(4) Calculate $MS_{Trt} = SS_{Trt}/df_{Trt}$ and $MS_{Err} = SS_{Err}/df_{Err}$.

(5) Calculate $F = MS_{Trt}/MS_{Err}$.

As a final check, calculate s^2 (i.e., the variance of all the scores in one large group) two different ways as indicated below. If these answers agree, the problem is probably correct.

    * from the "total" column in the table for the preliminary calculations:

$$s^2 = [n\Sigma x^2 - (\Sigma x)^2]/[n(n-1)]$$
$$= [100(83.802506) - (91.470)^2]/[100(99)]$$
$$= 13.4897/9900 = .001363$$

    * from the "total" row of the ANOVA table

$$s^2 = SS_{Tot}/df_{Tot}$$
$$= .13490/99 = .001363$$

10. The following preliminary values are identified and/or calculated.

	Bonds	McGwire	Sosa	total
n	73	70	66	209
Σx	29468	29296	26720	85484
Σx^2	11962970	12403606	10900378	35266954
$\bar{x}$	403.671	418.514	404.848	409.014
s^2	938.696	2069.732	1274.254	

$\bar{\bar{x}} = \Sigma n_i \bar{x}_i / \Sigma n_i$
    $= [73(403.671) + 70(418.514) + 66(404.848)]/209 = 409.014$

$\Sigma n_i(\bar{x}_i-\bar{\bar{x}})^2 = 73(403.671 - 409.014)^2 + 70(418.514 - 409.104)^2 + 66(404.848 - 409.014)^2$
    $= 9546.945$

$\Sigma df_i s_i^2 = 72(938.696) + 69(2069.732) + 65(1274.254)$
    $= 293224.13$

$s_B^2 = \Sigma n_i(\bar{x}_i-\bar{\bar{x}})^2/(k-1)$
    $= 9546.945/2 = 4773.47$

$s_p^2 = \Sigma df_i s_i^2/\Sigma df_i$
    $= 293224.13/206 = 1423.42$

$H_o: \mu_B = \mu_M = \mu_S$

H_1: at least one mean is different

$\alpha = .05$

C.R. $F > F_{206,.05}^2 = 3.0718$

calculations:

    $F = s_B^2/s_p^2$
    $= 4773.47/1423.42 = 3.3535$

conclusion:

    Reject H_o; there is sufficient evidence to conclude that at least one mean is different.

No. Apparently greater distance of home runs is not associated with greater number of home runs, for Bonds has the lowest distance but the greatest numbers. One can sometimes say, for example: "He doesn't hit home runs very often – but when he hits one, it really goes!"

11. The following preliminary values are identified and/or calculated. ["shelf 3" = shelf 3/4]

	shelf 1	shelf 2	shelf 3	total
n	6	6	4	16
Σx	1.19	2.73	.80	4.72
Σx^2	.3853	1.2445	.1846	1.8144
$\overline{x}$	.1983	.4550	.2000	.2950
s^2	.029857	.000470	.008200	

$\overline{\overline{x}} = \Sigma n_i \overline{x}_i / \Sigma n_i$

$\quad = [6(.1983) + 6(.4550) + 4(.2000)]/16 = .2950$

$\Sigma n_i(\overline{x}_i - \overline{\overline{x}})^2 = 6(.1983 - .2950)^2 + 6(.4550 - .2950)^2 + 4(.2000 - .295)^2 = .24577$

$\Sigma df_i s_i^2 = 5(.029857) + 5(.000470) + 3(.008200) = .17624$

$s_B^2 = \Sigma n_i(\overline{x}_i - \overline{\overline{x}})^2/(k-1) = .24577/2 = .12288$

$s_p^2 = \Sigma df_i s_i^2 / \Sigma df_i = .17624/13 = .01356$

$H_o: \mu_1 = \mu_2 = \mu_3$

$H_1:$ at least one mean is different

$\alpha = .05$

C.R. $F > F_{13,.05}^2 = 3.8056$

calculations:

$\quad F = s_B^2/s_p^2$

$\quad\quad = .12288/.01356 = 9.0645$

conclusion:

Reject H_o; there is sufficient evidence to conclude that at least one mean is different.

It appears that the cereals are not placed on the shelves at random, but that those with higher sugar amounts are on shelf 2 – at children's eye-level.

12. Since each group has equal size n, the simplified forms can be used.
The following preliminary values are identified and/or calculated.

	smokers	exposed ns	nonexposed
n	40	40	40
Σx	6899	2423	654
Σx^2	1746819	890393	163200
$\overline{x}$	172.475	60.575	16.350
s^2	14279.846	19067.174	3910.438

$k = 3$ $\qquad \overline{\overline{x}} = \Sigma \overline{x}_i/k$

$n = 40$ $\qquad\qquad = 83.133$

$s_{\overline{x}}^2 = \Sigma(\overline{x}_i - \overline{\overline{x}})^2/(k-1) \qquad s_p^2 = \Sigma s_i^2/k$

$\quad\quad = 12950.825/2 \qquad\qquad = 37257.458/3$

$\quad\quad = 6475.41 \qquad\qquad = 12419.15$

$H_o: \mu_1 = \mu_2 = \mu_3$

$H_1:$ at least one mean is different

$\alpha = .05$

C.R. $F > F_{117,.05}^2 = 3.0718$

calculations:

$\quad F = n s_{\overline{x}}^2/s_p^2$

$\quad\quad = 40(6475.41)/12419.15 = 20.8562$

conclusion:

Reject H_o; there is sufficient evidence to conclude that at least one mean is different.

The results seem to support the claim that secondhand smoke is harmful, but such a statement cannot be from the ANOVA. The conclusion is only that at least one is different. Determining exactly what that difference is requires more advanced techniques. It could be, for example, that the exposed and non-exposed non-smokers have significantly less cotinine levels than the smokers – but that their levels are not significantly different from each other.

13. a. $_5C_2 = 5!/2!3! = 10$
    b. P(no type I error in one t test) = .95
       assuming independence, P(no Type I error in ten t tests) = $(.95)^{10} = .599$
    c. P(no type I error in one F test) = .95
    d. the analysis of variance test

14. The following preliminary values are identified and/or calculated.

	Clancy	Rowling
n	12	12
Σx	848.8	969.0
Σx^2	61449.54	78487.82
$\bar{x}$	70.733	80.750
s^2	128.2806	21.9155

a. original claim: $\mu_1 - \mu_2 = 0$
   $\bar{x}_1 - \bar{x}_2 = 70.733 - 80.750 = -10.017$
   $s_p^2 = [(n_1-1) \cdot s_1^2 + (n_2-1) \cdot s_2^2]/(n_1 + n_2 - 2)$
   $\quad = [(11)(128.2806) + (11)(21.9155)]/(22)$
   $\quad = 75.098$ [with df = $df_1 + df_2 = 22$]
   H_o: $\mu_1 - \mu_2 = 0$
   H_1: $\mu_1 - \mu_2 \neq 0$
   $\alpha = .05$
   C.R. $t < -t_{22,.025} = -2.074$
   $\quad\quad t > t_{22,.025} = 2.074$
   calculations:
   $t_{\bar{x}1-\bar{x}2} = (\bar{x}_1 - \bar{x}_2 - \mu_{\bar{x}1-\bar{x}2})/s_{\bar{x}1-\bar{x}2}$
   $\quad = (-10.017 - 0)/\sqrt{(75.098)/12 + (75.098)/12}$
   $\quad = -10.017/3.5378 = -2.83129$
   conclusion:

   Reject H_o; there is sufficient evidence to reject the claim that $\mu_1 - \mu_2 = 0$ and to conclude that $\mu_1 - \mu_2 \neq 0$ (in fact, that $\mu_1 - \mu_2 < 0$).

b. Since each group has equal size n, the simplified forms can be used. In addition to the summary statistics above, the following preliminary values are noted.
   k = 2 $\bar{\bar{x}} = \Sigma \bar{x}_i/k$
   n = 12 $\quad = 75.7417$
   $s_{\bar{x}}^2 = \Sigma(\bar{x}_i - \bar{\bar{x}})^2/(k-1)$ $s_p^2 = \Sigma s_i^2/k$
   $\quad = 50.1668/1$ $\quad = 150.1961/2$
   $\quad = 50.1668$ $\quad = 75.098$

   H_o: $\mu_1 = \mu_2 = \mu_3$
   H_1: at least one mean is different
   $\alpha = .05$
   C.R. $F > F_{22,.05}^1 = 4.3009$
   calculations:
   $F = ns_{\bar{x}}^2/s_p^2$
   $\quad = 12(50.1668)/75.098 = 8.016$
   conclusion:

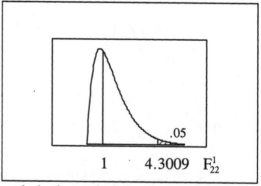

   Reject H_o; there is sufficient evidence to conclude that at least one mean is different.
c. critical value: $t^2 = (\pm 2.074)^2 = 4.301 = F$
   calculated statistic: $t^2 = (-2.83129)^2 = 8.016 = F$ [In general $t_{df,\alpha/2}^2 = F_{df,\alpha}^1$.]

Review Exercises

1. H_o: $p_{Mon} = p_{Tue} = p_{Wed} = p_{Thu} = p_{Fri} = 1/5$
   H_1: at least one of the proportions is different from 1/5
   $\alpha = .05$
   C.R. $\chi^2 > \chi^2_{4,.05} = 9.488$
   calculations:

day	O	E	$(O-E)^2/E$
Mon	98	75	7.053
Tue	68	75	.653
Wed	89	75	2.613
Thu	64	75	1.613
Fri	56	75	4.813
	375	375	16.747

$$\chi^2 = \Sigma[(O-E)^2/E] = 16.747$$

conclusion:
   Reject H_o; there is sufficient evidence to conclude that at least one of the proportions is different from 1/5.
Since the calls are not uniformly distributed over the days of the business week, it would not make sense to have the staffing level the same each day – unless the company staffed to handle the higher numbers of calls and had other work available to do during slack times.

2. H_o: $p_{Mon} = p_{Tue} = p_{Wed} = \ldots = p_{Sun} = 1/7$
   H_1: at least one of the proportions is different from 1/7
   $\alpha = .05$
   C.R. $\chi^2 > \chi^2_{6,.05} = 12.592$
   calculations:

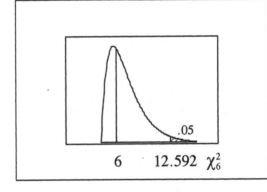

day	O	E	$(O-E)^2/E$
Mon	74	66.29	.8978
Tue	60	66.29	.5961
Wed	66	66.29	.0012
Thu	71	66.29	.3353
Fri	51	66.29	3.5249
Sat	66	66.29	.0012
Sun	76	66.29	1.4236
	464	464.00	6.7801

$$\chi^2 = \Sigma[(O-E)^2/E] = 6.780$$

conclusion:
   Do not reject H_o; there is not sufficient evidence to reject the claim that the gunfire death rates are the same for the different days of the week.
No, there is not support for the theory theat more gunfire deaths occur on weekends.

3. Refer to the following table and calculations.

		arson	rape	violence	stealing	coining	fraud	
USE	Y	50	88	155	379	18	63	753
		(49.11)	(79.21)	(139.93)	(358.55)	(16.90)	(109.31)	
	N	43	62	110	300	14	144	673
		(43.89)	(70.79)	(125.07)	(320.45)	(15.10)	(97.69)	
		93	150	265	679	32	207	1426

CRIME

$$\chi^2 = \Sigma[(O-E)^2/E]$$
$$= .016 + 0.976 + 1.622 + 1.167 + .072 + 19.617$$
$$.018 + 1.092 + 1.815 + 1.306 + .080 + 21.949 = 49.731$$

H_o: alcohol use and type of crime are independent
H_1: alcohol use and type of crime are related
$\alpha = .05$ [assumed]
C.R. $\chi^2 > \chi^2_{5,.05} = 11.071$

calculations:

[refer to the table and calculations at the start of the problem]

$\chi^2 = \Sigma[(O-E)^2/E]$
    $= 49.731$

conclusion:

Reject H_o; there is sufficient evidence to conclude that alcohol use and the type of crime committed are related.

Fraud seems to be different from the other crimes in that it is more likely to be committed by someone who abstains from alcohol.

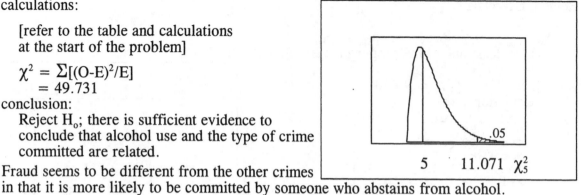

4. H_o: success in stopping to smoke is independent of the method used
   H_1: success in stopping to smoke is related to the method used
   $\alpha = .05$
   C.R. $\chi^2 > \chi^2_{1,.05} = 3.841$
   calculations:

REHOSPITALIZED?

		Y	N	
	E	622	3997	4619
DEPART		(584.02)	(4034.98)	
	L	631	4660	5291
		(668.98)	(4622.02)	
		1253	8657	9910

$\chi^2 = \Sigma[(O-E)^2/E]$
    $= 2.470 + 0.358$
    $2.157 + 0.312 = 5.297$

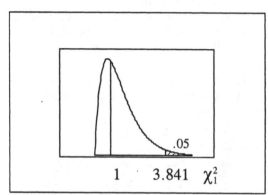

conclusion:

Reject H_o; there is sufficient evidence to reject the claim that whether a newborn is rehospitalized is independent of how soon it was discharged and to conclude that the two variables are related.

Yes, the conclusion changes if the level of significance becomes .01 [CV = 6.635]. This means we can be 95% confidence such a relationship exists, but not 99% confident.

5. H_o: $\mu_A = \mu_B = \mu_C$
   H_1: at least one $= \mu_i$ is different
   $\alpha = .05$
   C.R. $F > F^2_{14,.05} = 3.7389$
   calculations:
       $F = s^2_B/s^2_p$
         $= .0038286/.0000816$
         $= 46.90$
       P-value $= .000$ [from Minitab]

conclusion:

Reject H_o; there is not sufficient evidence to reject the claim that the three groups have the same mean and to conclude that at least one mean is different.

6. Since each group has equal size n, the simplified forms can be used.
   The following preliminary values are identified and/or calculated.

	oceanside	oceanfront	bayside	bayfront
n	6	6	6	6
Σx	2294	2956	1555	3210
Σx^2	944,422	1,494,108	435,465	1,772,790
$\overline{x}$	382.333	492.667	259.167	535.000
s^2	13469.867	7557.067	6492.167	11088.000

$k = 4$

$n = 6$

$s_{\bar{x}}^2 = \Sigma(\bar{x}_i - \bar{\bar{x}})^2/(k-1)$

$\quad = 45762.243/3$

$\quad = 15254.081$

$\bar{\bar{x}} = \Sigma\bar{x}_i/k$

$\quad = 417.292$

$s_p^2 = \Sigma s_i^2/k$

$\quad = 38607.100/4$

$\quad = 9651.775$

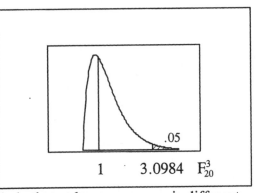

$H_o: \mu_{OS} = \mu_{OF} = \mu_{BS} = \mu_{BF}$

$H_1:$ at least one mean is different

$\alpha = .05$

C.R. $F > F_{20,.05}^3 = 3.0984$

calculations:

$\quad F = ns_{\bar{x}}^2/s_p^2$

$\quad\quad = 6(15254.081)/9651.775 = 9.4827$

conclusion:

Reject H_o; there is sufficient evidence to conclude that at least one mean is different.

Cumulative Review Exercises

1. scores in order: 66 75 77 80 82 84 89 94; $n = 8$ $\Sigma x = 647$ $\Sigma x^2 = 52847$

    $\bar{x} = 647/8 = 80.9$

    $\tilde{x} = (80 + 82)/2 = 81.0$

    $R = 94 - 66 = 28$

    $s^2 = [8(52847) - (647)^2]/[8(7)] = 74.41$

    $s = 8.6$

    five-number summary:

    $\quad x_1 = 66$

    $\quad P_{25} = (75 + 77)/2 = 76.0$ $[(.25)8 = 2,$ a whole number, use $x_{2.5}]$

    $\quad P_{50} = \tilde{x} = 81.0$

    $\quad P_{75} = (84 + 89)/2 = 86.5$ $[(.75)8 = 6,$ a whole number, use $x_{6.5}]$

    $\quad x_8 = 94$

2. Consider the table at the right.

	A	B	C	D	
M	66	80	82	75	303
F	77	89	94	84	344
	143	169	176	159	647

    a. $P(C) = 176/647 = .272$

    b. $P(M) = 303/647 = .468$

    c. $P(M$ or $C) = P(M) + P(C) - P(M$ and $C)$

    $\quad\quad = (303/647) + (176/647) - (82/647) = 397/647 = .614$

    d. $P(F_1$ and $F_2) = P(F_1) \cdot P(F_2 | F_1) = (344/647) \cdot (343/646) = .282$

3. $H_o:$ gender and selection are independent

    $H_1:$ gender and selection are related

    $\alpha = .05$ [assumed]

    C.R. $\chi^2 > \chi_{3,.05}^2 = 7.815$

    calculations:

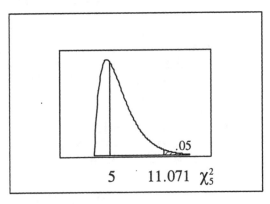

G	SELECTION				
E		A	B	C	D	
N M		66	80	82	75	303
		(66.97)	(79.15)	(82.42)	(74.46)	
D F		77	89	94	84	344
E		(76.03)	(89.85)	(93.58)	(84.54)	
R		143	169	176	159	647

$\chi^2 = \Sigma[(O-E)^2/E]$

$\quad = .014 + .009 + .002 + .004$

$\quad\quad .012 + .008 + .002 + .003 = .055$

conclusion:

Do not reject H_o; there is not sufficient evidence to reject the claim that gender and selection are independent.

4. $n = 4$ $\Sigma xy = 26210$ $n(\Sigma xy) - (\Sigma x)(\Sigma y) = 4(26210) - (303)(344) = 608$
$\Sigma x = 303$ $\Sigma x^2 = 23105$ $n(\Sigma x^2) - (\Sigma x)^2 = 4(23105) - (303)^2 = 611$
$\Sigma y = 344$ $\Sigma y^2 = 29742$ $n(\Sigma y^2) - (\Sigma y)^2 = 4(29742) - (344)^2 = 632$

$r = [n(\Sigma xy) - (\Sigma x)(\Sigma y)]/[\sqrt{n(\Sigma x^2) - (\Sigma x)^2} \cdot \sqrt{n(\Sigma y^2) - (\Sigma y)^2}]$
   $= 608/[\sqrt{611} \cdot \sqrt{632}] = .978$

original claim: $\rho \neq 0$
H_o: $\rho = 0$
H_1: $\rho \neq 0$
$\alpha = .05$ [assumed]
C.R. $r < -.950$ OR   C.R. $t < -t_{2,.025} = -4.303$
     $r > .950$ $t > t_{2,.025} = 4.303$

calculations: calculations:
   $r = .978$ $t_r = (r - \mu_r)/s_r$
                      $= (.978 - 0)/\sqrt{(1-(.978)^2)/2}$
                      $= .978/.146 = 6.696$

conclusion:

Reject H_o; there is sufficient evidence to conclude that $\rho \neq 0$ (in fact, $\rho > 0$).

5. $d = y - x$: 11 9 12 9;
$n = 4$ $\Sigma d = 41$ $\Sigma d^2 = 427$ $\bar{d} = 10.25$ $s_d = 1.50$
original claim: $\mu_d > 0$
H_o: $\mu_d = 0$
H_1: $\mu_d > 0$
$\alpha = .05$ [assumed]
C.R. $t > t_{3,.05} = 2.353$

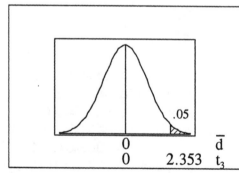

calculations:
   $t_{\bar{d}} = (\bar{d} - \mu_{\bar{d}})/s_{\bar{d}}$
      $= (10.25 - 0)/(1.50/\sqrt{4})$
      $= 10.25/.750 = 13.667$
conclusion:

Reject H_o; there is sufficient evidence to conclude that $\mu_d > 0$.

6. summary statistics
   males: $n_1 = 4$ $\Sigma x_1 = 303$ $\Sigma x_1^2 = 23105$ $\bar{x}_1 = 75.75$ $s_1^2 = 50.917$
   females: $n_2 = 4$ $\Sigma x_2 = 344$ $\Sigma x_2^2 = 29742$ $\bar{x}_2 = 86.00$ $s_2^2 = 52.667$
   $\bar{x}_1 - \bar{x}_2 = 75.75 - 86.00 = -10.25$
H_o: $\mu_1 - \mu_2 = 0$
H_1: $\mu_1 - \mu_2 \neq 0$
$\alpha = .05$ [assumed]
C.R. $t < -t_{3,.025} = -3.182$
     $t > t_{3,.025} = 3.182$
calculations:

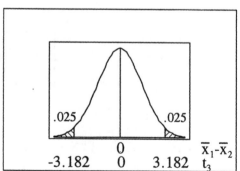

   $t_{\bar{x}_1 - \bar{x}_2} = (\bar{x}_1 - \bar{x}_2 - \mu_{\bar{x}_1 - \bar{x}_2})/s_{\bar{x}_1 - \bar{x}_2}$
          $= (-10.25 - 0)/\sqrt{50.917/4 + 52.667/4}$
          $= -10.25/5.089 = -2.014$
conclusion:

Do not reject H_o; there is not sufficient evidence to reject the claim that $\mu_1 - \mu_2 = 0$.